KT-385-412

Handbook of

ELECTRON TUBE AND VACUUM TECHNIQUES

by

Fred Rosebury

Massachusetts Institute of Technology

ADDISON-WESLEY PUBLISHING COMPANY, INC.

READING, MASSACHUSETTS

Printed in the United States of America

ADDISON-WESLEY PUBLISHING COMPANY, INC.

Headquarters:
Reading, Massachusetts 01867

School Division Office:
3220 Porter Drive, Palo Alto, California 94304

Sales Office:
411 Elm Street, Dallas, Texas 75202

Sales Office:
10–15 Chitty Street, London W 1, England

Preface

The scientific technology required in fabricating and processing electron tubes and other high-vacuum devices differs from, yet overlaps, other bodies of knowledge. For this reason we feel there is a need for a handbook or manual in which the various highly specialized techniques are set forth in some detail so that workers will not have to consult a great many other sources of information.

The present work represents a collection of notes on procedures and materials pertaining to the broad field of constructing and processing tubes and many other kinds of evacuated devices. There is no intention of invading the domains of physics, physical electronics, metallurgy, and other scientific disciplines which are basic and supportive to the making of successful devices. On these subjects, as relating to high vacuum, there is already a considerable body of classical and current literature, from which much of the material in this book has been freely drawn. The aim of this work is to supplement the basic principles, to outline procedures and techniques for performing the operations peculiar to this field, and to assemble tables and other aids to help the technician.

This book is a new version of the TUBE LABORATORY MANUAL (first and second editions) produced by the Research Laboratory of Electronics at the Massachusetts Institute of Technology. This volume, as a first public edition, greatly amplifies the material in its forerunner, with much new data and a comprehensive glossary that is practically an encyclopedia.

At the risk of appearing naive, we attempt in this glossary to palliate the tendency by some authors in current physical journals to use terms of their own or others' coining without sufficient clarification. The lay reader, seeking information in that literature, is often confused and frustrated by words and phrases of whose meaning the authors assume widespread knowledge.

Many of the subjects and techniques discussed are under current and exhaustive investigation in many quarters, and as in all the physical sciences today, new information is continually appearing. It is therefore inevitable that between the writing and the publication of such a work, some of the data will become obsolete and new words and meanings will appear.

For some of the information contained herein, we are indebted to the personnel of the Tube Laboratory and to other workers, companies, and laboratories that have kindly given us permission to reproduce material which was either printed publicly or contained in private communications. Acknowledgements are freely made.

References to particular commercial products are not intended as endorsement, but simply to indicate those materials and devices about which we have some knowledge.

Cambridge, Massachusetts F.R.
July, 1964

Trade Names

Reference is made within the text to the following trade names:

Trade Name	Registered Trademark of
Advance	Driver-Harris Company
Aloxite	Carborundum Company
Alundum	Norton Company
Apiezon "N"	J. G. Biddle & Company
Armco Ingot Iron	Armco Steel Corporation
Armco Iron	Armco Steel Corporation
Arochlor 1254	Monsanto Chemical Company
CerAlloy 420	Ronson Metals Corporation
Ceramvar	Wilbur B. Driver Company
CM-R 41 Alloy	Cannon-Muskegon Corporation
Crystolon Hot Rods	Norton Company
De-Oxo	Baker & Company
DNS Type #1, Platinum Plating Solution	J. Bishop & Company
Eastman 910 Adhesive	Eastman Chemical Products, Inc.
Easy-Flo	Handy & Harman
Equipto	Precision Equipment Company
Fernico	General Electric Company
Ferrovac E	Crucible Steel
Fiberglas	Owens-Corning Company
Fiberfrax	Carborundum Company
Fluorel	Minnesota Mining and Manufacturing Company
Freon	E. I. du Pont de Nemours Company
Globars	Carborundum Company
Inco 225	Huntington Alloys of International Nickel Company
Inconel (Inconel Alloy 600)	International Nickel Company
Invar	Société Anonyme de Commentry-Fourchambault et Decazivílle (Acieries d'Imphy)
Kasil #1	Philadelphia Quartz Company
Kel-F Plastic	Minnesota Mining and Manufacturing Company
Kovar	Westinghouse Electric Corporation, Carborundum Company

Trade Name	Registered Trademark of
Lava (#1137)	American Lava Company
Linde Molecular Sieves	Union Carbide Corporation
Lucite	E. I. du Pont de Nemours Company
Marinite	Johns-Manville Company
Molykote	Alpha-Molykote Corporation
Monel Alloy R-405	International Nickel Company
Monel Alloys	International Nickel Company
Mu metal	Allegheny Ludlum Steel Corporation
Narcoil	NRC Equipment Corporation
Neoprene	E. I. du Pont de Nemours Company
Nichrome V	Driver-Harris Company
Nickel 200	International Nickel Company
Nicoro (braze alloy)	Western Gold & Platinum Company
Nilvar	Driver-Harris Company
Nioro	Western Gold & Platinum Company
Niromet 42 Alloy	Wilbur B. Driver Company
Niromet 46 Alloy	Wilbur B. Driver Company
Niron 52 Alloy	Wilbur B. Driver Company
Nivac P	Crucible Steel Company of America
Nylon	E. I. du Pont de Nemours Company
Philips Cathodes	North American Philips Company
Picein	Schrader & Ehlers Company
Pyrex	Corning Glass Works
Pyroceram Brand Cement #45	Corning Glass Works
Rene 41	General Electric Company
Rodar	Wilbur B. Driver Company
Rodine #50	American Paint Company
Silastic	Dow-Corning Corporation
Silicone	Dow-Corning Corporation
Teflon	E. I. du Pont de Nemours Company
Therlo	Driver-Harris Company
Tophel-Nial	Wilbur B. Driver Company
Tophet	Wilbur B. Driver Company
Transite	Johns-Manville Company
Tygon	U. S. Stoneware Company
Viton	E. I. du Pont de Nemours Company
Vycor	Corning Glass Works
Zytel	E. I. du Pont de Nemours Company

Acknowledgements

The author wishes to express his appreciation to the firms and institutions who have permitted the use of material for the following figures.

Figs. 7, 8, 9. Courtesy of Intertech, Inc., Natick, Mass.

Fig. 19. From data compiled by W. E. Forsythe and A. G. Worthing, *Astrophys. J.* **61**, 146–185 (1925). Courtesy of University of Chicago.

Fig. 26. By permission of Varian Associates.

Figs. 38, 53, 54, 58, 60, 61. By permission of copyright owners, O. H. Caldwell and M. Clements, Electronic Development Associates, New York, N. Y. Reproduced from *The Electronic Handbook*, edited by R. R. Batcher and W. Moulic, 1944.

Figs. 46, 89, 93, 94, 120. Adapted from Saul Dushman's *Scientific Foundations of Vacuum Techniques*, second edition, John Wiley and Sons, New York, N. Y.

Figs. 48, 59. After C. J. Smithells, *Metals Reference Handbook*, Interscience Publishers, Inc., New York, N. Y., 1949.

Figs. 66–75. By permission of Corning Glass Works, Corning, N. Y., 1961.

Figs. 90, 91. Reproduced by permission of the Refractories Division of the Carborundum Company, Latrobe, Pa.

Figs. 117, 118, 119. After J. D. Cobine, *Gaseous Conductors*, by permission of the publisher, Dover Publications, Inc., New York, N. Y.

Fig. 132. Courtesy of Consolidated Vacuum Corp., Rochester, N. Y.

Fig. 139. Courtesy of Handy & Harman.

Figs. 146, 147. Courtesy of General Electric Company.

Figs. 148, 151, 153. By permission of Sylvania Electric Products, Inc., Towanda, Pa.

Fig. 149. After Fansteel Metallurgical Corporation. From W. Espe and M. Knoll, "Werkstoffkunde der Hochvakuumtechnik," Berlin, 1946.

Contents

Cleaning of Electron Tubes and Vacuum Components

It is generally recognized that the greatest problem facing the designer and builder of vacuum tubes and vessels is that of removing or reducing contamination from component parts. Submicroscopic particles, gases, and vapors from the environment can and do have harmful effects on the processing and operation of vacuum systems, and on the life and performance of electron tubes. At the outset, therefore, it is to be stressed that a kind of cleanliness beyond that of mere apparent surface purity and sterilization are to be sought after as far as possible.

Contaminants can roughly be divided into five categories. It will be seen that some of these can be changed into others: those given below under *A* and *C* usually decompose on heating to form those under *B*, *D*, and *E*, and under some conditions those under *B* and *D* can be degraded further into gases and vapors (*E*).

A. Environmental contaminants: dust, lint, soot; from the air, floors, walls, ceilings, furniture, clothing, body (e.g. hair and skin).

B. Water-soluble salts: electrolytes such as mineral salts (sodium chloride, etc.) and nonelectrolytes (various organic materials).

C. Nonwater-soluble organic materials: hydrocarbons such as greases and oils; lubricating and cutting compounds, either from direct contact or as a spray or mist in the air. Wherever there is an odor of machine oil, there is certainty of contamination from this source. Oily or tarry constituents of smoke, from chimneys and tobacco, and industrial vapors of all kinds are also sources of contamination. To be avoided are the fatty acids—oleic, stearic, palmitic, and sterols—from skin and soaps, etc.

D. Nonsoluble chemically combined materials: oxides, silicates, sulfides, nitrides, borides, and other such contaminants. They are often found closely adhering to the surfaces of materials.

E. Contaminating gases: heating in hydrogen or vacuum generally removes these.

Critical tube assembly work and handling of parts are to be done in a well-sealed room in which the walls and ceiling are coated with a good quality semigloss, flexible paint and the floor is covered with a composition asphalt or rubber tile kept clean and waxed. Air conditioning is to be provided through filters, in two or more stages, which exclude the smallest particles possible;

and the relative humidity is to be kept below 50 percent. Electrostatic precipitation is useful under some conditions but is not to be taken as a cure-all.

To detect and count dust particles, expose a clean glass plate to the atmosphere in question and then examine it with a low-power microscope. Some dust particles on metal parts will float off in clean water; the surface of the water can then be examined under low power. Dust in a room can, of course, be seen by the Tyndall effect, which is very sensitive.

Water-soluble salts (see *B* above) are removed by the use of plenty of clean water, both cold and hot. (These contaminants change the electrical conductivity of ultrapure water and can be thus detected.) Demineralized water is preferable to distilled, and tap water may be used in the first stages of rinsing.

The materials included in *C* above, and some of the contaminants of *D*, are likely to produce colored stains on metal parts during heating. These are often removed by reduction in hydrogen. The contaminants listed in *C* above can be detected by a test in which the article is sprayed with fine droplets from an atomizer,[1] e.g. an artist's airbrush. On clean surfaces a uniform continuous film of water is formed, rather than individual droplets, and foreign matter (finger prints) shows up dramatically, like images being developed on a photosensitive surface. In the so-called "water-break" test,[1] which is somewhat less sensitive, the piece is immersed in clean water; the film of draining water on a really clean surface remains unbroken until fairly uniform or symmetrical interference-color fringes are formed. Contaminants cause breaks or sharp irregularities such as "islands" to appear in the color fringes.

As a control on the atomizer or water-break tests, a fingerprint is placed on a piece of freshly cleaved mica, a surface which is known to be perfectly clean. The fresh surface is quickly subjected to the test. Failure to develop the contaminated area, and no other area, indicates that the atomizer spray may have been too coarse and the test insensitive. Airborne or other environmental contamination can be detected by exposing a piece of freshly cleaved mica to the atmosphere in the work area, and then employing the atomizer test.

In rooms where critical assembly is carried on, there should be as little traffic as possible. Parts and supplies can be brought in through sliding-panel cabinets.[2] Unless they have urgent business, all visitors should be excluded. The critical assembly room is partitioned off from a larger room which is air conditioned, and the air in the inner room is further filtered. An electrostatic

---

[1] "Detection, Removal and Control of Organic Contaminants in the Production of Electron Devices," D. O. Feder and D. E. Koontz; ASTM Special Publication No. 246, 1959, p. 40; "Generation of Clean Surfaces in High Vacuum," R. W. Roberts, *Br. J. Appl. Phys.*, **14,** 537–543, 1963; "Adsorption and Decomposition of Hydrocarbons on Clean Metal Films," R. W. Roberts, *ibid.*, 485–487, 1963.

[2] "Planning and Operating a Clean Shop," W. T. Dyall and L. C. Herman, *ibid.*, p. 13. "Measuring and Controlling Dust," P. R. Pondy and G. E. Helmke, *ibid.*, p. 3. "Operation Snow White—An Approach to Higher Reliability in Receiving Tubes," K. D. Johnson, *ibid.*, p. 32.

precipitator and a dehumidifier are useful. Relative humidity in rooms where oxide cathodes are fabricated should not exceed 40 percent. The inner room should have a slight positive pressure with respect to the outer room so that contaminant particles might be excluded. Except for the air conditioner and filter openings, the walls, floors, ceilings, and doors should be as well sealed as possible. Materials of contruction, such as plaster, building board, wood, and cement, should be well covered with a good grade of gloss or semigloss paint.

For special work a so-called "dry-box" can be used[1] to protect against contamination which escapes other methods of prevention (operator's breath, dandruff, etc.). The dry-box can also be used with special inert atmospheres when required, such as in the handling of activated cathode surfaces.

It is recommended that the operators wear wrap-around nylon or Orlon gowns and head coverings in all areas where critical tube work is being done, and necessary visitors are to be provided with the same articles before entering. Rubber finger cots can be used but the operators must guard against touching the exposed palm of the hand or face with them. Nylon gloves are to be used with the same precaution. A preferred type of nylon glove is one which fits well and is full-fashioned and, preferably, woven from a single filament so as to reduce the likelihood of frayed ends. The gloves can be washed and rinsed thoroughly in distilled water, and should be discarded as soon as any sign of pilling or wear is noticed. Contact of nylon gloves with acetone and similar solvents is to be avoided.

CLEANING PROCEDURES

The chemical cleaning procedures (given below) are not sufficient by themselves to ensure complete freedom from contamination. Ultrasonic methods can be used,[2] but only in conjunction with other procedures. All metal parts must be fired or heat-treated by one of the various techniques outlined below.

As a typical example of a specific cleaning procedure used in a tube laboratory, the following private communication is given here, courtesy of A. F. Amos, Tube Project Engineer of the Owen Harries Consulting Engineers, Ltd., Devonshire, Bermuda:

Preliminary Memorandum on Cleaning Electron Tube Parts:

1. Vapor-degrease metal parts in a suitable solvent such as perchlorethylene.

2. All parts (including glass and containers for transport or storage) are ultrasonically agitated in a 0.05 percent solution of a surface-active (wetting) agent in deionized water, made by passing tap, or preferably distilled, water through a mixed-bed deionizing column. All tap water must be tested periodically with silver nitrate for the presence of chlorides.

---

[1] See Reference 2, K. D. Johnson, p. 2.

[2] "An Ultrasonic System for Eliminating Physical Contaminants from Electron Devices," D. E. Koontz and I. Amron, ASTM Special Publication No. 246, 1959, p. 22. (*cf.* p. 561)

3. All the parts and containers, both metal and glass, are then washed for 15 minutes in overflowing deionized water.

4. Boil all parts and containers for 30 minutes in hydrogen peroxide (1%), analytical quality. *Warning:* If the parts include tungsten leads sealed into glass, it has been found that if the seals are not well fused, this process may produce a leaky seal.

5. For nickel parts, an alternative for step 4 is to fire at 400°C in air, to produce a light oxidation; for stainless steel parts, a firing at 900°C for 5 minutes may be substituted.

6. If step 4 is elected, all parts and containers are next washed in overflowing deionized water for 15 minutes. The surplus water is then removed with a jet of dry nitrogen gas by means of a spray gun. A filter is used in the gas line, which should preferably be Tygon tubing. The parts are then baked in dry nitrogen gas at 200°C for 15 minutes to complete drying. A stainless steel seamless oven is used, with a small positive nitrogen pressure applied to the inside. (If step 5 is used, omit step 6.)

7. The glass parts are then regarded as clean and ready for assembly. Metal parts are deoxidized by firing in *dry hydrogen:* 900°C for nickel and copper-nickel alloys, 1175° for stainless steel.

Note 1. The cleanliness of the parts is tested at appropriate stages by either the water-break or the atomizer test. In the case of the water-break test, the parts are dipped into a beaker of overflowing deionized water and withdrawn. In the case of the atomizer test, the parts are sprayed from a fine-particle atomizer. If, in both instances, a uniform, unbroken film of water is left on the part, hydrophobic contaminants are not present. The atomizer test is the more sensitive.

Note 2. If the parts include electrodes which will be subject to high electrostatic fields, they are to be electropolished after step 7 is completed. This electropolishing is intended to remove the crystallized surface produced by the firing procedures. After the electropolishing is finished, steps 2, 3, and 6 are repeated to clean the parts before use in a vacuum.

The following formulas, given by use in alphabetical order, have been found useful.

A-1. Cleaning of aluminum (not stained)

1. Degrease if oily (see DEGREASING below).
2. Use 2-8 oz/gal NaOH, Na_2CO_3, or TSP, 180–200°F.
3. If smut forms, immerse for a few seconds in *bright dip*:

   H_2SO_4 . . . 2 gal
   HNO_3 . . . 1 gal
   Water . . . 1 qt
   HCl (or NaCl) . . . $\frac{1}{2}$ oz
   Use at room temperature

A-2. Cleaning of aluminum (if stained from heat treatment, etc.)

1. Degrease if oily (see DEGREASING below).

2. Immerse for one minute in:

   HF . . . 1 part
   HNO_3 . . . 1 part
   Water . . . 98 parts
   Use at room temperature

3. Follow with treatment A-1 above.

B-1. Cleaning of silver-copper brazing alloys

1. Matawan #48W (Hanson-VanWinkle-Munning Co.) 8 oz/gal (water).
2. Use at 180–210°F for 5 minutes or more.
3. Rinse work in cold water.
4. Rinse in hot distilled or deionized water.
5. Rinse in methanol, reagent quality.
6. Dry in warm-air oven.

(Nichrome, nickel, or stainless steel baskets can be used to immerse the work in the cleaners.)

Cathodes: See N-1A, p. 12.

C-1. Chromic-sulfuric cleaning fluid

1. CrO_3 (chromic acid or chromium trioxide) saturated solution in:
2. Hot H_2SO_4, concentrated, 1.84 specific gravity (sp. gr.)

This solution is preferred for electron tube work because of the absence of alkaline salts likely to remain in crevices.

When the solution becomes greenish or diluted, it is to be discarded. If flushed down the drain, it is to be accompanied by copious quantities of water.

a. For use, cover the parts with the supernatant only—no crystals.
b. Heat on a hot plate to 80–90°C; remove from heat and allow to cool for 5 minutes.
c. Pour off the acid and rinse in hot running water for 10 minutes.
d. Rinse in 5 changes of deionized water for 5 minutes.
e. Boil in fresh deionized water for 5 minutes.
f. Drain and dry parts in hot-air oven at 80°C. Metal parts can be rinsed in reagent-grade methanol before drying, to speed the process. **Ceramic[1] parts should be dried immediately after step d.**

A proprietary ready-mixed chromic-sulfuric cleaning solution (Chromerge) can be obtained from the Emil Greiner Co., New York 13, N.Y.

---

[1] Do not use this procedure for boron nitride. See p. 172.

C-2. Bright dip for copper and brass

Water . . . 1960 ml
H_2SO_4 . . . 1730 ml (sp. gr. 1.84)
HNO_3 . . . 285 ml (concentrated)
HCl . . . 10 ml (concentrated)

C-2A. Cleaning of copper

1. Degrease (*see* DEGREASING D-1).
2. Immerse for 10 seconds in 50% (vol) HNO_3.
3. Rinse in cold tap water to stop the reaction.
4. Repeat acid treatment, if required, to obtain uniform surface.
5. Rinse for 10 minutes in cold tap water.
6. Rinse in two changes of distilled or deionized water.
7. Dry with hot-air blower.

C-3. Cleaning of copper (Becco Process: Food Machinery & Chemical Corp., Becco Division, Buffalo 7, New York)

This process is not a bright dip but removes oxides and leaves a clean crystalline surface. Solution is made up as follows:

1. Ammonium persulfate (Becco) . . . 20–25 gm,
   Tap water, tepid (not hot) . . . 100 ml.
2. Work should be thoroughly degreased before copper is immersed (see DEGREASING D-1).
3. Immerse work in solution 10 to 60 seconds (or as long as 2 minutes in stubborn cases). A slight agitation is desirable.
4. Rinse thoroughly in cold tap water, followed by cold distilled or deionized water. Dry at room temperature (fan or blower may be used). **Do not heat.**

(*Note:* This material is only mildly acid (pH 4.4 in saturated solution), nonfuming, nontoxic. It passivates copper surfaces.)

C-4. Cleaning of copper (for printed circuit material, etc.)

1. *Solution:* 5% (weight) HCl, or 2% (weight) H_2SO_4.
2. *Solution:* 10% (weight Na or KOH in tap water at 90°C. Immerse for 30 seconds after brief rinse from first solution. Room temperature.
3. Mechanical cleaning: pumice, grade FFF . . . 1 part (weight),
   water . . . 10 parts (weight).
   Rub with clean cotton or cloth.
4. Rinse in running tap and distilled water; dry in air blast.

C-5. Cleaning of copper[1]

Ultrasonic agitation in the following solution:

Formic acid HCOOH . . . 60% (vol)
Hydrogen peroxide H_2O_2 . . . 10% (vol of 30% superoxol)
Water, deionized . . . 30% (vol)

D-1. Degreasing procedure

(*Note.* Degreasing in liquid solvents is likely to be ineffective because in industrial atmospheres, or places where there are oil burners, internal-combustion engine exhausts, gas burners, etc., an open container or bottle will pick up, even in a very short time, oil- or grease-bearing dust particles. Also, if fingers are dipped into the solvent, it is obvious, as evidenced by the severe drying action on the skin, that the oily dermal secretions have gone into the solvent and will subsequently leave an oily residue on anything put into the solvent.)

Immerse the work successively in the following baths at room temperature. All the solvents are to be reagent grade and fresh. 1. Acetone. 2. Trichlorethylene. 3. Trichlorethylene (second bath). 4. Trichlorethylene (third bath). 5. Methanol. 6. Acetone (second bath). 7. Dry in warm-air blast or oven at 80°C.

D-2. Cleaning and descaling of Dumet wire[1]

The work is to be ultrasonically agitated in the following solution:

Formic acid (HCOOH) . . . 60% (vol)
Hydrogen peroxide (H_2O_2) . . . 10% (vol of 30% superoxol)
Deionized water . . . 30% (vol)

The nickel extensions on Dumet leads can be cleaned in the same solution.

G-1. Glass-cleaning solution

Hydrofluoric acid (HF) . . . 4 vol (concentrated)
HNO_3 . . . 33 vol (concentrated)
Water . . . 60 vol
Dreft (or any suitable detergent without filler) . . . 2 vol

Use solution at room temperature. Some workers have found this solution to be more effective in removing grease and carbonaceous matter than the conventional chromic-sulfuric cleaning fluid (C-1).

The proportions of the acids given can be varied widely, according to R. H. A. Crawley ("A Universal Reagent for Cleaning Glassware and Silica," *Chemistry and Industry,* **45,** 1953, p. 1205–6).

---

[1] "The Preparation of Ultraclean Electron-Tube Components by Chemical Etching," D. E. Koontz, C. O. Thomas, W. H. Craft, and I. Amron, ASTM Special Technical Publication No. 246, 1959, p. 136.

G-1A. Glass- and mica-cleaning solution[1]

(*Note:* If metallic contaminants are present, use solution C-1 or G-1 above.)

The following solution is suitable for cleaning new glass, preparatory to sealing in assemblies:

1. Boil in 5% (of 30%) H_2O_2. Add sufficient NH_4OH to give a pH of 11.0.
2. Rinse thoroughly in flowing deionized water.
3. Dry in clean atmosphere.

If small amounts of metal are present as contaminants on the glass, add up to 75% formic acid to solution G-1A.

The solution of hydrogen peroxide, formic acid, and water may be used without danger of etching the glass.

I-1. Electrolytic cleaning of iron and steel

Make up the following solution:

Matawan #48W (Hanson-VanWinkle-Munning Co. Matawan, New Jersey),

8 oz/gal of tap water.

Use at 180–210°F.

Current density 40–200 ASF. Work is anodic.

Electrodes: steel or lead.

Time: 1–2 minutes for light work; more for heavy scale.

(*Note:* Discard solution weekly. Scrub cathode and tank thoroughly.)

I-1A. Iron and steel etch[2]

Make up the following solution:

Formic acid (HCOOH) . . . 45% (vol)
H_2O_2 . . . 45% (vol)
Deionized water . . . 10% (vol)

Use at 80°C for 2 minutes.

K-1. Electrolytic cleaning of Kovar (for oxidized metal)

H_2SO_4 . . . 5–10% (weight)
Quinoline . . . 1% (weight) or Rodine #110[3] inhibitor
Water . . . to make 100% (weight)

With the above solution, use carbon electrodes or another piece of clean Kovar. Alternating current should be 10–12 volts. Current density is 1440 amp/ft^2 (or 10 amp/in^2). Time is variable; it depends on size and condition of piece. In some cases it may be necessary to remove loose oxide with a cloth or

---

[1] See footnote for C-5.
[2] See C-5 reference.
[3] American Paint Company, Ambler, Pennsylvania.

brush. The formula was obtained from the manufacturer of Kovar, Stupakoff Division of Carborundum Co., Niagara Falls, New York, and Latrobe, Pennsylvania.

Cleaning of Kovar (see pp. 329, 337)

K-2. Hydrogen firing of glass-Kovar seals

Oxide on the exposed metal portions of seals may be removed by the reduction action of a hydrogen atmosphere, but this method should be used with extreme caution for vacuum seals because of the danger of removing the oxide where the glass joins the metal. Satisfactory results have been obtained by raising the seals to 600°C in hydrogen for 30 minutes and then gradually cooling in hydrogen to at least 200°C before removal. The time in the deoxidizing zone depends on the degree of oxidation. Close control of furnace temperature is essential, and the reducing procedure must be followed by the regular glass-annealing program to remove strains on the glass. Annealing must be done in hydrogen or in some other nonoxidizing atmosphere.

K-3. Cleaning of Kovar and nickel (see also pp. 12–14)

Acetic acid, glacial . . . 750 cc
Nitric acid, concentrated . . . 250 cc
Hydrochloric acid, concentrated . . . 3 cc
Temperature 60°C

K-4. Kovar, iron, nickel; removal of oxides

1. Make up the following solution (inhibited hydrochloric acid):
   HCl (sp. gr. 1.19) . . . 1000 parts (vol)
   Rodine (see K-1 solution) #50, . . . 5 parts (vol)
   Tap water . . . 1000 parts (vol)
2. Add the acid to the water, then add the Rodine #50, and mix well.
3. Temperature for use is 80°C.
4. Immerse parts in solution for a length of time sufficient to dissolve the oxide scale. Heavy scale is removed with a stiff brush.
5. Repeat step 4 if required.
6. Rinse thoroughly in running hot tap water.
7. Rinse in deionized water.
8. Rinse in methanol (reagent grade) or acetone (reagent grade).
9. Dry in air oven at 80°C for 5 minutes.

K-5. Electropolishing of Kovar, stainless steel, and nickel

Solution:

H_2SO_4 (1.84 sp. gr; 66°Be) . . . 1000 ml
Water . . . 370 ml
Glycerin (USP) . . . 1370 ml

While stirring add the acid slowly to the water; avoid overheating. Cool to room temperature, then add the glycerin and mix thoroughly. Use carbon or lead cathode (negative electrode) immersed in the solution.

1. Connect a positive wire to the work and immerse in the solution at room temperature.
2. Raise the voltage to 7.5 for about 30 seconds. A small change in the voltage and time might be necessary to obtain a clean, bright surface.
3. Remove and rinse thoroughly in running tap water.
4. Rinse with deionized water and drain.
5. Boil in two changes of deionized water. Drain between changes.
6. Rinse in methanol (reagent grade) and dry—unless parts are to be plated immediately, in which case omit this. Drying temperature should not be over 70°C.

M-1. Cleaning of mica

1. Degrease (see D-1).
2. Boil in deionized water 2–5 minutes.
3. Rinse in clean, fresh methanol (reagent grade), and dry in oven at 80°C for several hours, or overnight.

M-1A: Cleaning of mica (Use procedure for cleaning glass, as in G-1A; see also p. 374.)

Mo-1. Cleaning of molybdenum

Solution A (mix in the order given):

Deionized water . . . 65 ml
CrO_3 . . . 20 gm
H_2SO_4 (sp. gr. 1.84 tech. grade) . . . 35 ml
(Add the acid slowly while stirring.)

Solution B (mix in the order given):

Tap water . . . 6 vol
HNO_3 (concentrated commercial) . . . 13 vol
HF (concentrated commercial) . . . 1 vol

Solution C:

Tap water . . . 18 vol
NH_4OH (concentrated) . . . 2 vol

1. Immerse parts in Solution B and rinse briefly in tap water.
2. Immerse parts in Solution A and agitate for 30 seconds.

3. Drain off and rinse immediately in hot running tap water.
4. Boil in Solution C for 5 minutes.
5. Drain off and rinse in tap water.
6. Rinse thoroughly in deionized water.
7. Boil in fresh deionized water 10 min. Pour off.
8. Rinse in fresh methanol, reagent grade.
9. Rinse in fresh acetone, reagent grade.
10. Drain as thoroughly as possible and dry in oven not over 80°C.

(*Note:* Solution A can be used until it turns green; then discard. Molybdenum parts cleaned by this method should be silvery bright. The surfaces may be slightly etched.)

Mo-2. Cleaning of molybdenum (and tungsten); removal of oxides

1. Cover parts to be treated in 15% NaOCl (Clorox or equivalent) and heat to about 70°C. Remove parts by inspection when clean; do not overclean. A further oxide may form on molybdenum which will be removed later.
2. Rinse thoroughly in cold or warm tap water. If there are recesses, rinse for one-half hour, or vacuum-boil, with several changes of water, to remove all NaOCl. Discard NaOCl solution when it is no longer effective.
3. Prepare the following solution:

   NH_4OH, 28% . . . 1 part
   H_2O_2, 30% . . . 1 part
   Deionized water . . . 2 parts

   (chemicals are to be reagent grade)

   Place the solution in or near sink; keep tongs handy. **Do not heat.** Immerse a few parts which have had treatment, as in step 1 above, into this solution until clean. If not clean after about 30 seconds, remove from solution and rinse to remove loosely adhering oxide. Repeat if necessary. **Keep the work load small to minimize heating of the solution.** If quite a large quantity of work is to be done, the solution (step 3 above) should be cooled with an outer jacket of cold running water. **Flush mixture down drain immediately after using, or if heating takes place; otherwise, a violent reaction may occur.**
4. Rinse work in running tap water for one-half hour, or repeat vacuum-boiling as in step 2 above. The last vacuum rinse should be in deionized water, or if vacuum is not used, in several changes of deionized water.
5. Rinse in reagent-grade methanol.
6. Dry in air at room temperature or in oven at not more than 80°C.

Mo-3. Cleaning of molybdenum[1]

This solution produces an etched surface.

Formic acid HCOOH . . . 45% by vol
Hydrogen peroxide (30% H_2O_2) . . . 45% by vol
Deionized water . . . 10% by vol

Use at 80°C for 2 minutes. Rinse thoroughly in flowing deionized water.

Mo-4. Dissolving molybdenum mandrel from coiled-coil tungsten heaters

(same source as Mo-3 above; see also T-4)

Formic acid . . . 50–75% by vol
H_2O_2 (30%) . . . 25–50% by vol

Treat for 10–15 minutes at 65–70°C, then rinse thoroughly in deionized water. The molybdenum mandrel is completely removed without visual change in the tungsten coil.

N-1A. Cleaning of nickel cathode bases and parts

1. Vapor-degrease in acetone or methyl ethyl ketone.
2. Select by microscopic examination.
3. Scrub in fresh acetone (reagent grade).
4. Rinse in fresh acetone.
5. Boil in distilled water 5 minutes.
6. Rinse in fresh acetone.
7. Dry in warm dry nitrogen blast.
8. Select by inspection.
9. Heat-treat at 925°C in wet hydrogen for 15 minutes.
10. Etch in the following solution:

HCl (concentrated) . . . 10% by vol
Deionized water . . . 90% by vol

Boil parts in this solution for 10 minutes, then add: equal amount of H_2O_2, 30% reagent grade . . . 5%. Continue boiling for an additional 15 minutes.

11. Wash in cold running tap water.
12. Wash in boiling distilled water for 10 minutes.
13. Rinse in fresh acetone 1 minute.
14. Rinse in absolute methanol (reagent grade).
15. Dry in air at 100°C.
16. Inspect. Under 10–15× magnification the nickel should look uniformly etched.

---

[1] "The preparation of Ultraclean Electron Tube Components by Chemical Etching," D. E. Koontz, C. O. Thomas, W. H. Craft, and I. Amron; ASTM Spec. Tech. Publication #246, 1959, p. 136.

17. Heat-treat at 925–1000°C for 15 minutes in wet hydrogen. For materials in excess of 0.010 inch thick, a longer time will be needed. The hydrogen is bubbled through distilled water.
18. Vacuum-fire so that the cathode surface temperature reaches 850°C. No bucket is used.

N-1B. Cleaning of nickel for cathodes and fluorescent screen bases[1]

1. Agitate in clean acetone.
2. Boil in the following solution for 5 minutes:

   sodium carbonate . . . 40 gm
   sodium hydroxide . . . 13 gm
   sodium cyanide . . . 13 gm
   (all chemicals are reagent grade)
   Distilled or deionized water . . . 1 liter

3. Boil five minutes in deionized water.
4. Rinse in acetic acid, 5% in deionized water, at 50°C.
5. Agitate in three changes of deionized water.
6. Rinse in clean methanol, reagent grade.
7. Dry in warm air blast or oven not over 80°C.
8. Just previous to cathode coating, the pieces are to be hydrogen- or vacuum-fired at 900°C.

N-2. Cleaning of nickel; removal of oxides

Prepare the following solutions; use reagent-grade chemicals.

Solution A:

Tap water . . . 1500 ml
H_2SO_4 (1.84 sp. gr.) . . . 500 ml
HNO_3 (1.42 sp. gr.) . . . 500 ml
Acetic acid, glacial . . . 500 ml

Solution B:

Tap water . . . 1000 ml
H_2SO_4 (1.84 sp. gr.) . . . 1500 ml
HNO_3 (1.42 sp. gr.) . . . 2250 ml
Allow to cool, then add:
NaCl . . . 30 gm

Solution C:

Tap water . . . 1000 ml
NH_4OH (28%) . . . 20 ml

---

[1] This is the solution and treatment given by F. Rosebury in the R.L.E. *Tube Laboratory Manual* under the designation C1-A.

1. For slightly oxidized nickel parts, heat Solution B under hood to 35°C and immerse work for 5 to 30 seconds.
2. Rinse in tap water. Work should now be bright.
3. Dip briefly in Solution C.
4. Rinse in running tap water.
5. Rinse in deionized water.
6. Boil in two changes of fresh deionized water; drain thoroughly after each boil.
7. Rinse in methanol, reagent-grade.
8. Dry at room temperature, or in air oven not over 60°C.
9. For heavily oxidized nickel parts, heat solution A under hood to 60–70°C and immerse work for a time just sufficient to remove the oxide. Check closely at short intervals. Do not overclean.
10. Remove parts and rinse thoroughly in running tap water.
11. Follow the step 3 procedure above.

N-3. Cleaning of nickel; removal of oxide from nickel-plated tube-base pins

1. Dip in HCl (1.18 sp. gr. tech. grade) and agitate gently for minute.
2. Rinse immediately in running tap water; drain thoroughly.
3. Immerse in 10% NH_4OH and agitate gently for 1 minute.
4. Rinse thoroughly in running tap water.
5. Rinse in two changes of deionized water; shake to remove excess water.
6. Rinse in fresh methanol, reagent-grade; agitate gently for 1 minute. Shake to remove excess methanol.
7. Dry in air oven at 80–100°C for one-half hour.

N-4. Electrolytic cleaning of nickel

1. Degrease parts as in D-1.
2. Electrolytic bath:

Tap . . . 300 ml
H_2SO_4 (1.84 sp. gr.) . . . 170 ml
H_3PO_4 (1.84 sp. gr.) . . . 550 ml
Temperature for use . . . 60°C
Anode . . . carbon rod
Cathode . . . nickel work pieces

Immerse work in this solution at temperature given and adjust dc voltage so that bubbling just begins around work piece. Avoid excessive current. **Caution:** This solution rapidly attacks and dissolves nickel.

3. Rinse thoroughly in hot running tap water.
4. Rinse in two changes of deionized water.
5. Rinse in fresh methanol, reagent grade.
6. Dry in air blast or oven not over 80°C.

SS-1. Cleaning of stainless steel

1. Degrease as per D-1.
2. Agitate for 30 seconds in the following solution:

   Tap water . . . 750 ml
   HCl (concentrated) . . . 250 ml
   HNO_3 (concentrated) . . . 200 ml

3. Rinse thoroughly in running tap water and then immerse in HNO_3 (concentrated).
4. Repeat steps 2 and 3 if necessary for a uniform surface.
5. Rinse in running hot tap water for 10 minutes.
6. Rinse in two changes of deionized water. If there are deep recesses or holes, boil in deionized water.
7. Rinse in acetone or methanol, reagent-grade.
8. Dry under infrared lamps or in air oven at 80–100°C.

SS-2. Cleaning, brightening, and passivating stainless steel

Solution: HNO_3 (concentrated) . . . 1 part
Tap water . . . 4 parts

1. Immerse in solution at room temperature until desired appearance is obtained. Warm solution gently if action is too slow.
2. Rinse thoroughly in hot, running tap water.
3. Follow steps 6 to 8 in SS-1 above.

SS-3. Cleaning, oxide removal, and passivation of stainless steel

Solution A (for oxide removal); mix in order given:

Tap water . . . 25 vol
HNO_3 (69% technical grade) . . . 10 vol
HF (50% technical grade) . . . 15 vol

Use polyethylene or rubber-lined vessel. Glass vessel may be used if for a short time and immediate use. **Do not keep in glass.**

Solution B (for passivation):

Tap water . . . 4 vol
HNO_3 (69% tech. grade) . . . 1 vol

PROCEDURE:

1. Immerse parts in solution A for not more than 20 minutes at a maintained temperature of 55–60°C. Agitate frequently. Take out and rinse in running tap water to check for oxide removal. Heavy oxidation may require longer times. Discard the solution whenever cleaning time becomes too long.
2. Rinse thoroughly in running tap water.
3. If passivation is not required, rinse in deionized water and drain well.

4. Boil in two changes of fresh deionized water, draining well after each.
5. Rinse in methanol, reagent-grade.
6. Dry in air at room temperature or in air oven not over 80°C.
7. **Passivation** (also for parts that are to be plated): Immerse in solution B after step 2 above. Agitate frequently.
8. Rinse thoroughly in tap water and drain.
9. Proceed from step 3 above.

SS-4. Electropolishing stainless steel[1]

Make up the following solution:

H_2SO_4 (1.84 sp. gr.) . . . 1000 ml
Water . . . 370 ml
Glycerin (USP) . . . 1370 ml

Stirring, add the acid slowly to the water; avoid overheating. Cool to room temperature, then add the glycerin, and mix.

1. Connect negative cable to carbon or lead cathode immersed in the bath.
2. Connect the positive cable to the work and immerse in the bath at room temperature.
3. Raise the voltage to 7.5 for about one-half minute. A small change in voltage and time may be necessary to get clean, bright surfaces.
4. Rinse thoroughly in running tap water.
5. Rinse with deionized water and drain.
6. Boil in deionized water, two changes.
7. Rinse in reagent-grade methanol and dry in air oven not over 70°C. **If parts are to be plated immediately, do not dry** but transfer them to the plating bath **while wet.**

TA-1. Cleaning of tantalum

1. Dip in hot 20% HCl solution.
2. Rinse thoroughly in distilled or deionized water.
3. Dip in chromic-sulfuric cleaning fluid (C-1) at 110°C.
4. Rinse thoroughly in hot, running tap water, then thoroughly in hot distilled or deionized water.
5. Parts should be dried in clean, warm air, avoiding all dust or contamination. The metal should not be wiped with paper or cloth, or handled with fingers. Store in dust-tight containers. Tantalum is to be vacuum-fired before using (see p. 511).

TI-1. Cleaning of titanium

Pickle the metal in a solution of 20–30% HNO_3 with 2% HF at 54°C. If the titanium has been heated not higher than 600°C, this treatment should be sufficient to remove contamination.

---

[1] See also p. 22.

T-1. Cleaning of tungsten

Solution:

Sodium hypochlorite (Clorox or equivalent) 15% . . . 1 vol
Water . . . 5 vol

1. Cover the tungsten pieces in a freshly prepared solution.
2. Boil 5–8 minutes, or until the oxide can easily be rinsed off under tap water as shown by a test piece taken from the bath.
3. Rinse thoroughly in running tap water, then in deionized water.
4. Rinse in reagent-grade methanol, unless parts are to be electropolished, in which case a tap water rinse is sufficient.

This procedure will give tungsten a clean, matte finish which can be easily electropolished (see T-3 and T-4 below) to a bright surface. If this cleaning is not used on heavily oxidized parts, the subsequent electropolishing may remove excessive metal before the oxide is entirely removed.

T-1A. Tungsten and molybdenum; removal of oxides

See Mo-2, p. 11.

T-2. Tungsten and molybdenum heaters and filaments; cleaning prior to coating with aluminum oxide

1. Boil 5 minutes in 20% KOH solution.
2. Rinse thoroughly in running tap water.
3. Rinse in three changes of deionized or distilled water at room temperature.
4. Dry in warm air blast or in oven at not more than 80°C.

T-2A. Tungsten and molybdenum; electropolishing or electrolytic cleaning (not to be used for heaters or filaments)

Solution:

KOH or NaOH (USP) flake or stick, 20% (by weight) in water.

Use at room temperature.

1. Use alternating current, 5–10 volts, with carbon electrode.
2. Vigorous gassing should occur. Treat the work for about one-half minute, then lower the voltage and examine the piece. Repeat if necessary. The tungsten will have a matte surface and be free of oxide.
3. Rinse thoroughly in running tap water and drain.
4. Rinse in three changes of deionized or distilled water.
5. Rinse in methanol (reagent grade).
6. Dry in oven not over 70°C.

T-3. Electropolishing of tungsten and molybdenum

Solution: Same as in T-2A above.

The treatment is the same as in T-2A above except that direct current is used; the negative cable is connected to the carbon electrode.

T-4. Dissolving molybdenum from tungsten coils

See also Mo-4, p. 12.

Solution:

HNO_3 (concentrated) . . . 5 parts by vol
H_2SO_4 (sp. gr. 1.84) . . . 3 parts by vol
Water . . . 2 parts by vol
Temperature for use . . . 90°C

1. Completely cover coils with solution. Cover vessel with glass to prevent spattering.
2. Allow coils to remain in solution until all evidence of chemical action has stopped.
3. Pour off solution and rinse thoroughly in distilled water, and then in three changes of deionized water. Drain and dry in reagent-grade methanol.

This solution may be used repeatedly until exhausted.

ELECTROPOLISHING[1]

Since most machined metal surfaces are not completely smooth, i.e., they show irregularities (projections and depressions), it is sometimes required to obtain a polished surface without the introduction of embedded polishing compounds, etc. Electropolishing is a means of reducing or eliminating these irregularities.

During electropolishing, an oxide or hydroxide film is formed on the work by electrochemical action; the exterior of this film is constantly dissolved into the electrolyte by the action. When proper balance conditions are met, a constant anodic film thickness is maintained, and this also maintains the electrolyte and protects the work from localized attack.

In most electropolishing techniques mechanical agitation of the work or the solution is beneficial in keeping the electrolyte active and facilitating oxide or hydroxide dissolution. Some baths require heating for best operation.

Electropolishing is similar to electroplating (see p. 23), but since metal is to be removed rather than deposited on the work, the work pieces are made positive (anodic). For optimum results cathode-to-anode ratios should be at least 2 : 1, except for electropolishing the inside of work pieces.

For electropolishing irregularly shaped work, the anode-cathode distance should be increased to avoid excess action at points of highest current density. Conforming cathodes may be required in some cases. When electropolishing the inside of cylindrical cavities, etc., a round cathode rod placed exactly in the center gives best results.

---

[1] Source: *Metal Finishing Guidebook & Directory,* Metals & Plastics Publications, Inc., Westwood, New Jersey (1962).

Cathodes may be of steel, stainless steel (302, 304), copper, or lead. The precautions to be taken in electropolishing are, in general, the same as those for electroplating (p. 24, with special attention to item 2).

Bright electropolished finishes are obtained at higher temperatures for longer times, while short times at lower temperatures tend to produce satin finishes.

Thorough rinsing is mandatory after treatment. In concentrated acid solutions, warm rinse water is more effective than cold. However, if a solution is used which is likely to attack the work during transfer, a fast cold-water rinse is indicated. Too high rinse temperatures should be avoided because they tend to cause a pickling action. After thorough rinsing with cold or warm running water, a hot water rinse may be used to facilitate drying. Wetting agents in the final rinse may be used to prevent spotting.

All the baths given below are in water unless otherwise indicated.

EPA-1. Aluminum (alkaline bath)

Sodium carbonate	15%
Trisodium phosphate (TSP)	5%
Temperature, °C	74–88
Current density, amp/ft^2	50–60 (at start)

EPA-2. Aluminum (acid bath)

Fluoboric acid	2.5%
Temperature, °C	29.5
Voltage (dc)	15–30
Current density, amp/ft^2	10–20

EPA-3. Aluminum (acid bath)

Sulfuric acid	1–60%
Hydrofluoric acid	0.2–1.5%
Current density, amp/ft^2	100
Temperature, °C	60

EPA-4. Aluminum (acid bath—cold)

Perchloric acid	34.5%
Acetic anhydride	64.5%
Current density, amp/ft^2	10
Temperature, °C	13.3

EPA-5. Aluminum (acid bath)

Phosphoric acid	35–45%
Glycerol	30–40%
Water	20–30
Current density, amp/ft^2	35–40
Temperature, °C	66–82

(Sulfuric acid can be added to this bath optionally.)

EPA-6. Aluminum (acid bath)

Sulfuric acid	4.7%
Phosphoric acid	75%
Chromic acid	6.5%
Al^{+++} and Cr^{+++} ... to	6%
Current density, amp/ft^2	150
Temperature, °C	79–82
Voltage (dc)	10–15

EPA-7. Aluminum (acid bath)

Phosphoric acid	10%
Sulfuric acid	60%
Nitric acid	1%
Current density, amp/ft^2	200
Temperature, °C	96

(Nitric acid has the same effect as the chromic acid in EPA-6.)

Copper (and alloys)

Cleaning of copper and high copper alloys can be accomplished preparatory to electropolishing by the Becco process (see details in C-3).

EPC-1. Copper and high-copper alloys (warm bath)

Arsenic acid	15% (weight)
Phosphoric acid	55% (weight)
Chromic acid	3% (weight)
Water	27% (weight)
Temperature, °C	54
Current density, amp/ft^2	500

EPC-2. Copper (cold bath)

Water	100 parts (weight)
Chromic acid	12.5 parts (weight)
Sodium dichromate	37.5 parts (weight)
Acetic acid	12.5 parts (weight)
Current density, amp/ft^2	250–1000
Temperature, °C	30

EPC-3. Copper (cold or warm)

Sulfuric acid	14% by weight
Phosphoric acid	49% by weight
Chromic acid	0.5% by weight
Water	36.5% by weight
Temperature, °C	15.6–77
Current density, amp/ft^2	100–1000

EPC-4. Copper (hot bath)

Phosphoric acid in cyclohexanol	40% by volume
Temperature, °C	100

Current density, amp/ft^2	200
Time, minutes	5

EPC-5. Copper (neutral—warm bath)

Sodium tripolyphosphate	14–16 oz/gal
Boric acid	4–5 oz/gal
pH	7–7.5
Temperature, °C	52–57

EPC-6. Copper (ac bath)

Ammonium phosphate	100 parts (weight)
Citric acid	100 parts (weight)
Potassium phosphate	25 parts (weight)
Water	1000 parts (weight)
Voltage (ac)	6–25
Current density, amp/ft^2 (ac)	75–575

Nickel and nickel alloys (see also K-5, N-4)

Nickel should be cleaned preparatory to electropolishing by one of the procedures given in N-1A, N-1B, N-2, N-3.

EPN-1. Nickel (sulfuric acid bath)

Sulfuric acid	70%
Water	30%

EPN-2A. Nickel (sulfuric-chromic acid bath)

Sulfuric acid	60% minimum
Chromic acid	to saturation
Water	as required

EPN-2B. Nickel (sulfuric acid/glycerin bath)

Sulfuric acid	60% minimum
Glycerin	200 ml/liter
Water	as required

EPN-2C. Nickel (nickel sulfate bath)

Nickel sulfate	240 gm/liter
Ammonium sulfate	45 gm/liter
Potassium chloride	35 gm/liter

EPN-3. Nickel (phosphoric acid bath)

Orthophosphoric acid	15–70%
Sulfuric acid	15–60%
Water	balance

EPN-4. Nickel (sulfuric/phosphoric acid bath)

Sulfuric acid	14%
Phosphoric acid	49%
Chromic acid	0.5%
Water	36.5%

An electropolishing bath for Kovar, stainless steel, and nickel is given in K-5. Electropolishing baths for tungsten and molybdenum are given in T-2A and T-3. An electropolishing bath for stainless steel is given in SS-4. Additional baths for stainless steel are given below.

EPSS-1. Stainless steel (phosphoric acid bath)

Phosphoric acid	75–100%
Water	0–25%
Current density, amp/ft^2	300
Temperature, °C	66

EPSS-2. Stainless steel (phosphoric/sulfuric/glycerin bath)

Phosphoric acid	5 parts
Sulfuric acid	4 parts
Glycerin (USP)	1 part
Current density, amp/ft^2	450
Voltage	9

EPSS-3. Stainless steel (sulfuric/phosphoric acid bath)

Sulfuric acid	15%
Phosphoric acid	63%
Current density, amp/ft^2	50 minimum
Temperature, °C	27–80

EPSS-4. Stainless steel (phosphoric/lactic/sulfuric acid)

Lactic acid	33%
Phosphoric acid	40%
Sulfuric acid	13.5%
Current density, amp/ft^2	75–300
Temperature, °C	71–93

EPSS-5. Stainless steel (phosphoric/butyl alcohol bath)

Phosphoric acid	90%
Normal butyl alcohol	10%
Current density, amp/ft^2	75–750
Temperature, °C	82

EPSS-6. Stainless steel (nitric/acetic acid bath)

Nitric acid	70%
Acetic acid	30%
Current density, amp/ft^2	75 minimum
Temperature, °C	24 maximum

(This bath can be used with ac.)

EPSS-7. Stainless steel (sulfuric/fluoboric/oxalic acid bath)

Sulfuric acid	48%
Fluoboric acid	14%
Oxalic acid	1%

Current density, amp/ft^2 50–250
Temperature, °C 60–76

It is understood that the values given for all liquid acids in the electropolishing baths are for concentrated strength. All quantities are by volume unless otherwise stated.

Electroplating and Stripping

PLATING IN GENERAL

Electroplating procedures which seem most adaptable to laboratory scale have been chosen. Large articles or those requiring heavy deposits should usually be handled by commercial plating concerns. Information on other types of baths than those given, and on special procedures, can be found in the following references:

Electroplating and Engineering Handbook, edited by A. K. Graham, Reinhold Publishing Corp., New York, 1955.

Modern Electroplating, H. P. Coats, Electrochemical Society, New York, 1942.

Guidebook and Directory, thirtieth edition, Metal & Plastics Publications, Westwood, New Jersey, 1962.

Protective Coatings for Metals, R. M. Burns and A. E. Schuh, Reinhold Publishing Corp., New York, New York, 1939.

"ASTM and AES Specifications and Tests for Electrodeposited Coatings," published by the American Society for Testing Materials, Philadelphia, Pennsylvania.

Electroplating on Aluminum and Its Alloys, published by Aluminum Company of America.

Practical Nickel Plating, second edition, published by International Nickel Company, New York, New York, 1961.

"Finishes for Metal Products," *Materials & Methods,* September, 1955, p. 117.

"Properties and Uses of Electroplates," Engineering Department, U.S.N. Ordnance Test Station, Inyokern, Calif., *Materials in Design Engineering,* February, 1959, p. 121.

"Nickel Plating Aluminum," M. W. Riley, *Materials & Methods,* July, 1954, p. 96.

"Guide to Electroplated Coatings," R. J. Fabian, *Materials in Design Engineering,* **55,** 95–106, 1962.

Also consult the following periodicals: *Electroplating, Metal Finishing, Metal Progress, Monthly Rev. Am. Electroplating Soc., Proc. Am. Electroplating Soc., Trans. Electrochem. Soc., Plating.*

The cleaning process and preparation of metal surfaces for plating are extremely important for proper adhesion and a good plate. (See previous sections, pp. 3–17.)

In general the work piece and the plating anode should have about equal surface area.

To avoid thin tarnish films on plated surfaces (especially important in silver plating), as soon as the work is plated, rinse thoroughly in hot running water, dip in clean reagent-grade methanol, and dry in warm air at not more than 80°C. When transferring work from one bath to another, drying should be avoided.

Some precautions for electroplating are given by Savage and Strothman[1] as follows:

1. Avoid sharp corners; use fillets with as large a radius as possible. This applies to protruding as well as recessed edges and corners.
2. Horizontal surfaces should be avoided; top flats collect sediment and produce poor and porous plate; bottom flats trap gas, which may prevent plating entirely.
3. Drill holes to vent gases and drain solution in recesses.
4. Sandblasting (of steel) aids in plating.
5. Cleaning and pickling is of paramount importance for good plating and adhesion.

When applying more than one deposit on a given material, it is generally considered desirable to electroplate in a certain specified order:

Steel. In the case of ordinary steels, the first deposit should be copper. This may be followed by silver, nickel, or gold, depending on requirements (see COPPER PLATING ON STEEL, p. 27).

Copper may be plated directly with gold, silver, or nickel.

Kovar should have an initial flash or strike of copper or nickel before silver or other plating is applied.

Brass can be silver-, gold-, or nickel-plated directly, but an initial copper strike is desirable.

Stainless steel and other high-chrome alloys may be nickel-plated, using a Watts-type bath (NiP-2, p. 29) at the higher temperatures. The metal must be thoroughly cleaned (not passivated) by one of the formulas given in the cleaning section.

---

[1] "Electroplating Large Complex Shapes," F. K. Savage and E. P. Strothman, *Materials & Methods,* August, 1952, p. 94.

Chromium plating is usually carried out in this order: copper, nickel, chromium (on steel).[1]

Molybdenum. See NiP-7, p. 31.

USE OF STOP-OFF LACQUER: This is a nitrocellulose lacquer resist, usually with a red dye added for identification. It is to be applied to the clean work piece by dipping, spraying, or brushing (to those areas where no plating is wanted). The lacquer is removed after plating by immersion in ethyl acetate or acetone.

PLATING AND STRIPPING BATHS

The following formulas and procedures are suggested for laboratory-scale operations in electroplating, stripping, and miscellaneous coating or decoating.

CRP-1. Chromium-plating bath. (From "Glass to Metal Seals of Strong Adherence," *Services Electronics Research Lab. Tech. Journal.,* **4,** February, 1954. This paper discusses the use of very thin, chromium-rich layers on other metals for the purpose of making glass seals.)

Formula:

Chromic acid	250 gm
H_2SO_4 (1.84 sp. gr.)	2.5 gm
Water	1 liter
Sp. gr. of bath	1.17
Temperature for use	52–55°C
Current density	600 amp/ft^2
Rate of deposition (estimated)	0.0001 inch/4 minutes

CuP-1. Copper plating on aluminum

Formula:

ZnO	10–13 oz
NaOH	55–70 oz
Water	1 gal

Use at room temperature.

1. Degrease parts (see D-1, p. 7).
2. Immerse in 20% NaOH solution for 30 seconds.

[1] There is evidence that a double layer of nickel under chromium is more effective than the standard copper-nickel-chromium procedure. See "The Corrosion Behavior and Protective Value of Copper-Nickel-Chromium and Nickel-Chromium Coatings on Steel," C. H. Sample, Symp. on Props., Tests & Performance of Electrodeposited Metallic Coatings, Spec. Tech. Pub. No. 197, Amer. Soc. for Testing Materials, 1956. (A reprint of this paper is available from the International Nickel Co., 67 Wall St., New York 5, New York.)

3. Rinse thoroughly in warm tap water.
4. Dip in 20–50% HNO_3 solution.
5. Rinse in cold running tap water. **(This rinsing must be thorough to remove all traces of acid.)**
6. Immerse the work in the formula given above.
7. Rinse thoroughly in cold running tap water.
8. Dip in concentrated HNO_3 until all action ceases.
9. Rinse thoroughly in cold running tap water.
10. Repeat step 6.
11. Copper-plate in regular copper plating bath (see below).

CuP-2. Copper plating on magnesium

Formula: Same as for CuP-1 above.

1. Sandblast parts to be plated, and degrease.
2. Immerse in 20% NaOH solution.
3. Rinse thoroughly, first in cold then in hot running tap water.
4. Dip briefly in concentrated HNO_3 and rinse thoroughly to remove all traces of acid.
5. Dip in chromic-sulfuric cleaning fluid (C-1, p. 5).
6. Rinse thoroughly.
7. Copper-plate as for aluminum (see above). A thickness of 0.001 inch of copper plate makes a good base for ordinary soft soldering.

CuP-3. Copper plating bath, Rochelle salt type (alkaline)

Formula:

NaCN	35 gm
CuCN (cuprous)	26.5 gm
$KNaC_4H_4O_6 \cdot 4H_2O$ (Rochelle salt)	45 gm
Na_2CO_3	15 gm
Water, distilled or deionized	1 liter
Adjust pH by addition of NaOH to	12.5–13.0
Amount of NaOH required, approximate	3.75 gm

1. Add chemicals in the order given to about 750 ml of water at 60–70°C. Dissolve each chemical completely by stirring.
2. Bring volume to 1000 ml.
3. Adjust the pH, if required, with small additions of NaOH.
4. Temperature for use, 60–70°C.
5. Current density for plating, 15 amp/ft^2 without agitation, but the bath is to be agitated in operation.
6. Anodes: annealed sheet copper, electrolytic or OFHC grade.
7. This bath will deposit about 0.0001 inch of copper at 15 amp/ft^2 in 4 minutes.

8. The bath should be filtered and treated with activated carbon (plating grade) at intervals of not more than a month.

CuP-4. Copper dip for Kovar and cold-rolled steel (Electroless)

Formula:

$CuSO_4 \cdot 5H_2O$ (blue copper sulfate)	180 gm
H_2SO_4 (1.84 sp. gr.)	40 ml
Water	960 ml

Use at room temperature. Can be applied with a brush or swab or by immersion.

CuP-5. Copper plating bath for stainless steel

Formula A (use C.P. or reagent-grade chemicals):

$NiCl_2$ (nickel chloride)	240 gm
HCl (concentrated)	80 gm
Distilled or deionized water	1 liter

This bath is to be aged before use by plating onto a steel cathode for several hours, with agitation.

Formula B: Rochelle salt copper bath CuP-3, above.

1. Preplate the stainless steel work pieces with nickel in the bath of formula A, using depolarized, plating-grade nickel anodes, at a voltage of 5–6. Working temperature of the bath is 25°C and the current density is 30 amp/ft^2. Make the work **anodic** for 2 minutes then **cathodic** for 6 minutes. For parts which have been already nickel-plated, make the work **cathodic** for 3 minutes.

2. Filter this bath and clean the container every 2 months; age the bath as indicated above after each filtering.

3. After the work has been thoroughly rinsed, plate in the Rochelle salt copper bath, CuP-3, p. 26.

4. After plating rinse thoroughly in tap water then in distilled or deionized water.

5. Rinse in fresh methanol, reagent-grade, and dry in air oven not over 70°C.

CuP-6. Copper plating on steel

Use copper plating bath, Rochelle salt type (CuP-3, p. 26). Connect the dc of 1–2 volts to the work and anodes *before immersing. Remarks:* The plated surface will have the same character as the unplated surface. **Do not interrupt the plating process once it has started.** Move the work around several times during plating. To remove any oxide film that forms, immerse the work in hydrochloric acid of 1.19 sp. gr. for a short time, not long enough to etch the surface. Rinse thoroughly in tap and distilled or deionized water (the latter near boiling). Immerse in methanol and dry in air oven not over 75°C.

CuP-7. Copper plating bath, acid

Formula (use C.P. or reagent-grade chemicals):

$CuSO_4 \cdot 5H_2O$	200 gm
Distilled water	500 ml
When dissolved completely, add:	
H_2SO_4 (add slowly while stirring)	63 gm
Distilled water ... to make	1 liter
Phenolsulfonic acid (prepared by adding H_2SO_4 to phenol, equal quantities of each, at room temperature)	6 ml
Temperature for use	room
Agitation	yes
Current density	60 amp/ft^2

Anodes: rolled, annealed, electrolytic, or deoxidized copper.
Time for deposition of 0.0001 inch at 60 amp/ft^2: 2 minutes.

For deposits greater than 0.001 inch, the bath must be filtered frequently.
Ferrous work must be treated in a cyanide copper bath (CuP-3, p. 26) for a short time, as a strike, before acid copper plating.

AuP-1. Gold plating

Formula (use C.P. or reagent-grade chemicals):

Potassium gold cyanide	86 gm
Potassium cyanide	100 gm
Potassium hydroxide	136 gm
Potassium sulf*ite*	68 gm
Distilled or deionized water	7 liters

Anode: 24k gold sheet or wire.

AuP-2. Gold plating, electroless

Atomex, an immersion gold bath, is manufactured by the Chemical Division of Engelhard Industries, 113 Astor St., Newark 2, New Jersey. This material operates by a replacement process. The manufacturer states that it adheres firmly to most metals and has excellent throwing power. Usual thickness of coating is about 0.000003 inch or 1 mg/in^2, self-limiting. It is suitable for iron, diecastings, carbon steel, and soft solder. Time of immersion is 3 minutes at 140°F or $1\frac{1}{2}$ minutes at 194°F. For nickel the time is 15 minutes at 140°F, less at 194°F. For copper, temperature should not be over 170°F. The pH of the solution is 7–8. Parts to be gold-coated are to be cleaned by the most suitable methods (see section on cleaning). Atomex is sold in 200 cc units containing $\frac{1}{2}$ oz (troy) of fine gold. (See "Immersion Bath Produces Uniform Gold Coatings on Metals," *Materials in Design Engineering,* **46** (5), October, 1957, pp. 183–4.)

NiP-1. Nickel plating, fluoborate[1]

Formula:

Nickel fluoborate, $Ni(BF_4)_2$	220–440 gm
Water	1000 ml
Temperature for use	38°–77°C
pH (colorimetric)	2.0–3.5

The pH of the warm solution is adjusted by adding nickel carbonate if the pH is too low or fluoboric acid if too high. The solution is then purified by electrolysis (plating a test sample at low current density with agitation). Normal current density is about 25 to 75 amp/ft^2. This bath has about the same throwing power as the Watts nickel bath (see below), gives soft, low-stressed deposits, and is suitable for electroforming.

NiP-2. Nickel plating, Watts-type bath

Formula:

Nickel sulfate, plating grade	900 gm
Nickel chloride, hexahydrate, plating grade	170 gm
Boric acid, plating grade	115 gm
Distilled or deionized water	4 liters
pH	4.5–6.0
Operating temperature	45–70°C
Current density	20–100 amp/ft^2

(Increasing temperatures with agitation permits higher current densities.) This bath has good throwing power and gives smooth deposits with good physical properties.

NiP-3. Nickel plating, chloride-type bath

Formula:

Nickel chloride hexahydrate (plating grade)	120 gm
Boric acid (plating grade)	12 gm
Water, distilled	4 liters
pH	2.0
Operating temperature	60°C
Current density	25–100 amp/ft^2

Nickel deposits from this bath are fine-grained, hard, smooth, and less ductile than from the Watts-type bath, NiP-2. This solution permits the use of a lower voltage and less power consumption. Use glass or hard rubber plating cells.

[1] Courtesy of the Allied Chemical Corporation, General Chemical Division, 40 Rector Street, New York 6, New York.

NiP-4. Nickel strike bath (preliminary to regular plating)

Formula:

Nickel chloride hexahydrate (plating grade)	220 gm
Hydrochloric acid, concentrated c.p.	120 ml
Distilled water	1 liter

Purify this bath by plating at low current density (2–4 amp/ft^2) on a test sample, then remove precipitates and sludge by filtration. Agitation during electropurification is desirable. Under normal plating conditions, the presence of copper and iron as impurities is shown as a dark deposit.

Operating temperature	25°C (room)
Voltage	6 dc
Current density	150–200 amp/ft^2
Time of immersion	1 minute

After immersing in the strike bath, rinse the work and transfer without drying to the standard Watts bath (NiP-2) as soon as possible.

NiP-5. Nickel plating, electroless[1]

Formula (use reagent-grade chemicals and distilled water):

	Bath 1	*Bath 2*
Nickel chloride hexahydrate	30 gm/liter	30 gm/liter
Sodium hypophosphite ($NaH_2PO_2 \cdot 5H_2O$) Add slowly while stirring (this is a replenisher ingredient)	10 gm/liter	10 gm/liter
Sodium citrate ($Na_3C_6H_5O_7 \cdot 5H_2O$)	100 gm/liter	0.0 gm/liter
Sodium hydroxyacetate ($NaC_2H_3O_3$)	0.0 gm/liter	50 gm/liter
Ammonium chloride	50 gm/liter	0.0 gm/liter
Alkali for neutralizing (this is a replenisher ingredient)	NH_4OH	NaOH
pH of baths	8–10	4–6
Rate of deposition (mm/hr)	0.008	0.015
Rate of deposition (in/hr)	0.0003	0.0006
Appearance of deposits	bright	semibright
Temperature of baths	90–98°C	90–98°C

Both baths should be continuously filtered. Nickel deposits are quite brittle but can be softened by heat treatment (above 600°C in hydrogen).

[1] "Electroless Plating Comes of Age," Dr. Abner Brenner (NBS) *Metal Finishing*, Nov.-Dec., 1954. A reprint of this paper can be obtained from the International Nickel Co., 67 Wall St., New York 5, New York.

Useful life of the baths is 10–30 gm nickel/liter. Use glass plating cells for laboratory-scale operations.

NiP-6. Nickel strike bath for steel, Kovar, and copper

Procedure (use reagent-grade chemicals and distilled water):

1. Immerse parts in boiling cleaning fluid (C-1, p. 5) to remove contamination and grease. (**Caution:** this solution is highly corrosive.)
2. Rinse thoroughly in running cold tap water.
3. Pickle in 7% H_2SO_4 at 70°C for 5 minutes.
4. Repeat step 2.
5. Immerse in the following solution:

Nickel sulfate hexahydrate	30 gm
Distilled water	4 liters
pH	3.2–3.5
(Adjust pH with NaOH or H_2SO_4 solutions.)	
Operating temperature	77°C
Time of immersion	1–2 minutes
(If coatings are too heavy, they will peel.)	

6. Repeat step 2.
7. Rinse in 5% NH_4OH. A rinse in a 10% solution of NaCN before step 7 removes iron and nickel salts.
8. Rinse in distilled or deionized water.
9. Rinse in fresh methanol.
10. Dry in air oven, not over 80°C.

NiP-7. Nickel plating molybdenum

1. Degrease and fire the molybdenum pieces in hydrogen at 900°C.
2. Without handling immerse in the following solution (20 seconds at room temperature):

HNO_3 (concentrated)	4 parts by volume
H_2SO_4 (concentrated)	2.5 parts by volume
Distilled water	3.5 parts by volume

3. Rinse thoroughly in running tap water.
4. Deplate for 1 minute at 200 ma/cm^2 in dilute chromic-sulfuric cleaning fluid (C-1, p. 5).
5. Rinse thoroughly and quickly in running tap water.
6. Strike in bath NiP-4 or NiP-6.
7. Plate in bath NiP-2 or NiP-3 (p. 29).
8. Rinse thoroughly first in tap water and then in distilled or deionized water.
9. Rinse in reagent-grade methanol.
10. Dry in air oven not over 80°C.

Pt-1. Platinizing solution (platinum black) for conductivity cells, etc.

Formula:

Chloroplatinic acid ($H_2PtCl_6{\cdot}6H_2O$) deliq.	0.3 gm
Distilled or deionized water	10 ml

(This constitutes a 3% solution.)

Add a few drops of a 5% solution of lead acetate [$Pb(C_2H_3O_2)_2$] in distilled water.

The platinum black is formed by simple immersion.

Pt-2. Platinum plating[1]

The solution is sulphato-dinitrotoplatinous acid: $H_2Pt(NO_2)_2SO_4$, prepared commercially as DNS Type No. 1 Platinum Plating Solution. The platinum concentration for good deposits should be above 4 gm/liter (5 gm/liter is recommended). Platinum anodes, completely insoluble, are used. The concentration of the solution is maintained by addition of DNS as necessary. The pH of the solution is to be kept below 2.0; variations below this figure have only a slight effect on current efficiency. Current densities up to 25 ASF can be used, but cracking may occur above 20 ASF. At 10 ASF there is no cracking, but a current density of 5 ASF is recommended for building up heavy deposits. Temperature of the bath should be between 30° and 70°C. The deposition rate at 50°C is 0.0001 inch per 2 hours at 5 ASF. For fast plating this can be changed to 30 minutes, using a 15 gm/liter concentration at 20 ASF. The solution may need to be filtered after a few days' use due to a slight precipitate. During use, the bath gradually darkens to an orange-red color, but this has no effect on plating. Plating from DNS can be applied successfully to copper, brass, silver, nickel, lead, and titanium. Because of the bath acidity, plating cannot be used on iron, tin, zinc, or cadmium unless these have an undercoat of nickel or silver. Deposits from this bath are bright and lustrous. Up to 0.0005 inch on polished copper, the deposits are nonporous, but above 0.001 inch, some cracking may occur. Less cracking occurs on pre-etched surfaces.

Rhodium plating (see p. 464)

AgP-1. Silver strike bath

Formula (use reagent-grade chemicals only):

Silver chloride (AgCl)	26 gm
Sodium cyanide (NaCN)	272 gm
Distilled or deionized water	4 liters

---

[1] Source: "Bright Platinum Plating," N. Hopkin and L. F. Wilson, *Platinum Metals Review*, **4**, (2), 1960, p. 56; Johnson, Matthey & Co., Ltd., London.

The work is to be immersed with *current leads connected* and power on, to prevent deposition of silver by simple immersion. Use a low current density at room temperature; immersion for one minute should be sufficient.

AgP-2. Silver plating bath

Formula (use plating-grade or reagent-grade chemicals):

Silver cyanide (AgCN)	165 gm
Potassium cyanide (KCN)	160 gm
Potassium hydroxide (KOH)	45 gm
Potassium carbonate ($K_2CO_3 \cdot 2H_2O$)	250 gm
Distilled or deionized water	4 liters
Temperature for use	25°C
Current density	5–15 amp/ft^2
Voltage (dc)	1 or 2

This bath produces a matte silver finish. For brighter finishes, add 1 ml of a 60% ammonium thiosulfate [$(NH_4)_2S_2O_3$] solution for each 10 liters of bath.

Tin plating (See p. 541)

STRIPPING PROCEDURES

CdS-1. Stripping cadmium from steel, brass, copper

Formula:

HCl (concentrated)	2 liters
Antimony trioxide (Sb_2O_3)	30 gm
Distilled or deionized water	500 ml

Cadmium plate on steel, brass, and copper is removed by simple immersion in this solution at room temperature.

CdS-2. Stripping cadmium from steel, brass, copper

Formula:

Ammonium nitrate (NH_4NO_3)	120 gm
Distilled or deionized water	1 liter

Cadmium plate on steel, brass, and copper is removed by simple immersion at room temperature.

CdS-3. Stripping cadmium from steel; electrolytic bath

Formula:

Sodium cyanide	300 gm
Sodium hydroxide	55 gm
Distilled or deionized water	4 liters

Use at room temperature with steel cathodes.

Voltage (dc)	6

CdS-4. Stripping cadmium from brass

Simple immersion at room temperature in 10% HCl in distilled or deionized water. **Caution:** This solution will attack the brass.

CuS-1. Stripping copper alloys (brass, bronze, copper) from steel; electrolytic

This is the same as CdS-3 above.

NiS-1. Stripping nickel from steel

Simply immerse in concentrated nitric acid at room temperature. Keep the work dry and cover the vessel to keep out water.

NiS-2. Stripping nickel from steel; electrolytic

Formula:

H_2SO_4 (1.84 sp. gr.)	2350 ml
Glycerin (USP)	30 ml
Distilled or deionized water	1420 ml
Use at room temperature.	
Voltage (dc)	6
Cathodes	lead (Pb)

The stripping rate will be increased by a larger water ratio, but pitting may occur with too much water. Copper sulfate crystals, 30 gm/liter of solution, may be added instead of glycerin to reduce pitting of steel.

NiS-3. Stripping nickel from brass and copper; electrolytic

1. Use NiS-2 (above) as directed for stripping nickel from steel.
2. (Alternative method)

Formula:

HCl (concentrated)	55 ml
Distilled or deionized water	4 liters
Temperature of use	25°C (room)
Cathodes	carbon

AgS-1. Stripping silver from brass or other copper alloys

Formula:

H_2SO_4 (1.84 sp. gr.)	19 parts by volume
HNO_3 (concentrated)	1 part by volume

Simple immersion is at 80–85°C. Keep work and solution free from water.

Stripping tin (see p. 541)

ZnS-1. Stripping zinc from steel; electrolytic

Use CdS-3 (p. 33) as directed for stripping cadmium.

ZnS-2. Stripping zinc from brass and other copper alloys

Formula:

HCl (concentrated)	120 ml
Distilled or deionized water	1 liter

Simple immersion is at room temperature.

Formex S-1. Removal of formex insulation from wires, etc.

Formula:

Formic acid	50 ml
Water	50 ml

Formex insulation is removed by simple immersion in this solution at room temperature.

Heat-treating and Brazing

HYDROGEN BRAZING: GENERAL (see also pp. 172–187, 258)

Controlled atmosphere-brazing and heat-treating offer certain very definite advantages over other methods of performing these operations. When copper, nickel, Monel, Kovar, silver, stainless steel, and other metals and alloys are worked with, they come out bright and clean, and usually stress-relieved, as a result of uniform heating. If due consideration is given to the design of surfaces at joints, dimensional tolerances of fits, placing of the solder, jigging (or otherwise holding the parts to be brazed together), as well as the time and temperature schedules, no special skill is required to produce clean, brazed joints with good vacuum properties and a high degree of uniformity.

All materials to be brazed in hydrogen should be degreased and chemically clean, and should not be handled with bare hands prior to firing. The secretions of the skin contain, in addition to oils and fatty acids, inorganic salts that are difficult to remove and that cause staining of the work through the action of the heat.

Various materials, including those mentioned above, can be joined. Under certain conditions, tungsten, molybdenum, chromium- and aluminum-containing alloys, as well as various ceramics and other nonmetallic substances, can be successfully brazed.

Copper. Ordinary electrolytic copper can be brazed in hydrogen but is unsatisfactory for vacuum devices when hydrogen-fired because the reduction of the oxide particles always present in it forms water-vapor in the intergranular spaces. The pressure resulting from this gas during heat treatment tends to rupture the metal (i.e., to cause hydrogen embrittlement). When nonporosity and ductility are rigidly required, oxygen-free, high-conductivity (OFHC) copper or vacuum-melted copper[1] must be used. A convenient brazing alloy for copper is the silver-copper eutectic alloy—72% silver, 28% copper—which has a sharp melting point at 779°C. Since this material will enter into diffusion with the copper parent metal during brazing operations, alloys of different composition and higher melting points will be formed. An examination of the equilibrium diagram for silver-copper alloys, to be found in any metallurgy text, will illustrate this graphically. Advantage may be taken of this effect where two or even three brazing operations on the same piece are required.

If the first operation is done at some temperature above 779°C, a considerable part of the joint will contain copper in excess of the 28% eutectic value and will have a melting point that approaches as a limit the temperature at which the operation was done. If, then, the second brazing operation is done at a temperature between 779°C and that of the first operation, the metal in the joint formed in the first operation will not flow. In this serial type of brazing, the temperature must, of course, be accurately controlled: the more serial operations, the greater the accuracy that is required.

Copper can also be joined by other solders in the hydrogen furnace. Two requirements must be met in normal operation: the solder should have no ingredients that will vaporize, such as lead, zinc, and cadmium. Brazing materials with such volatile constituents should not be used in or on vacuum devices that are to be outgassed by heating above 150°C. (See brasses and bronzes, p. 172.) The use of solders containing such constituents is treated elsewhere in this section. The brazing alloy used should have a flow point safely below the melting point of the copper itself. These requirements are met by the silver-copper eutectic already mentioned; by other alloys comprising silver and copper; by a gold-copper alloy containing 80% gold and 20% copper, melting at 890°C; by a gold-nickel eutectic (gold 82.5%, nickel 17.5%, melting point 950°C); by pure silver, melting point 960°C; and, with some caution, by a copper-gold alloy, copper 62.5%, gold 37.5%, melting point 1040°C. There are also some lower melting point brazing alloys containing indium (see the table on pp. 176–187). Pure gold can also be used by the diffusion method; the parts to be joined must be accurately machined and held together under pressure, with the gold (as foil, wire, or electroplate) making intimate contact. By this method the gold will diffuse into the copper, if it is held in hydrogen sufficiently long under pressure at a temperature below the melting point of gold. (Temperatures as low as 500°C have been reported.)

Copper parts can also be joined by silver-plating the contact surfaces. Where joints can be made with good contact over the surfaces to be bonded—

[1] See p. 219.

by press or close mechanical fit (with allowance for plating thickness)—the same procedure as that for the silver-copper eutectic can be followed. The interface of the silver-copper is in some places a thin layer of eutectic composition even before firing. This will melt first, and more silver and copper will dissolve in the liquid phase at 779°C, so long as there is enough silver to maintain the eutectic composition. Higher temperatures and longer periods will result in silver-copper alloys with a higher melting point, in the same manner as though the process were initiated with the eutectic.

By judicious use of silver plate, highly satisfactory vacuum-tight joints can be made. The silver plating may, if necessary, be limited to definite areas by the use of stop-off lacquer during the plating process (p. 25). In brazing, the silver can be prevented from flowing to surfaces where its presence is undesirable by coating these surfaces with aluminum oxide in a nitrocellulose binder. This is the same material that is used to coat tungsten heaters for vacuum tubes. The binder is burned off harmlessly during firing; the alundum can be brushed off the work after it has cooled, since the soldering temperatures are not high enough to sinter the ceramic material.[1]

In designing joints for controlled atmosphere brazing, consideration must be given to capillary and gravity flow. Because molten solder will act like any other liquid, and because materials such as copper in a hydrogen atmosphere present a very clean (wettable) surface, the solder will flow up into small cracks and gaps, and even upward along exposed surfaces. Therefore, the precautions are to avoid excessive solder, apply stop-off lacquer where required when plating, and position work in the furnace so that gravity may work to advantage; do not use as brazing jigs, fixtures, or supports any metal, which may become attached to the work by the excess solder's running onto it. When the use of a jig is required in brazing copper, nickel, Kovar, or other metals in ordinary or wet hydrogen, it is common practice to use austenitic (nonmagnetic) stainless steel, Nichrome, or "K" Monel[2] for those parts of the jig which, by being in contact with the work, might otherwise be brazed fast. Such jigs should be prefired in wet hydrogen to produce a protective coating of green chromium oxide, to which the brazing solder will not adhere, because this oxide is very tenacious and reducible only in pure, dry hydrogen or vacuum.

Steels. Cold-rolled, hot-rolled, and carbon steels: Many of the remarks about copper apply to other materials, especially in respect to design, machining, and fit of parts to be joined. The steels mentioned can be brazed with the same solders used for copper. One very successful method for joining steel is copper brazing, in which pure copper is used as a solder (melting point 1083°C). The steel should be previously nickel- and/or copper-plated. Since neither copper

---

[1] For the same purpose, a proprietary ready-mixed compound is available: NICRO-BRAZ Green Stopoff, made by Wall Colmonoy Corp., Detroit, Michigan.

[2] Monel Alloy K-500 (Huntington Alloy Products Division of the International Nickel Co., Inc., Huntington 17, W. Va.).

nor silver diffuses into iron to any extent, the remarks on diffusion of silver into copper do not apply. Success in hydrogen-brazing unplated steel and stainless steel with various solders has been achieved by a purification of the hydrogen. See p. 41 *et seq.*

The use of solders other than pure copper is dictated by the kind of metals to be joined to steel; copper-brazing is obviously unsuitable for joining steel to copper.

Nickel, monels, and related alloys. These can all be brazed in the hydrogen furnace; those containing chromium and aluminum can be handled in pure, dry hydrogen (see p. 42). Nickel can be copper- or silver-brazed without special treatment.

Beryllium copper should be copper- or nickel-plated before brazing because, in wet hydrogen, an oxide of beryllium tends to form which might prevent successful brazing.

Brass and zinc-bearing bronzes. Copper-zinc alloys should not be brazed in the furnace used for other electron tube parts because zinc easily vaporizes at silver-brazing temperatures to contaminate the walls of the muffle. Also, there is a loss of zinc, with consequent change in composition. In brazing such alloys, a time-temperature schedule should be worked out that will ensure fast heating and melting of the solder so that the volatile ingredients are not subjected to excessive evaporation. Brass and other volatile metal-bearing alloys can be handled by the method of bottle brazing described below.

Kovar,* an iron-nickel-cobalt alloy, presents no difficult problems and can be handled much like nickel and its alloys. In joining Kovar to Kovar or Kovar to steel, nickel, or nickel alloys, copper brazing is feasible. The gold-copper and gold-nickel alloys can be used with success for brazing Kovar to copper, also pure silver to pure gold. Silver-copper eutectic can be used if the Kovar has previously been stress-relieved above 850°C and copper-plated. These precautions are necessary to prevent intergranular penetration of the silver into the Kovar, and the consequent liability of the Kovar to cracking. Kovar should always be brazed with quick-melting solder, i.e., pure metals, or simple binary alloys such as eutectics. Intergranular growth occurs in Kovar when it is exposed to solders having a wide melting range, with resultant penetration of the solder. If the Kovar piece has not been previously annealed above 850°C, this penetration of the solder between grains may eventually result in fracture, especially if the part is to be repeatedly heated and cooled. In general, Kovar should be copper- and/or nickel-plated at the junction for any kind of brazing or soldering operation.

---

* The physical and mechanical properties of Kovar are given on pp. 322 *et seq.*

PREPARATION OF THE WORK FOR BRAZING

Some of the steps to be taken in preparing the work for brazing in the hydrogen furnace have already been indicated. The parts should be clean, and firmly held together by jigs, clamps, screws, wire, or weights. Allowance must be made for differences in expansion among work pieces of different materials. Since copper, nickel, and certain other metals become quite soft at brazing temperatures, weights are sometimes preferred to clamps or screws.

Care should be exercised to see that nothing can loosen or fall or strike the walls of the furnace as the work is pushed through. In the conventional horizontal, ceramic-muffle furnace, the pieces should be loaded into a nickel or stainless steel box or tray. If a cover is used, it should be provided with holes or vents large enough to allow free circulation of hydrogen. Massive pieces or work with interior spaces or cavities that connect with the outside only through small orifices should be preheated in the front part of the furnace so that (a) both work and muffle are protected against thermal shock, and (b) the hydrogen has time to displace the air in the interior spaces. When such cavities are large, it is advisable to purge them with dry nitrogen immediately previous to preheating and after cooling, to remove the danger of explosion.

Temperature of brazing will depend on the kind of solder used, as outlined above. The duration of heating can usually be determined conveniently by placing a small piece of solder in some position where it can be seen while the work is in the heated part of the muffle, but where it will not drip on the muffle or the work (if this is not wanted). Sometimes a ring or piece of solder that is on the work can be observed directly, or a small piece can be attached where it will do no harm and where it can be conveniently seen. Experience will dictate how much time to allow after the solder melts for the work to remain in the heated part of the furnace. If the pilot piece of solder is in contact with the main body of the work, only a short time will be required; a somewhat longer time will be necessary if the pilot is attached to or in contact with a jig or tray that is less massive than the work, since the more massive sections will heat more slowly.

In pure, dry hydrogen-brazing, where the work cannot be seen, it will be necessary to rely on the accurate calibration of the thermocouple, which is placed near the work.

BOTTLE BRAZING

Although this method does not involve the use of a furnace, it is convenient for working with vaporizable materials and applying localized heating (zone heating) to assembled work.

In rough outline the method is shown in Fig. 1. A Pyrex or Vycor bell jar covered with a protective screen made of heavy expanded metal is hung with suitable counterweights under an exhaust hood. Hydrogen is admitted through a flow gauge and metal tube to the inside **top** of the bell jar. A molybdenum

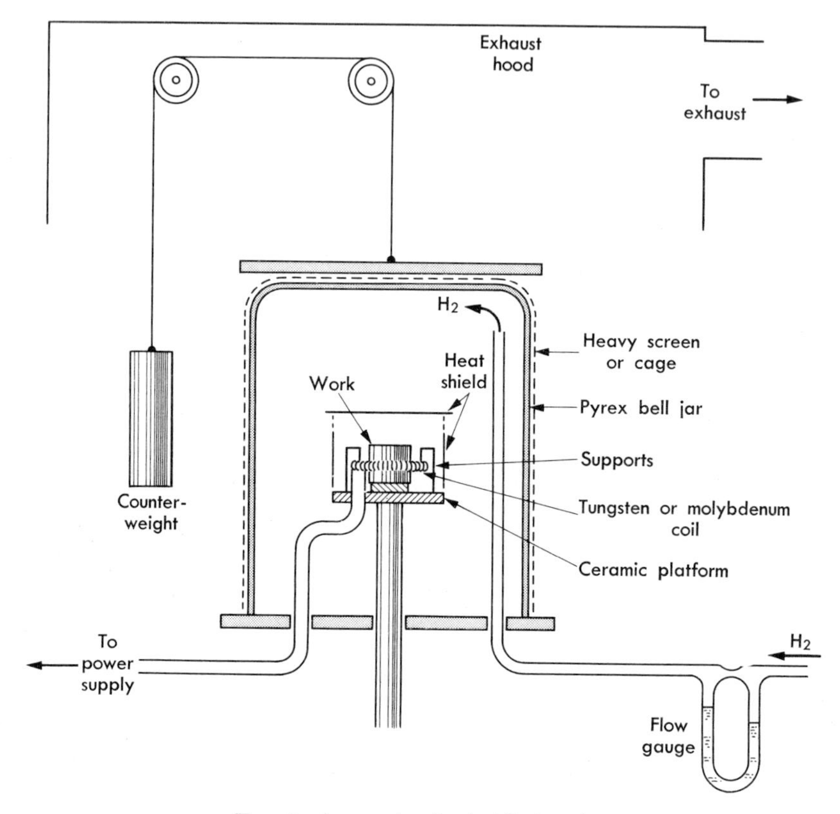

FIG. 1. Apparatus for bottle brazing.

or tungsten heating coil is placed around or near the part of the work that is to be heated, and is supported in several places to prevent sagging or short-circuiting. The work is mounted on a suitable refractory ceramic platform so that it will be about halfway up inside the bell jar, and is surrounded by sheet nickel or molybdenum heat shields. Another heat shield is placed so that it will protect the top of the bell jar. Adequate copper leads, heavy enough to dissipate the heat at the ends of the radiation coil, are brought out to a variable power supply. Space is provided at the bottom of the bell jar for the hydrogen to flow out and away; it is drawn off by the exhaust hood.

In operation, hydrogen is allowed to flow at moderate pressure for a length of time sufficient to displace **all** the air in the bell jar. This can be easily calculated, since the volume of the bell jar and the flow-rate of the hydrogen are known. The pressure should be sufficient to prevent air from reentering at the bottom, and some overflow, say about 20% additional time, should be allowed as a safety factor. Samples of the gas can be taken with an inverted test tube placed with its mouth next to the bottom of the bell jar; this may be carried a safe distance away with the thumb over the opening. A lighted match is held to the opening of the inverted test tube; if the gas in the tube burns upward slowly and quietly, the mixture is safe. An explosive mixture will be indicated by an audible "pop."

When the bell jar is filled with hydrogen, the current is turned on and the voltage raised slowly from zero. As the work receives the radiated heat, the operation is observed closely. A face shield should be worn by the operator. When the solder reaches its flow point, there will be, if vaporizable material such as zinc or cadmium is present, some clouding of the walls of the bell jar due to condensed vapors, but this is usually not sufficient to obscure the operation. No fluxes are to be used. The work should be clean before setting up. Any of the brazing alloys or pure metals mentioned above can be used, although bottle-brazing is generally confined to hard solders with intermediate melting points (Easy-Flo and Sil-Fos made by Handy & Harman Co.; Phos-Copper, by Westinghouse Co., for example). One advantage of bottle-brazing is that work which has parts of less rugged materials, such as glass, already attached can be brazed by properly disposing the heating coil, and by using auxiliary sheet nickel or molybdenum heat shields to protect such parts from excessive heat. The hydrogen is allowed to flow at a reduced rate after the solder has flowed and the power has been shut off and until the work has cooled enough to be exposed to the air without risk of oxidation or cracking.

STAINLESS STEEL

Stainless steels and other chrome-bearing alloys cannot ordinarily be brazed in tank or wet hydrogen without special treatment because the water-vapor and/or oxygen content of the atmosphere used is sufficient to form a protective film of chromium oxide on the metal that prevents the solder from wetting or adhering. See below.

HEAT-TREATING, DEGASSING, CLEANING, AND BRAZING AUSTENITIC STAINLESS STEEL IN DRY HYDROGEN[1]

Some of the austenitic, nonmagnetic stainless steels, such as types 302, 304, 305, and 347, are useful for making electronic tube parts and vacuum vessels. The presence of chromium in these alloys, however, makes ordinary wet-hydrogen furnace treatment difficult because of the formation of oxides from the moisture and/or oxygen content of tank hydrogen, and because of diffusion of these and other contaminants through the walls of porous muffles that are ordinarily used in atmosphere furnaces.

In pure, dry hydrogen, chromium oxide is reduced at temperatures above 1050°C. If a piece of clean, polished, austenitic stainless steel that has been oxidized by chemical treatment or by heating in air or wet hydrogen is heated

[1] Cold-rolled, plain carbon and tool steels, as well as Invar and other nickel alloys, can be treated in the same way as stainless steels.

to about 1050°C in dry hydrogen, its original bright condition is fully restored.[1] Indeed, on cooling, the color is whiter than before because the surface is no longer passivated. (For ordinary industrial or domestic uses, the metal should be treated in one of the chemical passivating baths.) When the pieces are to be used as internal parts of electron tubes or structures, the naked, clean surface is highly desirable so that assembly and evacuation will take place as soon as practicable after firing, and with the cleanest possible handling techniques, that is, in contaminant-free, low-humidity work areas, and with the use of gloves, finger cots, and instruments.

Experience has shown that contamination, from whatever source, including oxygen and water vapor, is almost invariably present in ceramic muffles. On firing, the austenitic stainless alloys are extremely sensitive to the formation of a light layer of green chromium oxide, which, as a possible gas source, is undesirable on electron tube elements. Also, in brazing, the presence of the oxide effectively prevents the wetting that is necessary for obtaining vacuum-tight joints. (This property is, of course, turned to advantage when stainless steel jigs and fixtures are used to hold copper, nickel, Kovar, and other metals for brazing in ordinary or wet hydrogen in ceramic muffles, and it also prevents the sticking of tungsten and molybdenum to previously oxidized stainless steel mandrels on which these refractory metals, as filaments or heater wires, are to be annealed and formed in tank hydrogen.)

It has been found that very little or no oxidation takes place on stainless steel when ordinary tank hydrogen is used in a glass, silica, Vycor, or quartz muffle (i.e., in a nonporous muffle) or retort. As a precaution, however, the dew point of regular-grade tank hydrogen should be measured because some variation in moisture content is to be expected. For satisfactory results, the dew point should be not higher than −50°C. (Although the dew point of dissociated ammonia, 75% H_2, 25% N_2, is very low when formed from anhydrous gas, there is some reason to believe that a degree of *nitriding* may occur.)

If the hydrogen is found to contain moisture, or if a small oxygen content is suspected, a simply constructed drying train, together with the use of a catalytic deoxidizer, will assure good results. Figures 2 and 3, show the arrangement of this train. Oxygen is converted to water-vapor and is then trapped out by the drying column,[2] the construction of which is shown in Fig. 2.

The body is a length of 1¼-inch IPS stainless steel pipe threaded at both ends and fitted with two stainless steel caps that have been drilled and fitted with smaller pipe fittings and needle valves. After the pipe is filled, the caps are screwed on and sealed with pipe compound. The length of the pipe is not critical; to some extent it will be determined by the volume of the muffle or

[1] Stainless steel components of high-voltage devices should be polished *after* firing with clean aluminum oxide abrasives and then subjected to an ultrasonic or detergent treatment. Only the purest alumina should be used.

[2] This device is fabricated to order by Intertech, Inc., 131 Bacon Street, Natick, Massachusetts.

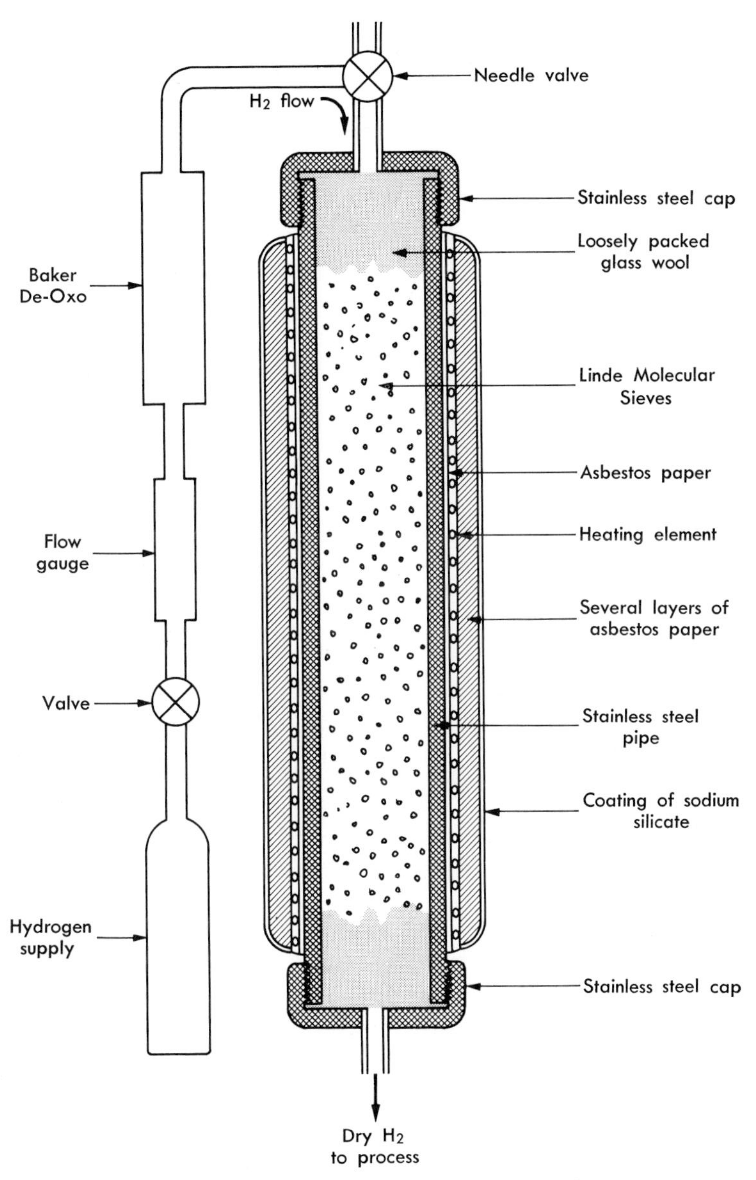

FIG. 2. Construction of hydrogen-drying column.

retort it is required to supply. Lengths varying from one to three feet may be used. The resistance winding is for the purpose of reactivating the drying chemical.[1] Reactivation, performed at infrequent intervals, is accomplished by heating to temperatures between 150° and 300°C while passing a small *reverse*

[1] Molecular Sieves, Linde Division of Union Carbide Corp., New York 17, New York. Type 5A, 1/16 inch pellets (see p. 377).

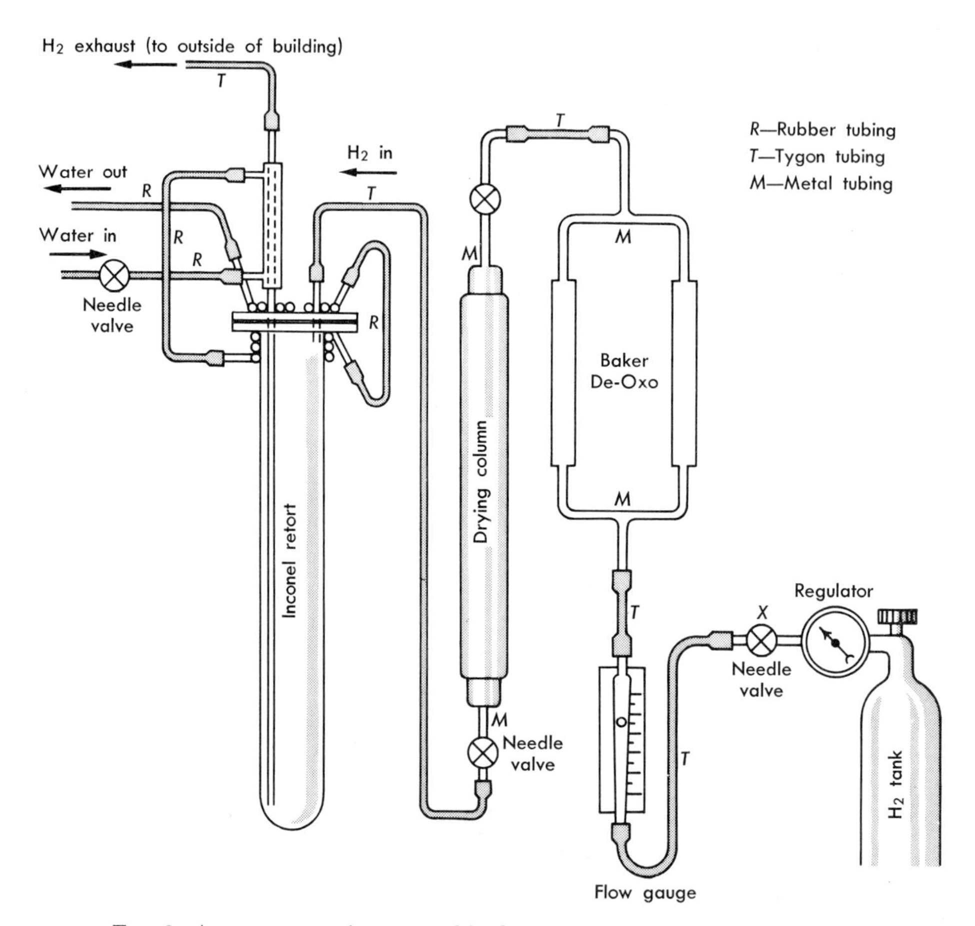

FIG. 3. Arrangement of water and hydrogen connections for dry H_2 process.

flow of dry, inert gas, such as oil-pumped nitrogen, through the column. A moisture-breathing test can be used to determine roughly when most of the adsorbed water has been removed; the total time for complete regeneration will be approximately double this interval. The material can be reactivated many times.

The heater for a 3-foot drying column has 76 turns of #20 B & S gauge Nichrome V wire wound over asbestos paper on 32 inches of the pipe. This is 40 feet of wire having a cold resistance of 25 ohms; it can be plugged directly into the 115-volt ac line and will produce a maximum temperature of about 300°C. The ends of the winding are conveniently anchored by winding an 8-inch piece of the same wire around each end over the asbestos paper, twisting them tightly, and then twisting the beginning and end of the main winding over the stub thus formed, allowing about 8 inches of the main winding for a pigtail.

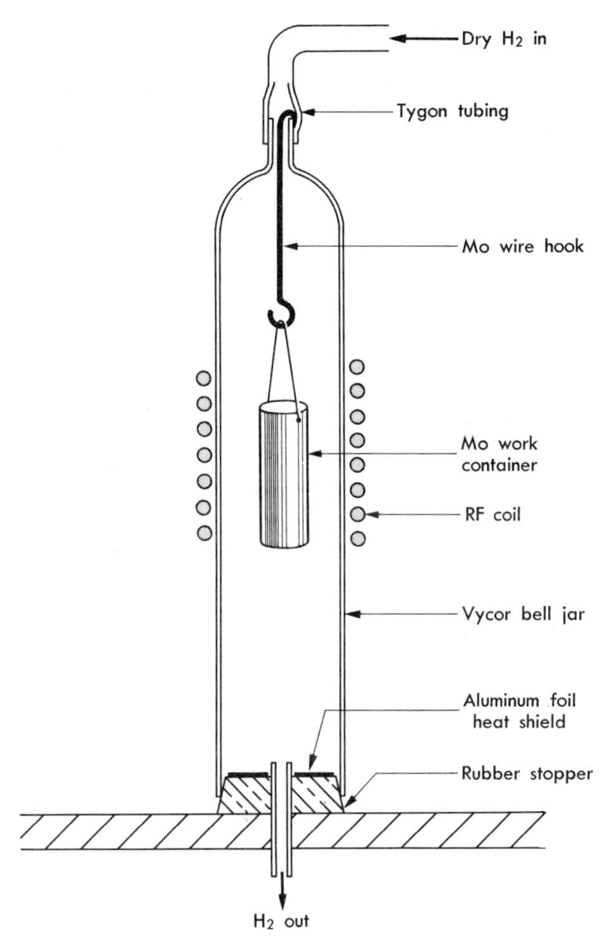

FIG. 4. Heat-treating with RF in dry hydrogen.

If it is feasible or desirable to heat work pieces by RF induction, a Vycor bell jar can be used, as shown in Fig. 4. This vessel should be long enough so that when the work is positioned in the middle, the top and bottom of the jar are not excessively heated. Several small air blowers can be disposed about the jar for cooling; they should not be placed too close to the RF coil. Temperatures as high as 1800°C have been attained in such an arrangement when the work is placed in cylindrical molybdenum containers ("buckets") with covers, preferably made from tubing and free of sharp edges or discontinuities which could become overheated. By this means it is possible to sinter the alundum coatings on electron tube tungsten heaters (for indirectly heated cathodes) with satisfactory results. Temperatures in this process are measured with an optical or radiation pyrometer.

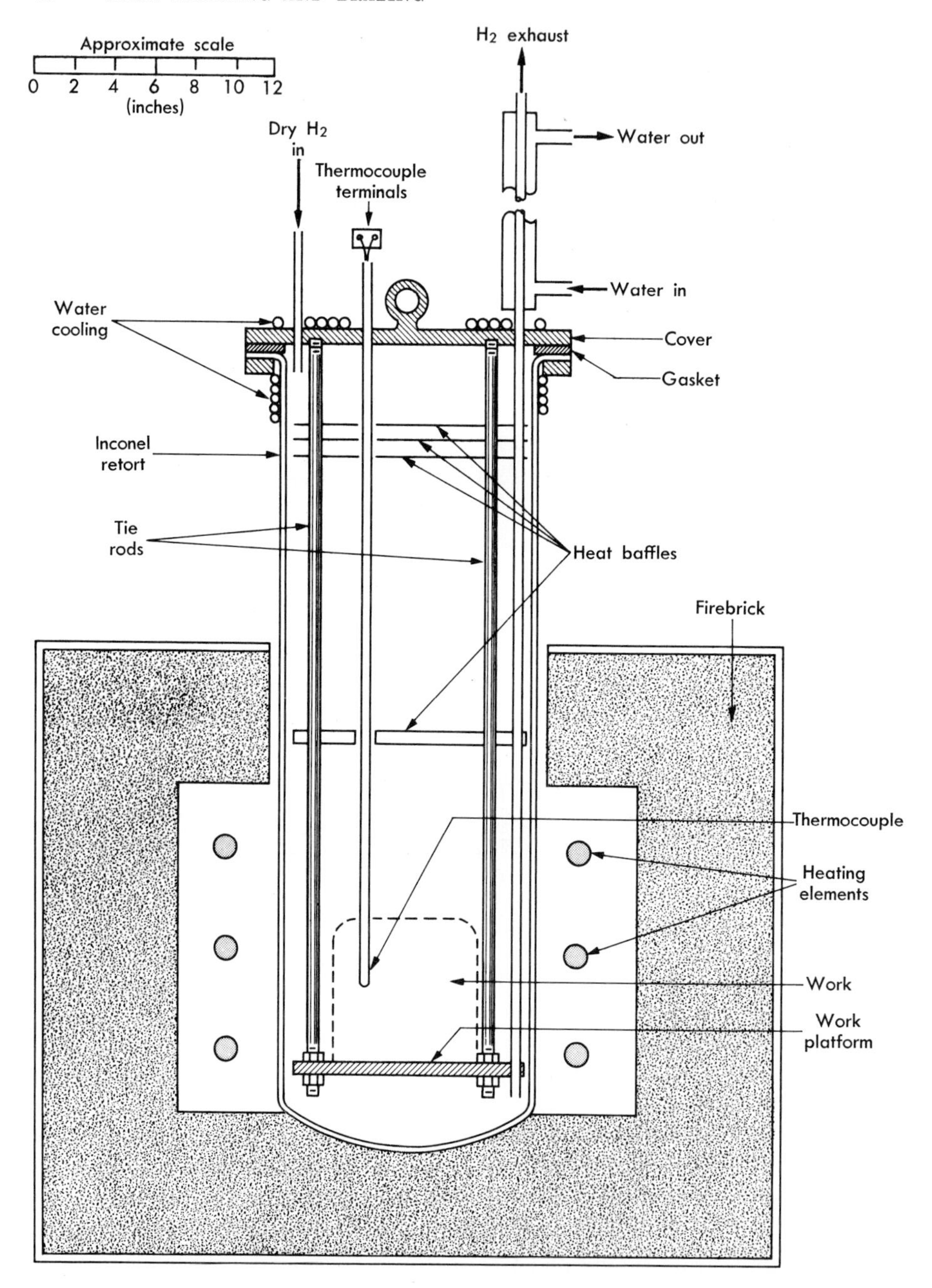

FIG. 5. Construction of Inconel retort for dry-hydrogen firing.

For large work, or for work which cannot be heated by RF induction, a metal retort is used, as shown in Fig. 5. One such retort, 14 inches in diameter, is made from a welded gas-tight annealed Inconel alloy 600 (14 gauge—0.064 inch) sheet about 4 feet long. The heat baffles nearest the top plate are 20-gauge (0.032 inch) stainless steel sheet; the work platform at the bottom and the central baffle are stainless steel plate $\frac{1}{2}$ inch thick and a little smaller in diameter than the inside of the retort to allow free circulation of the hydrogen. The four tie rods are also stainless steel $\frac{1}{2}$ inch in diameter. It is important to introduce the hydrogen through the short stainless steel tube ($\frac{1}{4}$ inch outside diameter, 1/32 inch wall) at the top. The gas is exhausted from a stainless steel tube of the same diameter which reaches almost to the bottom of the retort. The thermocouple is of the platinum-rhodium type, enclosed in a plugged and seal-welded stainless steel tube of a length that allows the junction to be at the same level as the work on the lower platform. The couple is thus in air, and the wires are insulated and protected with two-hole alumina tubing. Not shown in Fig. 5 are three special curved clamps made from heavy steel channel and fitted with machine bolts for tightening. Ordinary C-clamps can also be used. These clamps keep the top gas-sealed with a soft Neoprene or Silastic gasket $\frac{1}{8}$ inch thick. The upper parts of this apparatus are water-cooled, as shown, with several turns of $\frac{1}{4}$-inch soft copper tubing, soft-soldered to the neck of the retort and to the cover plate, which is a circle of $\frac{3}{4}$-inch-thick hot-rolled steel, copper plated, provided in the center with a ring-bolt for convenience in hoisting.

The heating chamber or furnace is constructed of firebrick, K-28[1] inside (hot zone), and K-20[1] outside; it has an outer sheath of Marinite, asbestos millboard, Transite, or sheet metal. A welded angle-iron or Equipto frame keeps the structure together. The bricks are not cemented.

The six heating elements can be of the silicon carbide type, either Globars or Crystolon Hot Rods. These are connected in parallel pairs to a three-phase autotransformer, which may have secondary taps brought out to a dead-front switch on the control panel. The use of an ammeter as an aid to limit the current in each circuit is imperative.

All exterior tubing in any of these arrangements in which hydrogen is carried must be either metal (copper, stainless steel) or Tygon. The use of ordinary rubber tubing should be avoided because its use tends to introduce harmful contaminants into the hydrogen.

Spent hydrogen in this process is carried in metal tubing to a safe point outside the building. Or it could be stored for reuse, if required, by pumping it into a cylinder. Note that in the Inconel retort, there is a water-cooling jacket around the hydrogen exhaust tube which is for the purpose of safely lowering the temperature of the gas below its flash point. (See the flow diagram, Fig. 3.) A curve showing the operation of this retort is given in Fig. 6.

---

[1] Product of Babcock & Wilcox Company, New York, New York.

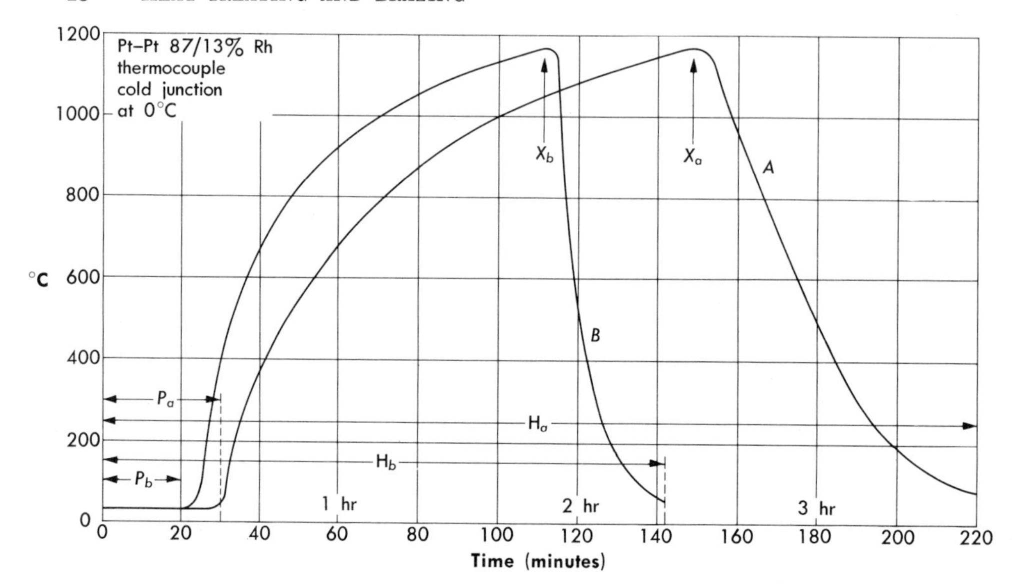

FIG. 6. Operation and behavior of Inconel retorts in dry-hydrogen furnace. *A*—14-inch Inconel retort; *B*—3-inch Inconel retort; P_a, P_b—purging period, no power applied to furnace; H_a—average hydrogen flow 19 liters/min, total consumption 4180 liters (146 ft³); H_b—average hydrogen flow 5 liters/min, total consumption 700 liters (24 ft³); X_a, X_b—points at which power is shut off and retort withdrawn from furnace.

For small work, or work on a laboratory scale, a retort can be constructed of Inconel alloy 600, scaled down from the design shown in Fig. 5. Such a retort and its interior structure are shown in Figs. 7 and 8. A three-foot length of 3-inch IPS-wrought Inconel alloy 600 pipe with a cap or plate heliarc-welded to the bottom and an Inconel flange at the top form the retort; the interior structure is made of type 304 stainless steel, with the tie rods, platform, and baffles welded together as shown. The operation and characteristics of such a retort, heated by four Globars in series on a 230-volt single-phase line, in which the current is controlled with a variable autotransformer, are shown in the curves of Fig. 6. Note that the work is allowed to cool in the retort, with the hydrogen flowing, to some temperature below 100°C, whereupon the gas can be shut off and the retort opened. Cooling of the retort is expedited by hoisting it out of the furnace, the overall dimensions of which are 19½ inches square by 23 inches high, and it can be built to stand on an angle-iron frame so that the heat is kept off the floor.

In operating the Inconel retorts, it is necessary and expedient to purge the chamber with hydrogen for 20 to 30 minutes before applying power to the heaters. Dry nitrogen should also be used as a purge before introducing the hydrogen to remove the air. The hydrogen flow during the purging and initial heating portion of the cycle is about 20 liters per minute, after which it can be reduced somewhat. In the 6-inch Vycor bell jar, a flow of hydrogen of 20 liters

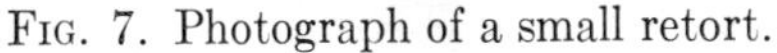

Fig. 7. Photograph of a small retort.

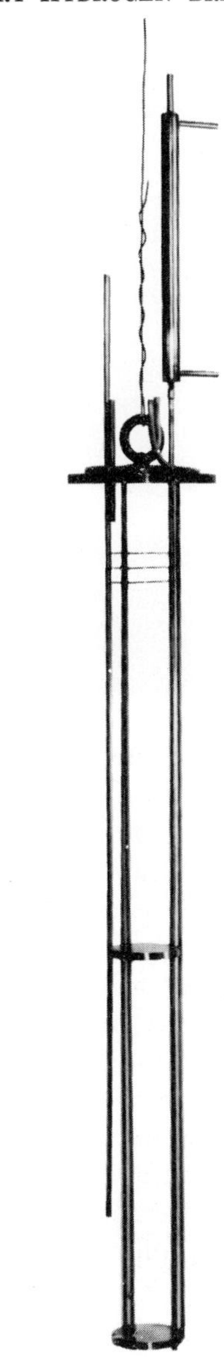

Fig. 8. Photograph of internal structure of small Inconel retort.

per minute is also maintained for about 20 minutes before applying heater power. After the heating is finished this flow can be reduced. As a safety precaution, dry nitrogen is to be used at the end of the cycle as a purge to clear the retort of hydrogen before opening it to the air. Sometimes the work may still be hot enough to cause ignition and explosion if air is admitted prematurely. The nitrogen and hydrogen can be connected into the system by using a three-way "tee" valve in place of the needle valve at point X in Fig. 3.

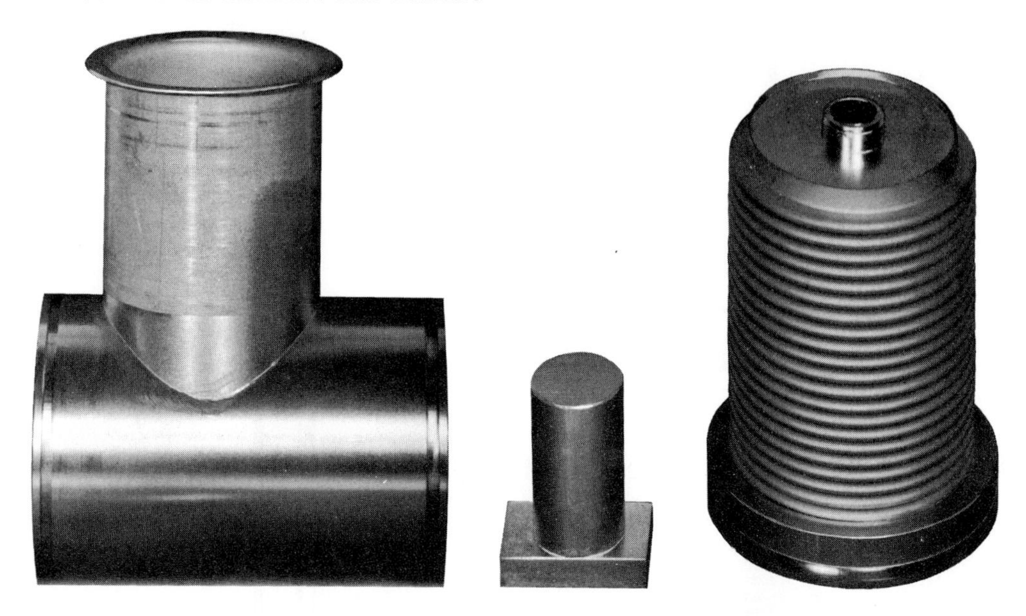

FIG. 9. Photograph of specimens of dry-hydrogen brazed assemblies.

It is necessary to condition the Inconel retort with its internal structure by heating under actual operating conditions (to about 1100°C) for one hour or more. This will reduce any scale or oxide inside the retort and on the welds. The outside of that portion of the retort which is in the heated part of the furnace chamber will become oxidized, but only a little scale will form after hundreds of hours of operation. Test pieces of previously oxidized stainless steel are used to indicate when the interior of the retort is ready for use. This conditioning process is to be repeated whenever the equipment has been idle for three weeks or more, although this period might have to be shorter in severe industrial environments.

In routine operation at 1100°C, brazing with pure copper or with 62.5% copper, 37.5% gold alloy (m.p. 1040°C) is easily accomplished. Assemblies thus brazed (see Fig. 9) are simultaneously outgassed and cleaned. The melting point of the copper-gold alloy is approximately the minimum temperature required for the reduction of chromium oxide in dry hydrogen.

Work pieces can be supported on silica, quartz, Vycor, or Fiberfrax[1] sheet, or on Inconel racks or trays. Porous materials such as firebrick and the like should not be used for supporting fixtures because such materials are likely to contain enough contaminating gases (air, water vapor) to interfere with the process of hydrogen reduction.

---

[1] The type 970-H refractory paper will withstand continuous temperatures of 1250°C, has no organic binders, and resists wetting by molten braze materials. It comes in thicknesses of 0.020 inch, 0.040 inch and 0.080 inch and in widths of 12 inches, 24 inches and 48 inches.

The Inconel retort should not be used with ordinary tank or wet hydrogen because such use will result in oxidation of the interior of the retort and its structure. When the retort is next used with dry hydrogen, the products of the consequent reduction are likely to oxidize the work. For use with wet hydrogen in the same furnace, a similar retort made of stainless steel instead of Inconel can be built.

Two or more retorts can be used on a schedule in which the furnace is kept at heat, the retorts being inserted one after the other. While the first is cooling, a second is heating, due precaution being taken to purge and cool each retort before and after, as outlined above. In this way many batches of work can be processed with a saving of time.[1]

If the procedure is followed carefully, as given above, complete success can be achieved in cleaning and bright-brazing the austenitic stainless steels, Inconels, Monels, low and high carbon steels, Armco iron, and Mu-metal.

Induction Heating: Radio-Frequency (RF) Heating, Bombarding

The work to be heated is surrounded by a water-cooled coil (inductor) of copper or copper tubing which is connected by special water-carrying cables to the vacuum tube RF oscillator. For maximum energy transfer, the inductor should be as closely coupled to the work as possible but not in contact with it (see p. 221). When work is to be heated in a vacuum, with the inductor outside, the vacuum vessel walls are of nonconducting material such as glass or quartz. If the work is to be raised to a high temperature, e.g., tantalum to 1000°C or higher, the vessel must be of such size, and the work so centered or positioned, as not to cause overheating, softening, and/or collapse of the vacuum vessel by radiated heat.

Since the heating is roughly proportional to the coupling (i.e., for a given piece of work a surrounding coil of small diameter will transfer more energy than one of larger size), a coil appropriate to the work should be chosen.[2]

---

[1] The retorts described in this section are fabricated by Intertech, Inc., 131 Bacon St., Natick, Massachusetts. See also "Safe Operation of Hydrogen Atmosphere Laboratory Furnaces," M. A. Cocca, General Electric Research Laboratory Report #58-RL-2013, Schenectady, N.Y., June, 1958.

[2] Helpful hints on the construction of induction coils as well as general information on application of RF heating will be found in "High Frequency Heating Review," published by Lepel High Frequency Laboratories, Inc., Woodside, New York.

Inductors can be made of solid copper stock, shaped to fit irregularly shaped work pieces, and either bored out for water cooling or with copper tubing brazed or soldered to them for most efficient heat exchange. Coils may be helical, spiral, conical, double-wound, oval, rectangular, or any other shape to fit the job. When the work is not to be raised to a high temperature, and when a closer control of heating is required, a coil of larger diameter should be used.

Metals such as nickel, Kovar, steel and stainless steel, copper, Monels, etc., will begin to evaporate *in vacuo* at red heat, and the evaporated material will condense on the walls of the vacuum vessel, gradually building up toward complete opacity. Thus the temperature of the work will be actually higher than is apparent through this obscuring film; caution is therefore to be exercised in applying RF power beyond a given point, since sudden melting may occur before the operator can shut off the generator. Also, build-up of evaporated metal on the inside walls of the vessel may result in puncture of the wall because of high-voltage breakdown induced through the metallic film which might, in addition, cause local overheating of the vessel. Work pieces which have sharp edges, holes, or other discontinuities should be heated with caution, because the RF-induced heat tends to concentrate at such discontinuities. Consideration is also to be given to work which has several diameters, where attempts to heat the smaller diameter may result in overheating the larger in view of the difference in coupling to the inductor.

An approximate formula for calculating heat transfer is

$$WST = \text{Btu/min.}$$

W is the weight of material in pounds, S is the coefficient of specific heat (see the table on p. 53), and T is the required temperature in °F. No allowance is made in this formula for normal heat losses, which may be 25 to 50% or more in air or hydrogen, considerably less in vacuum.

The frequency determines the heat penetration: the higher the frequency, the less the penetration. For surface-heating of metals, most commercial generators operate at a frequency in the neighborhood of 450 kc/sec.

The power output rating of an induction-heating generator is given by:

$$\text{kw} = 2.93 \cdot (\text{weight in pounds}) \cdot (\text{specific heat}) \cdot (\text{temperature rise °F}) \cdot (10^{-4}).$$

Because of hysteresis, magnetic materials at temperatures up to the curie point (p. 231) heat more rapidly than nonmagnetic materials, which heat by eddy currents only. The lower the resistivity, the lower the eddy current losses and hence the less heating; that is, more power is required to heat a piece of copper than a similar piece of nickel to a given temperature.

If localized heating is to be applied over a small area, a *current transformer* can be used to advantage. This is essentially an impedance-matching step-down RF transformer which allows the use of a single-turn work coil, with reduced voltage but little loss of power, and a concentration of energy in a small space (see pp. 221–222).

Multiturn coils should be proportioned so that the length does not exceed four times the diameter. When long lengths of work are to be heated, the work should be progressively fed through the coil.

For maximum energy transfer, the turns of a coil should be closely spaced without actually touching. Fiberglas sleeving (without binder) is useful for insulating the turns. Inductors are commonly made of ordinary soft copper tubing, joined to the cables with brass compression or flare-type fittings. Annealing and partial flattening are sometimes resorted to in order to bring the turns closer together; this results in more even distribution of the heat.

If possible, coils should have full turns, especially those with only one or a few turns. In single-turn inductors for use with the current transformer, the turn should be, in effect, a continuous ring with a very small gap; the smaller the gap the more uniform the field. In coils with more than one turn, the leads should be brought out close together near the coil; they may be separated beyond the coil. This does not apply to coils of five turns or more, since a high degree of uniformity of the field at the ends of the coil is not expected.

SPECIFIC HEATS OF SOME METALS*

METAL	SPECIFIC HEAT	METAL	SPECIFIC HEAT
Aluminum	0.21	Molybdenum	0.07
Brass, bronze	0.09	Nickel	0.11
Carbon (gas)	0.20	Platinum	0.03
Carbon (graphite)	0.17	Silver	0.06
Copper	0.09	Tantalum	0.04
Gold	0.03	Tin	0.06
Iron, steel	0.12	Tungsten	0.03
Lead	0.03	Zirconium	0.07

* From "Handbook of Chemistry and Physics," forty-first edition, 1959–60, edited by C. D. Hodgman, Department of Chemistry, Case Institute of Technology, Cleveland 6, Ohio.

Since the voltages employed in induction heating are high enough to cause serious or fatal injury, adequate precautions should be taken for protection of personnel. Metal tables or frames that are part of, or close to, an induction-heating generator should be thoroughly grounded to a cold-water pipe. The rubber covering on the cables used to connect the generator to the inductor is, as a rule, not high-voltage insulation; contact with these cables should therefore be avoided.

Condensation of water on the inductors sometimes occurs in humid weather; breakdown troubles from this source can be reduced by increasing the spacing of the turns, by covering the coil with unsaturated Fiberglas sleeving, or by reducing the water flow.

Glass-to-Metal Seals[1]

A true glass-to-metal seal is defined as one in which an inorganic glass is heated to the point where intimate contact ("wetting") is attained upon a hot metal surface and is retained when the glass and metal are cooled to room temperature. This requires, among other factors, that the glass and metal components have somewhat similar expansion coefficients (see the table on pp. 56–59) and *rates* of expansion, although there are exceptions, as noted below.

Internal seals (1a, 1b, 2, and 3 in Fig. 10) are those in which the metal, in the form of wire, rod, ribbon, or tube, is surrounded by glass.

External seals (4 and 14 in Fig. 10) are those in which a band, tube, or cup of metal adheres to the edge of a glass insert, which may be a round

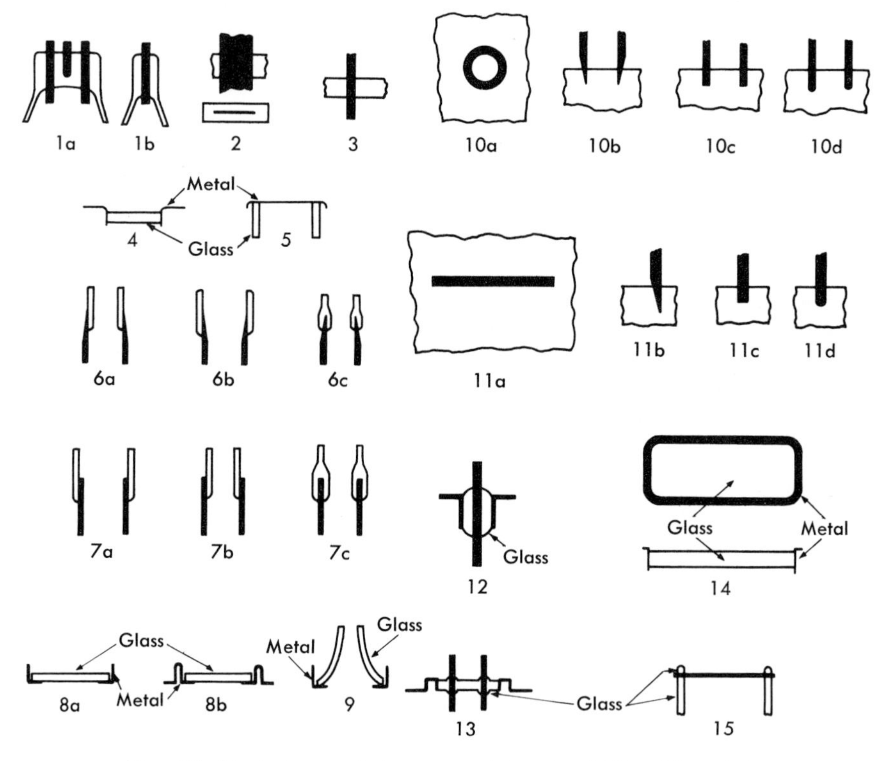

FIG. 10. Basic types of glass-to-metal seals. (After Monack.)

[1] "Glass-to-Metal Seals in Electronic Components and Applications," A. J. Monack, *Electrical Manufacturing* (now *Electro-Technology*), February, 1947. Data, tables, and figures are by courtesy of the publisher and copyright owner, C-M Publications Corp., 205 East 42nd Street, New York 17, New York. (See also pp. 282 *et seq.* and 322 *et seq.*)

button or disc or it may be square or any other shape, in which case the stresses are always greater and more complex than in a simple round button or disc.

Since glass is much stronger in compression than in tension, the differences in coefficients of expansion of the glass and metal components may be somewhat greater in external than in internal seals. Where expansion mismatch occurs, the ratio between the outside diameter of the tube in an external seal and its wall thickness should not be less than 15:1, with a maximum wall thickness of 0.010 inch. Where expansion-coefficient differentials are small, as in Kovar-to-glass seals (see p. 322 *et seq.*) these restrictions do not apply.

A tubular seal is "inside tubular" (6b, 7a in Fig. 10) when the metal is surrounded by glass and "outside tubular" (6a, 7b) when the glass is surrounded by metal.

The tubular seals (6a, b, and c in Fig. 10) are so-called "Housekeeper" seals (see p. 63). The metal, such as copper or stainless steel, having a widely different expansion coefficient, is formed to a thin edge so that it is able to yield as it expands with heat relative to the glass, and the stresses in the glass do not exceed its tensile strength.

Edge seals (10a, b, c, and d and 11a, b, c, and d in Fig. 10) are those in which the edge of the metal is embedded in glass. These resemble tubular seals in that they may be either normal edge or "Housekeeper" type (pp. 63–66), but the geometry and applications differ.

Butt seals (5, 9, and 15 in Fig. 10) are made by sealing a metal disc or ring to the end of a piece of glass tubing. This seal can be effective if the metal, e.g., copper, does not exceed 0.005 inch in thickness in the type of 5 in Fig. 10 or 0.030 inch in the type of 15. Thicker metal (e.g., Kovar) can be used where the expansion match is good.

Window seals (8a and b in Fig. 10) may be of any shape, although the round window is subject to less severe and complex stresses. As in 8b, the metal part (e.g., thin copper) can be formed with a deep ridge around the seal. This allows it to expand.

Combinations of the above types are also possible. The seal labeled 12 in Fig. 10 shows a "feed-through" or eyelet seal, consisting of internal and external seals. The center conductor is sometimes a metal tube of small diameter. Figure 10 shows a "button-stem seal" (13) in which the metal band around the edge is an external seal and the individual wires which pass through the button are internal seals.

Hard glasses, generally borosilicate, are those with thermal expansion coefficients below $5 \times 10^{-6}/°C$. Soft glasses, such as soda-potash-lead and soda-potash-lime (see the table, on page 270), are those with expanision coefficients above $5 \times 10^{-6}/°C$. Expansions are determined over the range 0°–300°C in both cases.

Glass-to-Metal Seal Combinations‡

A. METALS USED WITH SOFT GLASSES

METAL	COMPOSITION (PERCENT)	HEAT TREATMENT	OXIDE LAYER	KIND OF GLASS (CORNING NUMBERS)	COEFFICIENT OF THERMAL EXPANSION (cm/cm/°C × 10^{-6})
Chrome iron	Fe 72, Cr 28	Wet H_2 or cracked gas firing to oxidize	Cr_2O_3 (plus Fe_2O_3?)	Internal seal: 024, 008, 8160, 001	Metal: 10.8 (20°–500°C) Glass: 8.9–9.6
Dumet†	Core: Ni 42, Fe 58; Cu sheath: 18–28 by weight	Oxidize to light straw color in air. Surface to be smooth and free from scratches	CuO_2 (plus flux if used)	012, 001, 008; 8160—risky	Dumet: radial 9.2, axial 6.5; Glass: 8.9–9.2
Cold-rolled steel SAE 1010 unplated; or Ag-, Ni-, or Cu-plated	C 0.1, Mn 0.4, P 0.04, S 0.05, bal. Fe	Fire after plating	Fe_3O_4 (plus Fe_2O_3 if unplated)	Internal seal: 1990, 1991; External seal: any soft glass	Steel: 13.0; Glasses # 1990, 1991: 12.7; Other soft glass: 8.9–9.6
Sylvania #4, Driver-Harris #14; Carpenter #426	Fe 52, Ni 42, Cr 6	Wet H_2 fire to oxidize	Cr_2O_3 (plus Fe_2O_3?)	001, 012, 8160	Metal: 9.0 Glass: 8.9–9.2
Platinum	Pure Pt, or Pt/Ir alloy	None	Apparently none	012, 001, 008, 8160	Metal: 9.0 Glass: 8.9–9.2
Allegheny 4750*					Metal: 9.1 (20°–400°C)
52 Alloy*	Fe 50, Ni 50				Metal: 9.5 (20°–450°C)

* Allegheny 4750, 52 Alloy, "Ni 50, Fe 50," and Carpenter #49 are all quite similar in their properties. In alloys with nickel content of 47–50%, the specific resistance falls off very rapidly with increasing nickel proportion. This accounts for the relatively wide differences in specific resistance values shown for these alloys.

‡ Table data from Monack and other sources.

GLASS-TO-METAL SEAL COMBINATIONS‡

TYPE OF SEAL	STRESSES	THERMAL CONDUCTIVITY cgs	SPECIFIC RESISTANCE AT 20°C (μohm-cm)	COMMERCIAL FORMS	METAL
Internal	Axial and tangential compression; radial tension	0.06	72.0	Wire, rod, sheet, ribbon, punched and stamped forms	Chrome iron
External (usually)	Radial and tangential compression				
Internal	Radial and axial tension; tangential compression	about 0.4	4.6	Wire to 0.032 inch diameter; borax-coated†	Dumet†
Internal	None with proper anneal	0.108	18.0	Wire, sheet, ribbon, etc.	Cold-rolled steel SAE 1010, etc.
External	Radial and tangential compression				
Internal (others possible)	None with proper anneal	0.032	34.0	Any wrought form	Sylvania #4, D-H #14, Carpenter #426
Internal	Radial compression; axial and tangential tension	0.164	10.0	Wire, tube, sheet, ribbon, rings, etc.	Platinum
		0.037	51.0	Wire, sheet, strip	Allegheny 4750*
		0.04	43.0	Wire, rod, ribbon, etc.	#52 Alloy*

(*cont.*)

† A variety of Dumet wire known as MULtiLAYER is obtainable from Metals & Controls Division of Texas Instruments, Inc., Attleboro, Mass. A gold-plated Dumet wire having good weldability and long shelf-life is offered by General Electric Co., Lamp Metals and Components Dept., Cleveland 17, Ohio.

GLASS-TO-METAL SEAL COMBINATIONS (*continued*)

B. METALS USED WITH HARD GLASSES

METAL	COMPOSITION (PERCENT)	HEAT TREATMENT	OXIDE LAYER	KIND OF GLASS (CORNING NUMBERS)	COEFFICIENT OF THERMAL EXPANSION (cm/cm/°C × 10^{-6})
Tungsten (ground and polished)	Commercially pure W	None	Before beading: W_2O_5 plus WO_3 (W_4O_{11}?). After beading: mostly WO_3	772, 707, 3320, 775, 705, 750, 704, 7991	Metal: 4.6 Glass: 3.6–4.8
Molybdenum (ground and polished)	Commercially pure Mo	None	Before beading: Mo_2O_5 (plus MoO_3). After beading: mostly MoO_2	704, 705, 706, 7052	Mo: 5.5 Glass: 4.6–5.0
Kovar, Fernico, Rodar, Therlo, Sealvac-A	Fe 54, Ni 28, Co 18 (approx.)	900°–1100°C in H_2 (15 minutes to 4 hours)	CoO, NiO (plus Fe_3O_4?)	705, 704, 706, 7052, 7056	Metal: 5.0 Glass: 4.6–5.0
Allegheny #42	Ni 41, Mn 1, Fe 58	Wet H_2 fire to oxidize	—	704, 706, 708, AJ	Metal: 5.2 (25–100°C) Glass: 4.6–5.0
Copper, OFHC, or electrolytic	High-purity Cu	None	After sealing: Cu_2O (plus some CuO before)	Theoretically, any	Cu: 16.0 Glass: 3.3–9.6
Stainless steel #304	Cr 18, Ni 8, Mn 2, Si 1, bal. Fe	Wet H_2 fire to oxidize	Cr_2O_3 (plus Fe_2O_3)	7052	Metal: 10.6 Glass: 4.6

TYPE OF SEAL	STRESSES	THERMAL CONDUCTIVITY cgs	SPECIFIC RESISTANCE AT 20°C (μohm-cm)	COMMERCIAL FORMS	METAL
Internal	With 772, 3320, 775, radial compression to radial tension, axial and tangential tension, depending upon anneal. With 707, 750, 705, 704, 7991 radial tension, axial and tangential compression	0.38	5.5	Ground and polished rod (drawn wire)	Tungsten (ground and polished)
Internal	Radial compression, tangential and axial tension—approaching strain-free with proper anneal	0.35	5.7	Ground and polished rod (drawn wire)	Molybdenum (ground and polished)
Usually internal, external, tubular, occasionally others	None with proper anneal	0.046	49.0	Rod, wire, sheet, ribbon, cups, tubing, eyelets, etc.	Kovar, Fernico, Rodar, Therlo, Sealvac-A
—	—	0.038	67.0	Wire, rod, ribbon, etc.	Allegheny #42
Thin-edge tubular (Housekeeper), ribbon, butt	Usually complex stress system	0.92	1.7	Sheet, ribbon, thin-edge tubes, cups, etc.	Copper OFHC (or electrolytic)
Thin-edge tubular (Housekeeper)	Usually complex stress system	0.049	72.0	Any wrought form	Stainless steel Type 304

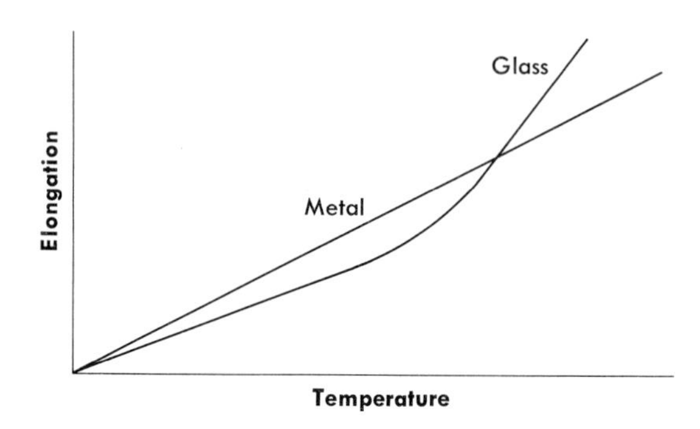

FIG. 11. Typical forms of glass and metal thermal-expansion curves.

Except in windows and combination seals, soft glasses have been used for all types of internal, external, tubular, and edge, while the hard glasses have found their greatest application in internal and tubular seals, although the other types are possible. In making glass-to-metal seals with all types of glasses, a perfect expansion match is not possible (see the table on p. 61), because while the elongation of a piece of metal is usually a linear function of temperature, that of glass is not. This is illustrated in Fig. 11. The alloys Kovar, Fernico, Therlo, Rodar, and Sealvac-A come closest to matching certain hard glasses (see the table on pp. 56–59). Because a thermal hysteresis may be said to exist in glass, it is important that all glass-to-metal seals be heated and cooled slowly. The magnitude of strain in a seal is normally and largely determined by the divergence of the glass and metal expansions at the glass-annealing point (see the table on p. 271, column 11). Important metals[1] used commercially in making seals are also given in the table on pp. 56–59.

In most glass-to-metal seals, the procedure involves the formation of one or more oxides on the metal surface by heating to the proper temperature. These oxides are readily "wet" by the fused glass to form a glass-oxide-metal transition. There is some evidence, however, that good hermetic seals can be made without the presence of oxide, e.g., as in the case of platinum.

The temperature of the metal during sealing nearly always exceeds that of the glass. Wires and rods can be "beaded" (precoated with glass, see p. 163), which allows the making of a glass-to-glass seal with greater facility. It is not usual, however, to bead soft-glass internal seals with Dumet (see the tables above and p. 230), chrome iron, and Sylvania No. 4. Hard glasses can be beaded on tungsten, Kovar, etc.

Theoretical evaluation of stresses in many types of glass-to-metal seals can be made, but values obtained in this way must be accepted with caution because, as a rule, unknown factors for differential cooling of glass and metal,

---

[1] Monack. See the reference on p. 54.

Stresses in Glass-to-Glass and Glass-to-Metal Seals (kg/mm^2)*

	7050	7052	7070	7040	3320
7050	0	−0.9	+1.7	−0.7	+1.8
7052	+0.9	0	+2.7	−0.3	+2.4
7070	−1.7	−2.7	0	−2.5	+0.2
7040	+0.7	+0.3	+2.5	0	+2.4
3320	−1.8	−2.4	−0.2	−2.4	0
7720	−1.9	−2.7	−0.2	−2.6	+0.5
7740	−3.1	—	−1.4	—	−1.6
7750	+0.1	−0.7	+2.0	−0.5	+1.6
Tungsten	−2.1	—	+1.2	−3.2	+0.7
Kovar	+1.9	0	+	−0.4	+

	7720	7740	7750	Tungsten	Kovar
7050	+1.9	+3.1	−0.1	+2.1	−1.9
7052	+2.7	+	+0.7	+	0
7070	+0.2	+1.4	−2.0	−1.2	—
7040	+2.6	+	+0.5	+3.2	+0.4
3320	−0.5	+1.6	−1.6	−0.7	—
7720	0	+1.9	−1.9	−0.1	—
7740	−1.9	0	−2.7	−3.5	—
7750	+1.9	+2.7	0	+1.5	−1.4
Tungsten	+0.1	+3.5	−1.5	0	
Kovar	+	+	+1.4		0

* Courtesy of H. R. Lillie, Corning Glass Works, Corning, New York.

plastic flow of glass during cooling, changes in properties of glass by heat treatment, and the exact temperatures at which strains appear in glasses can greatly modify these mathematical considerations. (See the table above.) Results should, whenever possible, be based on direct observation by polarized light (see p. 285). Figure 12 below is useful as a guide to the kind of stresses to be expected in internal seals in normal seal-making practice.

In addition to Mr. Monack's informative paper, mentioned on page 54, the reader is referred to the bibliography on p. 66.

The table above gives some glass-to-glass and glass-to-metal seal combinations. This table represents the approximate amounts of stress that can be expected with more or less normal treatment in seals of common sizes and types, and with both materials having nominal properties. Since the stress depends on geometry and on the annealing treatment, the table can be taken only as a rough guide to the expected final condition. In addition, the experimental error in determining the expansion curves (cf. p. 324) and inferring the stress is equivalent to about 0.2 kg/mm^2; accordingly, stress values of this order represent a very close match.

1. Expansion of glass greater than expansion of metal ($k_g > k_m$)
   a. On cooling
      Radial stress, $p_r = (-)$ compression
      Tangential stress, $p_t = (+)$ tension
      Axial stress, $p_z = (+)$ tension
   b. On heating
      Radial stress, $p_r = (+)$ tension
      Tangential stress, $p_t = (-)$ compression
      Axial stress, $p_z = (-)$ compression
2. Expansion of metal greater than expansion of glass ($k_m > k_g$)
   a. On cooling
      Radial stress, $p_r = (+)$ tension
      Tangential stress, $p_t = (-)$ compression
      Axial stress, $p_z = (-)$ compression
   b. On heating
      Radial stress, $p_r = (-)$ compression
      Tangential stress, $p_t = (+)$ tension
      Axial stress, $p_z = (+)$ tension

FIG. 12. Types of stress during heating and cooling of internal seals (Monack). The relationships shown above do not hold for Dumet because of the difference between radial and longitudinal expansions.

Values less than 1 kg/mm^2† indicate a satisfactory match. If the value is 1 to 2 kg/mm^2, greater care must be taken in producing a good bond, and the danger of breakage increases with the size of the article. Stresses up to 3 kg/mm^2 can be tolerated under ideal conditions if the seal is not expected to have to withstand subsequent minor abrasion. Values in excess of 3 indicate an undesirable condition and are generally omitted from the table, being indicated by an algebraic sign to show direction of stress. The positive and negative signs indicate the sense of the stress: the positive sign means that the material in the left-hand column contracts more on cooling, and vice versa.

As a special case of tungsten wires (intended to carry current) sealed into glass presses, etc., the table below shows the safe carrying capacity, in

SAFE-CARRYING CAPACITY OF TUNGSTEN WIRE WITHOUT UNDUE HEATING WHEN SEALED INTO GLASS*

SIZE WIRE (INCHES)	AMPERES	SIZE WIRE (INCHES)	AMPERES
0.010	1	0.050	15
0.015	2	0.060	20
0.020	3	0.080	25
0.025	4	0.100	40
0.030	6	0.125	50
0.035	8	0.150	70
0.040	10		

*Courtesy of L. W. Ryan, Research Laboratory of Electronics, Massachusetts Institute of Technology, Cambridge, Massachusetts.

† 1 kg/mm^2 = 1423 psi.

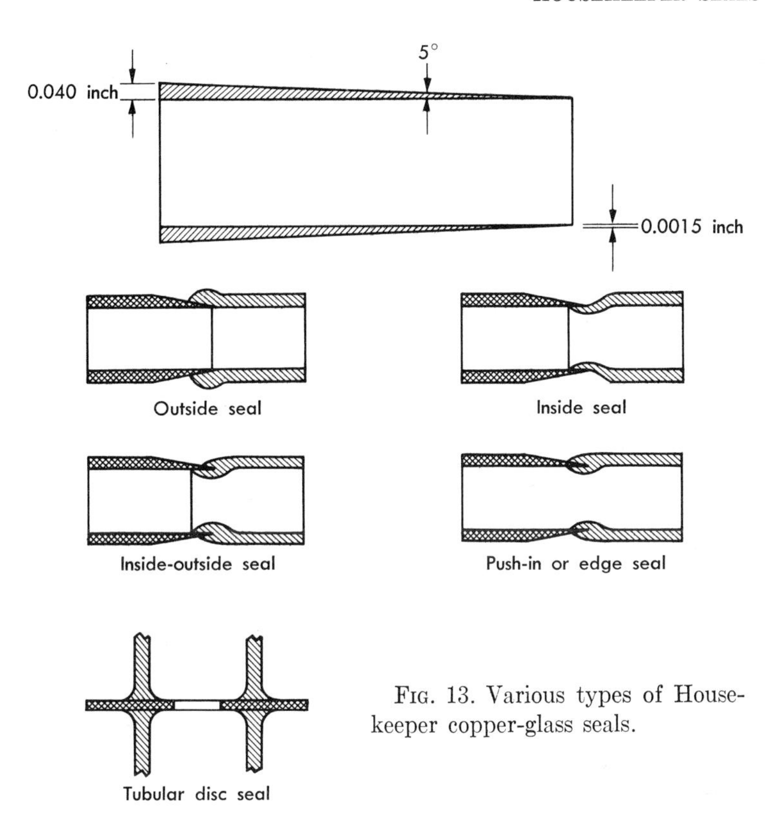

FIG. 13. Various types of Housekeeper copper-glass seals.

amperes, of various sizes of wire. Heating of the wire will not be excessive if the values in the table are followed. These values are for single-lead presses. When there is more than one lead, increase the size by one step in the table, e.g., a single tungsten lead 0.050 inch in glass will carry 15 amp without overheating, but if 15 amp are to be carried by each of two leads, the wire size should be 0.060 inch (see p. 559).

Housekeeper seals (Copper-to-glass).[1] Although the coefficient of expansion of copper is much greater than that of the glasses commonly used in electron tube work, a satisfactory vacuum seal can be made which utilizes the property of glass to "wet" copper oxide, some of which diffuses into the glass and forms a transition phase. For a satisfactory seal, the oxide layer should be no more than a few tenths of a micron thick (thus exhibiting spectral colors—see below) and may consist of various oxides. The copper piece is tapered down to a very thin feather edge (see Fig. 13) so as to form an elastic component which can follow the expansion and contraction of the glass. The surface of the feather edge must be smooth and polished. After degreasing and hydrogen-

[1] "The Art of Sealing Base Metals Through Glass," W. G. Housekeeper, *J. Am. Inst. Elec. Engrs.,* **42,** 954, 1923. U.S. Pat. 1,294,466; also, *Materials Technology for Electron Tubes,* second edition, W. A. Kohl, Reinhold Publishing Co., New York, 1959.

firing at 800°C in tank hydrogen, the copper piece is often borated by heating to redness in air and quenching in a concentrated solution of sodium borate. The color of the copper at the seal site should have a uniform deep red to purple sheen. If mottling or spotting occurs, contamination is present, and the parts should be discarded or recleaned and refired.

The glasses employed for this type of seal are usually the soft glasses, but, theoretically, any type of glass can be used. The copper and glass are heated to a temperature of about 1000°C (dull orange) in air and brought together. It is customary to apply a thin layer of glass to the metal before sealing it to the main glass-tube body. This is a process called beading, and it facilitates the glass-to-metal bond.

Copper-glass seals must be carefully annealed in an oven immediately after glassing (see the table on pp. 270–272; also the table on p. 58). When cool, the assembly is chemically cleaned to remove the excess copper oxides (see pp. 6, 20). Precautions must be taken to prevent undermining of the seal by the cleaning reagents.

It is to be remembered that only OFHC copper (see p. 219) is to be used if best results are to be obtained. The thickness at the feather edge should be 0.0015 ± 0.0005 inch and the taper should be about 5°, extending back from the edge until the wall is 0.040 inch thick. The taper should be chosen so as to compromise with both strength and elasticity.

All the seals shown in Fig. 13 can be accomplished by induction heating, and the outside, inside, inside-outside, and push-in seals can be done by lathe, using a flame.

Housekeeper seals (Stainless steel-to-glass).[1] A feather-edge seal similar to that employed with the copper-to-glass type can be made with 304 stainless steel where the greater strength and nonmagnetic properties of this alloy are required. Although Pyrex (Corning code 7740) glass can be used, Corning code 7052 FN is preferred for most applications because its coefficient of expansion ($4.6 \times 10^{-6}/°C$) is larger than that of other hard glasses, and therefore it matches the metal somewhat better. It readily wets the oxidized stainless steel; it seals well to other hard glasses, including 7740, and on the other end it can be sealed directly to molybdenum. Like 7740, its optical quality is high.

The piece of stainless steel tubing is cut to length and then fired before final machining in dry hydrogen (dew point −40°C or lower) at 1065°C for 15 minutes. The strain-free piece is then machined to the dimensions shown in Fig. 14. To obtain an edge whose thickness is uniform around the periphery, a cut must first be taken from the inside. The tubing is then put on a mandrel for machining the outside. The most important feature is the second cut of about 0.001-inch depth (shown dashed), which gives sufficient flexibility to the

[1] "Method of Sealing Stainless Steel to Glass," J. E. Benbenek and R. E. Honig, *Rev. Sci. Instr.*, **31**, 460, 1960.

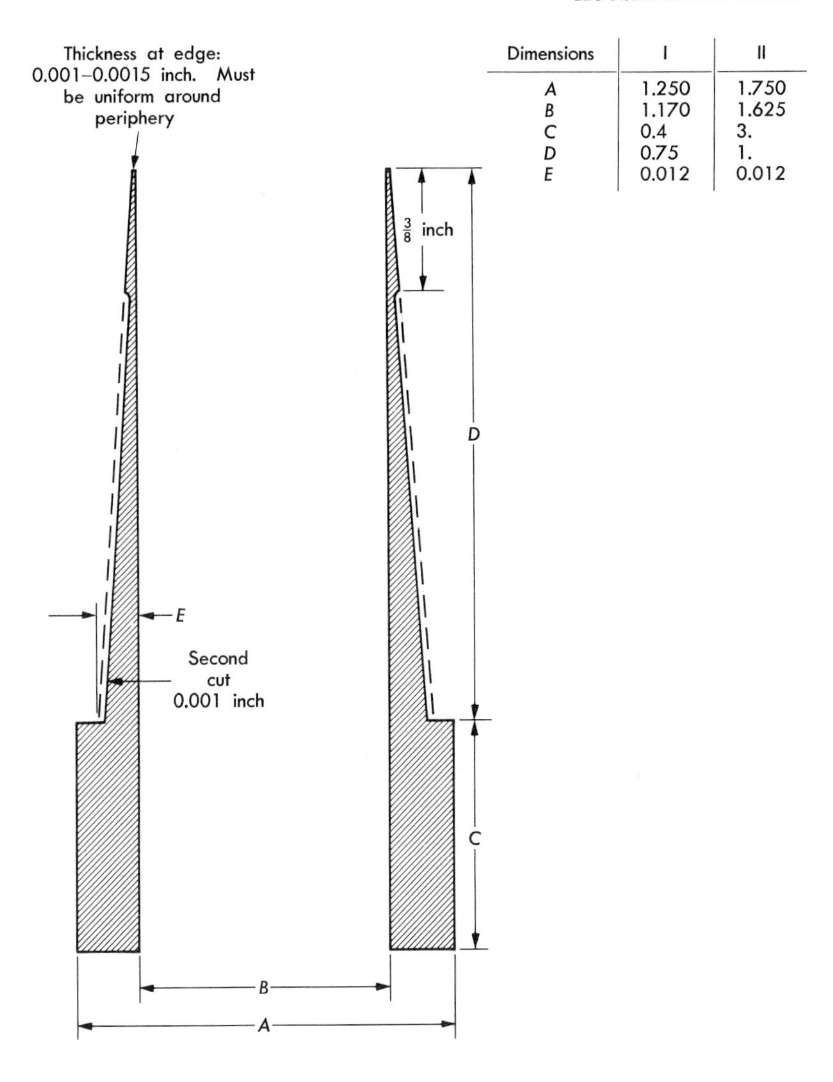

Dimensions	I	II
A	1.250	1.750
B	1.170	1.625
C	0.4	3.
D	0.75	1.
E	0.012	0.012

FIG. 14. Dimensions of stainless steel part for stainless steel-to-glass seals (not drawn to scale; all dimensions are in inches). (After Benbenek and Honig.)

tapered end. For the edge to be smooth, it should be not less than 0.001 inch thick, but it should not be heavier than 0.0015 inch to avoid stiffness.[1] After machining, the part is degreased and then oxidized by firing in wet hydrogen at 800°C. If it is to be welded into an outer collar within 2 inches of the glass seal, a snug-fitting copper plug is inserted and the heliarc welding is done before glassing. (Brazing to other metal members can be done before glassing by the method described on pp. 41–51.) After being joined, the piece may re-

---

[1] See note on following page.

quire remachining on the end opposite to the feather edge, for truing. The assembly is then degreased and finally vacuum-fired with the copper plug in place, at 1000°C for 15 minutes. The stainless steel part is now ready for glassing.

J. E. Benbenek calls attention[1] to an improved method of making stainless steel-to-glass housekeeper seals. The fragile edge of 0.001 inch to 0.0015 inch, as described above, is difficult to machine and does not tolerate the heating required for large-diameter seals, although small-diameter seals can be handled as above. The machining of this edge was modified by increasing the undercut to 0.002 inch, or greater, depending on the tapered-end thickness of the stainless steel tubing, and to within $\frac{1}{8}$ inch of the edge of the tubing instead of the $\frac{3}{8}$ inch shown in Fig. 14. This increases the edge thickness from 0.002 inch to 0.004 inch. This modification results in thicker and stronger seals and easier machining and glassing operations, making larger diameter seals possible.

Sealing. The stainless steel part is chucked in a lathe and wrapped to within $\frac{1}{2}$ inch of the end to be glassed with wet asbestos paper tape to keep it cool. A piece of the glass is shaped to overlap the exterior of the feather edge by about 0.050 inch and fused to the outside of the metal (beading). Care is taken to point the flame on the glass rather than on the metal to prevent overheating the thin edge. The glass is flame-cut at a distance of $\frac{1}{8}$ inch from the feather edge and then carefully rolled inside to complete the internal beading of the stainless steel tube. Finally, a glass tube is sealed to the beaded edge, and the assembly flame annealed.

Dimensions of the stainless steel part are shown in Fig. 14.

Glass to Metal Seals—Bibliography

"Glass-to-Metal Seals," A. W. Hull and E. E. Burger, *Physics,* **5,** 384, 1934.

"Analysis of Thermal Stresses," H. Poritzky, *ibid.,* **5,** 406, 1934.

"Analysis of Strains and Stress in Glass," A. J. Monack and E. E. Beeton, *Glass Industry,* **20,** 127, 185, 223, 257, 1939.

"Color in the Polariscope," A. J. Monack, *ibid.,* **21,** 513, 1940.

"Glass-to-Metal Seals II," A. W. Hull, E. E. Burger, and L. Navias, *J. Appl. Phys.,* **12,** 698, 1941.

"Glass-Metal Seals," A. J. Monack, *Glass Industry,* **27,** 389, 446, 502, 556, 1946.

"Stresses in Seals," A. W. Hull, *J. Appl. Phys.,* **17,** 685, 1946.

"Selection of Alloy Tubing for Glass Sealing," M. W. Keenan, *Electronic Design,* October 14, 1959, p. 38.

"Sealing Pyrex Glass to Stainless Steel and to Inconel," S. O. Colgate and E. C. Whitehead, *Rev. Sci. Instr.,* **33,** 1122, 1962.

Ultrahigh Vacuum and its Applications, R. W. Roberts and T. A. Vanderslice, Prentice-Hall, Inc., Englewood Cliffs, New Jersey, 1963, pp. 114–117.

---

[1] Private communication.

See also: References to aluminosilicate glass-to-molybdenum seals, p. 281; list of metals and alloys suitable for glass-to-metal seals, p. 283; Kovar-to-glass seals, p. 322; solder glass (Corning) for making glass-to-glass seals at lower than normal glassblowing temperatures, p. 486.

Metal and Ceramic Bonding

Certain metals and ceramics can be bonded together in vacuum-tight seals for use at high temperatures. There exist two general methods for accomplishing this.

1. Certain easily oxidized "active" metals, in combination with brazing metals or alloys, produce a bond in which the brazing material, under the influence of, or with the aid of the "active" metal, melts and flows at a temperature lower than the softening point of the ceramic. In simple terms, the theory appears to be that the "active" metal, in this case titanium, zirconium, or tantalum, in the form of their hydrides, due to thermal action, and in an inert atmosphere such as helium, argon, or in a vacuum, forms an oxide which is compatible with the ceramic (also often an oxide), or takes the part of a scavenger to prevent the parent metal from oxidizing. The hydrogen given off during the process is said to give some cleaning action also because of its reducing activity.

This process has the advantages that only one firing is required, a bond with excellent mechanical strength and vacuum tightness is obtained, and with the use of proper materials, only a simple mechanical assembly is required, with a minimum of jigging. Materials for this process are commercially available, such as titanium-cored solders,[1] in which the active metal is protected up to the point of melting of the solder. A nickel-titanium brazing material for forming hermetic feed-through insulators is available.[2] This is in the form of a wire having a nickel-clad titanium core. Formed into a ring and placed over the stem to be bonded, then vacuum-fired at 1040°C, the wire melts and forms a seal. The material contains 28.5 to 31% by weight of nickel, which forms a eutectic alloy when melted.

2. The solid-state process, an outstanding example of which is the so-called "moly-manganese" method (see below), differs from the active metal process in that temperatures at or near the softening point of the ceramic are utilized,

---

[1] "Titanium-Cored BT," Handy & Harman, 850 Third Avenue, New York 22, New York.

[2] Little Falls Alloys, Inc., 189 Caldwell Avenue, Paterson, New Jersey.

and usually in a hydrogen atmosphere. In this process molybdenum and manganese in powder form are applied to the ceramic with a binder by brushing, spraying, or dipping. The material is confined to the areas which are to be brazed. The coated ceramic is then fired in a hydrogen atmosphere at a temperature slightly below the softening point of the ceramic (for aluminum oxide about 1350°C). The ceramic and metal pieces are then assembled with preplaced brazing alloy in the form of rings, discs, washers, or, in some cases, electrodeposited copper, nickel, silver, or combinations of these and other metals. The assembly is then fired in hydrogen at a temperature suitable for the braze material.

The moly-manganese method produces strong bonds which can be reproduced with good success. It also has the advantages that very good dimensional control of metallized areas is achieved, and the process is not supersensitive to slight atmosphere and temperature variations. It has disadvantage over the "active" metal process in that two firings are required, and that the hydrogen atmosphere tends to discolor and impair the electrical properties of some ceramics. (High-purity alumina appears to be relatively free of these defects, and is widely used.)

In both methods, cleanliness is imperative. Metal and ceramic parts should be cleaned by an ultrasonic method (see p. 561), stored in approved containers, and not handled except with gloves or instruments.

Jigs and fixtures for brazing should be avoided if possible, or reduced to a minimum by proper design of the assemblies.

Blind gas pockets must be rigorously avoided in metal-ceramic assemblies, since the presence of small amounts of oxygen, especially in the "active" metal process, can spell failure.

Careful consideration in any type of metal-to-ceramic brazing must be given to the coefficients of thermal expansion of the metal and ceramic parts to be joined. Considerable stresses are set up in all metal-to-ceramic bonds, even when the best available expansion match is used. When the metal surrounds the ceramic, a compressive stress on the latter is obtained, and this is preferable to the reverse type of seal (ceramic surrounds the metal). Ceramics are generally quite strong in compression and notably weak in tension. Here, again, high-purity alumina exhibits the best properties.

Detailed instructions for making the so-called "moly-manganese" seals are given below.

"Moly-manganese" ceramic-to-metal seals (according to Coors).[1] The ceramic parts used for most electrical and mechanical applications must be joined to one or more metal parts to make up the complete ceramic and metal assembly. Usually the seals between the ceramic and metal must be vacuum-tight. They must also be able to withstand high temperatures and mechanical shock and vibration.

---

[1] Technical Data Sheet 0500, courtesy of Coors Porcelain Company, Golden, Colorado.

The ceramic composition used for ceramic and metal assemblies must have certain important characteristics: (a) vacuum tightness, (b) good mechanical properties, (c) high thermal shock resistance, (d) resistance to high temperatures, (e) economical fabrication to precision tolerances, (f) uniformity from one batch to another (for large production runs). In addition, for electronic and electrical applications, the ceramic must have good dielectric properties.

Of all ceramic compositions, high alumina ceramics most nearly meet all the requirements. The 85% alumina (Coors AD-85) is suitable for most general requirements, such as feedthroughs in dc or low-frequency applications. More stringent electrical requirements are met by 94% (Coors AD-94), 96% (Coors AD-96), 99% (Coors AD-99), or 99.5% (Coors AD-995), in order of ascending quality. If high-heat dissipation and thermal conductivity are required, a beryllium oxide ceramic can be used.

Choice of metal. For good design the coefficients of expansion of the ceramic and of the metal must be properly matched. Otherwise, the stresses that develop during temperature changes could result in failure of the seal. Metals commonly used include nickel-iron alloys, Kovar, nickel, stainless steel, certain types of Monel, copper, and molybdenum. Choice of the metal depends upon the application and upon the type of seal to be used.

Design of ceramic-to-metal seals. The type of seal between ceramic and metal is a basic consideration in designing ceramic and metal assemblies. There are four seals commonly used: (a) external, (b) tapered, (c) internal, and (d) butt. The external seal, Fig. 15(a) (a compressive seal), takes ad-

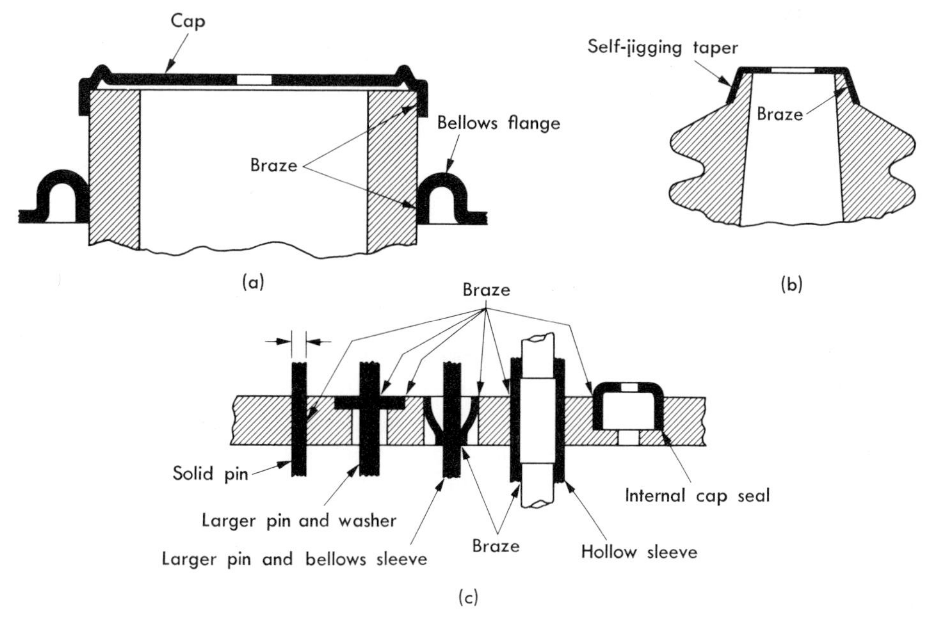

FIG. 15. (a) External seal. (b) Tapered seal. (c) Internal seals.

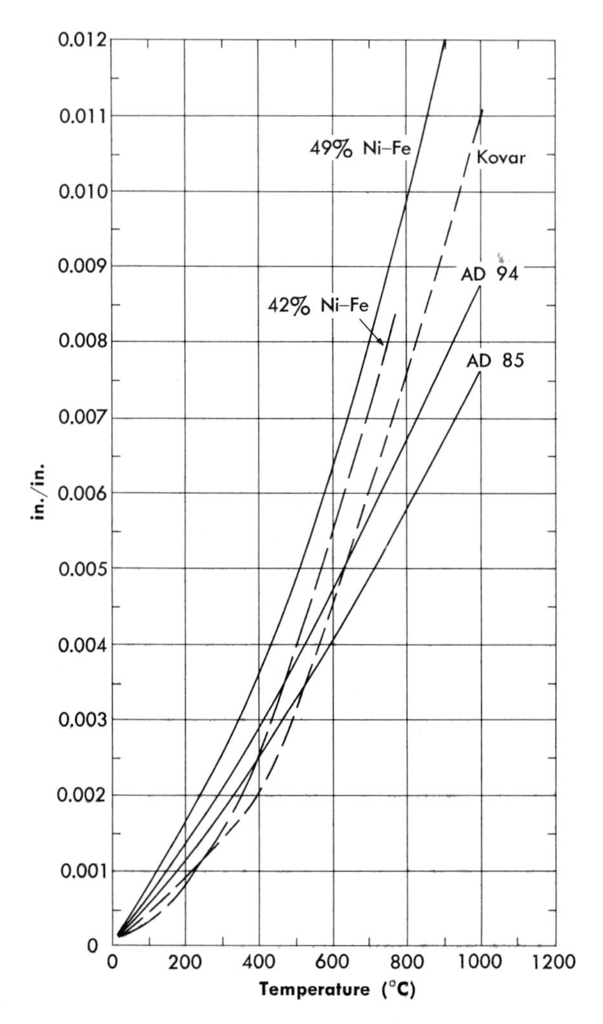

FIG. 16. Thermal expansion characteristics. (After Coors Porcelain Company.)

vantage of the fact that the strength of a ceramic is many times greater under compression than under tension. Compressive strengths of alumina ceramics may be over 200,000 psi, depending upon the particular composition. Tensile strength is 17,000 to 35,000 psi. It is obviously best, whenever possible, to design the ceramic and metal assembly so that the seal is under compression. This is true with an external seal because the coefficient of expansion of the metal is greater than that of the ceramic.

Tapered seals, Fig. 15(b), are used to a great extent in terminal insulator designs. In addition to being a compressive seal, the tapered seal has several other advantages. It is self-jigging, an important design consideration; also the taper minimizes the gap between metal and ceramic so that tolerances can be more open and, accordingly, costs can be less.

The stresses of an internal seal, Fig. 15(c), present more complex problems than those of an external seal. Because the metal has a greater expansion coefficient than the ceramic, cracks may develop in the ceramic during heating if the metal is too heavy or too strong. Because the radial stresses are tensile, the seal may open during cooling, unless the metal is ductile enough to be held by the seal. One solution is to select an alloy which matches as closely as possible the expansion characteristics of the ceramic. Kovar (see pp. 322–338) is a good choice because its expansion curve (Fig. 16) is fairly close to that of high alumina ceramic. Molybdenum also has a good expansion coefficient. Nickel can be used because it is very ductile and is able to absorb stresses.

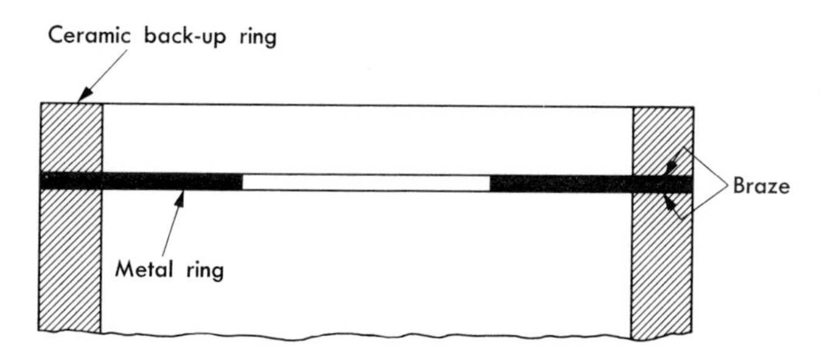

FIG. 17. Butt seals.

Butt seals (Fig. 17) between ceramic and metal are sometimes used. Most frequent use is with the stack-type seal in which ceramic and metal parts are stacked one upon the other. This is the strongest type of butt seal—with ceramic on each side of the metal. However, whenever possible, the ceramic part should be designed with a shoulder or some other device such as the cap in Fig. 15(a) so that an external seal can be used instead of a butt seal.

Where large metal parts must be joined to ceramic, the flange should be shaped to provide a bellows-type action which absorbs stresses during temperature changes. An example of this is the flange on a terminal insulator; see Fig. 15(a).

For good design it is always best to use the thinnest possible metal cross section. The thinner the metal, the smaller the stresses set up on the seal and the ceramic. The metal for external seals should be held to a maximum thickness of 0.020 inch to 0.030 inch [Fig. 15(a)]. For internal seals the metal should not ordinarily be thicker than 0.010 inch to 0.015 inch. However, it is sometimes possible to braze solid leads up to 0.030 inch in diameter for special purposes [Fig. 15(c)]. Tubing, rather than solid wires or rods, is often used for larger leads, since a tube can adapt itself to stresses more readily than a solid section; see Fig. 15(c). For a butt seal the metal should not exceed 0.015 inch in thickness. However, thicker metal can be used in making stacked assemblies; see Fig. 17. The resulting combined stresses are divided between the ceramic pieces on each side of the metal. A ceramic back-up ring should be used wherever space permits.

Moly-manganese procedure. This method can be used to metallize alumina or beryllia parts for brazing. It is well suited to precision, quantity production.

A powdered mixture of 80% molybdenum powder and 20% manganese powder of 1–5 micron size and of over 99% purity is suspended in a solution consisting of a nitrocellulose binder with other vehicles. The function of the binder is to keep the metal particles in suspension and to cause the powder to adhere to the ceramic surface before firing. The binder is completely burned off during firing.

The metallizing mixture is applied in a uniform thickness to the ceramic surface which is to be brazed. Application can be by brushing, spraying, screen printing, or roller or dip coating. Care must be taken to restrict the metallizing to the desired areas on the ceramic.

After it is dry, the ceramic part is placed in a closely controlled hydrogen-atmosphere furnace at temperatures ranging from 1350° to 1525°C, depending upon the particular ceramic body used. The part is held at a maximum temperature for 20–30 minutes and is then cooled to nearly room temperature in the hydrogen atmosphere. During firing, the metal powders sinter and combine with the ceramic, penetrating the surface to form a strong bond. The metallized coating is usually 0.001 inch to 0.0015 inch thick.

Plating the metallized ceramic. To prepare the moly-manganese surface for proper brazing, a second coating is required so that the braze material will wet the metallized area on the ceramic when making the metal seal. For most brazing materials used, the metallized areas on the ceramic are nickel-plated. Copper plating may be overlaid on the nickel if desired. The metallized and plated ceramic piece is now refired in hydrogen at approximately 1000°C, after which it is ready for brazing to the metal parts.

Various braze materials can be used to effect seals. A partial list follows (see the table on pp. 174–187):

Silver-copper eutectic	mp 779°C
Pure silver	mp 960
Gold-nickel alloy	mp 950
Copper-gold alloy	mp 980–1120
Pure copper (OFHC)	mp 1083
Platinum alloy	mp 1160

The brazing operation is done in a hydrogen atmosphere in much the same manner as metal-to-metal brazing (see pp. 35, 41, 172, 258). Ceramic parts should be designed so that they will be self-jigging, if possible, during brazing. The fit between the ceramic part and the metal part should be extremely close for most brazing materials. Large fillets must be avoided to prevent possible unequal thermal contraction between the ceramic and the brazing material, and to keep stresses at a minimum. When a moderately ductile brazing material, such as silver or copper, is used, this precaution is less important.

For complex assemblies several brazing operations are often required. If only one brazing material were to be used, all seals would have to be made at the same time and at the same temperature. Therefore, when more than one braze is necessary, brazing materials with different melting points are used. This allows each joining operation to be made at a lower temperature than the one preceding it. Metal-to-ceramic bonds have a tensile strength of 9,000–12,000 psi.

Metal-to-Ceramic Bonding—Bibliography

H. Pulfrich, U.S. Patent 2,163,407, June 20, 1939.

"German Centimeter and Decimeter Tubes," Intelligence Report (TUB-1) Office of the Theater, Chief Signal Officer, APO 887 (1945).

"High-Temperature Metal-Ceramic Brazed Seals," R. J. Bondley, *Electronics,* **20,** 97, 1947.

"Technical Report #104," C. S. Pearsall and P. K. Zingeser, Research Laboratory of Electronics, M.I.T., 1949.

H. J. Nolte and R. F. Spurck, *Television Engineering,* **1,** 14, 1959.

"Air Force Technical Report #6101," W. Knecht, February, 1950.

Ceramic Age, R. J. Bondley, **58,** 15, 1951.

Materials Technology for Electron Tubes, second edition, W. H. Kohl, Reinhold Publishing Co., New York, 1959.

"Metallizing and Bonding Nonmetallic Bodies," F. C. Kelley, U.S. Patent 2,570,248, October 9, 1951.

"Proceedings of the WADC Ceramic Conference on Cermets," WADC Technical Report 52–327, October 6–8, 1952.

A. G. Pincus, *J. Am. Ceram. Soc.,* **36,** 152, 1953.

J. A. Stavrolakis, *et al.,* WADC Technical Report 53–356, October, 1953 (Armour Research Foundation, Illinois Institute of Technology).

L. Navias, General Electric Research Laboratory Report RL-833, April, 1953.

"Ceramic-to-Metal Seals for Vacuum Tubes," T. L. Evans, *Ceramic Age,* August, 1954.

"High-Temperature Metal-Ceramic Seals," H. Bender, *Ceramic Age,* April, 1954.

"Ceramic Tube Mount for Automatic Assembly," R. N. Palmer, *Electronics,* August, 1954, p. 162.

"Reliable Tubes for Automatic Production," W. R. Wheeler and T. L. Evans, *Radio Electronic Engineering,* September, 1954.

" 'Stacked Tubes' in Production," *Tele-Tech,* August, 1954, p. 59.

W. D. Kingery, *et al., J. Am. Ceram. Soc.,* **36,** 363, 403, 1953; *ibid.,* **37,** 18, 42, 1954.

"Review of High-Temperature Metal-Ceramic Seals," Hayne Palmour, III, *J. Electrochem. Soc.,* **102** (7), July, 1955, pp. 160c–164c.

"Active Metal Sealing in Metal-Ceramic Hermetic Terminal Applications," Hayne Palmour, III, American Ceramic Society, Symposium on Sealing, Cincinnati, Ohio, April 26, 1955.

"The Application of Reactive Metal Seals," D. D. Mickey, Jr., Second Annual Technical Meeting on Electron Devices, Session IIIc-5., Washington, D.C., October, 1956.

"Sealing Metal and Ceramic Parts by Forming Reactive Alloys," J. E. Beggs, I. R. E. Transactions of the Professional Group on Component Parts, Vol. CP-4, No. 1, March, 1957.

"Experiments in the Design of Ceramic Electron Tubes," F. Brand, H. Jacobs, and C. LoCascio, *Ceramic Age,* **63,** May, 1954, pp. 18–23.

"Ceramic-to-Metal Bonds," G. R. VanHouten, *Materials in Design Engineering,* December, 1958.

"Metal-to-Ceramic Seal Technology Study, Final Technical Report," S. S. Cole, Jr., H. W. Larisch, J. E. Inge, and K. H. Styhr, Jr., Electron Tube Division, Sperry Gyroscope Co., Great Neck, New York. Prepared for Rome Air Development Center, Air Research & Development Command, U.S.A.F., Griffiss Air Force Base, New York. (Sperry Report No. Na–8240–8216.) (RADC–TR–60–236) October, 1960. Available from ASTIA Document Service Center, Arlington Hall Station, Arlington 12, Virginia.

"Active Metal Soldering of Crystalline Quartz," M. E. Knoll, *Rev. Sci. Instr.,* **32,** 83, 1961.

"Ceramic Metallizing Mixes," R. Keller, SEL Electron-Devices Techniques Bulletin No. 101, Stanford Electronics Laboratory, Stanford University, Stanford, California, September 1, 1959.

"Metallurgical Phenomena Associated with Active Metal Bonding," F. W. Clinard, Sandia Corporation; for U.S. Atomic Energy Commission (SCTM 215–61(11)), October 1961. Available from Office of Technical Services, U.S. Department of Commerce, Washington 25, D.C.

"Dielectric to Metal Seal Technology Study," M. Berg, A. C. Grimm, and F. F. Marinaro, Radio Corporation of America, Electron Tube Division, Lancaster, Pa., First Quarterly Report prepared for Rome Air Development Center, Air Force Systems Command, U.S. Air Force, Griffiss Air Force Base, New York (RADC–TDR–62–401), July 1962.

"Dielectric to Metal Seal Technology Study," P. D. Strubhar, A. C. Grimm, and F. F. Marinaro, Radio Corporation of America, Electron Tube Division, Lancaster, Pa., Second Quarterly Report prepared for Rome Air Development Center, Air Force Systems Command, U.S. Air Force, Griffiss Air Force Base, New York (RADC–TDR–62–401), October 1962.

"Dielectric to Metal Seal Technology Study," A. C. Grimm and P. D. Strubhar, Radio Corporation of America, Electron Tube Division, Lancaster, Pa., Third Quarterly Report prepared for Rome Air Development Center, Air Force Systems Command, U.S. Air Force, Griffiss Air Force Base, New York (RADC–TDR–63–249), December 1962. Available from Office of Technical Services, U.S. Department of Commerce, Washington 25, D.C.

"Ceramic-Metal Seals for High-Power Tubes," C. Johnson, S. S. Cole, Jr., I. Waraska, and K. H. Styhr, Jr., Final Technical Report, Electron Tube Division, Sperry Gyroscope Co., Division of Sperry-Rand Corporation, Great Neck, N.Y. prepared for Rome Air Development Center, Research and Technology Division, Air Force Systems Command, U.S. Air Force, Griffiss Air Force Base, New York (RADC–TDR–63–43), January 1963. Available from ASTIA Document Service Center, Arlington Hall Station, Arlington 12, Virginia.

"Ceramic-to-Metal Seals for High Temperature Operation," E. L. Brundige and G. S. Hanks, Los Alamos Scientific Laboratory, University of California, Los Alamos, N.M. (LAMS–2917), August 1963. Available from Office of Technical Services, U.S. Department of Commerce, Washington 25, D.C.

"A Nineteen-Inch Diameter Bakeable Metal-Ceramic Seal," K. Kirchner, *Trans. Am. Vacuum Soc.,* **10,** 170–175, 1963.

Ultrahigh Vacuum and its Applications, R. W. Roberts and T. A. Vanderslice, Prentice-Hall, Inc., Englewood Cliffs, New Jersey, 1963, pp. 117–119.

"Dielectric to Metal Seal Technology Study," A. C. Grimm and P. D. Strubhar, Radio Corporation of America, Industrial Tube and Semiconductor Division, Lancaster, Pa., Technical Report prepared for Rome Air Development Center, Air Force Systems Command, U.S. Air Force, Griffiss Air Force Base, New York (RADC–TDR–63–472) October 1963. Available from Office of Technical Services. U.S. Department of Commerce, Washington 25, D.C.

Tube Laboratory Procedures

Outgassing of tube components by vacuum-firing. In addition to the methods of outgassing tube parts and materials by firing in the hydrogen furnace, the firing of metal parts in vacuum is a very useful and often mandatory method of outgassing, especially in the case of tantalum, columbium, titanium, zirconium, and the like. Other metals, such as stainless steel, tungsten, molybdenum, nickel, steel, Monel, etc., can be vacuum-fired, as can certain nonmetallic materials such as ceramics.

An exhaust station suitable for outgassing tube parts is shown in Fig. 18. The refrigerated baffle is of a type which can be used with liquid nitrogen, Freon, or cold water, the choice of a coolant depending on the nature of the work. For many kinds of vacuum-firing, the ionization gauge may be omitted. In this category would be included materials which are expected suddenly to emit large quantities of gas on heating, a condition which might burn out the ionization gauge filament. A clean Penning gauge should be capable of reading down to the low 10^{-7} torr scale, which is adequate for most routine vacuum-firing and brazing.

A shield consisting of a cylindrical length of Vycor glass is provided inside the Pyrex bell jar for three reasons: (a) as a heat shield for the bell jar, (b) to receive evaporated material and thus prevent a leakage path for the RF field directly on the bell jar, and also for ease in cleaning after firing, and (c) the shield is more easily replaced than the bell jar in case of breakage. The bell jar is accurately ground to the water-cooled metal plate so that only a small amount of stopcock grease (Apiezon "N") is required to effect a seal.* Alternatively, a Neoprene or silicone rubber gasket may be used instead of the ground seal.

The work is suspended in the middle of the bell jar, which should be clean and freshly (but lightly) greased at the start of each operation. Tantalum or molybdenum wire can be used to hang the object in the bell jar. For small parts—screws, nuts, tabs—also ceramic insulators and other nonconducting material, use is made of a tantalum or molybdenum "bucket" or cylindrical

---

* See the table of vapor pressures on p. 140.

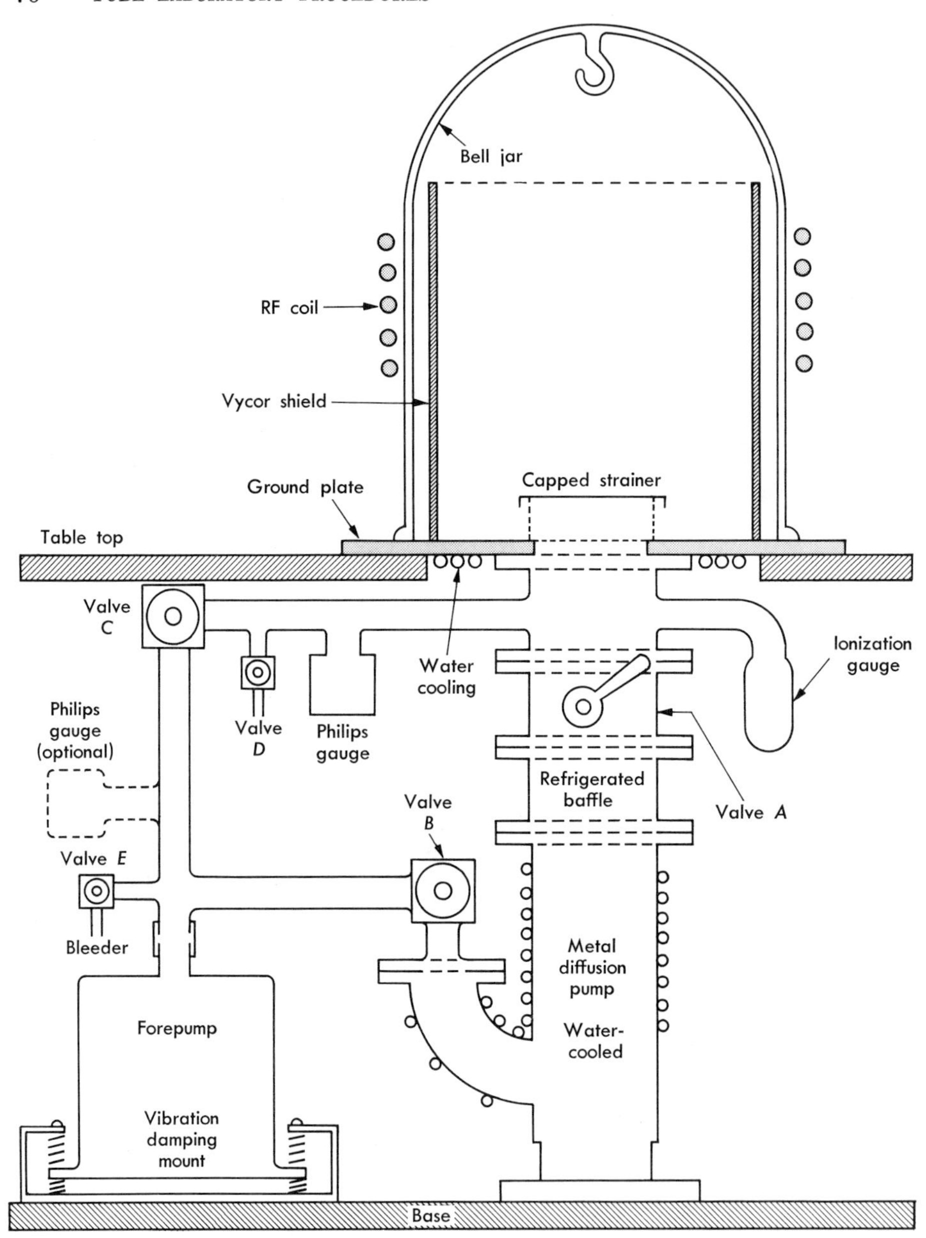

FIG. 18. Arrangement of apparatus for vacuum firing.

box with a double wall and with baffled or staggered holes that allow the evolved gases to be drawn off. A single-walled bucket may also be used.

All parts to be vacuum-fired should be degreased and chemically cleaned; that is, the firing schedule should be the last operation prior to assembly in the tube or device.

A coil connected to the RF generator is arranged around the bell jar (see p. 51 *et seq.*) to enclose the work in its field. It should be borne in mind that the closer the coupling, that is, the nearer the coil is to the work, the more power will be transferred and the greater will be the heating.

Two or more blowers should be provided if necessary to direct a stream of cooling air on the outside of the bell jar.

Operation of the vacuum-firing station. After the work is suitably suspended in the bell jar, valves *A* and *D* (Fig. 18) are closed, valves *B* and *C* are opened, and the forepump is started. When the pressure, as indicated by the Philips gauge (or thermocouple gauge in the same location), falls to 10 microns (0.01 torr) or lower, all water cooling is turned on and heating power is applied to the diffusion pump. When this pump has reached operating temperature (allow at least 15 minutes or more, depending on the characteristics of the pump used), valve *C* is closed and valve *A* is opened, whereupon the pressure should begin to drop to a lower value as the diffusion pump takes hold. The ionization gauge may be turned on when the Philips gauge reading shows the pressure to be within its range.

Pumping is continued in this manner until the pressure reaches the low end of the 10^{-5} torr scale, when the RF generator is turned on, and a small amount of power is applied to the work coil. This power should be raised cautiously from the lowest possible value, because the work may give off copious quantities of gas as soon as there is even a small rise in temperature. So much gas may be evolved that the pumps will be unable to remove it fast enough, and a bright glow discharge will occur within the bell jar. This should not be allowed to persist; it is stopped by shutting off or reducing the RF power, which should not be reapplied or raised again until the pressure has dropped.

The table below gives outgassing temperatures for various materials.

MATERIAL	TEMPERATURE °C (MAXIMUM)	
Tungsten	1000 20–30 minutes	Embrittlement takes place at higher temperatures
Molybdenum	1000 3 minutes	
Platinum	1000	
OFHC copper, beryllium copper	500–800	
Nickel	900–1000	
Monel, etc.	750–950	
Iron, steel	1000	
Stainless steel (austenitic)	1150	
Aluminum (commercially pure)	500	
Graphite	1500–1800	
Lava (No. 1137 previously air-fired)	800	
Alumina (high purity)	1000	

Copper alloys, such as brasses and some bronzes containing zinc, lead, cadmium, antimony, bismuth, and other volatile constituents, cannot be vacuum-fired at high temperatures because of excessive evaporation (see pp. 36, 38, 247, 564). OFHC copper may be fired at 800°C maximum. It is sometimes noticed that ceramics darken or discolor on vacuum- or hydrogen-firing; this is probably caused by the reduction of certain metallic oxides and may produce a greater or lesser degradation of dielectric properties.

The time required for outgassing will depend on the size and mass of the work piece. When the work can be held at its maximum temperature without an excessive rise in pressure, the RF power should be reduced somewhat and allowed to run 5 to 15 minutes. Massive pieces will continue to outgas for some time, since the heat will penetrate slowly. Materials with high electrical conductivity will require more RF power because heating is proportional to the IR drop. The maximum safe temperatures should not be exceeded; excessive temperatures will cause evaporation and sputtering, with possible injury to the work and to the Vycor tube or bell jar. Materials such as nickel, Kovar, Rodar, steels, copper, and Monels will begin to evaporate in vacuum at red heat, and the evaporated material will deposit on the glass, gradually building up toward complete opacity. Thus the temperature of the work will actually be higher than is apparent through this obscuring film; caution is therefore to be exercised in applying RF power beyond a given point, since sudden melting of the work may occur before the operator is fully aware of what is happening.

Consideration is also to be given to work which has several concentric diameters, where attempts to heat the smaller diameters may result in overheating the larger, in view of the difference in coupling to the RF coil.

After firing, the work is allowed to cool in vacuum. Massive pieces may take as long as several hours because of the poor heat losses.

The vacuum system in Fig. 18 is so arranged that the diffusion pump is bypassed for rapid cycling. The pumps need not be shut down if the bell jar is opened for removal of the work in the following manner:

1. Turn off the ionization gauge and the Philips gauge.
2. Close valve *A;* the fore- and diffusion pumps and the refrigerated baffle continue operating.
3. Valve *B* is to remain open; close valve *C* (bypass valve).
4. Allow air to enter slowly at valve *D*.
5. Remove work from bell jar; reload (in a fresh, clean bell jar if first is contaminated).
6. Valves *A* and *B* remain closed; close valve *D* and open valve *C*.
7. When the pressure as shown on the Philips gauge has fallen to 10 microns or lower, close valve *C* and open valve *A*, whereupon the pressure will fall rapidly to a point where heating of the work can again be started.

Between firing and assembly, the work should be handled with clean instruments only, and not exposed to the air any longer than necessary. It may be stored in the vacuum-firing bell jar after shutdown, with the valves *A, C,* and *D* closed.

Shutting down the vacuum-firing station. If the work is to remain in the bell jar, the system is closed down according to the following procedure:

1. Turn off the ionization and Philips gauges.
2. Close valves *A, C,* and *D*.
3. Turn off the refrigerated baffle and diffusion pump power—valve *B* open, forepump operating, cooling water in diffusion pump still flowing.
4. When the diffusion pump is cool, close valve *B* and shut down the forepump. Bleeder valve *E* is opened to prevent forepump-oil suck-back, then closed to keep out contamination.
5. Turn off all water cooling.

Storage of vacuum-fired components. Work that must be removed from the bell jar and stored until use should be kept in airtight, clean containers, preferably glass, stainless steel, or Teflon, although clean polyethylene or polyvinyl containers are permissible for short periods. Work should be at room temperature before being put into plastic containers of any kind. Small parts can be vacuum-fired in special constricted-tubulation glass tubes and sealed off under vacuum on the regular tube pumping stations. These storage tubes can, if required, be provided with a glass-frit filter in the tubulation so that when opened, the admitted air (or dry nitrogen, if desired) is dust-free.

Vacuum Systems—Bibliography

High-Vacuum Techniques, third edition, revised, J. Yarwood, John Wiley & Sons, Inc., New York, New York, 1955.

Vacuum Equipment and Techniques, Guthrie and Wakerling, McGraw-Hill Book Company, Inc., New York, New York, 1949.

Scientific Foundations of Vacuum Technique, second edition, revised, Saul Dushman (J. M. Lafferty, editor), John Wiley & Sons, Inc., New York, New York, 1961.

"Design of High-Vacuum Systems," Parts I and II, E. A. Bunt and R. J. McCulloch, *Industrial Chemist* (Br), October, 1952, p. 460.

"Vacuum Pumping Equipment and Systems," H. M. Sullivan, *Rev. Sci. Instr.,* **19,** 1, 1948.

An interesting paper for the amateur vacuum technologist will be found in *Scientific American,* **202,** 187, 1960. This article gives details on the construction and use of a vacuum system put together with relatively inexpensive materials.

"The Design of High-Vacuum Systems," C. M. Van Atta, Kinney Vacuum Division of New York Air Brake Co., Boston, Massachusetts, 1960.

Practical Vacuum System Design, Training Section, Industrial Relations Dept., Aerospace Division, The Boeing Company, Seattle 24, Washington.

"Techniques for Space Simulation Chambers," D. H. Holkeboer, *Trans. Am. Vacuum Soc.,* **10,** 292–296, 1963.

"Problems in the Construction and Operation of Bakeable and Nonbakeable Vacuum Systems," L. Holland, *Trans. Am. Vacuum Soc.,* **7,** 168–181, 1960.

"High Vacuum," A. R. Gardner, *Product Engineering,* **33,** 82, 1962.

Heater Design and Preparation

The purpose of the heater is to raise the temperature of the electron-emitting materials of the cathode sufficiently to produce the optimum thermionic emission. In the case of cathodes coated with barium and strontium carbonates, this temperature is approximately 850°C. (For the treatment of Philips dispenser-type cathodes, see p. 103.) However, while the tube is being evacuated, it is necessary to reduce these carbonates to oxides (see pp. 98–102) by raising the temperature of the cathode to approximately 1150°C and holding it there for several minutes in order to assure complete conversion.

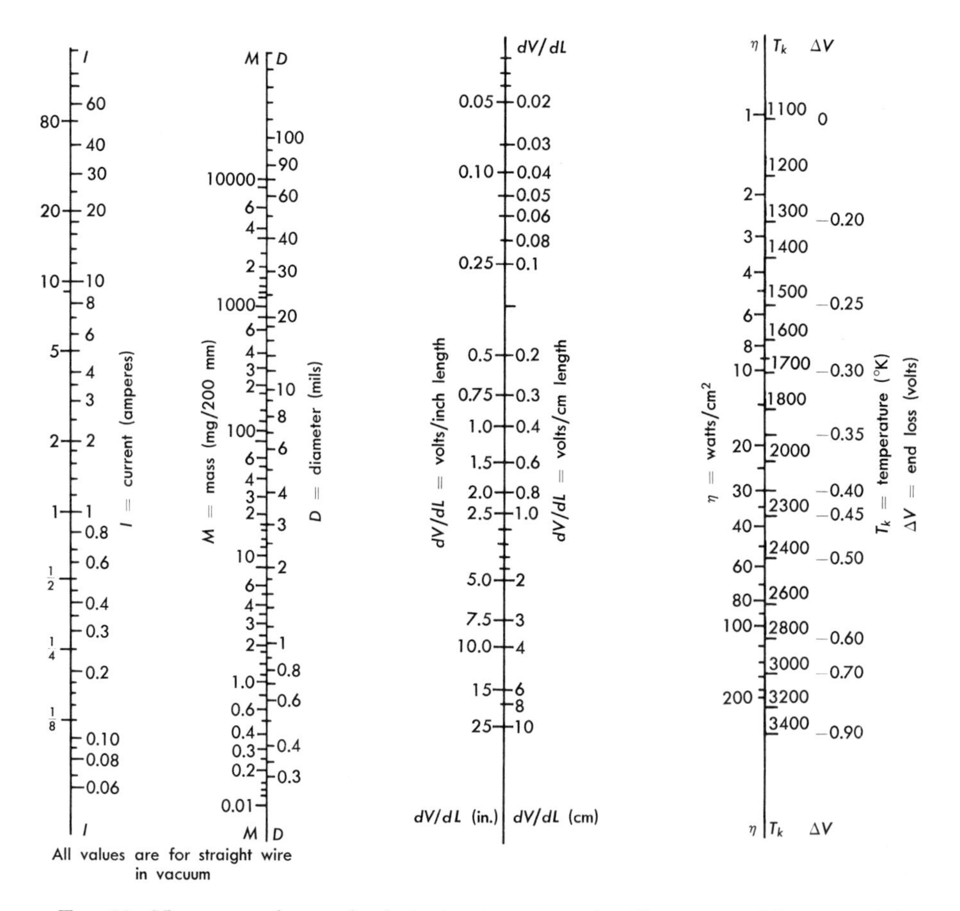

FIG. 19. Nomogram for use in designing tungsten wire filaments and heaters. (Note that for a temperature of 1700°K, a tungsten wire 0.005 in. in diameter will require a current of 1 amp and a voltage of 1 volt/in. or 0.4 volt/cm. The power requirements will be about 10 watts/cm² and the end losses will be 0.3 volt.

To accomplish this it has been found advisable to design the heater for a temperature of 1400°C (1700°K), which is safely below the softening temperature of the alundum-insulating coating on the heater wires. Figure 19 and the table below will be found useful in designing heaters and filaments of tungsten and molybdenum wire.

The heater usually consists of a coated tungsten wire or ribbon that has been wound on a mandrel or otherwise shaped to fit inside the cathode sleeve or recess. For some shapes it is necessary to anneal the wire on the mandrel in hydrogen. (See pp. 82 *et seq.*)

The heater is inserted in the cathode sleeve or mounted close to the cathode in such a way that there is no electrical leakage between them or between adjacent turns of the heater. This requires that the heater coating be hard and tough to withstand the abrasion incidental to mounting. The coating material which satisfies these conditions is an Alundum preparation compounded according to the following formula.

Approximately 0.08 lb of 1000-sec nitrocellulose (the binder) (Hercules Powder Company) is dissolved in equal parts of butyl alcohol and butyl

CURRENT AND VOLTAGE NECESSARY TO RAISE WIRE TO 1400°C*

WIRE SIZE (INCHES)	VOLTS		AMPERES	
	PER CM	PER INCH	TUNGSTEN	MOLYBDENUM
0.002	0.32	0.81	0.18	0.22
0.0025	0.28	0.71	0.26	0.31
0.003	0.25	0.63	0.34	0.41
0.0035	0.24	0.61	0.41	0.49
0.004	0.22	0.56	0.52	0.62
0.0045	0.21	0.53	0.60	0.72
0.005	0.20	0.50	0.72	0.86
0.0055	0.19	0.48	0.84	1.00
0.006	0.18	0.47	0.95	1.13
0.0065	0.18	0.46	1.05	1.26
0.007	0.17	0.44	1.20	1.44
0.0075	0.17	0.43	1.30	1.56
0.008	0.16	0.42	1.45	1.73
0.009	0.16	0.40	1.75	2.10
0.010	0.15	0.38	2.25	2.70
0.012	0.14	0.36	2.60	3.12
0.014	0.14	0.35	3.25	3.90
0.015	0.13	0.34	3.70	4.44
0.020	0.12	0.30	5.6	6.6
0.025	0.11	0.28	7.4	8.9
0.030	0.10	0.25	10.5	12.0
0.040	0.09	0.22	16.0	18.2

* The values given are for straight wire in vacuum.

acetate (about 1 gal of mixed solvents) to give a viscosity of 17.5 ± 0.1 centipoises at 74°F. To 1000 cc of this binder, 635 gm of Norton Company No. 38-900 special acid-washed Alundum are added. This mixture is then diluted with 705 cc of a mixture of equal parts butyl alcohol and butyl acetate. The mixture is rolled, to assure complete wetting of the particles, and then strained through several layers of cheesecloth as an additional precaution to remove coarse particles. A small amount of aniline dye (Sudan Red III, oil-soluble) is added for identification purposes, to distinguish it from the cathode spray described below. The material is agitated on a roller for one hour before use. It is applied by spraying with a De Vilbiss spray gun type CH or CV with a No. 90 air-cap and a type F fluid tip and needle. The air (or dry nitrogen) pressure is set at 35 psig, with a needle opening of one turn. The nozzle-to-heater distance will be determined by the size and number of heaters being sprayed, and will vary between 2 and 6 inches.

The size of mandrel required in winding helical heaters to a given outside diameter will have to be determined by trial and error. The wire will always spring open to a larger diameter when tension is released. However, when heaters are to be annealed in the hydrogen furnace on the mandrel, which may be grooved or threaded and machined from stainless steel (see below), there will be practically no change in dimensions. The finished mandrel is pre-oxidized in wet hydrogen at about 900°C. When winding the tungsten wire, hold it firmly in place so that it cannot change position when fired. The mandrel must be so designed that the wire can be unscrewed or otherwise easily removed. Firing of tungsten is done in hydrogen at 900–1000°C (see p. 555).

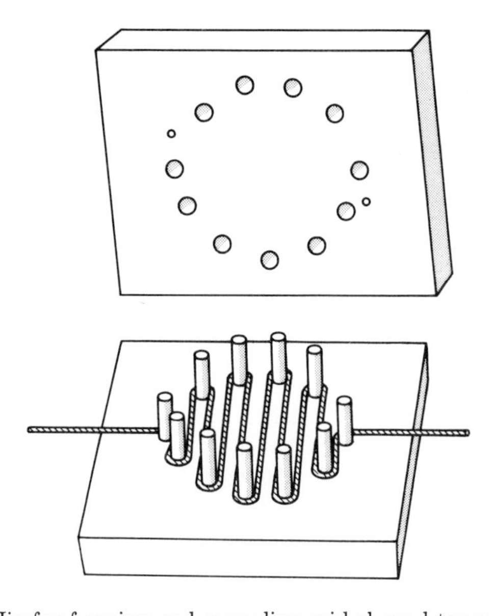

FIG. 20. Jig for forming and annealing grid-shaped tungsten heater.

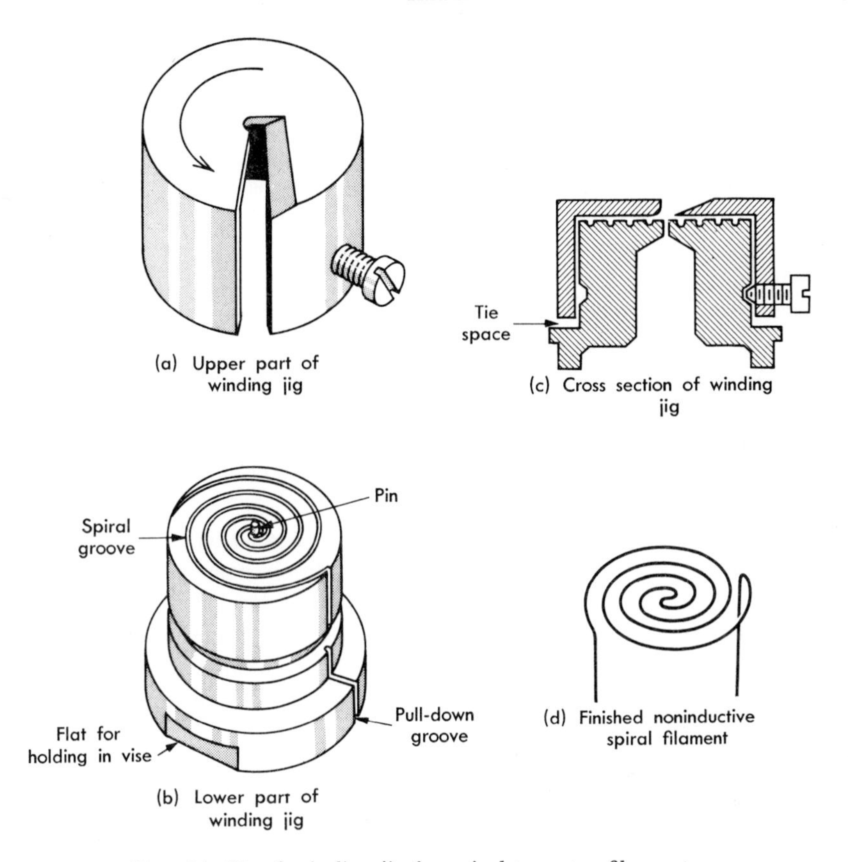

FIG. 21. Hand-winding jig for spiral tungsten filaments.

A simple jig for hand-forming and annealing a grid-shaped tungsten heater or filament is shown in Fig. 20. The parts are made of austenitic stainless steel (type 302 or 304) and prefired in wet hydrogen to form a layer of green chromium oxide which prevents sticking of the tungsten during firing.

If the ends must be perpendicular to the plane of the grid instead of as shown in the figure, the wire ends are bent into the desired position and fed through the holes in the upper plate before being fastened.

After the tungsten wire is formed, the upper plate is placed over the pins and fastened firmly against the lower plate, with the wire sandwiched perfectly flat between them, and then clamped together by two or more pieces of Nichrome wire tied around them. This assembly is then fired in tank hydrogen at the annealing temperature. The tungsten wire should not receive any further bending upon removal from the jig.

A suggested jig for winding and annealing a bifilar or noninductive spiral tungsten filament is shown in Fig. 21. The spiral groove is machined on the top of the flat surface to a depth and width which will accommodate the size of wire to be used. The upper part of the jig is dimensioned so that when the set-screw is turned in, the part can rotate on the lower half of the jig without binding, and yet lie flat on the tungsten wire to hold it securely in the grooves. A length of tungsten wire is folded in half with a pair of smooth round-nose pliers or by bending it around a smooth pin. This loop is then placed over the pin in the jig, the upper part of which is placed in position with the ends of the wire coming through the opening, and then rotated slowly in the direction indicated by the arrow. If lubrication is needed for the jig or the wire, a little dry molybdenum sulfide powder may be used. No oil should be used under *any* circumstances. When the outer end of the groove is reached, each end of the wire is bent down over the edge in turn and pulled down at one of the side grooves, which are 180° apart. Pieces of Nichrome wire are used to hold down the ends in place. These are looped around the jig at the position indicated (tie space). The leads may be made any length.

All parts of this jig, including the set-screw, are made of austenitic stainless steel.

The remarks on forming and firing on p. 82 also apply to this jig. A formed filament or heater can be produced which does not vary from the dimensions of the jig by any significant amount if the procedure for forming and heat treating are followed. With careful handling, a heater can be mounted immediately into the tube or device for which it was designed.

Heaters formed on jigs can be coated with alundum by the procedure described on pp. 81, 85.

If coating is desired after the heater has been formed to the required shape, it is prepared by boiling in 20% potassium hydroxide solution for five minutes, followed by a thorough rinsing in distilled or deionized water, and drying. Tungsten heaters and filaments should *not* be electrolytically cleaned or subjected to any strong chemical reagents such as nitric, hydrochloric, or sulfuric acids, or combinations of these, which cause etching of the surface leading to deformation and possibly to premature failure.

The Alundum coating is then sprayed on the tungsten wire to a thickness of about 0.003 inch (thicker or thinner coatings might be required in special conditions), and the heater is baked at 100°C for one-half hour in an air-oven to dry the binder or vehicle. The heater should be examined at this point for any defects. Small discontinuities in the sprayed coating may be remedied by local respraying.

The heater is now fired (sintered) in the high-temperature hydrogen muffle (see p. 552) at 1600–1650°C for 3 to 10 minutes, depending on the size of the heater; the exact time and temperature are to be determined by trial. Too high a temperature causes embrittlement of the metal and of the coating. Too low a temperature produces a soft coating which will change on standing because of incomplete decomposition of the spray constituents.

After firing, the heater is again examined for defects; if none are found, it is ready for welding or assembly into position in the tube structure.

Cataphoretic alundum coating for tungsten heaters. Tungsten heaters can be alternatively coated by electrocataphoresis according to the following procedure.[1]

In this procedure extreme cleanliness of utensils and constituents is to be observed, as microscopic contamination from dust, oil, grease, etc., may produce large effects, namely, irregularity of coating, bare spots, or failure to coat altogether.

Mixture CA:

Methyl alcohol, absolute (reagent quality)	600 cc
Deionized water, 2 megohms resistivity or higher	600 cc
Alundum #38–900 (Norton Company)	900 gm
Magnesium nitrate (reagent quality)	6 gm
Aluminum nitrate (reagent quality)	30 gm

Place this mixture in a 1-gallon porcelain ball mill, together with 7 pounds of B-2 flint pebbles (Paul O. Abbe Co.), and roll at about 50–60 rpm for 1 hour. Store this mixture in clean glass bottles with vinyl-lined caps tightly screwed on. These bottles are to be of a size suitable for rolling, which is to be done just prior to use to assure thorough dispersion of the solids.

Pour the CA mixture into a clean Pyrex cell equipped with a pure aluminum sheet electrode and a glass stirrer. A metal rack or clip, preferably of stainless steel, is to be provided for suspending the heaters in the mixture, but these racks or clips should at no time touch the liquid. The heaters should be well separated so as not to become enmeshed.

Connect the positive lead from a dc source of 30–100 v, 250-ma capacity, to the aluminum electrode. (The polarity does not appear to be critical; some workers prefer to connect the negative lead to the aluminum electrode.)

A second cell containing methyl alcohol (absolute, reagent quality) is prepared for rinsing off excess material from the coated heaters after cataphoretic treatment.

A third cell is provided containing a binder mixture which is prepared as follows:

Mixture CB:

N–50 ethyl cellulose (47–49 cps; Hercules Powder Co.)	85 gm
Butyl alcohol (butanol, reagent quality)	60 cc
Xylene, 3° (reagent quality)	3338 cc
Viscosity limits of this mixture	12–13 cps at 25°C

[1] U.S. Patent No. 2,307,018, January 5, 1943, issued to James Cardell, assigned to Raytheon Company, Waltham 54, Massachusetts.

The viscosity is adjusted by adding small amounts of either:
N–100 ethyl cellulose (80–105 cps) or
N–22 ethyl cellulose (18–24 cps)

For immediate use: to 425 cc of mixture CB, as adjusted, add

Xylene, 3° (reagent quality)	365 cc
Butyl alcohol (normal butanol, reagent)	45 cc

Firing boats made of sheet molybdenum about 0.010 inch thick are to be coated by spraying with the Alundum mixture on p. 81 and fired in wet hydrogen at 1450°C for 5 minutes.

Connect the negative lead from the dc power supply to the rack or clips and immerse the tungsten heaters in mixture CA for ½ to 2 seconds as indicated by a timer. The stirrer should be turned off while the heaters are in the bath.

Remove the heaters from the CA bath and immerse at once in the second cell containing the methyl alcohol. Agitate gently.

Immerse the heaters in the adjusted CB mixture. The stirrer in the CA bath is again started if more heaters are to be processed.

After immersion in the CB bath, the heaters are dried over a strip heater or radiant-heat lamp. Do not use a blower.

When dry, the heaters are removed from the clips (use only clean instruments to handle them) and placed in the coated molybdenum boats. They are then fired in wet hydrogen at about 1650–1675°C for 5 minutes (see p. 552).

TUNGSTEN FILAMENTS—DIRECT EMITTERS[1]

Tungsten wire or ribbon, including thoriated tungsten (p. 89), is used in making direct emitters to operate at temperatures considerably higher than the 1400°C value of the indirect heaters for oxide-coated cathodes. Consequently, somewhat different heat-treatment and handling will be required. Filaments at high temperatures have a tendency to sag or warp unless they are heat-treated and adequately supported. Special consideration should also be given to lead wires.

The smaller sizes of tungsten wire (up to 0.025 inch) should, for many purposes, be straightened. This is conveniently done by holding one end of a length in a vise and grasping the other end with pliers. Clip leads from a variable transformer are attached to each end of the wire and, while pulling with the pliers, the voltage is brought up slowly until the wire glows dull red. The tension is maintained until after the current is shut off. The wire may also be straightened by suspending appropriate weights at the end of the length and applying current as mentioned. (Do not stand with your feet beneath the weight!) The oxidation resulting from this operation can be removed by the

---

[1] See "Fine Wires in the Electron-Tube Industry," G. A. Espersen, *Proc. I.R.E.*, **34,** 116 W, 1946.

method given in T-2, p. 17. Tungsten wire for use as small formed heaters or filaments (see the following paragraph) generally requires no straightening, but if conditions call for it, the procedure should be carried out in hydrogen, forming gas, or in vacuum so that oxidation is prevented.

A tungsten filament to be operated in such a position that it might sag undesirably can be treated so that this effect is minimized. The filament is first formed in hydrogen on a stainless steel jig or mandrel, as described on pp. 82–84. It is then removed from the jig or mandrel and mounted on a press, or in a position similar to that which it will have in use, under a hydrogen bell jar. The hydrogen flow should be shielded or baffled so as not to impinge directly on the heated wire. The temperature is raised to something over 1400°C (white heat) and observed through a welder's head mask. Wherever sagging appears, the filament is poked or pushed from the open bottom of the bell jar with a piece of heavy copper wire formed into a hook at the end. The copper wire should not remain in contact with the filament longer than necessary because it will overheat and stick. It is to be noted that considerably more current will be required to heat the tungsten wire in hydrogen than in vacuum because of the high thermal conductivity of the gas. Use a fairly tall bell-jar and have the heated filament well up away from the bottom. During manipulation avoid excessive movement, which might cause turbulence of the hydrogen.

Tungsten emitters for use at 2500°K should be cleaned in the same manner as heaters (T-2, p. 17). The filaments should be formed (and firmly held on an oxidized stainless steel jig or mandrel for the larger sizes or more complicated shapes) and hydrogen-fired in wet hydrogen for 20–30 minutes at 950–1000°C. Since some brittleness will be produced by this treatment, the wire should be handled carefully, and mounted strain-free. Cleaning may take place after firing, but it is preferable to assemble the cleaned straightened wire on the clean (oxidized) mandrel. Hydrogen-fire and assemble in the tube immediately after firing if possible; otherwise, store the filaments in dust-free, preferably glass, containers. The filaments should be handled only with nylon gloves or instruments.

It is obvious that high-temperature tungsten filaments should not be spot-welded to nickel leads of inadequate size or close to the high-temperature zone. If nickel leads must be used, they should be heavy enough for operation at a maximum temperature of 700°C. The best lamp-making practice requires that tungsten filaments be attached to leads by clamping, crimping, or the use of small screws, rather than by welding, because of the tendency of welds to form low melting-point eutectics or alloys. Welds can be made to tungsten or molybdenum leads by the interposition of a flux (see p. 253) of tantalum or other refractory metal which will weld easily to tungsten. Tungsten-to-tungsten and tungsten-to-molybdenum welds are made with some difficulty, although small tungsten filament wires can be welded to heavy tungsten leads. The tungsten filament can, of course, be welded easily to tantalum wires.

The table below gives some of the physical properties of tungsten and molybdenum (*cf.* table on p. 89).

PROPERTY	TUNGSTEN	MOLYBDENUM
Density at 20°C (gm/cm^3)	19.3	10.2
Density at 20°C (lb/in^3)	0.697	0.368
Melting point (°C)	3400	2625
Linear coefficient of expansion (°C at 20°C)	4.0×10^{-6}	5.45×10^{-6}
Specific heat at 20°C (gm-Cal/gm/°C)	0.034	0.0624
Thermal conductivity at 20°C (Cgs)	0.399	0.349
Vapor pressure, mm Hg (approx.)		
1400°C	lower than 10^{-8}	lower than 10^{-8}
2000	lower than 10^{-7}	10^{-7}
2500	10^{-7}	10^{-4}
Electrical conductivity, % IACS	31	36
Electrical resistivity at 0°C microhm-cm	5.48	5.17
Temperature coefficient of electrical resistivity per °C (20–100°C)	0.00482	0.0047
Apparent positive work function (ev)	4.55	4.20
Apparent positive ion emission (ev)	11.93	8.60
First ionization potential (ev)	7.60	7.35
Magnetic susceptibility (cgs units) at 18°C	0.28×10^{-6}	0.04×10^{-6}
Tensile strength, wire, 0.025 inch unannealed (psi)	225,000	130,000
Hardness, Rockwell, wire, 0.025 inch unannealed	44C	100B
Young's modulus of elasticity, (psi)	52×10^6	42×10^6
Modulus of torsion, (psi)	21.48×10^6	21.3×10^6

Both tungsten and molybdenum are attacked vigorously by aqua regia. Tungsten is attacked only slightly by nitric acid in various dilutions up to full concentration, while molybdenum is attacked rapidly by the same reagent. This provides a convenient means of removing the molybdenum core from tungsten "coiled-coil" lamp filament wire. A mixture of nitric and sulfuric acids can also be used (see T-4, p. 18).

Treatment of coiled-coil tungsten filaments and heaters. This type of heater or filament is used when calculations call for medium- to high-resistance (i.e. more small wire) windings. It is the type used in ordinary incandescent

Some Properties of Tungsten and Molybdenum Compared with Copper and Nickel*

PROPERTY	COPPER	TUNGSTEN	MOLYBDENUM	NICKEL
Density	100	216	114	99
Melting point	100	314	242	135
Thermal conductivity	100	42	37	23
Electrical conductivity	100	31	36	14
Electrical resistivity	100	328	310	409
Linear expansion coefficient	100	26	30	81
Young's elasticity modulus	100	313	250	188

Note: In this table, the properties of copper are given an arbitrary value of 100. Properties of other metals are expressed as percentages of this value. Compare this table with the one on page 88.

* Courtesy of Fansteel Metallurgical Corporation, North Chicago, Illinois, 1954.

lamps, and comes in various sizes, nominally from 10 to 200 watts, or even heavier.

Coiled-coil heaters are formed on preoxidized stainless steel mandrels in the same manner as plain tungsten wire (see p. 82), except that the forming conditions are 1100°C for 30 minutes in wet hydrogen. The higher temperature and longer time are required because of the necessity of chemical treatment, which tends to produce stresses in the metal. After firing, the heater is removed from the mandrel and treated according to T-4 or in simple 50% nitric acid. After thorough rinsing and drying, the heater may be coated, if required, in the manner outlined on p. 81.

THORIATED TUNGSTEN EMITTERS[1]

Besides being the most prevalent type of cathode in transmitting tubes, the thoriated filament is found in many types of receiving tubes. It is usually of the filament type, and is operated in a temperature range in the neighborhood of 1975°K. The filament is made of pure tungsten wire to which a small amount of thorium oxide has been added as an alloy during manufacture. After being exhausted and baked, the thoriated filament is momentarily "flashed" or heated to a temperature high enough to drive some of the thorium oxide to the surface. It is then aged for some time at a lower temperature in a good vacuum so that some of the thorium oxide is reduced to metallic

[1] Abstracted from *The Electronic Engineering Handbook*, R. R. Batcher and W. Moulic, Electronic Development Associates, New York (1944).

Life Expectancy of Tungsten Filaments versus Input and Luminosity*

TEMPERATURE† (MAXIMUM °K)	COLOR TEMPERATURE (AVERAGE °K)	BRIGHTNESS† (PERCENT)	VOLTS (PERCENT)	WATTS (PERCENT)	CURRENT (PERCENT)	LUMINOUS INTENSITY (%)	LIFE (%)
2000	2024	10.4	55.0	38.7	70.3	10.4	1090000
2100	2128	18.4	63.6	48.7	76.5	18.6	100100
2200	2231	31.7	73.3	61.1	83.3	32.2	11400
2300	2335	52.1	83.5	75.2	90.0	52.2	1490
2400	2440	81.4	95.0	92.1	97.0	82.9	246
2450	2493	100.0	100.0	100.0	100.0	100.0	100
2500	2546	122.8	105.9	109.6	103.5	122.0	45
2600	2652	180.0	118.5	130.6	110.3	179.3	9.4
2700	2758	257.9	132.3	155.6	117.6	257.0	2.3

† Connection between the absolute temperature T of a tungsten filament and the intrinsic brilliancy C, in international candles per cm^2, is

$$T = \frac{10957}{6797 - \log C}.$$

* Courtesy of American Electro-Metals Corp., Yonkers, N.Y., 1941. See also p. 556.

thorium, which diffuses into the crevices and on the surface of the tungsten. The thorium becomes the active emissive element, the main function of the tungsten being to support and carry the heat which brings the thorium to the proper working temperature.

With the thoriated filament at an elevated temperature, the tube is baked (this is done preferably before activation, but can be done again afterwards), and the various metallic elements in the tube are subjected to heating by RF bombardment (see p. 101). The temperature attained by the elements during bombardment must be higher than any temperature reached in normal operation of the tube throughout its life; if this is not done, additional gas may be liberated later and the vacuum condition destroyed. *The activity of a thoriated tungsten filament may be permanently nullified by small amounts of gas* in the tube, as might be released during some later operating overload.

When properly prepared, the emission effectiveness of a thoriated filament may be a thousandfold that of tungsten alone at the same temperature. This huge improvement does not mean that the filament will be that much more efficient, since an increase of the order of 700°K in the temperature of pure tungsten alone would also show a similar increase.

In other words, thoriated filaments can be used at lower temperatures, but have to be treated rather carefully to maintain the prescribed operating temperature, or else unsatisfactory characteristics and shorter life result. *Pure tungsten, on the other hand, can handle greater variations in temperature without failure,* but requires more heating power.

Further data on thoriated tungsten cathodes.[1] The thoriated cathode was developed by Langmuir and his associates.[2] It is made by dissolving a small amount of thorium oxide and a little carbon in a tungsten filament.[3] The filament is first flashed at 2800°K for one minute to reduce some of the thorium oxide, then "formed" or activated by being operated *in vacuo* at a temperature somewhat above normal, usually about 2200°K. At this temperature some thorium works its way to the surface of the cathode where it deposits in a layer one atom deep. If the process is continued indefinitely, more thorium is brought to the surface, but the layer is never more than one atom deep, the additional thorium merely displacing some that has already formed and so gradually reducing the supply of this metal in the cathode. This cathode is ordinarily operated at a temperature of about 1950 to 2000°K. Like the oxide-coated cathode, it should not be operated at temperatures either above or

[1] *Fundamentals of Vacuum Tubes,* third edition, A. V. Eastman, McGraw-Hill Book Company, New York, New York, 1949. By permission.

[2] "The Electron Emission from Thoriated Tungsten Filaments," I. Langmuir, *Phys. Rev.,* **22,** 357, 1923.

[3] Commercial filament wire is obtainable 1% and 2% thoriated, for example, from General Electric Company, Lamp Metals and Components Department, 21800 Tungsten Road, Cleveland 17, Ohio (type NF and type 2% thoriated).

below the rated value if maximum life expectancy is to be realized. The emission efficiency is approximately 40–100 ma/w.

The emission of the thoriated cathode remains normal as long as the layer of thorium is intact, but as the cathode is used, the thorium is gradually dissipated, and after a period of time the emission begins to drop. This decrease in emission is not directly proportional to the decrease in area of the thorium coating, but is much more rapid. For example, when the thorium coating has been so reduced as to cover only about one-half the cathode, the emission will have decreased to less than 1% of its maximum. The minimum emission below which a tube is not usable varies with different tubes but is usually specified by the manufacturer.

Carbonization of thoriated cathodes. Both thoriated and oxide-coated cathodes, especially the latter type, are particularly subject to injury under positive-ion bombardment (see p. 101). By a process known as *carbonization* (sometimes called *carburization*), thoriated cathodes can be considerably protected against such bombardment and against too rapid evaporation of thorium at higher filament temperatures. Before being activated by the procedure described above, the cathode is operated at a temperature of somewhat over 1600°K in the vapor of some hydrocarbon such as naphthalene, benzene, or alcohol. The molecules of the vapor decompose upon striking the hot cathode, depositing carbon, which then combines with the tungsten to form tungsten carbide (W_2C). Since tungsten carbide is quite brittle, great care must be taken not to carry the process too far, about 3% carbon being satisfactory.

The evaporation of thorium from a carbonized cathode is only about 15% as great as from one not so treated. It is therefore possible to increase the operating temperature of the treated cathode and so increase its emission efficiency. Most high-voltage tubes are supplied with thoriated tungsten, carbonized cathodes, instead of with pure tungsten, as formerly.

Rejuvenation of thoriated cathodes. Tubes having thoriated cathodes or filaments that are found to have too low an emission may often be rejuvenated. Low emission is an indication that the surface layer of thorium has been partially dissipated. Generally an additional supply of thorium is still dissolved in the cathode in the form of thorium oxide, which may be brought to the surface reduced to thorium and made available for use by raising the temperature of the cathode temporarily. To do this the original activation process is repeated (see above). Flashing temperatures are obtained by applying about $3\frac{1}{2}$ times normal filament voltage, and forming or aging temperatures by about $1\frac{1}{2}$ times normal voltage. Flashing is not recommended for tubes having filament voltages higher than 5.0.[1]

---

[1] See also "Use of Thoriated-Tungsten Filaments in High-Power Transmitting Tubes," R. B. Ayer, *Proc. I.R.E.*, **40,** 591, 1952.

Nickel Bases for Oxide-Coated Cathodes[1]

The following material is from "Superior Tube Electronic Products," courtesy of the Superior Tube Company, Norristown, Pennsylvania. (Catalog No. 51, 1956.)

Cathaloy A-30. This is an active-grade nickel alloy designed for use in high-speed electron-tube production. Results of exhaustive testing commend it as a replacement for active alloys with silicon and magnesium reducing elements. Its chief advantages are long life, rapid activation, very low interface impedance, practically no interelectrode leakage caused by sublimed films, and high emission value. Hot yield strength is approximately 2500 psi. It may be used wherever an active alloy is now specified. It is recommended for general-purpose entertainment-type electron tubes.

Cathaloy A-31.[2] This is a premium-grade 4% tungsten nickel alloy designed for cathode use in ruggedized electron tubes. The need for this alloy for indirectly heated cathodes has been demonstrated by the increase in requirements for strength, long life, and reliability. It has also been shown that A-31 provides long life under fluctuating cathode temperatures. It has demonstrated hot yield strength of approximately 5000 psi. It is resistant to bowing during assembly and processing. Its recommended use is for any electron tubes subjected to shock, vibration, and varying heater voltages. A-31 is particularly desirable for applications requiring life test at 25% above rated heater voltage. Its great strength enables it to withstand approximately twice the shock-loading of alloys without tungsten.

Cathaloy A-32. This cathaloy contains 2.25% tungsten for high strength both at room temperatures during fabrication and at elevated temperatures during use. A-32 is particularly recommended where resistance to shock and vibration is needed. It is strong enough for most ruggedized tube applications. In addition, it has excellent emission characteristics, rapid activation during processing, freedom from excessive sublimation during both processing and use, and a very low rate of interface impedance formation during pulsing. Its hot yield strength, approximately 3750 psi, is surpassed only by that of Cathaloy A-31 and P-51.

Cathaloy P-50. This is a passive-grade nickel alloy designed for the most reliable type of electron tubes. Experiments have shown it to offer the low

---

[1] See the table on p. 94.

[2] Same as INCO 202 nickel.

Cathode Alloys*

ALLOY	ASTM GRADE	FORM	Cu MAX. %	Fe MAX. %	Mn MAX. %	C MAX. %	Mg MAX. %	Si MAX. %	S MAX. %	Ti MAX. %	OTHER	Ni+Co MIN.%
Active Cathaloy A-30		*L*, *W*, Disc	0.05	0.10	0.05	0.03–0.10	0.01–0.06	0.02	0.005	0.01	Al 0.03–0.08	99.25
Cathaloy A-31	7	*L*, *W*, Disc	0.10	0.10	0.05	0.03–0.10	0.01–0.06	0.02–0.06	0.005	0.02	W 3.75–4.25	94.50
Cathaloy A-32		*L*, *W*, Disc	0.05	0.10	0.05	0.03–0.10	0.01–0.06	0.02	0.005	0.01	Al 0.03–0.08 W 2.0–2.5	96.25
Passive Cathaloy P-50	22	*L*, *W*, Disc	0.04	0.05	0.02	0.05	0.01	0.02	0.005	0.01		99.50
Cathaloy P-51		*L*, *W*, Disc	0.04	0.05	0.02	0.05	0.01	0.02	0.005	0.01	W 3.75–4.25	95.25
Active D-H 799‡	2	*L* and Disc	0.04	0.05–0.10	0.05	0.08	0.01–0.10	0.12–0.20	0.005	0.01		99.25
INCO 225†	3	*L*, *S*, Disc	0.20	0.20	0.20	0.08	Not specified	0.15–0.25	0.008	Not specified		99.00
D-H 599‡	4	*L* and Disc	0.04	0.05–0.10	0.10	0.08	0.01	0.15–0.25	0.005	Not specified		99.25
D-H 399‡	6	*L*	0.04	0.05	0.02	0.08	0.01	0.15–0.25	0.005	Not specified		99.25
INCO 233†	10	*L*, *W*, Disc	0.15	0.20	0.30	0.08	Not specified	0.10	0.008	Not specified		99.00
INCO 220†	11	*L*, *S*, Disc	0.20	0.20	0.20	0.08	0.01–0.10	0.01–0.05	0.008	Not specified		99.10
Electronic Grade A Nickel (INCO 200)†		*S*, *W*,	0.20	0.30	0.35	0.15		0.20	0.008			99.00

L means lockseam, *W* means weldrawn, and *S* means seamless. Disc means used with disc-type cathodes.

* Superior Tube Company, Norristown, Pennsylvania. Catalog 51, 1956.

† International Nickel Co., Huntington Alloy designation. *Cf.* page 293.

‡ Driver-Harris Co.

rate of barium evolution, minimum sublimation, and freedom from interface impedance required of passive cathodes. Cathaloy P-50 is used for power output tubes requiring low grid emission and for tubes which need a seamless passive cathode. It is specially treated to provide good uniformity. Hot yield strength is approximately 2500 psi. This is the only passive cathode alloy available commercially in seamless and Weldrawn forms. It is also supplied in Lockseam cathode form.

Cathaloy P-51. This is a passive-grade nickel alloy designed for electron tubes which require the low rate of barium evolution, minimum sublimation, and freedom from interface impedance characteristic of passive cathodes, but which at the same time must operate under conditions of extreme shock and vibration. It may be used in any tube requiring a passive cathode. However, since its hot yield strength is approximately 5000 psi, it has approximately twice the resistance to shock and vibration of other passive cathode alloys. It is available commercially in seamless, Weldrawn, and Lockseam cathode forms.

OTHER CATHODE MATERIALS[1]

Cathodes are also supplied in six other cathode-base materials. They are active alloys in varying degrees, and one is a passive material. Their activity is dependent upon small amounts of silicon and/or magnesium present.

These standard materials are melted and offered by either The International Nickel Company (INCO) or Driver-Harris Company (D-H). For rapid activation, plus high-level dc emission, the silicon-activated alloys INCO 225 and D-H 599, 399, and 799 are most frequently used. For normal emission, with rapid activation, the silicon magnesium alloys INCO 220 and 233 are regularly employed. (See p. 289.)

Long life oxide-cathode tubes. Experimental tubes often do not require their oxide-coated cathodes to have exceptionally long life. Occasionally, however, a long-life cathode having good emission properties is needed. In order to achieve such a rugged cathode certain special precautions must be taken.

1. The need for eliminating contamination in *all* the tube components, including the grids, anodes, targets, supports, and envelope, calls for extreme emphasis on the remarks at the beginning of this book (p. 1). Certain glasses, even if clean, may, when heated, give off substances that adversely affect the cathode.[2]

2. Nickel bases of highest purity are required (see p. 293). The presence of silicon and aluminum in any but trace amounts is to be avoided. Magnesium may be present only in controlled amounts of 0.01 to 0.03%, and tungsten my be allowed up to 2%. A high-purity nickel has the disadvantage of passivity and long activating time, but the advantages to be gained are more than offset in freedom from materials that might "poison" the cathode.

3. All parts of the tube should be thoroughly outgassed either by vacuum firing (p. 75), hydrogen firing (p. 41), or, in the case of glass envelopes, long-baking at maximum temperature, after assembly but before cathode activation (breakdown).

---

[1] Superior Tube Company is now offering Alloy X-3012, an active-grade cathode alloy designed to have more features of the ideal nickel cathode alloy than do any other commercial alloys. Its basic composition of 2% tungsten, 0.1% zirconium, and controlled minimum amounts of residual elements give this material: (1) high strength, (2) excellent emission with (3) a low rate of sublimation, and (4) virtually no development of interface impedance. Alloy X-3012 can be obtained in seamless, Weldrawn, Lockseam, or lapseam cathode forms, or as disc cathode caps. This alloy can be fired at 700°C for 10 minutes in dry hydrogen without undue softening, as compared with 600°C for Alloy 220. At higher temperatures (up to 1000°C) the X-3012 has higher collapse strength. (This is an excerpt from Technical Service Report, Superior Tube Co., Technical Division, Norristown, Pennsylvania, April 24, 1959.)

[2] See L. F. Oldfield and R. D. Wright, *Glass Technology,* **3,** 59, 1962; B. Johnson, J. L. Lineweaver, and J. T. Kerr, *J. Appl. Phys.,* **31,** 51, 1960; T. W. Hickmott, *ibid.,* **31,** 128, 1960; *Ultrahigh Vacuum and its Applications,* R. W. Roberts and T. A. Vanderslice, p. 102, Prentice-Hall, Inc., Englewood Cliffs, N.J., 1963; L. H. James and G. Carter, *Br. J. Appl. Phys.,* **14,** 147, 1963; *Scientific Foundations of Vacuum Technique,* S. Dushman, 2nd edition, p. 469, John Wiley & Sons, Inc., New York, 1962.

4. Only highest purity chemicals are to be used in the preparation of cathode coatings. Some workers find that the calcium carbonate (see p. 97) in the cathode mixture, while accelerating cathode breakdown, sometimes tends to cause poor adherence of the coating to the nickel base.

5. A careful activation schedule should be followed. Current is to be applied to the heater in small steps, especially in tubes in which other elements near the cathode (closely spaced) might be heated and thus give off gases or vapors harmful to the coating. During the aging period, the cathode temperature should be held to a minimum for the same reason. It is most important that at no time during vacuum processing should the pressure in the tube be allowed to rise above 1×10^{-6} torr. This calls for a fast, well-trapped pumping system in which backstreaming of oil vapors near the cathode have been eliminated. In order to assure accurate pressure readings, the precalibrated gauge-tube is to be placed as close as possible to the tube or vessel being evacuated. A "nude" ionization gauge (p. 398) can be used to advantage. In any event, the ionization gauge elements and envelope must be thoroughly outgassed prior to heating the cathode.

6. If getters are used, they should be of the best quality, and should be outgassed cautiously, preferably before activation of the cathode. The same rule is to be applied to final firing of the getters just before seal-off.

7. In the case of glass tubes, heat is applied to the seal-off tubulation very cautiously at first, in order to desorb gases on the glass (which the baking temperature was not high enough to do). Here again the maximum allowable pressure (note 5) is to be strictly observed.

8. It is obvious from the foregoing that none of the operations in making a long-life tube can be done in a hurry, and this should be the tube technician's watchword.

Oxide-Coated Cathodes General[1]

The material commonly used as a base for barium-strontium oxide cathodes is a high-nickel alloy (see pp. 93, 293) which is prepared for use by one of several methods (see pp. 12, 13). Hydrogen- and/or vacuum-firing is done just before coating. Other metals, such as tungsten,[2] molybdenum, and tantalum, are sometimes used as bases for oxide cathodes of a directly heated

[1] See the bibliography on p. 102.

[2] "Chemical Reactions in Barium Oxide on Tungsten Emitters," R. C. Hughes, P. P. Coppola, and H. C. Evans, *J. Appl. Phys.*, **23,** 635–641, 1952; "Bariated Tungsten Emitters," R. C. Hughes and P. P. Coppola, *ibid.*, **23,** 1261–1262, 1952.

type, but these are not uniformly successful in respect to adherence of the oxide coating.

Cathode coating. The material used for cathode coating is normally a triple carbonate, although a double carbonate is sometimes used (see p. 96). The composition of this mixture varies slightly with the source (see the following table), generally consisting of equal parts of barium and strontium carbonates and a small amount of calcium carbonate.

COMPARATIVE SPECTROSCOPIC ANALYSES OF CATHODE-COATING MATERIALS

	MATERIAL ANALYZED					
CONSTITUENT	RAYTHEON BINDER B-71-5	RAYTHEON C-51-2	BAKER RADIO MIXTURE NO. 3	RCA 33-C-118	RCA 33-C-131	RCA 33-C-133
Aluminum		m_1		m_5	m_1	m_3
Barium		M	M_2	M	M	M
Calcium	m_1	m_2	m	m_5	m_4	m_1
Copper	t	m_1	m_1	m_1	m_2	m_2
Iron		t_1	m	m_2	m_1	t_2
Potassium		t		t	t	t
Magnesium	m_1	m_3	m	m_1	m_1	m_1
Manganese		m_1	t	m_2	m_1	t
Sodium	t_1	m_3		m_1	m_4	m_4
Lead		m_1	t_1	t_2	t_1	t_1
Silicon		t_2	m	m_4	t_1	m_2
Strontium		M	M	M	M	M

M means major; m means minor; t means trace; m_2 is larger than m_1.

Typically, the Raytheon Manufacturing Company C-51-2 (see third column) is composed of a binder (B-71-5) consisting of 1000-second nitrocellulose (Hercules Powder Company) dissolved in equal parts of butyl alcohol and butyl acetate (0.08 lb nitrocellulose to 1 gal mixed solvents) to give a viscosity of 17.5 ± 0.1 centipoises at 74°F. To 1700 cc of this binder is added 1600 gm of Radio Mixture No. 3 (J. T. Baker Company), which consists of 57.3% barium carbonate, 42.2% strontium carbonate, and 0.5% calcium carbonate. The mixture is ball-milled for 7 hours. For use, 1500 cc of the ball-milled suspension is diluted with 750 cc of the 17.5 cps binder.

In order to prepare the C-51-2 mixture for use in a spray gun, roll it for 1 hour in a half-gallon bottle at about 50 rpm. Spray-gun bottles are cleaned with acetone (reagent quality) and dried before the suspension is poured in. The spray gun is a De Vilbiss-type CH or CV with a No. 90 air-cap and an

"F" fluid tip and needle. Clean, filtered compressed air is to be used, or if the cleanliness of the air is doubtful, dry nitrogen may be used.

There should be a 0–50 psi pressure gauge at the air or nitrogen outlet. The actual spraying pressure is set at 30 to 35 psi, with the gun operating, and the spray gun air-cap is set at 10 to 18 turns, with the needle opening at ½ to 2 turns. The gun is held from 3 to 7 inches from the cathode and at an angle of 90° with respect to the cathode surface. Passes are made across the work in about 2 seconds, the number of passes depending on what coating thickness is required; 10 to 20 passes will yield a coating thickness of about 0.003 inch, which is an approximately optimum value. After spraying, the work is dried over a radiant heat lamp for 3 minutes, or placed in an air oven at 100°C for 15 minutes.

Spraying is to be done in an exhaust booth to protect the operator and materials. The gun, which is to be used only for cathode spray, is cleaned after use by removing the bottle containing the cathode coating mixture, substituting one containing clean acetone, and spraying this solvent through the gun. (After several spray passes, during spraying of cathodes, a pass or two is made with air or dry nitrogen only, so as to more quickly dry the previous coats.)

The cathode coating may also be applied to certain supports or bases with a brush.[1] A convenient size and quality is Windsor & Newton's or Grumbacher's Red Sable Watercolor Brush No. 5, which should be previously cleaned in acetone and dried. Cathodes may also be coated by dipping. Both brushing and dipping can be done repeatedly, allowing each coat to dry thoroughly, in order to build up the required thickness. Any unevenness can be corrected by scraping with a clean, sharp razor blade or X-acto knife after the coating is dry.

Activation of double- and triple-carbonate cathode coatings (barium and strontium; and barium, strontium, and calcium). The nickel bases for oxide-coated cathodes (see pp. 93 *et seq.*) are cleaned after forming by the N-1B process given on p. 13. They are then hydrogen-fired at 900°C for 10 to 30 minutes, depending on size and mass.

The prepared nickel base is coated by the procedures given above. The heater and other elements of the tube are then assembled[2] and placed on the vacuum system, consisting of a forepump, a three-stage oil diffusion pump, a

---

[1] The coating is applied in this way to nickel-screen cathodes, in which a single layer of nickel mesh is sintered in a special jig, over a solid nickel base. In this way a matrix is formed for the retention of larger quantities of the emitting material than could be accommodated on a smooth or etched surface.

[2] It is often a good plan, as a preliminary to the construction of a complex tube structure, to set up a test diode or multode having similar geometry, but with the cathode visible if possible, upon which activation and electrical tests can be made, so that when the final tube is being processed, the activation and parametric characteristics will have been approximately determined.

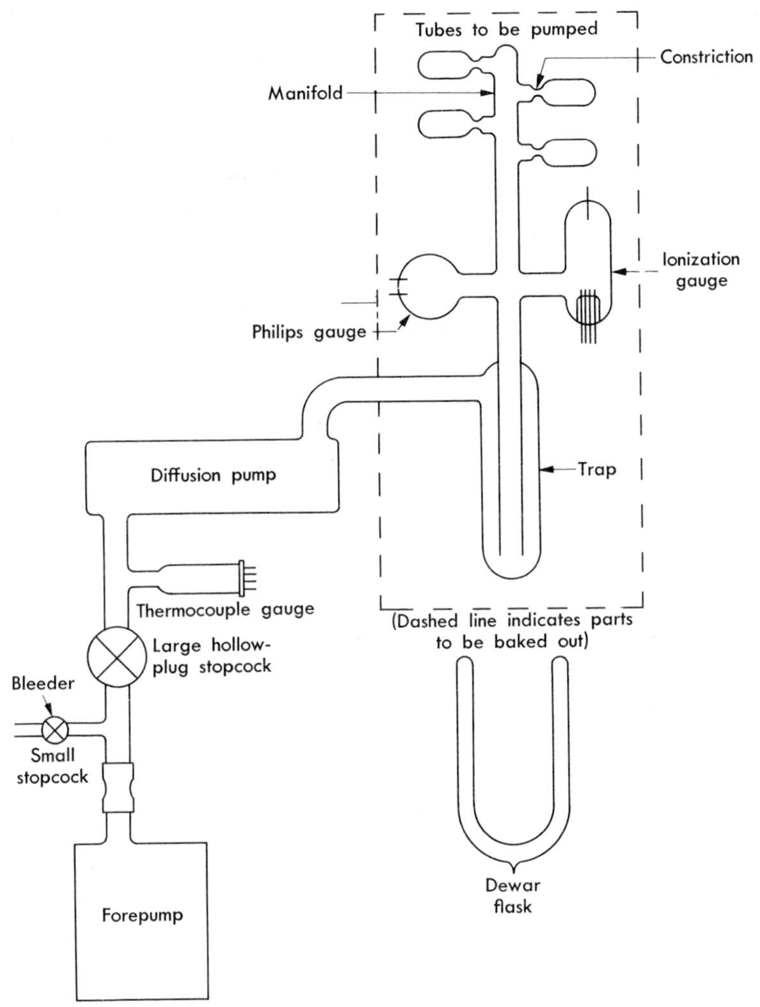

FIG. 22. Suggested vacuum system for pumping tubes.

refrigerated trap which can be baked out, a bake-out oven, ionization and thermocouple gauges, and stopcocks (see Fig. 22, also pp. 416 ff.).

When the pressure falls to 5×10^{-6} torr or lower, the tube is baked for at least one-half hour at 450°–500°C. In the absence of leaks, and with observance of cleanliness procedures (see pp. 1–3 *et seq.*), the pressure should fall to approximately 2×10^{-6} torr by the end of the bake-out at 450°C and to 1×10^{-7} torr or better when the tube has reached room temperature. With rigid cleaning and firing procedures for all tube components, and longer bake-out times, it is possible to attain pressures of 1×10^{-9} torr or lower.

The cold trap is now used with liquid nitrogen and is kept in place during the entire activation process.

A small ac voltage is applied to the heater and raised by small steps while the ionization gauge reading is watched. The pressure should not be allowed to rise above 5×10^{-5} torr at any time. If the temperature of the cathode is raised too rapidly, there is risk of blistering, flaking, or evaporating the coating. An initial sharp increase in pressure, observed when the heater current is first applied, is caused by outgassing of the heater itself.

Most of the decomposition products of the nitrocellulose binder are removed during the 450°–500°C bake-out; the remainder, if any, will all have been eliminated when the cathode coating has reached a temperature of about 700°C.

It has been found, in general, that if the pressure is not allowed to rise above 10^{-5} torr during the activation, this process will take place in as expedient a manner as is allowable in safe practice. The employment of very fast pumps and proper design of the vacuum system (elimination of constrictions, sharp bends, long runs of tubing, etc) permit more rapid activation. Certain types of cathode-base alloys allow faster activation than others (see pp. 93–95).

The rise in pressure with increase in temperature is due largely to the evolution of carbon dioxide with, perhaps, some water vapor and other gases. When the cathode becomes visibly incandescent, an optical pyrometer can be used for gauging the temperature.[1] The normal operating temperature for an oxide-coated cathode is between 800°C and 900°C, but during the activation, heating currents to produce cathode temperatures up to 1100°C may be applied for short periods (up to 30 seconds), at intervals of several minutes. This is called *flashing*. The maximum chemical change from carbonate to oxide occurs in the neighborhood of 900°C; the 1100°C temperature is applied in order to assure complete conversion of the coating, especially at the ends or edges of the cathode surface, where radiation losses are greater than in the middle.

For each increase in applied heater power during activation, the pressure will rise rapidly to a value approximately proportional to the increase in temperature. It should be allowed to fall before a further increase of heater power is applied. When the cathode temperature approaches 900°C, the rate of gas evolution will rise considerably, indicating that the peak of chemical conversion is being reached. Further increases in temperature beyond the peak will result in a decreasing evolution of gas, and the pressure will fall to a lower level when the normal temperature of 800°–900°C is resumed after flashing. When this condition occurs, a small dc voltage may be applied to the anode,

---

[1] In measuring temperatures of the emitting surface with an optical pyrometer, certain corrections must be made. The actual temperature is always higher than the value observed, since the light transmission of glass, especially at an oblique angle, is always less than 100%. Also the spectral emissivity of the hot surface, a variable quantity, depends on surface smoothness, color, and temperature. As a very rough guide, the real temperature of an oxide-coated surface may be of the order of 100°C higher than that observed with an optical pyrometer. See pp. 240–244 and 405.

or to the anode and grids, or other electrodes tied together electrically. The pressure will again begin to increase as soon as this voltage is sufficient to produce an electron current which causes the evolution of gas from those parts of the tube that are being bombarded. With tubes of applicable geometry, some electron bombardment may be tolerated with useful effects, namely, outgassing of the structure, but with certain designs, overheating may cause failure from expansion and warping of metal parts or cracking of ceramics.

A small anode current should be drawn continuously until the pressure drops to approximately 2×10^{-7} torr. At no time during the early stages of drawing current should the pressure be allowed to rise above 5×10^{-6} torr. Pressures in excess of this value may cause injurious discharges arising from positive ion bombardment. Oxide-coated cathodes are particularly susceptible to damage from this source.

A tube is said to be "hard" when changes in dc voltage on the anode, etc., produce little or no change in pressure.

In tubes where electron bombardment cannot be produced sufficiently from the cathode emission to outgas the structure, use is made of the RF induction heater (see page 51). The coil is placed around or near the outside of the tube and RF power is applied. RF bombarding must be used with understanding and caution.

Bombarding of tubes without oxide-coated cathodes is carried out at any time after bake-out. Ionization gauges may be bombarded after installation in a system. Anodes and other outer structures of tubes with oxide-coated cathodes can be bombarded twice, before and after activation. It is advisable to have a small amount of heater power on the cathode during the second bombardment to prevent condensation of gases and evaporated metals from heated anodes, etc. Excessive heating should be strictly avoided in any event. In general, tubes with oxide-coated or thoriated cathodes should be no more than lightly bombarded; that is, the temperature of the parts heated should not exceed an incipient red heat (about 550°C).

It is sometimes advisable to bake the tube again after drawing anode current and before flashing the getters (see p. 105). If a very hard tube is required, the baking, both first and second, is extended many hours. The second baking is done with the cathode at a temperature slightly lower than normal and with a small anode current being drawn.

In tubes with pure tungsten emitters, the procedure is the same except that the cathode or filament does not require activation beyond heating to slightly above operating temperature. Some gas will be driven off because tungsten, like other metals, has considerable gettering action. (*Cf.* **Water cycle,** p. 568.)

Seal-off (tip-off) of glass tubes is accomplished by first slowly heating the constriction, preferably with a Bunsen burner, to drive off gases in the glass. The cathode should be at or near operating temperature and a small dc current drawn during the seal-off operation. Allow the pumps to restore the low pressure before applying additional heat to the seal-off. The pressure should not be allowed to rise above 1×10^{-6} torr.

Oxide-Coated Cathodes—Bibliography

"Oxide-Coated Cathodes," A. S. Eisenstein, Advances in Electronics Series, **1**, 1–64, Academic Press, Inc., New York, 1948.

"The Performance of Nickel Alloys in Oxide-Coated Cathodes," T. H. Briggs; presented at meeting of A.S.T.M. Committee B-4-VIII-A, June 1, 1950.

"The Oxide-Coated Cathode," G. Hermann and S. Wagener, Chapman & Hall, London, 1951.

"Development and Use of a DC Emission Figure of Merit for Oxide-Coated Cathodes," T. H. Briggs and C. D. Richard, Jr., A.S.T.M. Bulletin #171, pp. 66–70, January, 1951.

"Elements of Thermionics," W. E. Danforth, *Proc. I. R. E.*, **39**, 485, 1951.

"Loss of Thermionic Emission in Oxide-coated Cathodes due to Mechanical Shock," D. O. Holland, I. E. Levy, and H. J. Davis, *Proc. I. R. E.*, **40**, 587, 1952.

"Directly Heated Hum-Free Cathode for CR Tubes," F. H. Nicoll, *Rev. Sci. Instr.*, **26**, 1206, 1955.

'Mounting Scheme for Large Cathodes," F. A. Braun, *ibid.*, **27**, 113, 1956.

"Electric and Magnetic Properties of the Oxide Cathode," R. J. Forman, Report of 15th Annual Conference on Physical Electronics, p. 10, 1955.

"Some Effects of Gases on Oxide Cathodes," J. Morrison, *ibid.*, p. 21.

"Use of Oxide Cathodes in Demountable Vacuum Systems," G. A. Haas and J. T. Jensen, Jr., *Rev. Sci. Instr.*, **28**, 1007, 1957.

"Results of Experiments on Behavior of Nickel for Cathodes Heated under Vacuum," J. Richard, *Le Vide* (Fr), p. 28, May 9, 1954.

"Relation between Oxide Cathodes and Gases at Very Low Pressures," S. Wagener, *Proc. Phys. Soc.*, **67B**, 369, 1954.

"Recent Advances in the Design of Thermionic Cathodes," D. W. Shipley, *Sylvania Technologist*, **VIII**, 103, 1955.

"Use of Platinum (Oxide-Coated) Filament in the Electron Microscope," F. W. Bishop, *Rev. Sci. Instr.*, **31**, 124, 1960.

"Techniques of Cathode Temperature Measurements as Applied to Commercial CRT's," P. P. Coppola, *ibid.*, **31**, 137, 1960.

"Source of Thermal Ions for Use in Gases at High Pressures," E. W. McDaniel and D. W. Martin, *ibid.*, **31**, 660, 1960.

"Use of Oxide-Coated Cathodes in High-Current Electron Accelerator," G. Davidson, S. Ozaki, and R. Weinstein, *ibid.*, **31**, 31, 1960.

"Cathode Interface Impedance Measurements," J. Tamiya, *ibid.*, **31**, 696, 1960.

"Trapping with Alumina and Its Effect on Cathode Activity," L. A. Harris, *ibid.*, **31**, 903, 1960.

"Thermionics and Cathodes" (a selective bibliography); Office of Technical Services, U.S. Dept. of Commerce, SB-431, September, 1960.

"Thermionic Electron Sources," G. A. Haas, N.R.L. Report 5657, U.S. Naval Research Laboratory, Washington, D.C., October 6, 1961.

"Studies of Electron Tube Materials and Thermionic Emission Processes," 7th Science Report AF19(604)–7286, General Telephone & Electronics Labs., Inc., Bayside, New York, prepared for Air Force Cambridge Research Laboratories, December 31, 1961. (OTS AD 271–101).

"The Effect of Impurity Migrations on Thermionic Emission from Oxide-Coated Cathodes," I. E. Levy, *Proc. I. R. E.*, **41**, 365, 1953.

"Preconversion of Oxide-Coated Cathodes," G. A. Haas and J. T. Jensen, Jr., *Rev. Sci. Instr.*, **30,** 562, 1959.

"On the High Residual Pressure Obtained during Activation of Valves Containing Oxide-Coated Cathodes," H. J. Curnow, *J. Sci. Instr.* (Br), **34,** 73, 1957.

"Progress in Electron Emission at High Fields," W. P. Dyke, *Proc. I.R.E.*, **43,** 162–167, 1955.

"Efficiency of Thermal Electron Emission," M. J. O. Strutt, *ibid*, **40,** 601–603, 1952.

"Fundamental Research on Raw Materials Used for Electron Emissivity on Indirectly Heated Cathodes," W. B. Nottingham, J. Cardell, and I. E. Levy, Summary Report of Work Accomplished on Contract N7onr–389, Task Order No. NR–074–251, Raytheon Mfg. Co., Newton, Mass., for Office of Naval Research.

"A 5% Bandwidth, 2.5 MW, S-Band Klystron," P. G. R. King, Paper No. 2624, International Convention on Microwave Valves, *Proc. I.E.E.* (*Br.*), **105B,** 8, 1958.

"Nickel Alloys for Oxide-Coated Cathodes," Catalog E-102A, Alloys for Electronics, Wilbur B. Driver Company, Newark, New Jersey, 1962, p. 7.

"Poisoning of Oxide Cathodes by Atmospheric Sulfur," H. A. Stahl, *Proc. I.R.E.*, **39,** 193, 1951.

"A Method for Extending the Life of Oxide-Coated Filaments in Hot-Cathode Ionization Gauges," J. W. Kelly, *J. Sci. Instr.* (*Br.*), **39,** 473, 1962.

PHILIPS CATHODES

Philips cathodes (also known as "dispenser," "L," "pressed," "impregnated" and "matrix" cathodes) take various forms, but basically they consist of a chamber of nonporous heat-conducting metal such as molybdenum (although such other metals as tungsten, tantalum, and columbium can be used) that has a "window" of porous tungsten, which constitutes the emitting surface. This porous material, made from partially sintered tungsten, is impregnated with barium, calcium, strontium, aluminum, beryllium, and other carbonates or thoriates, or mixtures of these. The chamber can also be constructed with a porous tungsten cylindrical wall. Unimpregnated porous tungsten can also be used, in which case it covers a compartment containing a reservoir of the emission-producing compounds, and is impregnated during the activation process. (See Figs. 23, 24, and 25.)

The chamber is provided with a coated tungsten heater (see pp. 80 *et seq.*). Activation[1] is accomplished by heating the emitting surface to a suitable temperature (in the neighborhood of 1300°C), which is needed to form a monomolecular layer of barium, etc., on the surface of the cathode. The operating temperature is about 1100°C.

Some of the formulations show much greater stability to air, water vapor, and carbon dioxide at atmospheric pressure than do conventional oxide-coated cathodes.

---

[1] Except for temperatures, the activation procedure is much the same as that given on p. 98 for oxide-coated cathodes. No cleaning is required as the cathodes are vacuum sealed when packed.

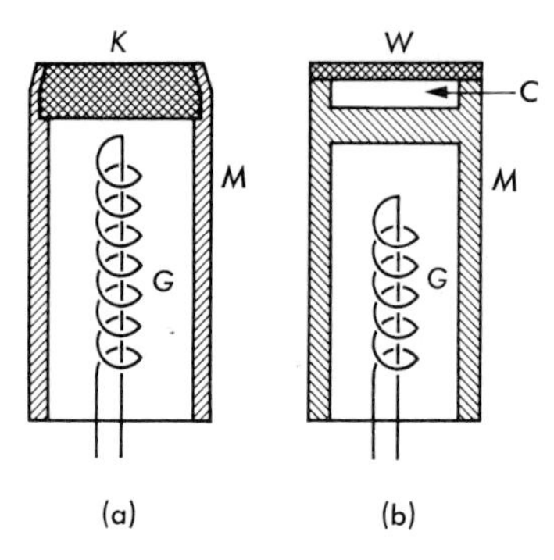

FIG. 23. (a) Flat impregnated cathode, K, in a molybdenum cylinder, M. The disc, K, is anchored by spinning over the lip of the cylinder. (b) L-cathode showing the porous tungsten disc, W, covering the chamber, C, containing the barium compound. G is the coated heater.

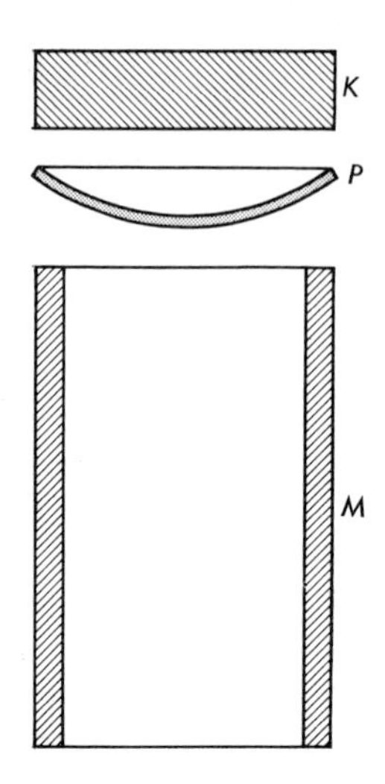

FIG. 24. Flat impregnated cathode, K, with separating shield, P. Assembly is made to the molybdenum cylinder, M, by a resistance-welding operation.

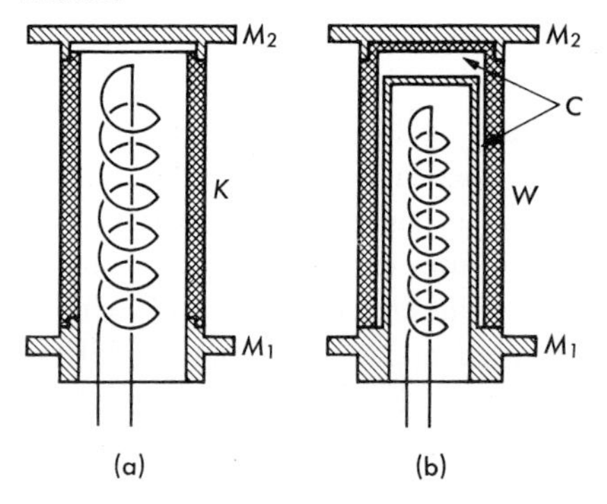

FIG. 25. (a) Cylindrical impregnated cathode, K, with molybdenum end pieces, M_1, M_2. (b) Corresponding L-cathode. The chamber, C, contains the barium compound.

Philips cathodes of this type show favorable emission, up to 10 amp/cm^2, with long life (about 1000 hours). Emissions up to several hundred amperes per square centimeter have been obtained for short times.

Philips cathodes—Bibliography

H. J. Lemmens, M. J. Jansen, and R. Loosjes, *Philips Tech. Rev.*, **11**, 341, 1949–50.

E. S. Rittner, R. H. Ahlert, and W. C. Rutledge, *J. Appl. Phys.*, **28**, 156, 1957.

W. C. Rutledge and E. S. Rittner, *J. Appl. Phys.*, **28**, 167, 1957.

"Dispenser Cathodes," I, Introduction and Synopsis by A. Venema; II, The Pressed Cathode, by R. C. Hughes and P. P. Coppola; III, The Impregnated Cathode, by R. Levi; *Philips Tech. Rev.*, **19**, 177–190, 1957/1958).

U.S. Patent No. 2,700,000, R. Levi and R. C. Hughes; January, 18, 1955.

U.S. Patent No. 2,700,118, R. C. Hughes, P. P. Coppola, and E. S. Rittner; January 18, 1955.

"Molded Nickel BaO Matrix Cathodes," commercially obtainable from Electron Emitters, Inc., 208 Depot Rd., Huntington Station, Long Island, New York.

A survey of all types of emitters is given by G. A. Haas in "Thermionic Electron Sources," NRL Report 5657, October 6, 1961.

Getters and Getter-ion Pumping

Certain metals and alloys are used in vacuum tubes to produce pressures lower than can be obtained with the pumps alone and to clean up or adsorb gases which are released from the materials of the tube structure during processing and after seal-off. This phenomenon is called gettering and can be produced in three ways: (a) by absorption of the gas directly during evaporation and condensation of fresh getter metal; (b) by adsorption of gases on the freshly condensed getter-mirror surface; and (c) by adsorption of gases by the getter with the aid of an electrical discharge which ionizes and accelerates the particles.

Ordinary atmospheric and chemically active gases (nitrogen, carbon dioxide, hydrogen, oxygen, carbon monoxide, water vapor) are adsorbed by the getter as a simple mechanical or chemical action (physisorption, chemisorption), which, in most cases, can be considered irreversible unless the condensed getter surface is reheated to a temperature much higher than would normally be encountered or is bombarded with electrons. Getters do not ordinarily adsorb the noble gases[1] (argon, helium, krypton, neon, and xenon).

The most common metal used as a simple getter is barium,[2] either alone or in combination with aluminum and/or magnesium. Since barium is chemically active, it is incased in some stable metal such as iron or nickel, which, as tubing, is drawn out and used either as wire or as a flattened strip.[3] This casing has a purposely thinned zone so that when heated, the barium can vaporize and diffuse through it. Vaporization occurs at temperatures between 900°C and 1100°C, although somewhat higher temperatures are sometimes employed. The getters are heated either by induction (see pp. 51, 221) or by passing current through them as wires whose ends are welded to current-carrying leads. If several getters are used in a tube, one of them can be deliberately burned out before seal-off. This is commonly done when there is a limited number of feed-through leads into the tube, and the two wires to which the getter is welded are primarily to be used for another purpose in the operation of the tube, e.g., to supply different voltages to grids or anodes, etc.

Other metals used as getters include cerium, lanthanum, didymium, thorium, praeseodymium, mischmetal (p. 375) and various mixtures of these with magnesium, aluminum, etc.[4] These can be used as foils, wires, or powder and applied in a suitable binder to other metal surfaces such as nickel. The get-

---

[1] See p. 109.

[2] "The Sorption of Hydrogen by Barium Getters," P. Della Porta and S. Origlio, *Vacuum* (Br) **11**, 26, 1961.

[3] KIC getters, Kemet Laboratories, Cleveland, Ohio.

[4] See "Materials for and the Mechanism of Gettering Multiple Component Gases," L. Epstein and L. J. Kaufman, Ronson Metals Corporation, Newark, New Jersey, Final Report AFCRL–63–7 for Air Force Cambridge Research Laboratories, January, 1963; obtainable from OTS, U.S. Department of Commerce, Washington, D.C.

tering capacity of CerAlloy 420 for various gases is shown in Table A[1] on p. 107.

The properties of other materials used as getters are given in Table B[1] on p. 107.

Barium and barium combinations are enclosed in the metal sheath in a freshly distilled or vacuum-melted condition, and must therefore be protected from the atmosphere if they are to be of value. The protective sheath, with thinned-down zone, is cut into pieces of the required length, the cutting action at the same time sealing the ends. The pieces are mounted in the tube structure by spot-welding.

Getter tablets or pellets are sometimes used. These are fired by RF induction-heating from outside the tube. In combination with magnesium, the maximum allowable proportion of barium for stability in the atmosphere is 30%, but in combination with aluminum and magnesium, up to 43% barium is permissible, the higher barium content making the getter easier to flash. These alloy pellets are held in or on a "flag" of thin nickel foil (0.005 inch), usually with a nickel screen over the pellet to protect it.

The vacuum pressure in the tube at the time of flashing the getter will determine the appearance and condition of the condensed deposit. Very slow heating of the getter results in adsorption of most of the residual gas in the tube before much condensation takes place, so that the pressure is actually very low during the bulk of the condensation which, under these conditions, presents a bright mirror appearance. On the other hand, if the temperature of the getter is raised very rapidly, condensation occurs before the getter action can operate completely, and this results in a discolored mirror appearance. Flashing of the getter in an inert atmosphere, such as argon, produces a black deposit which is not contaminated but porous and light-absorbing.

Getters that are to be RF-fired should be mounted in the tube close enough to the glass wall (but not in contact with it) so that good coupling can be obtained. Wire or strip getters should also be mounted near the wall so that the deposition area is limited. It is frequently necessary to further restrict the condensation area by the use of nickel gates or shields to prevent the sputtering of conducting films on the stem or structure of the tube, where such films might produce electrical short circuit or voltage breakdown.

TITANIUM-ION PUMPING

Freshly deposited titanium metal can be used as an efficient getter, and it has certain advantages over barium. Titanium is atmospherically stable, and the compounds of this metal which would normally be encountered in vacuum work have very low vapor pressures.

---

[1] Tables from "An Investigation into the Gettering Powers of Various Metals for the Gases Hydrogen, Oxygen, Nitrogen, Carbon Dioxide, and Air," L. F. Ehrke and C. M. Slack, *J. Appl. Phys.*, **11**, 129, 1940.

A[1]

GAS	BRIGHT DEPOSIT (LITER-MICRONS/MG)	DIFFUSE DEPOSIT (LITER-MICRONS/MG)
O_2	21.2	50.9
H_2	46.1	63.9
N_2	3.18	16.1
CO_2	2.2	44.8

B[1]

GETTER[2]	GAS	BRIGHT DEPOSIT (LITER-MICRONS/MG)	DIFFUSE DEPOSIT (LITER-MICRONS/MG)
Al	O_2	7.5	38.6
Al	N_2, H_2, CO_2	None	None
Ba	O_2 } at room temperature	15.2	45.0
	H_2	87.5	73.0
	N_2	9.5	36.1
	CO_2	5.21	59.5
Mg	O_2	20.0	202.0
	CO_2	None	Slight, not permanent
	N_2, H_2	None at room temperature	None at room temperature
Th	O_2	7.45	33.15
	H_2	19.45	53.7
U	O_2	10.56	9.26
	H_2	8.9	21.5
Mischmetal[3]	O_2	21.2	50.9
	H_2	46.1	63.9
	N_2	3.18	16.1
	CO_2	2.2	44.8
Zr, Ta[4]	O_2, H_2, N_2, CO_2		
Ti[5]			
Mo[6]	H_2		

[1] See footnote on p. 106.

[2] CETO getters (alloy of thorium, mischmetal, and aluminum) are described by W. Espe, M. Knoll, and M. P. Wilder in *Electronics*, **23,** 80, 1950, and by J. H. N. van Vucht in *Vacuum* (Br), **10,** 12, p. 170, 1960.

[3] See p. 375.

[4] Zirconium and tantalum are sometimes used in high-power tubes where they can be operated at elevated temperatures and where the action of physical adsorption (physisorption) of gases makes these two metals of value. The use of zirconium as a getter is described by O. Pressel, in *Vacuum* (Br), **10,** 141, 1960.

[5] Titanium is used very widely as a getter, especially in combination with ion pumping (see p. 106 *et seq.*).

[6] "Attainment of Ultra-High Vacuum, Reduction in Surface Desorption, and the Adsorption of Hydrogen by Evaporated Molybdenum," A. L. Hunt, C. C. Damm, and E. C. Popp., *J. Appl. Phys.*, **32,** 1937, 1961.

See also *Ultrahigh Vacuum and its Applications,* R. W. Roberts and T. A. Vanderslice, Prentice-Hall, Inc., Englewood Cliffs, New Jersey, 1963, pp. 26–29.

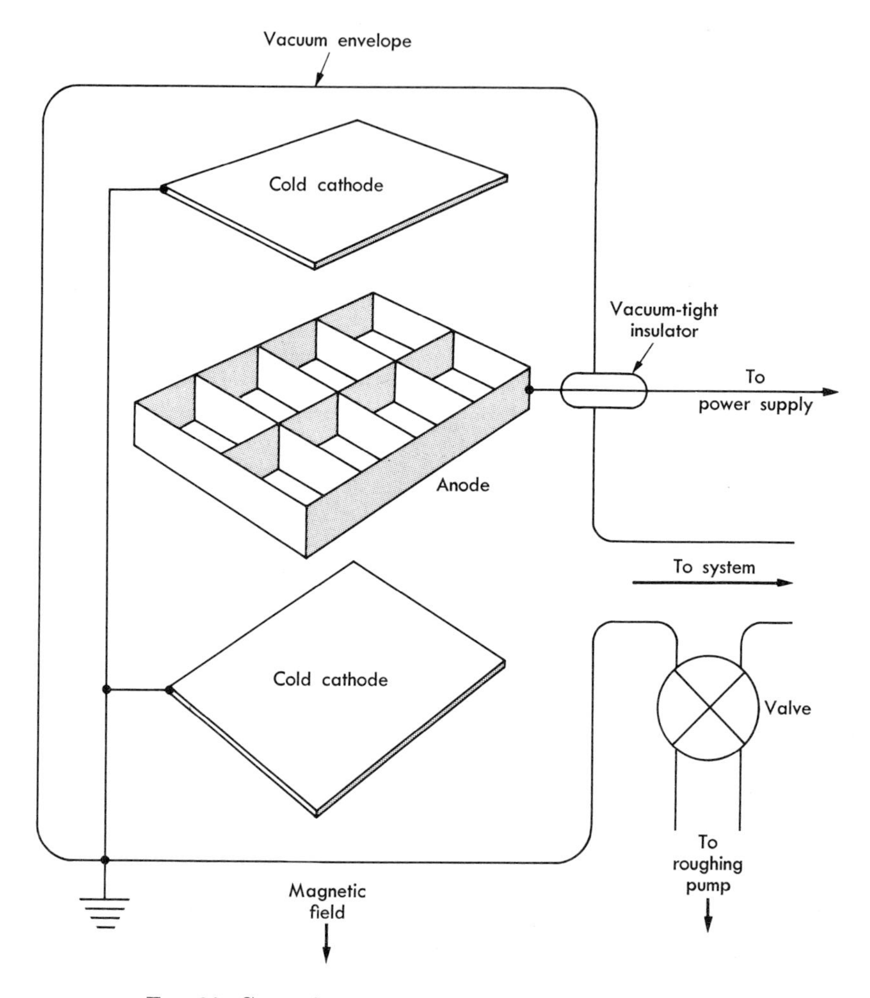

FIG. 26. Getter-ion vacuum pump (schematic drawing).

A titanium getter is easily made by winding a small-size titanium wire over a larger-diameter tungsten wire through which current is passed. Another method is to twist several titanium strands together with a number of tungsten wires of the same size (about 0.010 inch); this cable is then formed into a helix of a length convenient for the passage of sufficient current to heat it (about 4 inches is a good length).[1]

The gettering action can be greatly enhanced by the presence of a cold-cathode discharge or by any source of electrons such as a hot cathode. In

[1] "A Small Titanium Ion Pump (TIP)," J. G. King and J. R. Zacharias, *Quarterly Progress Report of the Research Laboratory of Electronics,* M.I.T., July 15, 1957.

commercial getter-ion pumps, one type[1] employs a continuously fed titanium wire which is consumed by thermal evaporation. Another type[2] comprises a Penning gauge (p. 431) with a magnetic field. This type can be used both as a pump and as a vacuum gauge. A single-element pump of this kind is illustrated in Fig. 26. The pumping action in getter-ion pumps occurs by virtue of ionization, excitation, and condensation of titanium on the pump walls, entrapping not only dissociated atmospheric gases but metastable molecules or atoms (p. 160) of the noble gases as well; these are held by permanent bonds. Titanium-ion pumps[2] are intended to operate from a forepump pressure of about 10 microns, and are capable of ultimate pressures down to 10^{-10} torr. Baking at 500°C is possible (with magnet removed) and provides a method of degassing or reactivating.

At low pressures the life of a titanium-ion pump is very long (40,000 hours at 10^{-6} torr). L. D. Hall states that one-half to one molecule of gas is pumped for each atom of titanium sputtered.

In practice the titanium-ion pump can be used in an all-metal or glass system, without rubber O-rings or grease seals, as shown in Fig. 26. A refrigerant trap can be installed. Thorough baking is required for lowest pressures, and the forepump and trap can be valved, pinched, or sealed off (or even removed). Some large tubes can be made with a small titanium-ion pump[3] permanently attached, to be operated as conditions warrant.[4] This is known as "appendage pumping."

---

[1] The "Evapor-Ion" pump of R. G. Herb, A. S. Divatia, and D. Saxon, *Phys. Rev.*, **89**, 897, 1953. This is commercially available from Consolidated Vacuum Corp., Rochester 3, New York. See their bulletin 6-2 (1961).

[2] The "Vac-Ion" pump of L. D. Hall, *Rev. Sci. Instr.*, **29**, 367, 1958; also *Science*, **128**, 279, 1958.

[3] Varian's "Vac-Ion" 5 liter/sec, No. V11402 is an example. This pump can also be used as a vacuum gauge when used with Varian's power supply VA-1304.

[4] See also "Properties of a Small Titanium-Ion Pump," A. Klopfer and W. Ermrich, *Vacuum* (Br), **10**, 1/2, 128, 1960; "Gas Sorption of Penning Pumps and Titanium Films," L. Holland and A. Harte, *ibid.*, p. 133; "Electron Tube Processing with Getter-Ion Pumps," L. Malter and H. Mandoli, *ibid.*, p. 121; "Magnetically Confined Cold-Cathode Gas Discharges at Low Pressures," R. L. Jepsen, *J. Appl. Phys.*, **32**, 2619, 1961; "Enhanced Hydrogen Pumping with Sputter-Ion Pumps," S. L. Rutherford and R. L. Jepsen, *Rev. Sci. Instr.*, **32**, 1144, 1961; "Electrical Characteristics of a Penning Discharge," J. C. Helmer and R. L. Jepsen, *Proc. I.R.E.*, December, 1961, p. 1920; "Pumping Characteristics of a Titanium-Droplet Getter-Ion Pump," L. Holland and L. Laurenson, *Br. J. Appl. Phys.*, **11**, 401, 1960; "Alternative Ion-Pump Configuration Derived from a More Thorough Understanding of the Penning Discharge," W. Knauer and E. R. Stack, *Trans. Am. Vacuum Soc.*, 10th Annual Symposium, 180–184, 1963; "Sputter-Ion Pumps for Low-Pressure Operations," S. L. Rutherford, *ibid.*, 185–190; *Ultrahigh Vacuum and its Applications*, R. W. Roberts and T. A. Vanderslice, Prentice-Hall, Inc., Englewood Cliffs, New Jersey, 1963, pp. 13–29.

Cryopumping

The chief feature of this method of pumping is refrigeration. The common use of a refrigerated trap in a vacuum system produces some degree of pumping action, as is well known; this may be enhanced with copper foil[1] and by various other ways to increase the cold surface. Cryopumping is usually associated with getter-ion pumping (see above) to obtain conditions in which no pump fluids are required. A consequent, very high order of cleanliness is maintained, with no "backstreaming" (reverse movement of oil particles from pumps, etc., which thus can impinge on clean metal surfaces to cause contamination).

The degree of vacuum attained depends to some extent on the kind of refrigeration used, liquid nitrogen producing lower pressures than mechanical (Freon) refrigeration, and liquid helium still lower.

In some cases, activated charcoal and other chemical agents such as Linde Molecular Sieves, activated alumina, or artificial zeolite[2] are used with or without refrigeration and ion-pumping to produce low pressures without oil or mercury pumps.[3] According to Jepsen *et al.*,[4] a water aspirator can be used for rough pumping in such a system.

Ultrahigh Vacuum

For the routine pumping of experimental or laboratory-scale tubes, pressures down to 10^{-8} mm Hg are usually considered adequate, and these are attainable by the methods already described above. However, for certain types of work, pressures that are several orders of magnitude lower are required.

The limiting factor in systems containing oil-diffusion pumps is the presence of oil vapors, some of which, despite the most careful and extensive refrigerant trapping, get back into the high-vacuum parts of the system[5] and, impinging upon hot cathodes or emitters or other hot surfaces, ultimately decompose to form hydrogen, carbon, carbon monoxide, carbon dioxide, methane, ethane, propane, and other hydrocarbon gases. The presence of oil vapor and

---

[1] "Copper Isolation Trap for Vacuum Systems," D. Alpert, *Rev. Sci. Instr.*, **24,** 1004, 1953.

[2] See pp. 151, 377, 572; also bibliography on p. 112.

[3] E. M. Robson, *Vacuum* (Br), **11,** 1, 1961.

[4] "Rough Pumping with Activated Charcoal," R. L. Jepsen, S. L. Mercer, and M. J. Callaghan, *Rev. Sci. Instr.*, **30,** 377, 1959; "Tube Exhaust Methods Use Simple Gear," J. H. O. Harries, *Electronics*, June 19, 1959; "Cryopumping for High Vacuum," I. Ames, R. L. Christensen, and J. Teale, *Rev. Sci. Instr.*, **29,** 736, 1958.

[5] "Backstreaming," see p. 161.

its decomposition products prevents the attainment of pressures lower than 10^{-7} to 10^{-8} torr.

Mercury-diffusion pumps are used by some workers. These must be used in a system having multiple refrigerant traps and the capacity of being baked out for long periods at relatively high temperatures to free it of mercury vapor.

Pressures below 10^{-8} can be attained by means of fast pumping, together with gettering, getter-ion pumping, and/or cryopumping (see above), and these usually involve isolating the high-vacuum section of the system from the diffusion pumps, if used, whether oil or mercury. Parts of a vacuum system can be isolated by sealing (p. 101), by pinching-off (p. 119), or by using high-vacuum valves. Obviously, valves with rubber or Neoprene O-rings or gaskets or with greased parts are not high-vacuum valves in the sense of this discussion. Teflon[1] or Kel-F[2] parts cannot be used because these materials will not withstand the elevated temperatures necessary for ultrahigh vacuum bake-out.[3]

A popular type of ultrahigh vacuum valve is that originally described by Alpert[4,5] in which a highly polished Kovar nosepiece is forced against a soft copper seat. A modification of this valve has been described by Brown and Coyle[6] in which the screw and nose (of Monel alloy 501, formerly known as KR-Monel) pushes into a soft copper seat with a Monel alloy 400 diaphragm.

Another modification of the Alpert valve is given by Bills and Allen[7] in which a vacuum-melted pure silver ring is compressed between two harder Monel alloy 400 components in such a way that the Monel pieces do not make contact until the silver is under extremely high pressure; deformation of the Monel parts is thus minimized or eliminated.

Use of the Alpert-type valve in gas-handling experiments is described by Carmichael and Trendelenburg.[8]

A large modified Alpert-type valve has been devised by Lange[9] in which a replaceable soft copper nose seats against the stainless steel body. This valve has an open conductance of approximately 100 liters/sec.

Other types of high-vacuum valves have been described in the literature. One of these, by Paty and Schurer,[10] utilizes metallic indium, whose low melt-

---

[1] See pp. 513–517.

[2] See p. 312.

[3] "Seals and Gaskets for Ultra-High Vacuum Systems," W. Steckelmacher, *Vacuum* (Br), **12**, 109, 1962; see also pp. 117 *et seq.*

[4] D. Alpert, *Rev. Sci. Instr.*, **22**, 536, 1951.

[5] D. Alpert, *J. Appl. Phys.*, **24**, 860, 1953.

[6] S. C. Brown and J. E. Coyle, *Rev. Sci. Instr.*, **23**, 570, 1952. The gold-copper brazing mentioned in this paper can now be done without hot-nickel plating by the method outlined on pp. 41–51.

[7] D. G. Bills and F. G. Allen, *ibid.*, **26**, 654, 1955.

[8] J. H. Carmichael and E. A. Trendelenburg, *Rev. Sci. Instr.*, **30**, 494, 1959.

[9] W. J. Lange, *ibid.*, **30**, 602, 1959.

[10] L. Paty and P. Schurer, *ibid.*, **28**, 654, 1957; see also S. Pakswer and J. Dowd, *ibid.*, **33**, 780, 1962; F. Sinclair, *ibid.*, **34**, 437, 1963.

ing point (156°C) and low vapor pressure (10^{-7} mm Hg at 540°C) make it adaptable as a fluid seal in a glass body. Another type, described by Nester,[1] comprises a tapered gold plug which is melted in place in a fine, tapered capillary glass tube. Since the gold and glass have different coefficients of expansion, throttling control is obtained by heating and cooling the glass capillary containing the gold plug. A pressure variation from 10^{-5} down to lower than 10^{-7} occurs between 20°C and 300°C, making this valve suitable for handling small flows of gas.

Another glass valve, devised by Sill,[2] makes use of tungsten-heating coils to soften a glass tube in which a hole is blown and subsequently sealed by surface tension. This valve can be outgassed by baking.[3]

Ultrahigh Vacuum—Bibliography

"New Developments in the Production and Measurement of Ultrahigh Vacuum," D. Alpert, *J. Appl. Phys.*, **24,** 860, 1953.

"The Production and Measurement of Ultrahigh Vacuum (10^{-8}–10^{-13} mm Hg)," P. A. Redhead, *Fifth National Symp. Vac. Tech. Trans.*, Pergamon Press, New York, 1958.

See "Ultrahigh Vacuum in Small Glass Systems," P. A. Redhead, E. V. Kornelsen, and J. P. Hobson, *Can. J. Phys.*, **40,** 1814, 1962; "Some New Techniques in Ultrahigh Vacuum," T. H. Batzer and J. F. Ryan, *Trans. Am. Vacuum Soc.*, 10th Annual Symposium, 1963, pp. 166–169; *Ultrahigh Vacuum and its Applications,* R. W. Roberts and T. A. Vanderslice, Prentice-Hall, Inc., Englewood Cliffs, New Jersey, 1963; "Diffusion Pumps and Ultrahigh Vacuum," NRC Equipment Corp., Newton, Massachusetts, Tech. Bulletin 0100–02, 1962.

Vacuum Techniques, Design Procedures, and Construction of Vacuum Tubes and Vessels

Although we regard the design and construction of vacuum devices as a highly specialized technology, those engaged in it must have a good knowledge of physics and must also know something about such other branches of science as chemistry, metallurgy, gas dynamics, and properties of materials.

---

[1] R. G. Nester, *ibid.*, **27,** 874, 1956.

[2] R. C. Sill, *ibid.*, **27,** 657, 1956.

[3] See also "Metal Bakeout Valve for Ultra-High Vacuum," C. M. Haaland, *Rev. Sci. Instr.*, **30,** 947, 1959; "Ultra-High Vacuum Valve," N. N. Axelrod, *ibid.*, **30,** 944, 1959; "Greaseless Vacuum Valve Useful in Kinetic Studies," W. R. Doty and P. R. Ryason, *ibid.*, **32,** 89, 1961; and "All-Metal Valve for Ultra-High Vacuum Use," R. B. Thorness and A. O. Nier, *ibid.*, **32,** 807, 1961.

In the building of successful tubes, the full implication of cleanliness has not yet been completely explored. We know now that we must look for a degree of cleanliness that exceeds the demands of the surgeon and the microbiologist. The internal structures of tubes must be far more than sterile; they must also be free of nonliving chemical and physical contamination in amounts comparable to the dimensions of the smallest bacteria, and these cannot be rendered harmless by simple heat and the use of germicides. Not only must the parts of the tubes themselves be superclean on the surface, but gases adsorbed from the atmosphere and from processing and handling must be removed from solid materials. (See in this connection pages 1–23.)

The materials to be used in vacuum devices must be chosen with certain considerations in mind. From the preceding paragraph it will be seen that materials which might be difficult to clean, that is, porous, rough-textured, loosely laminated, or friable, are to be avoided if possible. Consideration must be given to: what temperature the material must withstand in processing and use; whether or not it might give off injurious vapors; its magnetic properties; its susceptibility to machining, forming, and joining by welding or brazing; electrical resistivity or dielectric qualities; heat conductivity; thermal expansion; strength and rigidity, and other properties.

Avoid if possible:

1. Porous materials;
2. Rough-textured materials;
3. Loosely laminated materials;
4. Flaky or friable materials;
5. High vapor-pressure constituents (lead, antimony, bismuth, cadmium, zinc, etc.);
6. Too-low melting points, too-low evaporation-temperature materials;
7. Magnetic materials when structure is to be used in magnetic fields where their presence might distort the field;
8. Materials difficult to machine or form, or difficult to join by welding or brazing.

Porous materials. If ceramics are to be used, they should be dense and smooth in texture; the vacuum-tight ceramic bodies are preferable even for internal structures.

Materials like Alnico and products that are likely to have blow-holes (poorly made castings), internal gas pockets, and blind holes covered up with plating or brazing (see p. 134) can be a source of apparent leaks. Or bursts of gas, given off when the material is heated, might cause voltage breakdown.

Rough texture. This usually indicates that there is a surface porosity, and if the material has been chemically treated, vaporizable and injurious substances are given off on heating. Also, the gas-absorbing properties of a rough surface are very much greater than those of a highly polished one. Electropolishing is preferable to mechanical buffing, since the latter almost always results in burying or inclusion of buffing compounds or ordinary handling contaminants (oil, grease, finger marks) under the surface. Clean-technique polishing with pure aluminum oxide on a new and washed cotton wheel is permissible under proper conditions. If sandblasting is done, only washed, sharp steel grit should be used because the tiny particles of embedded steel may more easily be removed by chemical means than sand.

Loosely laminated materials. This designation applies particularly to sections that are seam- or spot-welded (metals) and also to mica that has been carelessly treated. If mica must be used, edges, holes, or other openings must be punched by special methods with very sharp precision dies. The methods used for fabricating sheet metal parts are not suitable for mica.

Flaky or friable materials. Mica also comes under this heading, since flakes of it are likely to fall off and settle on parts of the tube where they are not wanted, and where they might actually be harmful (cathode surfaces) unless special precautions are taken to prevent it. Glass and ceramics with sharp edges are objectionable for the same reason.

High vapor-pressure constituents. When the use of a metal or alloy is contemplated, the available literature[1,2,3] should be consulted. In general, for high-vacuum work where baking is to be carried out for the removal of water vapor and other adsorbed gases, the following constituents are to be avoided: lead, arsenic, antimony, bismuth, tellurium, cadmium, magnesium (except in small amounts, as in getters), mercury, rubidium, selenium, zinc, sulfur, phosphorus.

Low melting-point materials. Obviously, if vacuum vessels are to be baked during exhaust, solders or other materials which would melt or evaporate at the baking temperature cannot be used.

Magnetic materials. The following metals and alloys are **nonmagnetic** (or practically so):

1. stainless steels, austenitic (types 302, 304, 305 etc.)[4]
2. tungsten
3. molybdenum
4. copper
5. silver
6. gold
7. platinum
8. tantalum
9. titanium
10. beryllium copper
11. rhenium

[1] *Metals Reference Book,* C. J. Smithells; Interscience Publishing Co., New York.
[2] *Scientific Foundations of Vacuum Technique,* second edition, S. Dushman, John Wiley & Sons, New York, 1962.
[3] *Materials and Techniques for Electron Tubes,* second edition, Walter H. Kohl; Reinhold Publishing Corp., New York, 1959.
[4] Low permeability at room temperature.

12. columbium
13. Monel alloy K-500 and Monel alloy 501
14. Inconel alloys 600 and X-750
15. zirconium
16. palladium
17. Nichrome V
18. Tophet A
19. indium and gallium
20. tin
21. Monel alloy 403
22. aluminum, magnesium, and alloys

The following metals and alloys are **magnetic:**

1. steels—low, medium, and high carbon, including cold-rolled, tool, and high-speed steels
2. stainless steels—ferritic and martensitic (types 400 and 500 series; the hardenable varieties are likely to be magnetic)
3. nickel and high-nickel alloys (cathode nickels)
4. Monel alloys 400 and R-405
5. Kovar, Therlo, Rodar, Niromet, Niromet 46, Niron 52, Fernico (all glass-sealing alloys)
6. Ceramvar (ceramic-sealing alloy)
7. constantan
8. Advance
9. Nichrome and Nichrome IV
10. Tophet C
11. invar
12. Nilvar
13. René 41 and CM-R 41 alloy
14. cupro nickels
15. iron, cast iron, Alnicos, Armco iron
16. Mu metal
17. Illium and Stellite

Materials difficult to form or machine. Tungsten cannot be machined by conventional methods, although it can be formed by grinding, high-voltage, airbrasive, and plasmajet methods. Tungsten wire up to 0.030 inch can be bent with radii three times its diameter. Small wires, 0.010 inch or less, can be bent to much smaller radii, using a fine, round-nose tool or pin. Sharp-edged instruments should never be used with tungsten because even very small scratches produce weak spots. Tungsten wire greater than 0.030 inch in diameter can take bends only with the application of mild heat (100°–200°C) and not over a small radius. Small tungsten wire can be cut with *sharp* cutting pliers; the larger sizes should be cut with an abrasive wheel.

Molybdenum is variable in machinability and formability, depending upon its source and previous history (see p. 116). The round bar stock can usually be machined with sharp high-speed or carbide tools (kept sharp), although its brittleness may cause chipping. Work should be firmly chucked and tools well-supported; machines should be rigid and free of backlash. Molybdenum wire in sizes up to 0.040 inch can be formed without too much difficulty. Molybdenum sheet less than 0.020-inch thick can be stamped, drawn, or spun at room temperature, although it is preferable to apply mild heat to both work and tools (or dies).

Most of the other metals and alloys mentioned above have machining and forming properties which are more familiar. Each, however, has its own idiosyncrasies, but there are no extreme problems.

Spot welding. Tungsten and molybdenum can be spot-welded to *other metals* (except copper, silver, and high copper-silver alloys) without much difficulty, but not very successfully to each other or to themselves. The best method of spot-welding these metals to themselves is to use a condenser-discharge type of welder with tungsten electrodes, one of which is tapered to a small cone, and with rather critical adjustments of the timing, pressure, and current. The conditions are best found by experiment. Both metals can sometimes be spot-welded more easily on ac-type welders by roughening the metal in some way (etching, providing projections or points) and by using heavy current for very short times.

The interposition of another metal in the form of a thin foil (flux) provides a means of "welding" tungsten to tungsten, or to molybdenum, or molybdenum to itself. Actually, it is a brazing process rather than welding. Where temperature requirements allow it, nickel can be used; if higher temperatures are to be encountered in use, platinum or tantalum are used. For lower temperatures, certain brazing alloys (silver-copper, gold-copper, gold-nickel) can be used; the nickel-containing materials operate best. All these metals are readily obtainable as thin foils (0.001 inch or less).

METALS IN THE CONSTRUCTION OF VACUUM SYSTEMS

Many vacuum vessels—metal diffusion pumps: all-metal valves; chambers for studying electron, molecular, and plasma phenomena; etc.—are constructed with little or no glass. Special problems arise in designing such vessels.

Kinds of metal: Brass and aluminum are suitable when high bake-out temperatures will not be encountered. Brass, of course, can be readily soft- and hard-soldered. Aluminum may be soldered[1,2] or welded.[2] Both these metals are nonmagnetic. Nickel, Monel alloys 400 and R-405, and steel are used for metal tube envelopes; all three are magnetic and are easily soft- and hard-soldered and welded. The Heliarc process is capable of clean, vacuum-tight welds on these metals and also on Kovar and stainless steels. The low-carbon steels, such as type 1010, are suitable for vacuum work. The austenitic (18–8) stainless steels, such as types 302, 304, and 305, are very satisfactory when a high-strength, machinable, nonmagnetic metal is required. They may be hydrogen-brazed by the method described on p. 41 *et seq.*, or soft- and hard-soldered. Molybdenum is sometimes used for small vacuum chambers. A recent development[3] describes a high ductility (HD) molybdenum sheet in thicknesses from 0.005 inch to 0.100 inch (G. E. Marketing Letter No. 59–3,

---

[1] Information on aluminum soldering is contained in "Designing with Aluminum," No. 10, published by Kaiser Aluminum & Chemical Sales, Inc., 919 N. Michigan Ave., Chicago 11, Illinois, 1957.

[2] See "Simple Aluminum Soldering," H. Hirst, *Electronic Design,* p. 32, Andrew Corp., Chicago, Illinois, September 30, 1959.

Note: All the soft solders for aluminum appear to contain zinc and some lead and cadmium, which are to be used with caution in vacuum equipment.

[3] General Electric Co., Lamp Metals & Components Dept., Cleveland 17, Ohio.

"HD Moly Sheet," August 24, 1959.[1,2] Molybdenum round and bar stock should be tested for machining properties before any fabrication is attempted because there is considerable variation in temper among lengths received from the mill.

Copper is widely used for tube making, and only OFHC (oxygen-free, high-conductivity) or vacuum-melted metal should be used. After hydrogen-firing (see p. 35) or brazing, copper is very soft (as is nickel), and consequently the walls of a vacuum vessel made of copper should be thick enough to withstand atmospheric pressures.

Joints in demountable metal vacuum vessels may be made with flanged gasketed connections. Gaskets or O-rings are used (see p. 407 *et seq.*).

STEP-TYPE DEMOUNTABLE METAL VACUUM JOINTS

An ultrahigh vacuum, all-metal seal having certain advantages over previously reported metal seals[3,4,5,6] has been described by Lange and Alpert.[7] Figure 27 shows this seal in which a flat gasket of 0.040-inch OFHC copper is clamped between stainless steel flanges. The seal is made by tightening the bolts (12 are used on a 6-inch flange) until the copper gasket is roughly half its original thickness between the sealing edges.

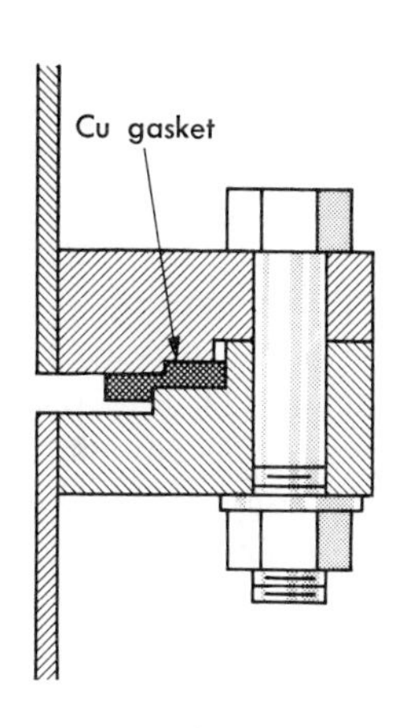

FIG. 27. Step-type demountable metal vacuum joint of Lange and Alpert.

This seal is more easily machined, with less stringent tolerances, than knife-edge seals (see p. 309). Further, the step flange can be more easily repaired in case of marring or scratching. Also, the copper washer is rigid enough to allow the assembly of vertical seals even when sealing to larger systems. The steps in the female flange serve to position and hold the gasket.

Variations, including negative as well as positive overlap of mating edges, and 45° bevel edges have been tested and found satisfactory. Repeated heat cycling (up to 70 times) at 450°C on an ultrahigh vacuum system did not show any greater leakage rates than that due to helium permeation through Pyrex glass.[8]

---

[1] General Electric Co., Lamp Metals & Components Dept., Cleveland 17, Ohio.

[2] See "Welding and Brazing of Molybdenum," Defense Metals Information Center Report No. 108, Battelle Memorial Institute, Columbus 1, Ohio.

[3] J. B. Mann, *Rev. Sci. Instr.*, **27**, 1083, 1956.

[4] P. J. van Heerden, *ibid.*, **26**, 1130, 1955.

[5] H. H. Pattee, Jr., *ibid.*, **25**, 1132, 1954.

[6] R. L. Sproull, *ibid.*, **22**, 410, 1951.

[7] W. J. Lange and D. Alpert, *ibid.*, **28**, 726, 1957.

[8] W. A. Rogers, R. S. Buritz and D. Alpert, *J. Appl. Phys.*, **25**, 868, 1954.

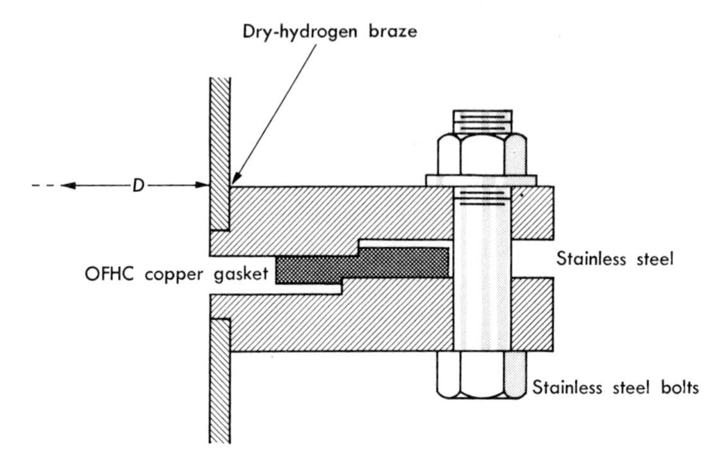

FIG. 28. Simplified form of step-type all-metal seal.

A simplified form of the Lange-Alpert step seal is shown in Figure 28. This is suitable for small vessels in which the diameter D of the tubing is not more than 2 inches. As a rough guide to dimensions for a 2-inch diameter tube, the flanges are $\frac{3}{8}$ inch thick and 4 inches in diameter, having 6 holes provided with $\frac{5}{16}$-inch stainless steel machine bolts (these can be lubricated with graphite or MoS_2 to prevent seizing). The OFHC copper gasket is $3\frac{1}{8}$ inches OD, $2\frac{1}{4}$ inches ID, and 0.040 inch thick, hydrogen-annealed at 950°C after machining. The copper should be smooth and free from scratches. Note that in this design the gasket is centered by the bolts. The edges of the steps in the stainless flanges should be slightly chamfered and smoothed so that considerable pressure can be applied to the bolts without shearing the gasket. Seals of this kind will withstand many heat cycles; some have been used without failure as traps in which the temperature range was from 500°C to liquid nitrogen temperature.

For a discussion of the theory and application of metal-gasket seals, see W. R. Wheeler, *Trans. Am. Vacuum Soc.*, 10th Annual Symposium, Macmillan Co., New York, 1963, pp. 159–165.

Metal gasket seals—Bibliography

"Aluminum Foil High-Vacuum Gasket," S. Ruthberg and J. E. Creedon, *Rev. Sci. Instr.*, **26**, 1208, 1955.

"Techniques in Evacuating and Pressurizing Metal Chambers," H. V. Neher and A. R. Johnston, *ibid.*, **25**, 517, 1954.

"Improved Metal-to-Metal Vacuum Seals," M. J. Higatsberger and W. W. Erbe, *ibid.*, **27**, 110, 1956.

"The Knife-Edge Vacuum Seal," G. W. Hees, W. Eaton, and J. Lech, *Vacuum,* **IV** (4), 438, 1954.

"Demountable Metal Vacuum Seal," T. Foote and D. B. Harrington, *Rev. Sci. Instr.*, **28**, 585, 1957.

A review of metal gasket design for vacuum systems is given by I. I. Papirov, *Pribory i Tekhn. Eksperim.*, **7**, 5, 1962.

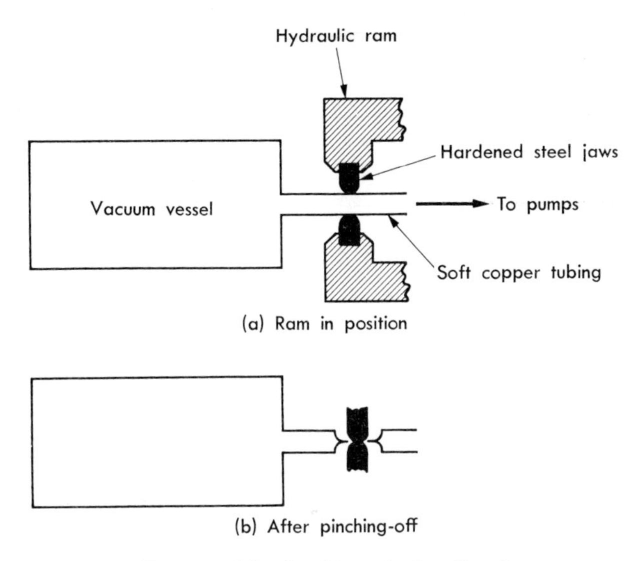

FIG. 29. Metal tubing pinch-off seal.

Metal Tubing Seal. A seal-off can be effected with metal tubing instead of glass, as in conventional tubes. Various sizes of tubing can be used, and it should be OFHC grade, cleaned and hydrogen-furnace annealed. The method of pinching-off is shown in Fig. 29.

For $\frac{1}{8}$-inch copper tubing, use a Starrett No. 1, 7-inch "Cutnipper" hand tool, with special rounded and parallel, hardened steel or carbide jaws, as shown in the figure. For larger tubing, use a hydraulic ram fitted with the jaws. The jaws should be lapped parallel and kept in highly polished condition because nicks or deep scratches might prevent the attainment of a perfect seal.

If the copper tubing, especially inside, is clean at the start of pumping, the pressure of the jaws produces a cold weld. A slight increase of pressure parts the tubing. Copper-tubing seals, properly made, are vacuum-tight. To protect the extremely thin feather edge, a small cover, made of sheet copper, is slipped over the end of the tubing, and the end is fluxed and dipped in molten solder.

Gas Filling of Tubes

A method for introducing gas at a known pressure into an evacuated tube is shown in Fig. 30. The procedure is as follows:

1. The vessel or tube to be filled is first evacuated and thoroughly baked in the usual way (see p. 99), with the two cold traps refrigerated as shown.

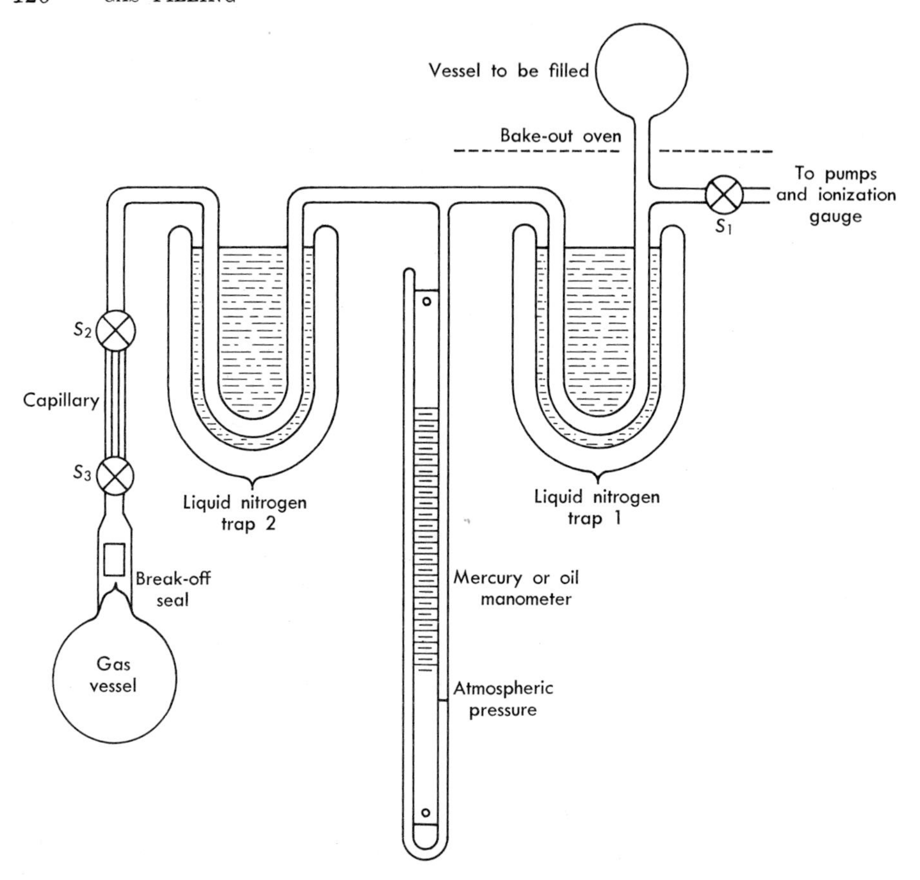

FIG. 30. Admitting metered quantities of gas to a vacuum tube. The manometer is filled before sealing onto the system, and when in the position shown (the system is at atmospheric pressure), the level is read as 760 mm. When pumped, the mercury levels in the two arms will become equal. Admission of gas, as described in the text, will be read as the difference (in mm) between the two levels. (See p. 348.) For gases which would be condensed in liquid nitrogen trap 2, the refrigerant is CO_2 (dry ice) instead of N_2; or under certain circumstances the trap may be omitted altogether. For oil manometers, see p. 354.

2. When the ionization gauge shows a pressure of 5×10^{-7} mm Hg or lower, this gauge is shut off and the stopcock S_1 is closed.

3. The reservoir, usually a standard 1- or 2-liter sealed Pyrex flask of the gas, of spectroscopic quality, at atmospheric pressure, is opened to the system by raising the iron slug with a magnet and allowing it to drop and break the internal seal. The stopcocks S_2 and S_3 are closed before and during this step.

4. With S_2 closed, S_3 is opened momentarily and then closed, allowing the capillary section to fill with gas at 1 atmosphere pressure (760 mm Hg).

5. Stopcock S_2 is then opened and closed, whereupon the mercury manometer will indicate a differential pressure which is direct reading.

6. It is advisable to flush out or purge the vacuum vessel two or three times with the gas required, and this is done by opening stopcock S_1 (S_2 and S_3 are both closed) for a few minutes to pump out the gas. The procedure of steps 4 through 6 is then repeated.

7. Final filling of the tube is accomplished by closing stopcock S_1 and repeating step 4 and 5 as many times as is needed to build up the required pressure. The mercury manometer in this case may be replaced by a Pirani or other type of gauge, in which case the refrigerated trap 2 may be omitted.

8. When the specified pressure has been attained, the tube is sealed off at the constriction.

HYDROGEN-FILLING BY DIFFUSION

As a special case, in filling tubes with hydrogen, use is made of the property palladium or nickel has of becoming slightly porous to pure hydrogen at an elevated temperature. As in Fig. 31, the palladium-leak tube is connected to the vacuum system, pumped down, and baked at the same time as the tube to be filled. A small flow of illuminating gas or tank hydrogen is introduced as shown, the excess being burned off at the jet. When sufficient voltage is applied to the heater to cause the metal tube to reach the required temperature, a small flow of pure hydrogen will pass through into the vacuum system. The procedure for filling will be similar to that described above, except that a stopcock is not needed, since no gas flows when the heater voltage is shut off. Only one refrigerated trap is required if a Pirani-type gauge is used.

Pure hydrogen can also be admitted to vacuum systems in the manner shown in Fig. 32. Tank hydrogen is admitted to the tube during heating so as to form uranium hydride (UH_3). The reaction is reversible so that hydrogen is evolved upon reheating the tube in a vacuum. The reaction is

$$2U + 3H_2 \rightleftharpoons 2(UH_3).$$

The quantity of gas reevolved is determined by the formula

$$\log p(\text{mm}) = 9.28 - \frac{4500}{T},$$

where p means pressure (mm Hg) and T means temperature in °C.

Both uranium and UH_3 are pyrophoric (i.e., flammable) in finely divided form. Uranium is used because its high molecular weight allows large hydrogen absorption. The reaction takes place in vacuum at above-room temperatures.

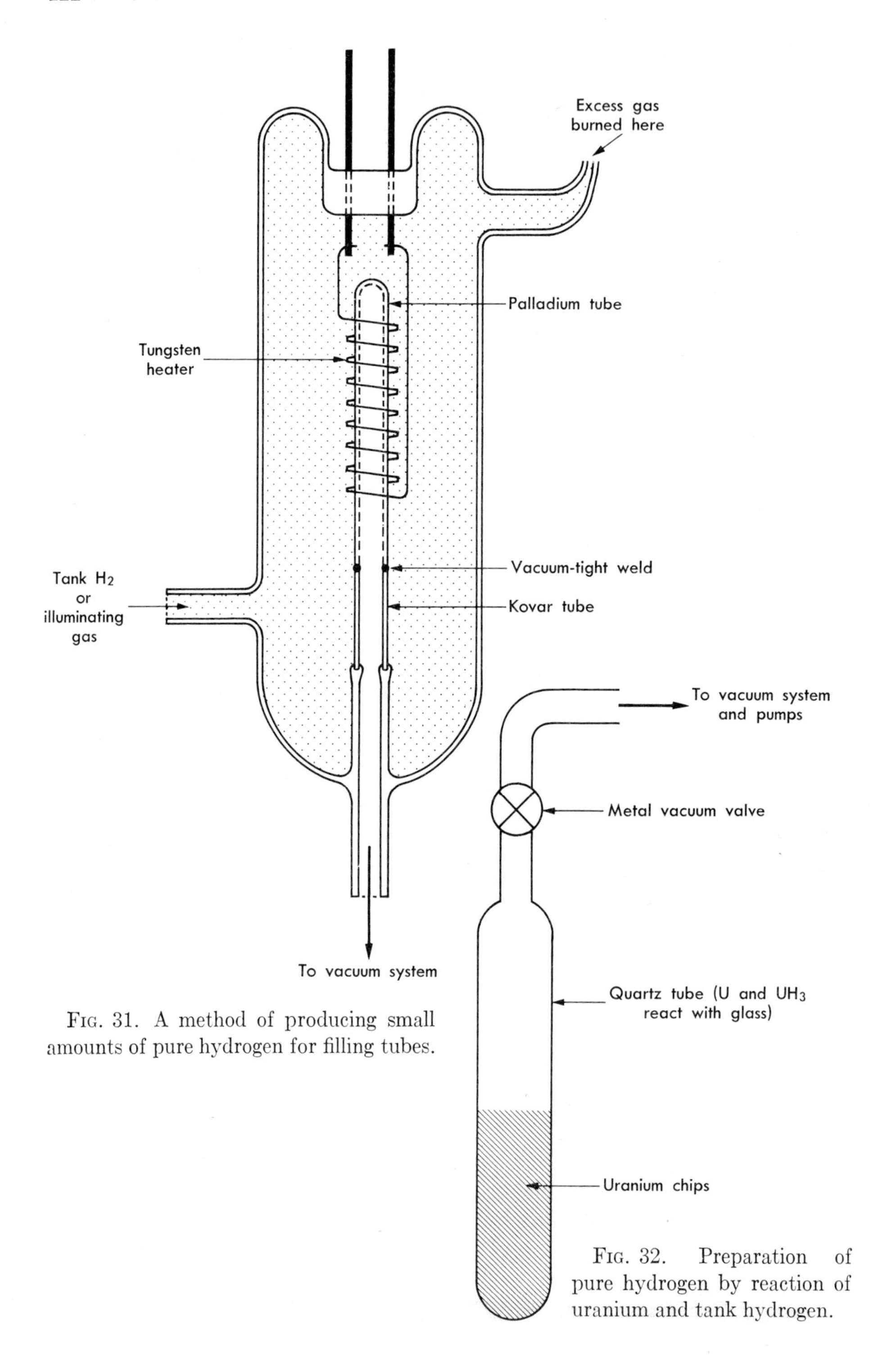

Fig. 31. A method of producing small amounts of pure hydrogen for filling tubes.

Fig. 32. Preparation of pure hydrogen by reaction of uranium and tank hydrogen.

Hydrogen diffusion leaks—Bibliography

Gases and Metals, C. J. Smithells, Chapman & Hall, London, 1937.

Metals Reference Book, C. J. Smithells, Butterworths, London, 1955.

Scientific Foundations of Vacuum Technique, second edition, S. Dushman, John Wiley & Sons, Inc., New York, New York, 1962.

"Iron and Nickel Leaks for Hydrogen," J. L. Snoek and E. J. Haes, *J. Appl. Sci. Research,* **A2,** 326, 1950.

Procedures in Experimental Metallurgy, A. U. Seybolt and J. E. Burke, John Wiley & Sons, Inc., New York, 1953.

"Diffusion of Gases through Nickel and Design of a Convenient Leak for Hydrogen and Deuterium," K. Landecker and A. J. Gray, *Rev. Sci. Instr.,* **25,** 1151, 1954.

"Nickel Diffusion Leaks for Hydrogen," E. R. Harrison and L. C. W. Hobbis, *ibid.,* **26,** 305, 1955.

"Use of Palladium Diffusion Membranes for Purification of Hydrogen," D. W. Juenker, M. van Swaay, and C. E. Birchenall, *ibid.,* **26,** 888, 1955.

"Permeability and Diffusivity of Hydrogen through a Palladium Tube," O. M. Katz and E. A. Gulbransen, *ibid.,* **31,** 615, 1960.

"Compact Palladium Diffusion Leak for Hydrogen," L. A. Noble, W. H. Sain, and R. K. Waits, *ibid.,* **31,** 789, 1960.

"Diffusion of Hydrogen through Palladium," R. C. Hurlbert and J. O. Konecny, *J. Chem. Phys.,* **34,** 655, 1961.

"Palladium-Diaphragm Hydrogen Pump," J. R. Young, *Rev. Sci. Instr.,* **34,** 374, 1963.

"Purity of Hydrogen Permeating through Pd; Pd–25% Ag, and Ni," J. R. Young, *ibid.,* p. 891.

"Thermal and Electrolytic Palladium Alloy Diffusion Cells (Complementary Methods of Obtaining Ultra-Pure Hydrogen)," A. S. Darling, *Platinum Metals Rev.* (Johnson, Matthey & Co., London), **7,** No. 4, 126, 1963.

Mercury vapor tubes: In filling tubes with mercury vapor, we customarily distill a small quantity of metallic mercury into the tube. This is conveniently done by the method shown in Fig. 33. No vacuum gauge is shown since the mercury pressure will be determined only by the presence of a noncritical amount of mercury (pool or globule) and the temperature of the tube after seal-off. However, for pumping purposes, an ionization gauge may be connected between the cold trap and the pumps, inside the bake-out oven area.

The procedure for mercury filling is as follows:

1. Evacuate and bake out the system, as shown in the figure. (The wet asbestos wrapping and the liquid nitrogen Dewar flask have not yet been installed.)

2. When the pressure at room temperature has dropped to 5×10^{-7} torr or lower, apply the refrigerant and the moist asbestos wrapping.

3. Break the internal seal of the mercury reservoir by raising the iron slug with a magnet and allowing it to fall. Apply heat to the mercury reservoir (a small Bunsen burner may be used in place of the electric heater, if desired). Saturate the asbestos wrapping with cold water and keep it wet. When the mercury boils, the vapors will condense and fall into the tube.

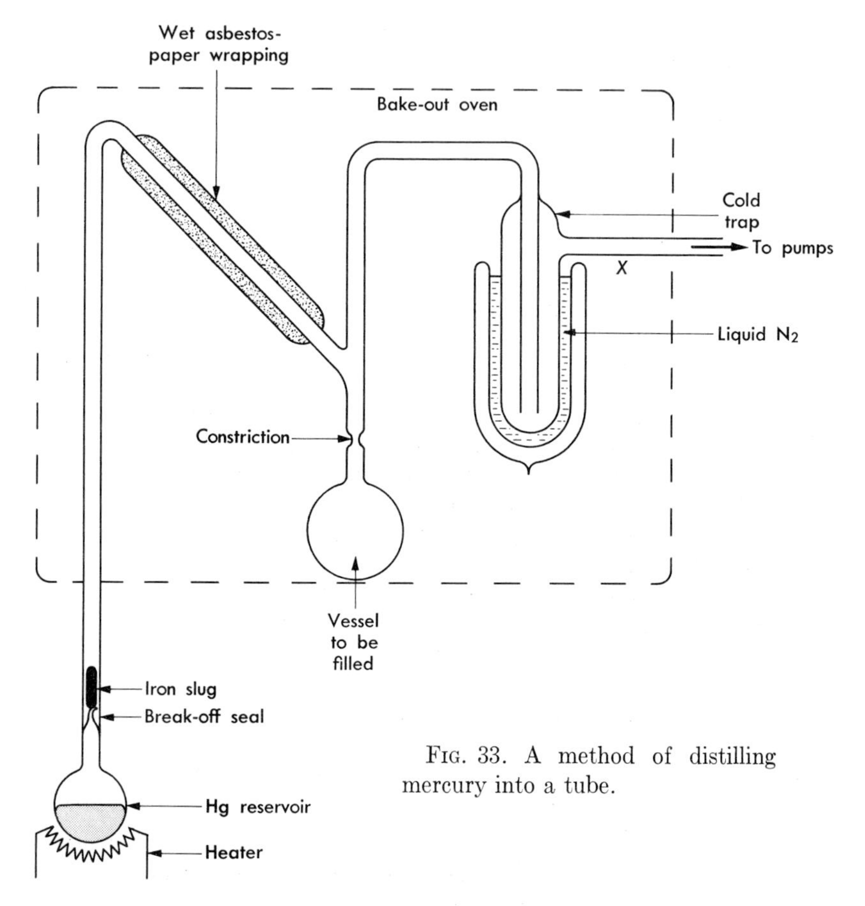

FIG. 33. A method of distilling mercury into a tube.

4. When the requisite amount of mercury has been thus distilled into the vacuum vessel, shut off the heater and seal off the vessel immediately.

5. If the apparatus is not to be used again immediately, it is advisable to seal off at the point X while the trap is under refrigeration in order to prevent mercury vapor from entering the vacuum pumps.

Metal Bellows

Where flexible joints are required and rubber or plastic tubing cannot be used, metal bellows can be installed. The table on pp. 126–127 shows various data for brass and bronze flexible bellows. Stainless steel bellows are listed on p. 125.

STAINLESS STEEL BELLOWS†

OUTSIDE DIAMETER	INSIDE DIAMETER	WALL	SEAM	CONVOLUTIONS	S-T CORP. DRAWING NO.
*$\frac{7}{16}$	$\frac{5}{16}$	0.0045	No	17	D-55472
*$\frac{17}{32}$	$\frac{3}{8}$	0.0045	No	22	D-39873
*$\frac{3}{4}$	$\frac{1}{2}$	0.0045	No	28	D-54076
$\frac{25}{32}$	$\frac{9}{16}$ (2 ply)	0.0060	No	11	D-55169
*$1\frac{1}{8}$	$\frac{3}{4}$	0.0055	No	20	D-56422
$1\frac{1}{4}$	$\frac{7}{8}$	0.0062	No	13 (15 available)	D-48512
*$1\frac{1}{2}$	1	0.0065	Yes	9	D-50599
$1\frac{11}{16}$	$1\frac{15}{64}$	0.010	Yes	2	D-50867
$1\frac{7}{8}$	$1\frac{1}{4}$	0.005	Yes	13	D-55728
*2	$1\frac{3}{8}$	0.0075	Yes	13	D-55170
$2\frac{1}{4}$	$1\frac{25}{32}$	0.011	Yes	2	D-51325
$2\frac{3}{8}$	2	0.0065	Yes	18	D-55747
$2\frac{3}{8}$	2	0.0065	Yes	22	D-55752
$2\frac{9}{16}$	$2\frac{9}{64}$	0.0075	Yes	7	D-54892
*$2\frac{7}{8}$	2	0.010	Yes	24	D-51471
$2\frac{7}{8}$	$2\frac{1}{2}$	0.0075	Yes	8	D-52132
$2\frac{15}{16}$	$2\frac{15}{32}$	0.0120	Yes	3	D-51324
$3\frac{1}{2}$	3	0.014	Yes	20	C-53713
*4	$3\frac{1}{2}$	0.014	Yes	31	C-55271
*$4\frac{1}{2}$	4	0.014	Yes	24	C-53716
*$6\frac{7}{8}$	$5\frac{1}{8}$	0.025	Yes	10	D-52102
*$15\frac{1}{2}$	13	0.013	Yes	11	D-53578
*21	18	0.021	Yes	8	D-52148
$23\frac{3}{32}$	$22\frac{3}{32}$	0.013	Yes	10	C-54871
*26	$21\frac{1}{2}$	0.025	Yes	5	D-52106
$26\frac{3}{8}$	$25\frac{5}{8}$	0.025	Yes	3	D-53253

Sizes marked with an asterisk should be selected whenever possible because these sizes will normally be more available than other so-called "mongrel" sizes.

Wall thicknesses may be varied to suit requirements, but in order to keep inventories flexible, the following wall thicknesses are considered preferred sizes: 0.0045, 0.0065, 0.010, 0.015 and 0.025 inch.

Number of convolutions can be varied to suit customers' requirements.

† Courtesy of Standard-Thomson Corporation, Waltham 54, Massachusetts, manufacturers of Hydron metal bellows.

Table of Sizes and Characteristics, Regular Hydron Bellows*

Size No.	Outside Diameter (inches)	Root Diameter (inches)	Wall Thickness (inches approx.)	Standard Number of Convolutions	Approx. Normal Free Length per Convolution (inches)	Effective Area Square Inches or Linear Volume (cubic inches)	†Maximum Deflection per Convolution (inches)	Spring Rate per Convolution (lb/in)	Flexibility Travel per Convolution (in inches for each lb/in^2)	†Maximum Pressure Internal (lb/in^2)	†Maximum Pressure External (lb/in^2)
1	$\frac{5}{16}$	$\frac{7}{32}$	0.003	21	0.030	0.06	0.003	1609	0.00004	700	770
2	$\frac{3}{8}$	$\frac{1}{4}$	0.004	20	0.033	0.08	0.006	1500	0.00008	750	820
	$\frac{3}{8}$	$\frac{1}{4}$	0.008	20	0.039	0.08	0.004	8320	0.00001	3000	3300
3	$\frac{15}{32}$	$\frac{5}{16}$	0.004	16	0.039	0.12	0.010	727	0.00017	350	385
4	$\frac{9}{16}$	$\frac{3}{8}$	0.004	26	0.045	0.17	0.012	707	0.00024	210	230
	$\frac{9}{16}$	$\frac{3}{8}$	0.005	26	0.043	0.17	0.011	1170	0.00015	290	310
5	$\frac{3}{4}$	$\frac{1}{2}$	0.004	28	0.055	0.31	0.018	472	0.0007	100	110
	$\frac{3}{4}$	$\frac{1}{2}$	0.005	28	0.053	0.31	0.017	650	0.0005	130	140
	$\frac{3}{4}$	$\frac{1}{2}$	0.006	28	0.050	0.31	0.015	1063	0.0003	180	200
6	$\frac{15}{16}$	$\frac{5}{8}$	0.004	11	0.083	0.48	0.025	236	0.0020	70	77
	$\frac{15}{16}$	$\frac{5}{8}$	0.006	11	0.077	0.48	0.024	603	0.0008	200	220
7	$1\frac{1}{8}$	$\frac{3}{4}$	0.004	11	0.084	0.69	0.029	172	0.0040	55	60
	$1\frac{1}{8}$	$\frac{3}{4}$	0.005	11	0.079	0.69	0.028	291	0.0024	80	88
	$1\frac{1}{8}$	$\frac{3}{4}$	0.006	11	0.074	0.69	0.027	552	0.0012	150	165
	$1\frac{1}{8}$	$\frac{3}{4}$	0.007	11	0.070	0.69	0.023	687	0.0010	200	220
8	$1\frac{5}{16}$	$\frac{7}{8}$	0.004	11	0.119	0.94	0.036	118	0.0080	50	55
	$1\frac{5}{16}$	$\frac{7}{8}$	0.005	11	0.108	0.94	0.034	253	0.0037	70	77
	$1\frac{5}{16}$	$\frac{7}{8}$	0.006	11	0.100	0.94	0.033	380	0.0025	85	94
	$1\frac{5}{16}$	$\frac{7}{8}$	0.007	11	0.096	0.94	0.030	578	0.0016	150	165
9	$1\frac{1}{2}$	1	0.004	13	0.121	1.23	0.043	110	0.011	35	39
	$1\frac{1}{2}$	1	0.005	13	0.118	1.23	0.042	148	0.008	45	50
	$1\frac{1}{2}$	1	0.006	13	0.115	1.23	0.041	310	0.004	70	75
	$1\frac{1}{2}$	1	0.007	13	0.111	1.23	0.039	418	0.003	110	121
	$1\frac{1}{2}$	1	0.008	13	0.106	1.23	0.034	646	0.002	120	132
10	2	$1\frac{3}{8}$	0.005	16	0.143	2.24	0.055	120	0.019	28	31
	2	$1\frac{3}{8}$	0.007	16	0.121	2.24	0.045	317	0.007	50	55
	2	$1\frac{3}{8}$	0.010	16	0.113	2.24	0.034	796	0.003	150	165

11	3	2	0.005	11	0.239	4.91	0.122	51	0.096	20	22
	3	2	0.007	11	0.217	4.91	0.105	103	0.048	30	33
12	$4\frac{1}{2}$	3	0.007	13	0.271	11.04	0.133	57	0.194	15	17
					EXTRA-FLEXIBLE HYDRON BELLOWS						
13	$\frac{11}{16} \times$	$\frac{3}{8}$	0.004	11	0.059	0.22	0.017	121	0.0018	135	150
	$\frac{11}{16} \times$	$\frac{3}{8}$	0.005	11	0.049	0.22	0.016	275	0.0008	200	225
14	$\frac{3}{4} \times$	$\frac{7}{16}$	0.004	11	0.062	0.28	0.024	135	0.002	95	105
15	$\frac{27}{32}$	$\frac{1}{2}$	0.004	11	0.075	0.36	0.027	133	0.003	80	88
16	$\frac{15}{16} \times$	$\frac{17}{32}$	0.004	11	0.091	0.42	0.035	69	0.006	75	80
	$\frac{15}{16} \times$	$\frac{17}{32}$	0.006	11	0.084	0.42	0.027	206	0.002	130	143
17	$1\frac{1}{8} \times$	$\frac{21}{32}$	0.004	11	0.100	0.62	0.047	62	0.010	55	61
	$1\frac{1}{8} \times$	$\frac{21}{32}$	0.005	11	0.087	0.62	0.034	108	0.006	65	72
	$1\frac{1}{8} \times$	$\frac{21}{32}$	0.006	11	0.076	0.62	0.029	226	0.003	130	143
18	$1\frac{5}{16}$	$\frac{3}{4}$	0.004	11	0.143	0.84	0.068	38	0.022	35	39
	$1\frac{5}{16}$	$\frac{3}{4}$	0.006	11	0.128	0.84	0.050	117	0.007	80	88
19	$1\frac{1}{2} \times$	$\frac{7}{8}$	0.004	11	0.181	1.11	0.087	59	0.019	30	33
	$1\frac{1}{2} \times$	$\frac{7}{8}$	0.005	11	0.163	1.11	0.067	68	0.016	40	44
	$1\frac{1}{2} \times$	$\frac{7}{8}$	0.007	11	0.150	1.11	0.055	176	0.006	75	83
20	2 ×	$1\frac{1}{4}$	0.005	15	0.190	2.07	0.095	75	0.028	25	28
	2 ×	$1\frac{1}{4}$	0.007	15	0.169	2.07	0.072	134	0.015	40	44
		For approx. inside diam. subtract twice wall thickness		May be decreased in every case and increased in some cases	Multiply by number of convolutions to obtain normal free length of bellows	$\pi[(D+d)/4]^2$ This figure expressed as cubic inches is the approximate volume per inch of length	Multiply by number of convolutions to obtain maximum deflection of bellows	Divide by number of convolutions to obtain spring rate of bellows	This is a calculated value multiply by number of convolutions to obtain flexibility of bellows		

* Table courtesy of Standard-Thomson Corporation, Waltham 54, Massachusetts, manufacturers of Hydron metal bellows.

† Maximum deflection is the greatest stroke which the bellows will withstand at zero pressure without taking a set. Maximum pressure is the highest pressure to which the bellows can be subjected at its normal free length without permanent deformation. Maximum deflection with maximum pressure can seldom, if ever, be used.

Procedure for Assembling Tubes

After the electrical requirements and consequent geometry of the tube have been decided upon, the first step is to formulate and draw up a mechanical design with complete dimensions. Then choose the kinds of materials to be used. At this point an excellent procedure is to organize a step-by-step plan in which the order or all operations are outlined. As an example, we give the following:

An experimental electron tube is required that has a 5UP cathode-ray gun, two tungsten-mesh grids, and a fluorescent target. The specifications are tabulated below.

MATERIALS NEEDED

ITEM	NUMBER REQUIRED	DESCRIPTION	DIMENSIONS AND NOTES
1	1	Envelope, Pyrex glass	3″ OD × 14″ long
2	1	Press, 10-lead, Pyrex; nickel leads, Kulgrid flex.	0.060″ leads, 3″ flare
3	1	Press, 1-lead, Pyrex; nickel lead, Kulgrid flex.	0.060″ lead, 3″ flare
4	2	Press, 1-lead Pyrex; nickel lead	1″ flare; thread end of lead $\frac{1}{8}$″ #0–80 thread
5	1	Press, 1-lead, Pyrex, nickel lead, short stub inside	1″ flare
6	1	Target, stainless steel	2½″ diam. 0.015″ thick; sandblast; dry H_2 fire
7	2	Grids, stainless steel double rings, tungsten knit mesh	2¾″ OD; dry H_2 fire
8		Aquadag (or other coating)	
9		Willemite (or other phosphor)	
13	1	CRT electron gun	Type 5UP
14	2	KIC barium getter wires	See p. 105

The assembly procedure is as follows (see Fig. 34):

1. Make a glass envelope (item 1) with open ends and side arms. Clean and store dust-tight.

2. Make one 10-lead press (item 2) for CRT gun (item 13). This is to have a constricted pumping tubulation and is to be flared to fit on the end of the envelope (item 1). Clean and store dust-tight.

3. Make one 1-lead press for target (item 6), with flare to fit on the other end of the envelope (item 1). Clean and store dust-tight.

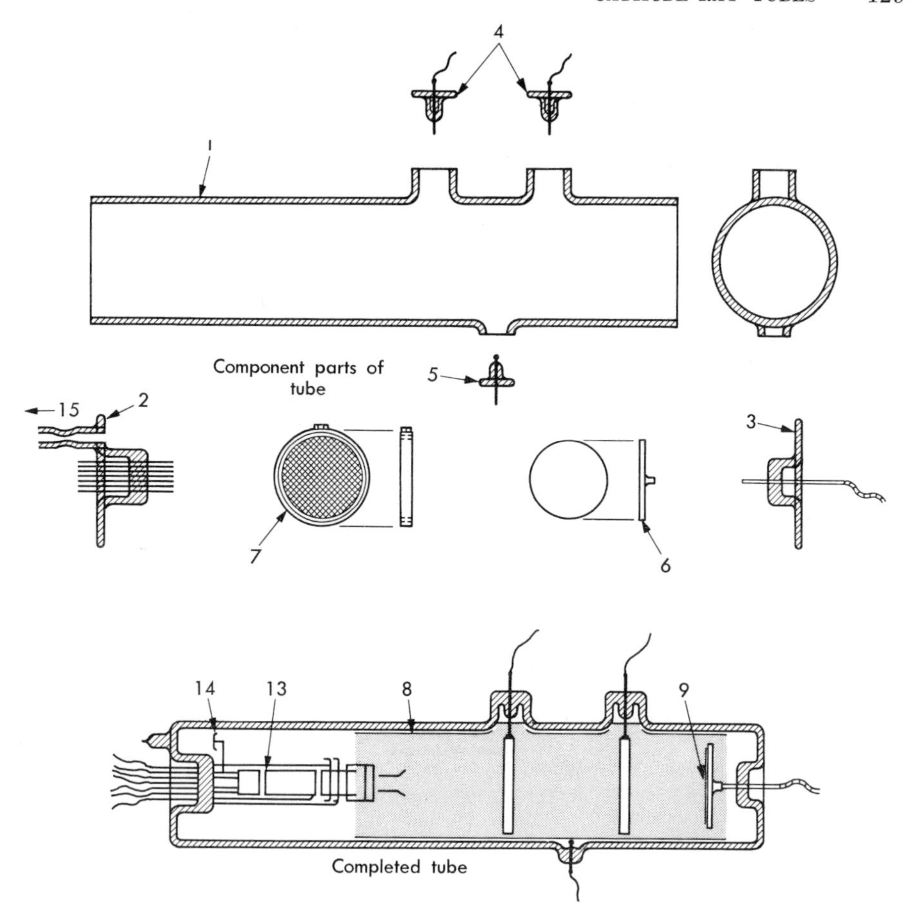

FIG. 34. Experimental electron tube illustrative of assembly schedule.

4. Make two 1-lead presses for grids (to fit on side arms of envelope, item 1). Inner ends of leads are to be exactly correct length and threaded for assembly later into grids (item 7). Clean and store dust-tight.

5. Make one 1-lead press to fit third side arm. Inner end of lead is to have short stub which will be covered with Aquadag (see step 8 below). Clean and store dust-tight.

6. Make disc for target. Blast one side lightly with steel-grit. Clean. Dry-hydrogen- or vacuum-fire at 1000°C and store dust- and moisture-tight until ready for step 9.

7. Make two grids. These are made like embroidery hoops: two stainless steel rings, one fitting inside the other, with clearance for the tungsten knit mesh. (See p. 472 and Fig. 137.) Outer ring is to have one #0–80 threaded hole and a #0–80 stainless steel nut spot-welded over the hole to form a boss. Assembly is by spot-welding. Each part (item 7) is to be cleaned and dry-hydrogen- or vacuum-fired at 1000°C. Store dust- and moisture-tight.

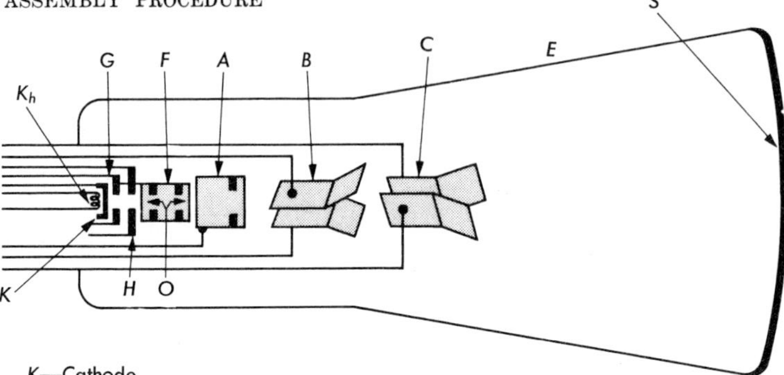

(a)

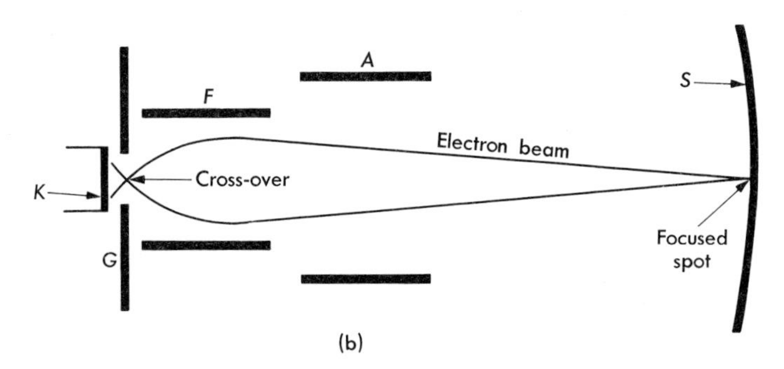

(b)

FIGURE 35

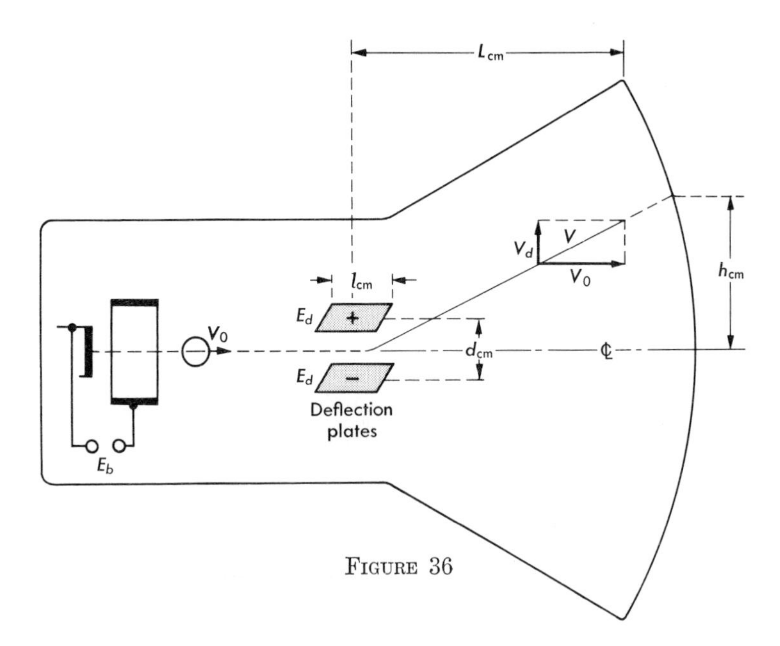

FIGURE 36

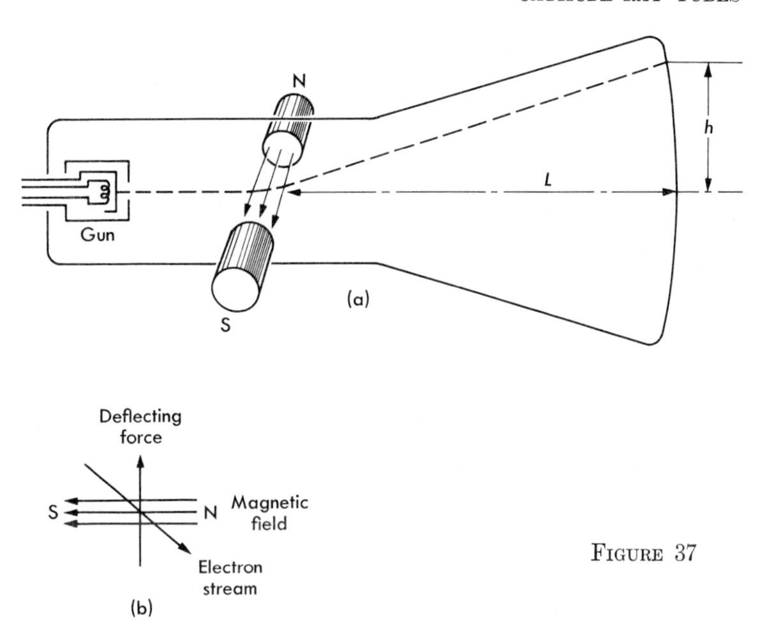

FIGURE 37

FIG. 35. (a) A simplified design of a cathode-ray tube with electrostatic focusing. Items K, K_h, G, H, F, O, and A comprise an electron gun (see p. 239). Electrodes F and A are the focusing system. (b) This figure shows how the electrons from the cathode in an electron gun are immediately redirected to a focus point, called the cross-over, which acts as the point of origin for the main focusing system. In this figure, F is the focus electrode and A is the anode.

FIG. 36. Cathode-ray tube, electrostatic focusing. Electrons entering a field between the deflection plates are diverted in proportion to the strength of the field and the length of time they are influenced by that field.

$$V_0 = 5.94 \times 10^7 \sqrt{E_b} (\text{cm/sec}), \qquad h = Ll\,E_d/2E_b d \ (\text{cm}).$$

FIG. 37. Cathode-ray tube, electromagnetic (or magnetic) focusing. (a) The amount of deflection h of a cathode ray passing through a magnetic field of flux density B (gauss) and length l will be

$$h = 0.298\,BlL/E_b,$$

where L is the distance from the deflecting field to the screen, and E_b is the second anode voltage. All dimensions are in centimeters. (b) The deflection by magnetic fields is at right angles to the lines of force and to the axis of the beam. After leaving the field, the beam continues on in the same line until it strikes the screen. (See also "Magnetic Focusing of Electron Beams," J. T. Mendel, *Proc. I.R.E.*, **43,** 327, 1955.)

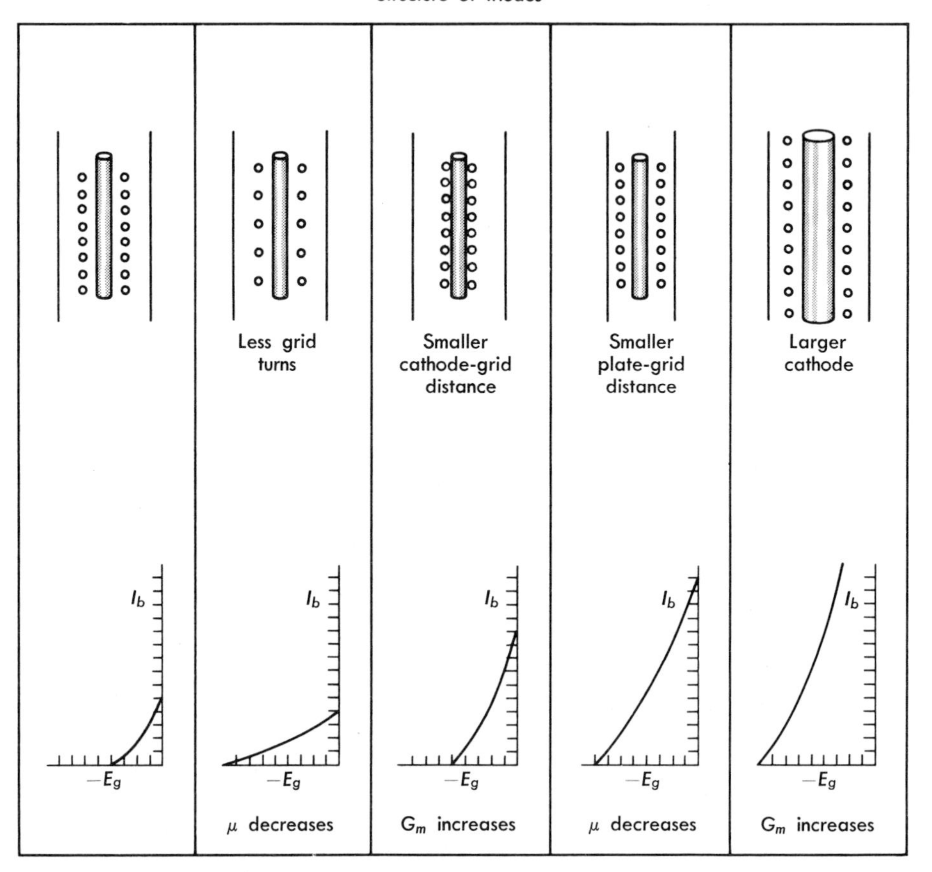

FIG. 38. Variations of tube characteristics with different geometries. Changes in the dimensions of the control grid in a triode have an influence on the control characteristics of the tube. This is illustrated in the figure which correlates the shape of the characteristic curve with grid spacing. Grids with less turns or which are closer to the anode (plate) decrease the amplification factor μ. With grids closer to the cathode or with cathodes of greater surface (emitting) area, the value of G_m (transconductance) is increased. A discussion of tube characteristics is given on pp. 546–548.

8. Coat part of inside of envelope (item 1) with conductive coating, as specified (see pp. 157, 199). Allow to dry, and bake. Store dust-tight.

9. Assemble target (item 6) to 1-lead press (item 3) by spot-welding.

10. Coat target with fluorescent material (see p. 251) as specified, and dry in oven.

11. Assemble grids (item 7) into envelope (item 1). Grasp stainless steel ring firmly with long forceps or tweezers and place in proper position inside envelope so that the 1-lead threaded presses can be screwed in from outside at the side arms. Screw in tight and glass-seal into side arms, making sure that grid is correctly aligned inside envelope.

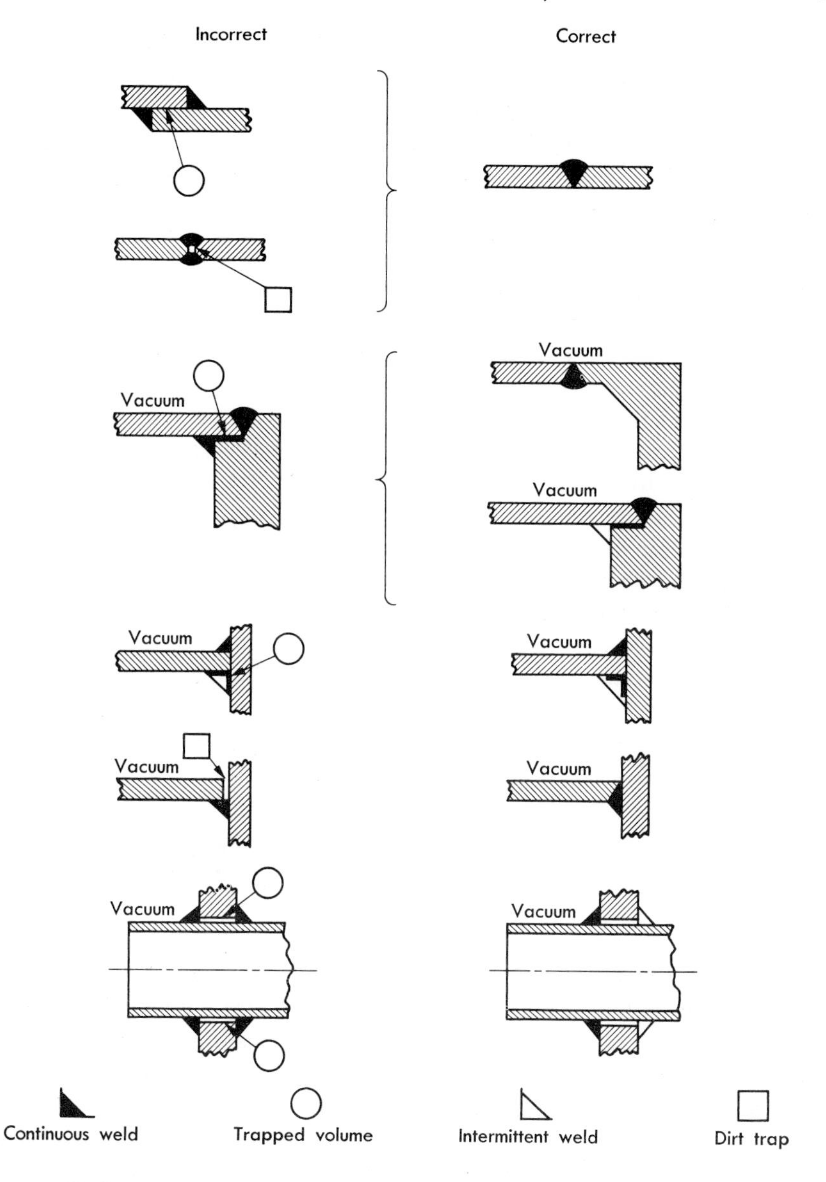

FIG. 39. Various welded joints in vacuum systems: examples of good and bad practices.

12. Seal in coated target mounted on 1-lead press (item 9).

13. Unpack fresh 5UP electron gun and attach to 10-lead press. Mount two getters on press in such a way that they can be fired by passing current. If the leads are for gun electrodes, the getter is to be burned out. If getters are to be fired by RF, they should be mounted so as to be positioned near inside surface of glass envelope. A gate or shield should be provided to prevent evaporated material from the getter coating the press, which could cause

shorting or flashover. Mounting of gun and getters is done while steps 11 and 12 are being performed by the glassblowers, so that the electron gun can be sealed to the envelope immediately after step 12.

14. Connect assembled tube to vacuum system immediately after step 13.
15. Pump, bake, activate, bombard, and age. (See p. 98 *et seq.*, also p. 149.)
16. Fire getters.
17. Seal off and shut down vacuum system.

The foregoing is intended only as a rough guide. It is obvious that some details, such as making the presses, annealing the glass components, etc., have been omitted. Because each new tube presents unique problems, a different procedure will be required for each.

It is important that closed spaces, pockets, or crypts be avoided in structures that are to be evacuated. Obviously, such spaces are gas traps, and as such they are difficult to evacuate, producing the effect of a leak. For example, if a machine screw is unavoidably to be used to hold two members together inside the tube in such a way that the screw is threaded into a blind hole, the screw should either be provided with a longitudinal groove or with a hole drilled axially through its center so that the blind hole can be pumped.

Pockets or crypts can also be created in brazing or welding parts together. Figure 39 shows some good and bad practices in making such joints in metal vacuum apparatus.[1]

Leak Detection

Defects in glass seals—small cracks, pinholes, or other faults—are detected directly with a Tesla coil sparker (see p. 493). When the electrode is passed near a leak, a bright spot will indicate its position.[2] (**Caution:** held too long in one position, the sparker is capable of puncturing the glass.)

Leaks in metal systems and in glass-to-metal or ceramic-to-metal seals cannot be detected by means of the sparker, but if there is a glass section in the system being pumped, the sparker may be used as follows:

If the leak is not so large that it precludes a discharge fluorescence, the sparker is held near the glass section so that the glow-discharge can be observed, and the places suspected of leaking are swabbed, brushed, or sprayed with carbon tetrachloride, acetone, or methanol. (**Caution:** the last two are flammable and can be ignited from the sparker.) Whenever the volatile liquid

---

[1] "High Vacuum Practice," H. Kronenberger, *British Chem. Engineering,* **3,** 26, January, 1958.

[2] *Cf.* "Electronic Leak Detector," D. J. Dowling, *J. Sci. Instr.* (Br), **37,** 147, 1960.

flows over a small leak, the suction and expansion cause it to freeze at the site, thus momentarily closing the leak, whereupon the character of the fluorescence will undergo a marked change.

The color and character of the fluorescence produced by the sparker are rough indicators of the pressure (see p. 213). At high pressures, above 10^{-2} torr, the glow will be bright, with a "snaky" character and a pink or violet color, indicating the presence of air. A greenish-gray tinge denotes the presence of decomposed oil vapors. With falling pressure, the glow becomes more diffuse, paler, and more blue and less red. The blue color, becoming fainter and more transparent as the pressure is reduced, is generally attributed to carbon dioxide and water vapor in or on glass and metal parts which have not been thoroughly baked or outgassed. At pressures in the neighborhood of 10^{-4} torr, only a faint local fluorescence may be seen, and at 10^{-5} the glow has practically disappeared ("black vacuum").

Leaks can also be detected by means of an indicating vacuum gauge of any type suitable for the pressure range encountered (see Fig. 40). When we use a thermocouple gauge (p. 440), for example, which is capable of measuring pressures down to about 1 micron Hg, if the site of the leak is bathed with one of the solvents mentioned above, the indicated pressure will at first drop momentarily as the solvent freezes, then rise rapidly as the solvent evaporates into the gauge. Some indicating gauges are more sensitive to solvent vapors than to air.[1]

When a system pumps down to pressures of 10^{-5} torr or thereabouts, and does not improve on continued pumping, the probability is (1) that something in the system is steadily outgassing because of (a) chemical action, (b) contamination, or (c) the presence of one or more crypts (see p. 134), and/or (2) that there exists a very small leak or porosity. No useful visible discharge can be obtained with the sparker at this pressure, but an ionization gauge (p. 303) is to some degree useful for finding leaks by the method described in the previous paragraph. In addition to the solvents mentioned, illuminating gas or hydrogen can be used. The section under suspicion is covered with a gas-tight box or container (a polyethylene bag is useful), open at the bottom, and the gas is introduced. The presence of a leak or porosity is indicated but not precisely located in this way. After the presence of a leak is definitely established, the open-bottomed vessel is removed and a small jet of the gas, such as from a hypodermic needle, is used as a probe. The presence of a leak is indicated by a sudden increase in pressure. Even though ionization gauges are less sensitive to hydrogen than to normal air, the hydrogen will be capable of entering a small leak at a much faster rate than air.

For leaks that are so small or obscure as to defy all these measures, use is made of the helium leak detector (see pp. 359–363, also the starred references

---

[1] Scientific Foundations of Vacuum Technique, second edition, Saul Dushman, John Wiley & Sons, New York, 1962.

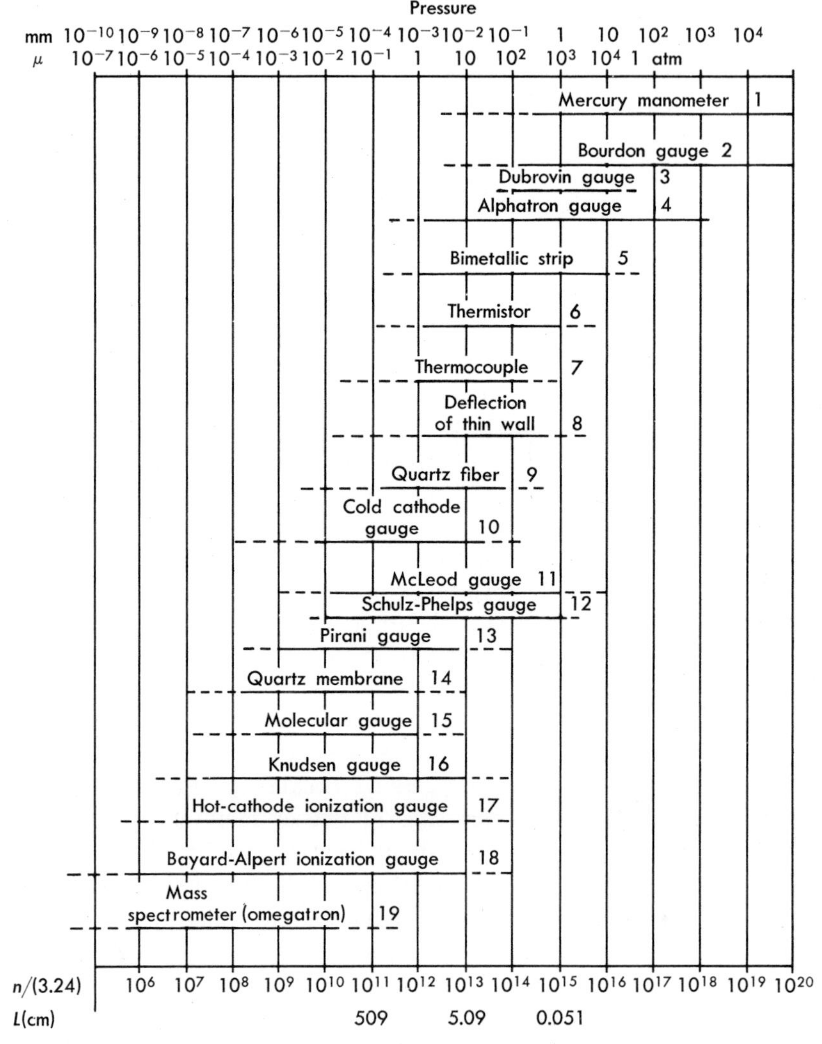

FIG. 40. Comparison of ranges of various vacuum gauges. The numbers to the right of the lines are keyed to the following page numbers: 1–348, 2–347, 3–353, 4–193, 304, 5–none, 6–347, 7–440, 8–347, 9–none, 10–431, 11–348, 12–471, 13–438, 14–none, 15–none, 16–321, 17–303, 18–162, 19–402. The full line indicates the usual range; the dashed portions to the left indicate sensitivities which have been, or may be, attained by specially designed constructions. The symbol n is number of molecules per cm^3 at 25°C; L is mean free path in cm for air at 25°C.

below). This instrument is a mass-spectrometer permanently adjusted for helium, connected into the vacuum system in such a way that when the open-bottomed vessel or jet of helium is used, the presence of minute amounts of helium entering a leak can be detected. In order to protect the rather delicate ionizing structure against gross leaks which might contaminate or burn out its filament, the tube or vessel to be tested is first roughed down with a separate pumping system consisting of a fast mechanical pump and a thermocouple gauge, the helium mass-spectrometer being isolated with a suitable valve which is opened only when the thermocouple gauge shows that a low pressure has been attained.

The halogen-sensitive leak detectors are preferentially used with Freon, which is nontoxic and nonflammable, but any halogen-compound gas can be used.

Leak Detectors and Various Methods of Application—Bibliography

J. B. H. Kuper, *Rev. Sci. Instr.*, **8**, 131, 1937.

J. H. Manley, L. J. Haworth, and E. A. Luebke, *ibid.*, **10**, 389, 1939.

E. J. Lawton, *ibid.*, **11**, 134, 1940.

* A. O. Nier, *ibid.*, **11**, 212, 1940.

Procedures in Experimental Physics, J. Strong and collaborators, Prentice-Hall, New York, pp. 93–150, 1942.

L. N. Ridenour, *Rev. Sci. Instr.*, **12**, 134, 1944.

R. B. Nelson, *ibid.*, **16**, 55, 1945.

H. Nelson, *ibid.*, **16**, 273, 1945.

* H. A. Thomas, T. W. Williams, and J. A. Hipple, *ibid.*, **17**, 368, 1946; also *Westinghouse Engr.*, **6**, 108, 1946.

* W. G. Worcester and E. G. Doughty, *Trans. Amer. Inst. Elec. Engrs.*, **65**, 946, 1946.

* A. O. Nier, C. M. Stevens, A. Hustrulid, and T. A. Abbott, *J. Appl. Phys.*, **18**, 30, 1947.

* R. B. Jacobs and H. F. Zuhr, *ibid.*, **18**, 34, 1947.

W. C. White, J. S. Hickey, *Electronics,* **21**, 100, 1948.

F. M. Penning, *Philips Tech. Rev.*, **11**, 116, 1949.

Scientific Foundations of Vacuum Technique, second edition, p. 353, S. Dushman, J. Wiley & Sons, Inc., New York, 1962.

Vacuum Equipment and Techniques, A. Guthrie and R. K. Wakerling, McGraw-Hill Book Co., New York, 1949.

F. H. Kloepper, L. W. Seagondollar, and R. K. Smith, *Rev. Sci. Instr.*, **23**, 245, 1952.

G. A. Alers, J. A. Jacobs, and P. R. Malmberg, *ibid.*, **24**, 399, 1953.

K. Ziock, *Glas und Hochvakuum Tech.*, **2**, 292, 1953.

R. B. Lawrance, *Chem. Eng. Progress,* **50**, 155, 1954.

T. B. Kent, *J. Sci. Instr.* (Br), **32**, 132, 1955.

E. Glueckauf and G. P. Kitt, *ibid.*, **35**, 220, 1958.

J. A. van Leeuwen and H. J. Oskam, *Rev. Sci. Instr.*, **27**, 328, 1956.

M. Varićak, *ibid.*, **27**, 655, 1956.

C. C. Minter, *ibid.*, **29**, 793, 1958.

C. C. Minter, *ibid.*, **31**, 458, 1960.

J. L. Peters, *ibid.*, **30**, 1093, 1959.

D. E. Swets, *ibid.*, **31**, 659, 1960.
N. R. Daly, *ibid.*, **31**, 721, 1960.
R. N. Bloomer and W. C. Brooks, *J. Sci. Instr.* (Br), **37**, 306, 1960.
D. J. Dowling, *ibid.*, **37**, 147, 1960.
J. R. Young, *Rev. Sci. Instr.*, **32**, 85, 1961.
S. Jnanananda, *High Vacua*, D. Van Nostrand Co., Inc., New York, 1949.
N. Milleron, *Trans. Am. Vacuum Soc.*, 10th Ann. Symp., 283–286, The Macmillan Company, New York, 1963.
W. Steckelmacher and D. Tinsley, *Vacuum* (Br), **12**, 145, 1962.
J. W. Ackley, *et al.*, *Trans. Am. Vacuum Soc.*, 9th Ann. Symp., 380–383, The Macmillan Company, 1962.
A. E. Barrington, *Rev. Sci. Instr.*, **33**, 1045, 1962.
R. W. Roberts, and T. A. Vanderslice, *Ultrahigh Vacuum and its Applications*, Prentice-Hall, Inc., Englewood Cliffs, N.J., 1963.

Vapor Pressure

All substances, no matter how inert or refractory, exhibit some vapor pressure, although at room temperature or lower the vapor is infinitesimally small, and often not measurable at all. However, as the temperature is raised, aside from atmospheric and other gases which have been adsorbed or absorbed, molecules of the substance itself are released and constitute a vapor which becomes perceptible with vacuum gauges.

Vapor pressure is expressed by the formula:

$$\log_{10} P = AT^{-1} + B \log_{10} T + CT + D,$$

where P means pressure in millimeters of mercury and T means absolute temperature in °K. A, B, C, D mean coefficients characteristic of the substance.[1] (See p. 563 for a discussion of the vapor pressure of alloys.)

Vapor pressures have been measured for many elements[1] and for other substances[2,3,4]. Using the empirical formula, Jensen[2] has measured the vapor pressure of some plastic materials:

$$\log_{10} P = A - B/T,$$

in which the constants A and B are given in his table reproduced on p. 139.

---

[1] R. E. Honig, "Vapor Pressure Data for the Solid and Liquid Elements," *RCA Review*, **23**, 567–586, 1962 (see pp. 142–148).

[2] N. Jensen, "Vapor Pressures of Plastic Materials," *J. Appl. Phys.*, **27**, (12), pp. 1460–1462, 1956.

[3] S. Dushman, *Scientific Foundations of Vacuum Technique*, second edition, John Wiley & Sons, Inc., New York, p. 696, 1962.

[4] See pp. 140–141.

In the table[1] on pp. 140–141, the pressures were measured on a system comprising a forepump, an oil- or mercury-diffusion pump, a cold trap with liquid nitrogen refrigerant, and a conventional ionization gauge. Except for the forepump, the system was all glass, and the sample was contained in a glass tube sealed to a manifold and close to the gauge. All samples were previously cleaned in a manner appropriate to the material, and the glass parts were heated for outgassing (to 450°–500°C) before each run. Temperatures were measured either with a Weston dial thermometer or a chromel-alumel thermocouple, calibrated in both cases. Heating of the sample was accomplished with a small tubular electric heater controlled with a Variac and placed around the glass tube holding the material.

TABLE OF CONSTANTS A AND B IN $\log_{10} P = A - B/T$ FOR SOME PLASTIC MATERIALS*

Material	A	B	Vapor pressure at 25°C torr
Mylar	3.0	3000	1×10^{-7}
Saran	6.4	4200	3×10^{-8}
Vinyl	11.5	5900	1×10^{-8}
Teflon	4.3	3400	1×10^{-7}
Nylon cloth	10.0	5600	1×10^{-9}
Hycar rubber	19.4	7400	4×10^{-6}
Butyl rubber	11.4	4900	1×10^{-5}
Polyethylene	7.4	4500	3×10^{-8}

* Jensen, *op cit.*

Comments on column headings in the following table: *Best initial pressure* (1) was that obtained after several hours of pumping with the sample at room temperature (2). Heat was then applied and held at a maximum (4) that depended on the material being studied long enough for the pressure to reach a stable value (3). The temperature was then allowed to fall. *Terminal pressure* (5) was taken several hours after the sample had again dropped to near room temperature (6), or until there was no appreciable further reduction in pressure.

The vapor pressures given in this table are not to be taken as absolute values, since, in most cases (the organic materials), some decomposition occurs with the application of heat. The measurements are therefore to be considered as comparative under the conditions of test, and as a guide in deciding what materials to use in vacuum devices.

[1] F. Rosebury, *Tube Laboratory Manual,* second edition, Research Laboratory of Electronics, M.I.T., Cambridge, Massachusetts, p. 125, 1956.

COMPARATIVE VAPOR PRESSURES OF VARIOUS LABORATORY MATERIALS*

MATERIAL	PRESSURES AND TEMPERATURES					
	(1) BEST INITIAL PRESSURE (torr)	(2) TEMPERATURE (°C)	(3) PRESSURE (torr)	(4) HEATED TO TEMPERATURE (°C)	(5) TERMINAL PRESSURE (torr)	(6) TEMPERATURE (°C)
Polyethylene wire insulation, gray color	4.5×10^{-6}	25	1.5×10^{-4}	at 200	6.0×10^{-7}	25
Polyethylene wire insulation, amber color	4.5×10^{-7}	26	1.0×10^{-4}	at 120	3.4×10^{-7}	27
Formvar-insulated copper wire, 16-gauge	1.7×10^{-5}	25	5.2×10^{-5}	at 250	2.0×10^{-7}	25
Teflon; $\frac{1}{8}''$ sheet	5.0×10^{-6}	25	3.3×10^{-5}	at 350	5.0×10^{-8}	50
Nylon; small piece from 1-inch round stock	1.2×10^{-6}	25	8.2×10^{-5}	at 104	2.1×10^{-7}	26
Glyptal; clear lacquer, coated on glass cane	1.7×10^{-6}	25	$>10^{-3}$	at 132	2.4×10^{-6}	25
Glyptal; red lacquer, coated on glass cane	5.0×10^{-7}	27	1.0×10^{-4}	at 224	6.8×10^{-7}	28
Neoprene O-ring; $\frac{1}{8}''$ section; new ring	2.0×10^{-6}	24	1.1×10^{-4}	at 100	1.4×10^{-6}	24
Picein wax, black (Vacuum Wax from Honeywell Co.)	2.5×10^{-7}	24	5.0×10^{-5}	at 123	1.8×10^{-7}	25
DeKhotinsky cement (Cenco); medium grade	1.2×10^{-6}	26	1.0×10^{-4}	at 73	1.0×10^{-6}	26
Silicone rubber: red (Roth Rubber Co., Compound 7-163)	1.2×10^{-6}	27	1.0×10^{-4}	at 150	1.6×10^{-6}	27

White silicone rubber O-ring	3.0×10^{-6}	25	3.5×10^{-5}	at 150	7.0×10^{-8}	25
Lubriseal stopcock grease (A. H. Thomas Co.)	5.5×10^{-6}	24	1.2×10^{-5}	at 130	5.2×10^{-6}	25
Apiezon "M" stopcock grease (Metropolitan-Vickers Co.)	2.2×10^{-6}	27	$>10^{-3}$	at 168	2.8×10^{-6}	27
Apiezon "N" stopcock grease (Metropolitan-Vickers Co.)	2.5×10^{-7}	23	9.0×10^{-6}	at 220	2.5×10^{-8}	23
Apiezon "Q" sealing compound (Metropolitan-Vickers Co.)	1.8×10^{-5}	25	2.0×10^{-4}	at 50	4.3×10^{-6}	25
Celvacene stopcock grease, medium (Consolidated Vacuum Co.)	1.7×10^{-7}	29	2.5×10^{-6}	at 247	1.0×10^{-8}	30
Insalute ceramic cement (Sauereisen-Cenco)	2.8×10^{-7}	24	6.5×10^{-6}	at 460	2.0×10^{-7}	22
Soft solder, 50–50; $\frac{1}{8}''$ wire	8.5×10^{-6}	27	1.1×10^{-4}	at 195	3.9×10^{-6}	27
Yellow brass	3.0×10^{-8}	24	1.0×10^{-6}	at 520	1.0×10^{-8}	28
Cadmium-plated steel (screws)	7.2×10^{-6}	29	1.5×10^{-4}	at 470†	8.0×10^{-7}	29
Teflon-silicone Rubber Elastomer Compound X-5-8 (Bacon Industries, Inc.)	8.0×10^{-7}	25	1.5×10^{-4}	at 225	3.0×10^{-7}	25
Plexiglas (Rohm & Haas Co.)	1.0×10^{-6}	25	2.0×10^{-4}	at 155	5.0×10^{-7}	25
Epoxy Resin, cured (Hysol Corp.)	5.0×10^{-6}	25	1.0×10^{-5}	at 130	4.0×10^{-7}	22

* See comments on p. 139.
† After all cadmium had been evaporated and condensed on an unheated part of the tube.

VAPOR PRESSURES OF THE ELEMENTS

This material on vapor pressure of the elements (see tables and graphs on the following pages) is from "Vapor Pressure Data for the Solid and Liquid Elements," by permission of the author, R. E. Honig (*RCA Review*, **23**, 567–586, 1962).

In his paper, Dr. Honig acknowledges the following major sources: "Selected Values for the Thermodynamic Properties of Metals and Alloys," R. R. Hultgren and collaborators, Report of the Minerals Research Laboratory, University of California, Berkeley, California, 1962; "JANAF Interim Thermochemical Tables," D. R. Stull and associates, Dow Chemical Co., Midland, Michigan, 1962; and "Thermodynamic Properties of the Elements," D. R. Stull and G. C. Sinke, *Advances in Chemistry*, Series 18, American Chemical Society, Washington, D.C., 1956.

In addition to these, about 125 articles and abstracts were consulted, out of which Dr. Honig gives some 75 references. The reader is referred to his paper for the list.

To compare vapor pressure data from various sources, the author plotted on log p versus log T, where p is in torr or atm and T in °K. Hultgren's data for many metals, tabulated as temperatures at given pressures, could be plotted directly. Stull's data, tabulated as log p (atm) at given temperatures, could be put directly on the log p versus log T plots, with the help of a special scale. Most of the individual references present experimental results in terms of the general equation:

$$\log_{10}p = AT^{-1} + B\log_{10}T + CT + DT^2 + E$$

where p means pressure, expressed in torr; T means absolute temperature, in °K; A, B, C, D, E mean coefficients characteristic of the element (in most cases only A and E are used).

The tables that follow present vapor pressure data over the range 10^{-11} to 10^3 torr, together with the temperature range of the original data.

Figures 41, 42, and 43 present the vapor pressure data in graphical form. To locate a given element, consult the column headed "Curve in Fig." in the tables on pp. 146–148. The letters s (solid) and l (liquid) on the figures have been appended to the chemical symbol if the melting point falls outside the range of the graph. When two elements fall on the same curve, and one of them is based on estimated values, the symbol of the letter is placed in a dashed circle. For some elements, there exist several different, but apparently equivalent, sets of vapor pressure data as determined by different workers. If these measurements appear equally reliable, the set nearest the mean has been selected.

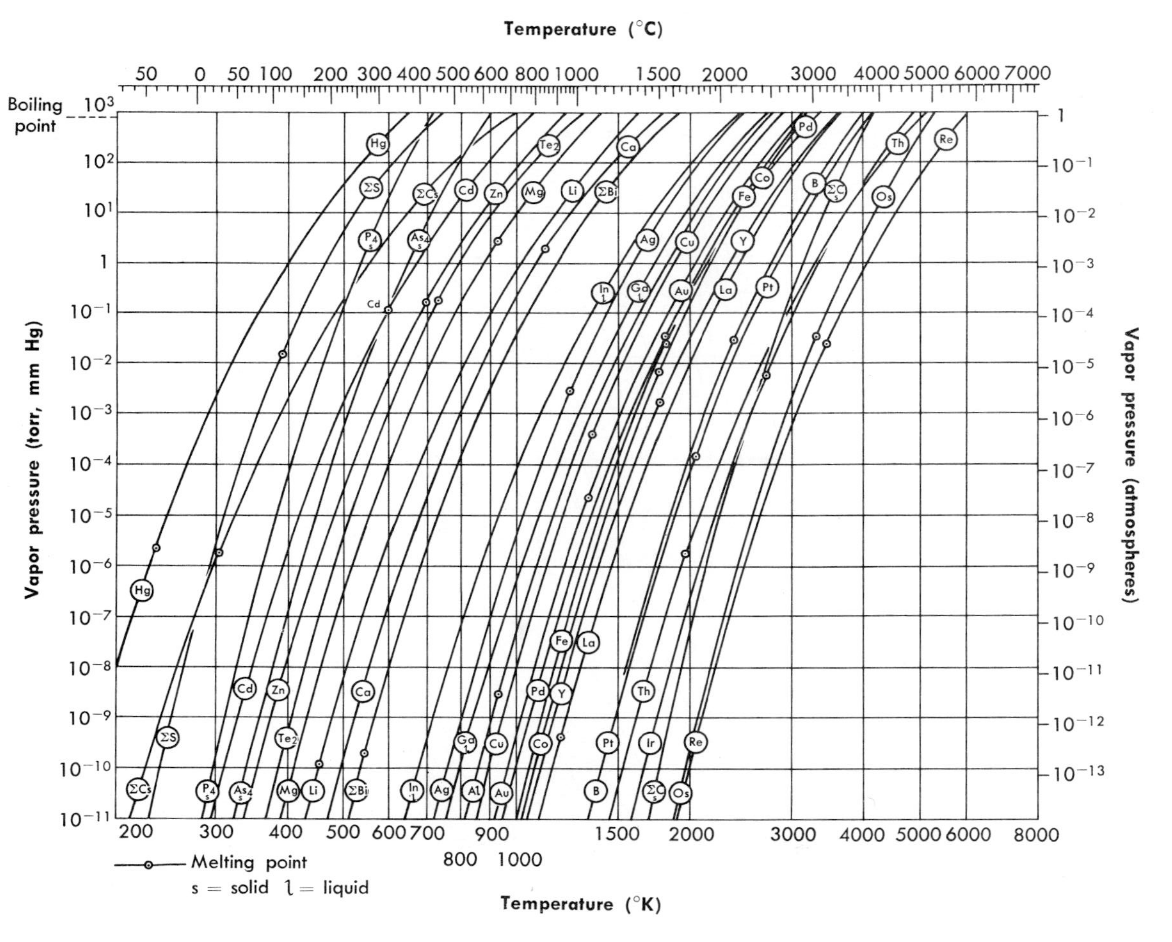

FIG. 41. Vapor-pressure curves of the elements.

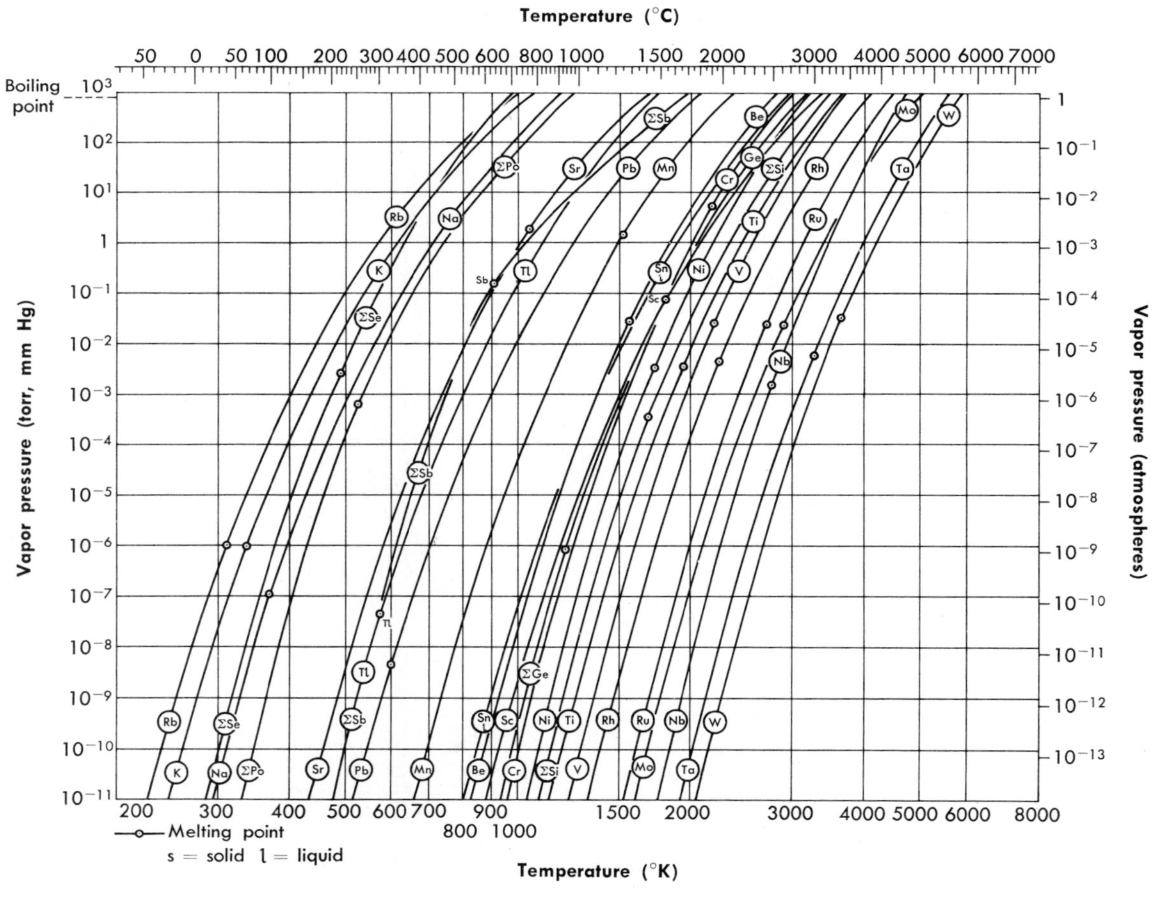

FIG. 42. Vapor-pressure curves of the elements.

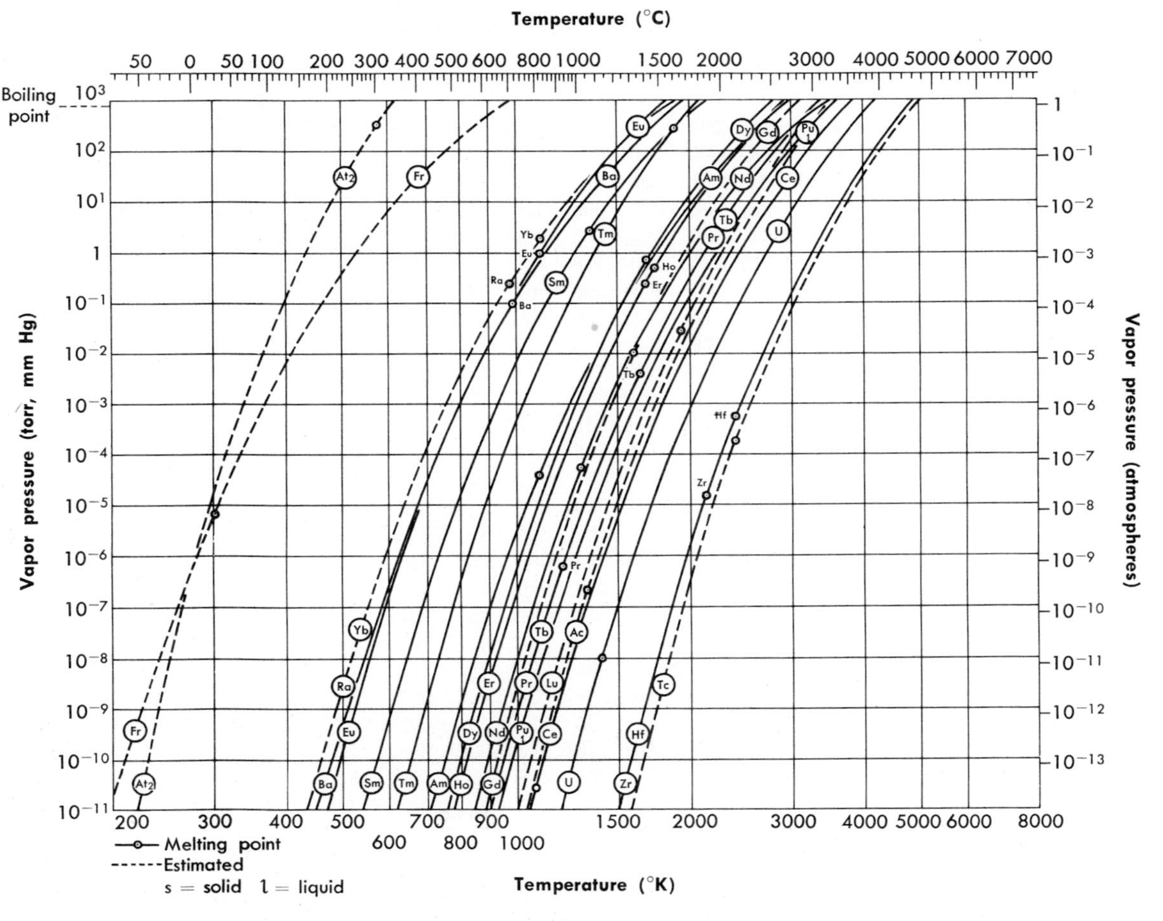

FIG. 43. Vapor-pressure curves of the elements.

VAPOR PRESSURES FOR THE SOLID AND LIQUID ELEMENTS

SYMBOL*	MP(°K)	BP(°K)	CURVE IN FIG.	DATA TEMP RANGE (°K)	TEMPERATURES (°K) FOR VAPOR PRESSURES (TORR)														
					10^{-11}	10^{-10}	10^{-9}	10^{-8}	10^{-7}	10^{-6}	10^{-5}	10^{-4}	10^{-3}	10^{-2}	10^{-1}	1	10^{1}	10^{2}	10^{3}
Ac	1320	3470	43	1873, Est.	1045	1100	1160	1230	1305	1390	1490	1605	1740	1905	2100	2350	2660	3030	3510
Ag	1234	2435	41	958–2200	721	759	800	847	899	958	1025	1105	1195	1300	1435	1605	1815	2100	2490
Al	932	2736	41	1220–1468	815	860	906	958	1015	1085	1160	1245	1355	1490	1640	1830	2050	2370	2800
Am	1200	2790	43	1103–1453	712	752	797	848	905	971	1050	1140	1245	1375	1540	1745	2020	2400	2970
As(s)	1090	886	41		323	340	358	377	400	423	447	477	510	550	590	645	712	795	900
At	575	610	43	Est.	221	231	241	252	265	280	296	316	338	364	398	434	480	540	620
Au	1336	3081	41	1073–1847	915	964	1020	1080	1150	1220	1305	1405	1525	1670	1840	2040	2320	2680	3130
B	2360	3850	41	1781–2413	1335	1405	1480	1555	1640	1740	1855	1980	2140	2300	2520	2780	3100	3500	4000
Ba	983	1895	43	1333–1419	450	480	510	545	583	627	675	735	800	883	984	1125	1310	1570	1930
Be	1556	2757	42	1103–1552	832	878	925	980	1035	1105	1180	1270	1370	1500	1650	1830	2080	2390	2810
Bi	544.5	1852	41		510	540	568	602	640	682	732	790	860	945	1050	1170	1350	1570	1900
C(s)	—	4130	41	1820–2700	1695	1765	1845	1930	2030	2140	2260	2410	2560	2730	2930	3170	3450	3780	4190
Ca	1123	1756	41	730–1546	470	495	524	555	590	630	678	732	795	870	962	1075	1250	1475	1800
Cd	594	1040	41	411–1040	293	310	328	347	368	392	419	450	490	538	593	665	762	885	1060
Ce	1077	3740	43	1611–2038	1050	1110	1175	1245	1325	1420	1525	1650	1795	1970	2180	2440	2780	3220	3830
Co	1768	3174	41	1363–1522	1020	1070	1130	1195	1265	1340	1430	1530	1655	1790	1960	2180	2440	2790	3220
Cr	2176	2938	42	1273–1557	960	1010	1055	1110	1175	1250	1335	1430	1540	1670	1825	2010	2240	2550	3000
Cs	301.8	955	41	300– 955	213	226	241	257	274	297	322	351	387	428	482	553	643	775	980
Cu	1357	2846	41	1143–1897	855	895	945	995	1060	1125	1210	1300	1405	1530	1690	1890	2140	2460	2920
Dy	1680	2710	43	1258–1773	760	801	847	898	955	1020	1090	1170	1270	1390	1535	1710	1965	2300	2780
Er	1770	2850	43	1773, Est.	779	822	869	922	981	1050	1125	1220	1325	1450	1605	1800	2060	2420	2920
Eu	1099	1764	43	696– 900	469	495	523	556	592	634	682	739	805	884	981	1100	1260	1500	1800
Fr	300	950	43	Est.	198	210	225	242	260	280	306	334	368	410	462	528	620	760	980
Fe	1809	3148	41	1356–1889	1000	1050	1105	1165	1230	1305	1400	1500	1615	1750	1920	2130	2390	2740	3200
Ga(l)	302.9	2676	41	1179–1383	755	796	841	892	950	1015	1090	1180	1280	1405	1555	1745	1980	2300	2730
Gd	1585	3000	43	Est.	880	930	980	1035	1100	1170	1250	1350	1465	1600	1760	1955	2220	2580	3100
Ge	1210	3100	42	1510–1885	940	980	1030	1085	1150	1220	1310	1410	1530	1670	1830	2050	2320	2680	3180

* (s): solid; (l): liquid.

Vapor Pressures for the Solid and Liquid Elements

SYMBOL*	MP(°K)	BP(°K)	CURVE IN FIG.	DATA TEMP. RANGE (°K)	Temperatures (°K) for vapor pressures (torr)														
					10^{-11}	10^{-10}	10^{-9}	10^{-8}	10^{-7}	10^{-6}	10^{-5}	10^{-4}	10^{-3}	10^{-2}	10^{-1}	1	10^{1}	10^{2}	10^{3}
Hf	2400	4745	43	2035–2277	1505	1580	1665	1760	1865	1980	2120	2270	2450	2670	2930	3240	3630	4130	4780
Hg	234.29	629.73	41	193– 575	170	180	190	201	214	229	246	266	289	319	353	398	458	535	642
Ho	1734	2842	43	923–2023	779	822	869	922	981	1050	1125	1220	1325	1450	1605	1800	2060	2410	2910
In(l)	429.3	2364	41	646–1348	641	677	716	761	912	870	937	1015	1110	1220	1355	1520	1740	2030	2430
Ir	2727	4810	41	1986–2600	1585	1665	1755	1850	1960	2080	2220	2380	2560	2770	3040	3360	3750	4250	4900
K	336.4	1031	42	373–1031	247	260	276	294	315	338	364	396	434	481	540	618	720	858	1070
La	1193	3610	41	1655–2167	1100	1155	1220	1295	1375	1465	1570	1695	1835	2000	2200	2450	2760	3150	3680
Li	453.69	1597	41	735–1353	430	452	480	508	541	579	623	677	740	810	900	1020	1170	1370	1620
Lu	1925	3300	43	Est.	1000	1060	1120	1185	1260	1345	1440	1550	1685	1845	2030	2270	2550	2910	3370
Mg	923	1376	41	626–1376	388	410	432	458	487	519	555	600	650	712	782	878	1000	1170	1400
Mn	1517	2309	42	1523–1823	660	695	734	778	827	884	948	1020	1110	1210	1335	1490	1695	1970	2370
Mo	2890	4924	42	2070–2504	1610	1690	1770	1865	1975	2095	2230	2390	2580	2800	3060	3390	3790	4300	5020
Na	370.98	1156.2	42	496–1156	294	310	328	347	370	396	428	466	508	562	630	714	825	978	1175
Nb†	2770	4640	42	2304–2596	1765	1845	1935	2035	2140	2260	2400	2550	2720	2930	3170	3450	3790	4200	4710
Nd	1297	3335	43	1240–1600	846	895	945	1000	1070	1135	1220	1320	1440	1575	1770	2000	2300	2740	3430
Ni	1725	3159	42	1307–1895	1040	1090	1145	1200	1270	1345	1430	1535	1655	1800	1970	2180	2430	2770	3230
Os	3318	5260	41	2300–2800	1875	1965	2060	2170	2290	2430	2580	2760	2960	3190	3460	3800	4200	4710	5340
P(s)	870	704	41		283	297	312	327	342	361	381	402	430	458	493	534	582	642	715
Pb	600.6	2016	42	1200–2028	516	546	580	615	656	702	758	820	898	988	1105	1250	1435	1700	2070
Pd	1823	3310	41	1294–1640	945	995	1050	1115	1185	1265	1355	1465	1590	1735	1920	2150	2450	2840	3380
Po	527	1220	42	711–1286	332	348	365	384	408	432	460	494	537	588	655	743	862	1040	1250
Pr	1208	3295	43	1423–1693	900	950	1005	1070	1140	1220	1315	1420	1550	1700	1890	2120	2420	2820	3370
Pt	2043	4097	41	1697–2042	1335	1405	1480	1565	1655	1765	1885	2020	2180	2370	2590	2860	3190	3610	4170
Pu(l)	913	3508	43	1392–1793	931	983	1040	1105	1180	1265	1365	1480	1615	1780	1975	2230	2550	2980	3590
Ra	973	1800	43	Est.	436	460	488	520	552	590	638	690	755	830	920	1060	1225	1490	1840
Rb	312	974	42		227	240	254	271	289	312	336	367	402	446	500	568	665	802	1000
Re	3453	5960	41	2494–2999	1900	1995	2100	2220	2350	2490	2660	2860	3080	3340	3680	4080	4600	5220	6050

* (s): solid; (l): liquid   † Columbium

(cont.)

VAPOR PRESSURES FOR THE SOLID AND LIQUID ELEMENTS *(cont.)*

SYMBOL*	MP(°K)	BP(°K)	CURVE IN FIG.	DATA TEMP. RANGE (°K)	TEMPERATURES (°K) FOR VAPOR PRESSURES (TORR)														
					10^{-11}	10^{-10}	10^{-9}	10^{-8}	10^{-7}	10^{-6}	10^{-5}	10^{-4}	10^{-3}	10^{-2}	10^{-1}	1	10^{1}	10^{2}	10^{3}
Rh	2239	4000	42	1709–2205	1330	1395	1470	1550	1640	1745	1855	1980	2130	2310	2520	2780	3110	3520	4070
Ru	2700	4392	42	2000–2500	1540	1610	1695	1780	1880	1990	2120	2260	2420	2620	2860	3130	3480	3900	4450
S	388.36	717.75	41		230	240	252	263	276	290	310	328	353	382	420	462	519	606	739
Sb	903	1908	42	693–1110	477	498	526	552	582	618	656	698	748	806	885	1030	1250	1560	1960
Sc	1811	3280	42	1301–1780	881	929	983	1045	1110	1190	1280	1380	1505	1650	1835	2070	2370	2780	3360
Se	490	952	42	550– 950	286	301	317	336	356	380	406	437	472	516	570	636	719	826	972
Si	1685	3418	42	1640–2054	1090	1145	1200	1265	1340	1420	1510	1610	1745	1905	2090	2330	2620	2990	3490
Sm	1345	2076	43	789– 833	542	573	608	644	688	738	790	853	926	1015	1120	1260	1450	1715	2120
Sn(l)	505	2891	42	1424–1753	805	852	900	955	1020	1080	1170	1270	1380	1520	1685	1885	2140	2500	2960
Sr	1043	1640	42		433	458	483	514	546	582	626	677	738	810	900	1005	1160	1370	1680
Ta	3270	5510	42	2624–2948	1930	2020	2120	2230	2370	2510	2680	2860	3080	3330	3630	3980	4400	4930	5580
Tb	1638	3295	43	Est.	900	950	1005	1070	1140	1220	1315	1420	1550	1700	1890	2120	2420	2820	3370
Tc	2400	4900	43	Est.	1580	1665	1750	1840	1950	2060	2200	2350	2530	2760	3030	3370	3790	4300	5000
Te	723	1267	41	481–1128	366	385	405	428	454	482	515	553	596	647	706	791	905	1065	1300
Th	1968	5020	41	1757–1956	1450	1525	1610	1705	1815	1935	2080	2250	2440	2680	2960	3310	3750	4340	5130
Ti	1940	3575	42	1510–1822	1140	1200	1265	1335	1410	1500	1600	1715	1850	2010	2210	2450	2760	3130	3640
Tl	577	1710	42	519– 924	473	499	527	556	592	632	680	736	803	882	979	1100	1255	1460	1750
Tm	1873	2005	43	809–1219	624	655	691	731	776	825	882	953	1030	1120	1235	1370	1540	1760	2060
U	1405.5	4090	43	1630–2071	1190	1255	1325	1405	1495	1600	1720	1855	2010	2200	2430	2720	3080	3540	4180
V	2190	3652	42	1666–1882	1235	1295	1365	1435	1510	1605	1705	1820	1960	2120	2320	2560	2850	3220	3720
W	3650	5800	42	2518–3300	2050	2150	2270	2390	2520	2680	2840	3030	3250	3500	3810	4180	4630	5200	5900
Y	1773	3570	41	1774–2103	1045	1100	1160	1230	1305	1390	1490	1605	1740	1905	2105	2355	2670	3085	3650
Yb	1097	1800	43	Est.	436	460	488	520	552	590	638	690	755	830	920	1060	1225	1490	1840
Zn	692.7	1184	41	422–1089	336	354	374	396	421	450	482	520	565	617	681	760	870	1010	1210
Zr	2128	4747	43	1949–2054	1500	1580	1665	1755	1855	1975	2110	2260	2450	2670	2930	3250	3650	4170	4830

* (l): liquid

Glossary of Terms

Absorption. A condition in which one material is impenetrated into the body of another (*cf.* Adsorption).

Acetone (CH_3COCH_3). A colorless, flammable liquid, miscible with water and alcohols in all proportions; density 0.792 gm per ml; boiling point 56.5°C. Acetone (reagent-grade) is useful for cleaning and degreasing electron tube parts and vacuum pumps, especially diffusion pumps, and for hunting leaks (*vide* Leaks, hunting for). See DEGREASING, p. 7. Mixed with solid CO_2 (dry ice), acetone is capable of producing a refrigerant temperature of −75°C or lower.

Activated carbon is used to remove impurities of a colloidal nature from electroplating solutions. The solution is filtered through it, and the carbon cannot in general be reactivated by washing, and is discarded when exhausted.

Activated charcoal. This material is used for adsorbing gases. The activating process consists of heating in dry air, inert gases, or vacuum to drive off contaminant gases and to produce a network of fine capillary spaces. When used in vacuum systems, the charcoal should not be in particles that are too small in size because the dust may penetrate into unwanted places. The charcoal thus used can be reactivated by heating *in vacuo*.[1, 2]

Activation of oxide-coated cathodes. See pp. 98 *et seq.* A typical schedule for the activation of the cathode in a 6.3-v cathode-ray tube electron gun is as follows:

After the tube is pumped and baked (see pp. 98 *et seq.*), the temperature is allowed to fall to room ambient, and the whole gun is heated gently by induction (see p. 51) to about 300°C for 5 minutes. Simultaneously with the induction-heat step, apply 5.5 v to the heater for 5 minutes or more. Shut off the induction heat

TABLE OF AGING SCHEDULE OF OXIDE-COATED CATHODES

HEATER (VOLTS)	GRID #1 (VOLTS)	GRID #2 (VOLTS)	ANODE #1 (VOLTS)	TIME MINUTES
6.3	0	0	0	1
12.5	0	0	0	$1\frac{1}{2}$
9.0	+5	+150	−100	10
9.0	0	0	0	10
6.3	0	0	0	5

[1] "Rough Pumping with Activated Charcoal," R. L. Jepsen, S. L. Mercer, and M. J. Callaghan, *Rev. Sci. Instr.* **30,** 377, 1959.

[2] "Tube Exhaust Methods Use Simple Gear," J. H. O. Harries, *Electronics,* June 19, 1959.

and raise the heater voltage to 7.5, maintaining it at this value for 5 minutes; then raise to 9 volts and hold for 5 minutes. Raise the voltage to 12.5 and hold for $1\frac{1}{2}$ minutes, then reduce the voltage to 7.5 for a minimum of 5 minutes. The getters are partially fired (p. 105) at this stage. Shut off heater voltage. The tube can be sealed off from the pumps 1 minute after the heater is shut off. At no time is the pressure allowed to rise above 5×10^{-6} torr.

Aging schedule: Aging can be done while the tube is still on the pumps, or it can be done after seal-off. (If done during pumping, the getter should not be fired until just before sealing-off.) See Table on preceding page.

Active cathode alloys. See pp. 93, 293.

Active metals in ceramic-to-metal sealing. See p. 67.

Adhesives and cements (see p. 194).

Adsorption. This is defined as the condensation or adhesion of gases, liquids, or dissolved substances on the *surface* of solids, as distinct from absorption (*cf.* above).

Advance alloy. A nickel-copper resistance alloy having the following properties:

Composition: Ni 43%, Cu 57%; specific resistivity at 20°C 49 microhm-cm or 294 ohms/cir mil ft; temperature coefficient of resistivity ±0.00002 (20°–100°C); specific heat 0.094 gm-cal/gm/°C; thermal conductivity 0.059 cgs[1] at 100°C. Approximate melting point 1210°C; coefficient of linear expansion 14.9×10^{-6}/°C at 20°–100°C; tensile strength at 20°C 60,000–100,000 psi. Density 8.9 gm/cc or 0.321 lb/in^3.

This alloy is useful for winding heavy-duty rheostats because of its high resistance and noncorroding properties. In finer sizes, its very small temperature coefficient of resistivity makes it useful for winding precision resistors over a limited temperature range. A gas-free grade suitable for electronic tube use is marketed as Advance II.

Advance is widely used as one of the elements in thermocouples, against copper, iron, and platinum. The alloy is similar to Constantan (*vide*). (See Thermocouples p. 525.)

Aging of cathodes (see ACTIVATION OF OXIDE-COATED CATHODES, above).

Aging of thoriated filaments (see p. 89).

Air (see ATMOSPHERE, p. 159).

Alcohols. The table below gives the properties of four common alcohols.

ALCOHOL:	METHYL	ETHYL	ISOPROPYL	BUTYL (*n*)
Synonym:	Methanol	Ethanol	2-Propanol	1-Butanol
Formula:	CH_3OH	CH_3CH_2OH	$CH_3CHOHCH_3$	$CH_3(CH_2)CH_2OH$
Melting point (°C)	−97.8	−115	−89	−89.5
Melting point (°F)	−144	−175	−128	−129
Boiling point (°C)	64.7	78.5	82.3	117.7
Boiling point (°F)	148	173	180	244
Density (gm/cm^3)	0.793	0.789	0.785	0.81
Molecular weight	32.04	46.07	60.09	74.12
Refractive index	1.331	1.362	1.377	1.399
Solubility in water (gm/ml at 20°C)	Inf	Inf	Inf	7.9

[1] See p. 520.

Because they will remove water, methyl and ethyl alcohols are suitable (in reagent-grade) for use as a dip preliminary to drying tube parts. Since methyl alcohol is more easily obtainable in pure form, it is frequently used for removing water. Isopropyl alcohol is sometimes applied as an additive to CO_2 gas used as a protective atmosphere for brazing, etc. The CO_2 is simply bubbled through the isopropyl alcohol, which decomposes on the heated surfaces to form carbon monoxide and hydrogen, both of which have a reducing (i.e., deoxidizing) effect.

Altitude and vacuum comparison (See H. E. Newell, Jr., *Science,* **131,** 385, 1960.)

ALTITUDE		PRESSURE torr	ALTITUDE		PRESSURE torr
MILES	FEET		MILES	FEET	
20	105,600	6.4	150	792,000	8×10^{-8}
40	211,200	0.19	200	1,056,000	9×10^{-9}
60	316,800	3.9×10^{-3}	250	1,320,000	2.5×10^{-9}
80	422,400	1.7×10^{-4}	300	1,584,000	8×10^{-10}
100	528,000	6.0×10^{-6}	426	2,250,000	1×10^{-10}

Alumel alloy. This was developed by the Hoskins Manufacturing Company (Detroit, Michigan) especially for use as the negative element, opposing Chromel P (Hoskins) as the positive element, in thermocouples. It has the composition Ni 94%, Mn 3%, Al 2%, Si 1%. Chromel-Alumel thermocouples are useful up to about 1350°C. (See Thermocouples p. 525.)

Alumina (see ALUMINUM OXIDE).

Alumina, activated, use in vacuum systems: It is reported[1, 2, 3] that backstreaming (p. 161) in vacuum systems using oil diffusion pumps can be minimized by the insertion of a trap containing activated alumina[4] or artificial zeolite[5]. The trap may be refrigerated in the conventional way (pp. 211–212), or an unrefrigerated trap of metal or glass can be used. Copper foil traps have also been used with some success.[2]

Periodic baking-out appears to be required because both the activated alumina and the artificial zeolite are susceptible to saturation with gases and vapors. If the materials are exposed to the atmosphere, some moisture is absorbed, but recovery is attained after pumping and baking. The alumina can be baked at temperatures up to 1000°C and the zeolite up to 600°C, but bake-out temperatures of 450°C are more common. Harris[2] makes use of a heater and a thermocouple built into the trap so that the actual temperature of the material can be determined.

---

[1] M. A. Biondi, *Rev. Sci. Instr.,* **30,** 831, 1959.

[2] L. A. Harris, *ibid.,* **31,** 903, 1960.

[3] M. A. Biondi, Paper No. 6 presented at American Vacuum Society Symposium, Cleveland, Ohio, October, 1960.

[4] Grade F-1, 8–14 mesh activated alumina; Aluminum Company of America, Pittsburgh 19, Pennsylvania.

[5] An alkali-metal aluminosilicate. The type used was 13X, manufactured by the Linde Company Division of Union Carbide Corp., New York, New York. *Cf.* p. 377.

Biondi[1] reports that alumina is slightly less effective as a trapping agent than zeolite, but is more stable in baking. Neither of the materials appears to be effective with mercury vapor.

Aluminum. In pure form, a ductile metal having good electrical conductivity, sometimes used in tube structures, especially in gas-discharge devices because of its freedom from sputtering. Aluminum is difficult to outgas thoroughly because of its relatively low melting point (660°C). Aluminum alloys have a wide range of mechanical properties. Soft aluminum (2S, 2SO)[2] is useful for making metal gaskets for demountable vacuum systems (see pp. 117–118) which are to be baked at temperatures not higher than 450°C. Aluminum is nonmagnetic, having a susceptibility (paramagnetic) of 0.65×10^{-6} cgs. See below for other properties.

Properties of Aluminum

Atomic weight	26.98
Melting point (°C)	646–657
Boiling point (°C)	2057
Specific gravity	2.7(20°C)
Density (lb/in³)	0.098
Electrical resistivity at 20°C (microhm-cm)	2.828
Conductivity (% IACS)	63
Thermal conductivity (cgs)	
−160°C	0.514
+ 20°C	0.57
300°C	0.64
400°C	0.76
600°C	1.01
Coefficient of linear thermal expansion in/in $\times 10^{-6}$ (commercial)	
20–100°C	24.0
20–300	26.7
20–600	28.7
Temperature coefficient of electrical resistivity	
25°C	0.0034
100	0.004
500	0.005
Specific heat (gm-cal/gm/°C)	
−250°C	0.0039
−100	0.1676
20	0.214
100	0.225
300	0.248
600	0.277
660 (liq)	0.25
Photoelectric work function	4.08
Mechanical properties (thickness 0.006–0.019 inch)	
Ultimate tensile strength (psi)	14,000 max.
Yield strength (psi)	4000
Elongation in 2 inches (%)	15 min.
Modulus of elasticity	
psi in tension	9.9×10^6
psi in compression	10.1×10^6
Resistance to corrosion	excellent
Weldability	excellent
Machinability	poor

[1] M. A. Biondi, Paper No. 6 presented at American Vacuum Society Symposium, Cleveland, Ohio, October, 1960.

[2] Some producers designate this as aluminum alloy No. 1100. It is approximately 99.0% pure. A higher purity (99.6%) is known as EC grade (Alcoa).

Aluminum oxide (ALUMINA, ALUNDUM, SAPPHIRE). Industrial alumina is a chemically inert, highly refractory material consisting mainly of Al_2O_3. It has a high electrical resistivity, good thermal conductivity, resistance to reduction, density, and non-porosity. At 1700°–1800°C it resists attack by all gases except fluorine. Fused Al_2O_3 has the following properties:

Purity	99.5%
Melting point °C	2000–2045
Maximum usable temperature	1950°C
Working temperature	1700°C
Density, specific gravity	3.95
Coefficient of linear thermal expansion	5×10^{-6}/°C (0–1000°C)
Specific heat (gm-cal/gm/°C)	0.21–0.27i
Hardness (Mohs' scale)	9.0
Tensile strength (psi; thousands)	25–27
Compressive strength (psi; thousands)	275–290
Flexural strength (psi; thousands)	40–65
Modulus elasticity (psi; millions)	40.2
Impact resistance, (in-lbs) (Charpy)	7.6
Porosity	gas-tight
Color	white (slightly grayish after H_2 firing)
Thermal conductivity (cgs) at	
20°C	0.047
38	0.052
430	0.083
870	0.104
Dielectric strength (volts/mil)	250
Volume resistivity (ohm/cm³) at	
25°C	$>10^{14}$
100	3×10^{12}
300	1.4×10^{10}
500	3.4×10^{8}
700	2×10^{8}
900	6×10^{7}
Te value (temperature at which 1 cm³ has a resistance of 1 megohm)	1000°C 1832°F
Dielectric constant	
1 Mc	9.4
10,000 Mc	9.2
Power factor, 1 Mc	0.0003
10,000 Mc	0.0008
Loss factor, 1 Mc	0.0028
10,000 Mc	0.0074

The properties given above are approximate. There is some variation among the various manufacturers (see table on next page).

Coors Dense High-strength Alumina Ceramics

MECHANICAL AND ELECTRICAL PROPERTIES

PROPERTY	UNITS	AD-85 (85% Al_2O_3—FORMERLY TYPE AB-2)	AD-94 (94% Al_2O_3—FORMERLY TYPE Al-200)	AD-96 (96% Al_2O_3—FORMERLY TYPE El-95)	AD-99 (99% Al_2O_3)	AD-995 (99.5% Al_2O_3)
Tensile strength						
70°F>(21° C)	psi	17,000–18,000	25,000–27,000	26,000–28,000	34,000–35,000	—
2000°F>(1093° C)	psi	8,000–9,000	9,000–10,000	13,000–14,000	21,000–22,000	—
Compressive strength	psi	Over 240,000	Over 300,000	Over 300,000	Over 300,000	Over 350,000
Flexural strength*						
70°F	psi	40,000–45,000	45,000–50,000	47,000–52,000	47,000–60,000	43,000–55,000
2000°F	psi	10,000–15,000	15,000–20,000	21,000–26,000	23,000–28,000	26,000–31,000
Modulus of elasticity	psi	31.9×10^6	40.2×10^6	42×10^6	50×10^6	50×10^6
Impact resistance	inch/lb. (Charpy)	6.8	7.6	—	—	—
Specific gravity*		3.38–3.44	3.58–3.64	3.68–3.74	3.80–3.90	3.82–3.87
Water absorption		None	None	None	None	None
Porosity		Gas tight†	Gas tight†	Gas tight†	Gas tight†	Gas tight†
Hardness	Rockwell 45N	75	78	78	80	81
Color		White	White	White	White	Pink
Working temperature (max.)	°C (°F)	1400(2550)	1700(3100)	1700(3100)	1725(3140)	1750(3182)
Specific heat	Btu/lb	0.18	0.19	0.19	0.20	0.20
Thermal conductivity	$Btu/hr/ft^2/°F/in.$					
70°F		92	140	140	202	202
600°F		50	74	74	108	108

PROPERTY	UNITS	AD-85 °F	AD-85 °C	AD-94 °F	AD-94 °C	AD-96 °F	AD-96 °C	AD-99 °F	AD-99 °C	AD-995 °F	AD-995 °C
Thermal coefficients of expansion	Per degree as noted										
−240° to 70°F (−151° to 21°C)		1.6×10^{-6}	2.9×10^{-6}	1.7×10^{-6}	3.1×10^{-6}	1.5×10^{-6}	2.7×10^{-6}	1.5×10^{-6}	2.7×10^{-6}	—	—
70° to 500°F (21° to 260°C)		3.3×10^{-6}	5.9×10^{-6}	3.7×10^{-6}	6.7×10^{-6}	3.7×10^{-6}	6.7×10^{-6}	3.5×10^{-6}	6.3×10^{-6}	3.8×10^{-6}	6.8×10^{-6}
500° to 1000°F (260° to 538°C)		5.0×10^{-6}	9.0×10^{-6}	4.2×10^{-6}	7.6×10^{-6}	4.6×10^{-6}	8.3×10^{-6}	4.5×10^{-6}	8.1×10^{-6}	4.6×10^{-6}	8.3×10^{-6}
1000° to 1800°F (538° to 982°C)		4.9×10^{-6}	8.8×10^{-6}	4.9×10^{-6}	8.8×10^{-6}	5.0×10^{-6}	9.0×10^{-6}	5.0×10^{-6}	9.0×10^{-6}	5.1×10^{-6}	9.2×10^{-6}

70° to 1800°F (21° to 982°C)		4.21×10^{-6}	7.58×10^{-6}		4.39×10^{-6}	7.91×10^{-6}		4.56×10^{-6}	8.22×10^{-6}		4.51×10^{-6}	8.12×10^{-6}		4.62×10^{-6}	8.33×10^{-6}	
Resistivity (ohms)																
25°C			$>10^{14}$			$>10^{14}$			$>10^{14}$			$>10^{14}$			—	
300°			4.6×10^{10}			9.0×10^{11}			3.1×10^{11}			1.0×10^{13}			—	
500°			4.0×10^{8}			2.5×10^{9}			4.0×10^{9}			6.3×10^{10}			—	
700°			7.0×10^{6}			5.0×10^{7}			1.0×10^{8}			5.0×10^{8}			—	
1000°			—			5.0×10^{5}			1.0×10^{6}			2.0×10^{6}			—	
Te value	°C		850			950			1000			1050			—	
Dielectric strength 25°C (ASTM $\frac{1}{4}$ inch thick specimens)	rms volts/mil 60 cycle ac Tests under oil		210–260 (330 for $\frac{1}{8}$ inch thick spec.)			220–240 (330 for $\frac{1}{8}$ inch thick spec.)			220–240 (330 for $\frac{1}{8}$ inch thick spec.)			220–240 (330 for $\frac{1}{8}$ inch thick spec.)			220–245 (330 for $\frac{1}{8}$ inch thick spec.)	
		25°C	500°C	800°C	25°C	500°C	800°C	25°C	500°C	800°C	25°C	500°C	800°C	25°C	500°C	800°C
Dielectric constant																
1 kc		8.18	13.86	—	8.89	11.76	—	8.97	10.92	—	9.30	11.25	—	—	—	—
1 mc		8.16	8.87	—	8.87	9.64	—	8.95	9.65	—	9.30	10.09	—	9.67	10.26	—
100 mc		8.16	—	—	8.93	9.4	—	8.95	9.45	—	9.30	9.88	—	—	—	—
85 kmc		8.08	8.26	—	8.75	9.05	—	8.90	9.40	9.90	9.30	9.88	—	9.44	9.88	10.3
14 kmc		—	—	—	8.72	9.05	9.41	8.90	9.40	9.90	9.30	9.85	10.41	9.58	10.06	10.55
24 kmc		—	—	—	8.72	9.05	9.41	8.90	9.40	9.90	9.30	9.85	10.41	9.22	9.67	9.98
50 kmc		—	—	—	8.67	—	—	8.70	—	—	9.30	—	—	—	—	—
Loss tangent (Tan δ)																
1 kc		0.0014	0.580	—	0.00019	0.215	—	0.0011	0.20	—	0.0042	0.14	—	—	—	—
1 mc		0.0009	0.024	—	0.000085	0.0078	—	0.000084	0.0039	—	0.0015	0.0052	—	0.00009	0.0023	—
100 mc		0.0009	—	—	0.00052	—	—	0.00024	—	—	0.00006	—	—	—	—	—
8.5 kmc		0.0014	—	—	0.001	—	0.0030	0.0006	0.0008	0.0028	0.00013	0.00017	0.00057	0.00008	0.00028	0.0006
14 kmc		0.0014	0.0033	—	0.0011	0.0018	0.0034	0.0007	0.001	0.0031	—	0.0002	0.00047	0.00020	0.00025	0.00042
24 kmc		—	—	—	0.0011	0.0025	0.0059	0.0082	0.0012	0.0032	0.00024	0.00025	0.00034	0.00034	0.00045	0.0007
50 kmc		—	—	—	0.0021	—	—	0.0068	—	—	0.00052	—	—	—	—	—
Loss factor																
1 kc		0.011	8.04	—	0.0017	2.53	—	0.0099	2.2	—	0.039	1.6	—	—	—	—
1 mc		0.0074	0.21	—	0.00075	0.075	—	0.00075	0.038	—	0.014	0.052	—	0.0008	0.023	—
100 mc		0.0074	—	—	0.0046	—	—	0.0022	—	—	0.0006	—	—	—	—	—
8.5 kmc		0.011	—	—	0.0087	—	—	0.005	0.007	0.028	0.0012	0.0017	—	0.0009	0.0028	0.006
14 kmc		—	—	—	0.0096	0.016	0.032	0.006	0.009	0.031	—	0.002	0.0049	0.002	0.0025	0.0044
24 kmc		—	—	—	0.0096	0.023	0.055	0.073	0.011	0.032	0.0022	0.0025	0.0035	0.0031	0.0044	0.007
50 kmc		—	—	—	0.018	—	—	0.059	—	—	0.0048	—	—	—	—	—

* Flexural strength and specific gravity values vary somewhat with method of manufacture and with the sizes of the parts. The ranges of values listed in this table take into account this total variation. Among similar parts formed in the same manner, the range is less than the above values would imply.

† Gas tight by helium mass spectrometer.

Aluminum oxide is useful in making ceramic-to-metal seals by the processes described on p. 67.

Because of its great hardness, aluminum oxide cannot be machined in the fired state, except by grinding. When it is necessary to do extensive machining on ceramic materials, other bodies should be used. (See LAVA pp. 196, 340–342 and BORON NITRIDE pp. 168 *et seq.*)

Industrial synthetic SAPPHIRE (100% Al_2O_3), as supplied by the Linde Company Division of Union Carbide Corp., New York, New York, is available in the form of windows, rods, tubing, boules, and other shapes. It is used as supports and spacers for vacuum-tube and microwave apparatus, as windows for klystrons and magnetrons, and as components for various ultraviolet and infrared devices. Some of the characteristics of this single-crystal nonporous material are given on p. 466.

Alundum is a trade name for aluminum oxide. See ALUMINUM OXIDE, above. Alundum is one of the materials used for coating tungsten heaters (Norton Company's No. 38–900 Special Acid-Washed). The procedure is described on p. 81 (sprayed coating) and on p. 85 (cataphoretic coating).

Alundum cement. This is an impure form of aluminum oxide mixed with other materials. It is used for constructing furnaces, setting firebrick, etc. It is usually mixed with water for application, allowed to dry thoroughly, and then cured by heating to temperatures above red heat. The exact temperature will be determined for the particular formulation. These cements are made by the Norton Company, Worcester, Massachusetts.

Ammonia, dissociated or cracked. Since ammonia gas is composed of 75% hydrogen and 25% nitrogen, by the use of commercially available dissociators, these gases can be separated and the mixture used in many heat-treating processes where hydrogen is called for. Because ammonia gas (NH_3) can be obtained commercially in an anhydrous form, the dissociated gas mixture has a very low moisture content, or dew point. Also, ammonia is considerably cheaper than hydrogen. (**Caution:** cracked ammonia is flammable and explosive, much like hydrogen.)

In some procedures the presence of nitrogen may cause nitriding (in some steels, for example), and for this reason the manufacturer of the metal or alloy should be consulted before heat-treating it in dissociated ammonia.

Amoil (see pp. 400, 401).

Amplification factor (see pp. 546 *et seq.*).

Angstrom unit, or **Angstrom.** A unit of length used in the measurement of light wavelengths and very thin films. It has the value: $A = 10^{-8}$ cm $= 10^{-7}$ mm $= 10^{-4}$ microns $= 10^{-1}$ millimicrons.

Annealing of glass. See pp. 267 *et seq.* Many pieces of shaped or blown glass are annealed before assembly, but after the metal parts of a tube are mounted in the glass envelope, annealing is usually not feasible because the high temperature would oxidize the metal elements unless a protective atmosphere is used. For this reason it is expedient to seal the tube onto the vacuum system, pump it, and bake as soon as possible after the last glassworking operation so that the bake-out performs the double function of outgassing and annealing on the glass.

Annealing of stainless steel (see pp. 41 *et seq.*)

Anode. The element in an electron tube which is at a positive potential with respect to the cathode and other elements, and thus attracts electrons, which are carried to the external circuit and are manifested as an electric current. The anode is also called the PLATE.

Anode, electroplating. The element in the plating bath which is connected to the positive side of the dc power supply. In most normal plating baths, such as silver, copper, gold, nickel, etc., the anode is in the form of a piece of the metal in a purified form. Thus, for silver plating, the anode would be a piece of silver in the form of a plate, sheet, rod, or wire. The shape used should be appropriate to the work in hand so as to obtain best "throwing power" (ability to plate into depressions, holes, cavities). The anode slowly dissolves in the bath, replacing the metal ions deposited on the work from the solution.

In some types of plating, and especially in electropolishing baths, the anode may be a passive element used only for the purpose of conducting the current into the bath. Steel, lead, stainless steel, carbon, and other materials are used (pp. 23 *et seq.*).

For some procedures, e.g., electropolishing, the work itself is made the anode for the purpose of removing metal.

Anodes, incandescent (see ELECTRON BOMBARDMENT).

Anodes, rotating. To prevent excessive evaporation or erosion of anodes or targets in high-power tubes (chiefly X-ray tubes), a method has been devised to rotate the anode or target, either by an external motor with vacuum-sealed coupling or by a motor or driven rotor inside the tube.[1]

Antimony (see Table of Vapor Pressures on pp. 144, 148). Solders or alloys containing antimony are not to be used in the construction of electron tubes or vacuum devices which are to be heated above room temperature.

Apiezon. A trade name for various products including vacuum waxes, greases, oils, and plastic cements made in England and sold in the United States by the J. G. Biddle Company, Philadelphia, Pennsylvania. The table on the next page shows some of the properties of these products.

Aquadag. Trade name for a proprietary colloidal suspension of graphite in water. Made by the Acheson Colloids Company, Port Huron, Michigan. Aquadag has 22% solids of fine-particle size in paste form, which can be diluted or thinned with distilled water. It has a density of 9.35 lb/gal. Meets U.S. Army Specification 2-130. Other suspensions of graphite in alcohol, water, nitrocellulose lacquer, glycerine, petroleum oil, castor oil, and alkyd resin are produced by the company. Some of these materials are useful for providing an electrically conductive coating inside glass tubes, to carry off electrostatic charges, etc. A tungsten and platinum whisker can be sealed into Pyrex for making contact, or buttons of Kovar or other alloys appropriate to particular glasses can be sealed into the tube wall (see pp. 58, 59 for combinations of glass-to-metal seals). In the use of Aquadag, adding 2–3% of potassium or sodium silicate to the suspension gives a tenaciously adhering conducting coating after baking at about 350°C. The coating is scratch-resisting, and will withstand a 450°C bake-out. See pp. 199 *et seq.*

Arc. A low-voltage arc can occur in a gas tube whose cathode is heated to incandescence, a phenomenon which is utilized in rectifier tubes. An alternating voltage applied to such a tube causes a heavy current to flow when the cathode is negative, but no current passes when the cathode is positive, since the anode does not emit electrons. However, if the voltage is made high enough, a gas discharge can occur with a negative anode; this is called flashback, and it must be avoided completely in rectifiers (see p. 288).

---

[1] A. Taylor, *J. Sci. Instr.*, **26**, 225, 1949; A. Taylor, *Rev. Sci. Instr.*, **27**, 757, 1956. (See also MOTION THROUGH VACUUM JOINTS in this Glossary.)

APIEZON OILS, GREASES, AND WAXES*

PRODUCT	APPLICATION AND USE	VAPOR PRESSURE (torr) AFTER EVOLUTION OF DISSOLVED AIR	MAXIMUM TEMPERATURE FOR SAFE USE (°C)	TEMPERATURE FOR APPLICATION
Oil A	Diffusion pumps	10^{-5} at room temperature		
Oil B	Diffusion pumps	10^{-7} at room temperature		
Oil C	Diffusion pumps	10^{-8} (approx.) at room temperature		
Oil J	Oil-sealed stopcocks, also places where a moderately viscous oil of low-vapor pressure is required	10^{-3} at 250°C; 10^{-8} (approx.) at room temperature		
Oil K	For places where an exceedingly viscous oil of low-vapor pressure is required	10^{-3} at 300°C; 10^{-9} to 10^{-10} at room temperature		
Grease L	Well-fitting ground joints (not for stopcocks).	10^{-3} at 300°C; 10^{-10} to 10^{-11} at room temperature	30	Room temperature
Grease M	For places where a grease of moderately low-vapor pressure is required	10^{-3} at 200°C; 10^{-7} to 10^{-8} at room temperature	30	Room temperature
Grease N	Glass stopcocks	10^{-3} at 200°C; 10^{-8} to 10^{-9} at room temperature	30	Room temperature
Grease T	For places where a grease of high melting point is required	10^{-8} (approx.) at room temperature	Up to 110	Room temperature
Soft wax Q (seal compound)	Unground joints	10^{-4} at room temperature	30	Room temperature
Med. soft wax W-40 (seal compound)	Semipermanent joints	10^{-3} at room temperature	30	40° to 50°C
Med. hard wax W-100 (seal compound)	Semipermanent joints	10^{-3} at room temperature	50	80°C
Hard wax W (seal compound)	Permanent joints	10^{-3} at 180°C	80	100°C

* These products are made in England and sold in the United States by the J. G. Biddle Company, Philadelphia, Pennsylvania, by whose courtesy this table is reproduced here.

Argon. (A). One of the rare, inert, or noble, gases comprising 0.94% of the earth's atmosphere. It is colorless, odorless, and nontoxic and does not combine with any other element. It is used in electronic and discharge devices, imparting the characteristic red fluorescence at pressures of about 3 torr.

Some of the properties of argon are as follows:

Atomic weight	39.944
Atomic number	18
Melting point, °C	−189.2
Boiling point, °C	−185.7
Density, gm/liters at 0°C	1.7837
Density, gm/liters at −186°C (liquid)	1.40
Density, gm/liters at −233°C (crystalline solid)	1.65

The solubilities in water of argon, oxygen, and nitrogen are:

	SOLUBILITY IN WATER AT		
	0°C	50°C	40°C
Argon	5.6 cm^3	3.01 cm^3	
Oxygen	4.89 cm^3	2.46 cm^3	
Nitrogen	2.33 cm^3		1.42

Armco iron. A highly purified form of domestic iron used for magnetic purposes with appropriate heat treatment. (See IRON, pp. 307 *et seq.*)

Asbestos. A heat-resistant mineral fiber. It is commercially combined with small amounts of organic binders and fibers such as paper and cotton, and sold as asbestos paper, textiles, and millboard. **Transite** is asbestos combined with portland cement. Asbestos products are not suitable for internal electron tube structures but are useful around the laboratory in making ovens, in glass-blowing, and in brazing and induction-heating procedures. Asbestos products should not be used in the hydrogen furnace because of their large gas and water porosity. (See also MARINITE, p. 356.)

Assembly of tubes (see pp. 2, 128).

Atmosphere. A unit of pressure (1 atm) equal to 760 mm of mercury (760 torr) at 0°C, which is the pressure of the earth's atmosphere at sea level. The mean free path is

$$6.5 \times 10^{-6} \text{ cm}, \quad \text{density } 13.595 \text{ gm/cm}^3.$$

The pressure of 1 atm is equal to

$$1.0133 \text{ bars} = 14.696 \text{ lb/in.}^2 = 1.0581 \text{ tons/ft}^2 = 29.921 \text{ in. of mercury}$$

at

$$32°\text{F} = 2116.2 \text{ lb/ft}^2 = 1033.2 \text{ gm/cm}^2 = 1.0133 \times 10^6 \text{ d/cm}^2 = 1.0332 \times 10^4 \text{ kg/m}^2.$$

Atmosphere is also a gas or mixture of gases surrounding an object or contained in a vessel.

Air (dry) has the following approximate composition:

CONSTITUENT GAS	MOLECULAR FRACTION (PERCENT)	MOLECULAR WEIGHT (O = 16.000)
Nitrogen (N_2)	78.09	28.016
Oxygen (O_2)	20.95	32.0000
Argon* (A)	0.93	39.944
Carbon dioxide (CO_2)	0.03	44.010
Neon* (Ne)	1.8×10^{-3}	20.183
Helium* (He)	5.24×10^{-4}	4.003
Krypton* (Kr)	1.0×10^{-4}	83.7
Hydrogen (H_2)	5.0×10^{-5}	2.0160
Xenon* (Xe)	8.0×10^{-6}	131.3
Ozone (O_3)	1.0×10^{-6}	48.0000
Radon* (Rn)	6.0×10^{-18}	222.

* The noble or inert gases. Compounds of some of the noble gases with other elements have been prepared. See R. J. Gillespie, in *Noble-Gas Compounds,* H. H. Hyman, Ed., University of Chicago Press, Chicago, 1963; H. Selig, *et al, Science,* **143,** 1322, 1964; B. Jaselskis, *ibid,* p. 1324.

Atmosphere, protective. This term denotes a gas or combination of gases used in heat-treating materials, by which oxidation or other undesirable chemical changes are inhibited or prevented. The gas may exclude oxidation by virtue of its inertness (helium, argon, neon, and, in certain cases, nitrogen and carbon dioxide), or it may protect by *reduction* of oxides (hydrogen, dissociated ammonia, carbon monoxide, carbon dioxide plus isopropyl alcohol vapor). The gas or gas mixture is usually flowing at a low rate through the furnace chamber or muffle and, in the case of H_2, CO, and cracked ammonia, can be burned off outside the furnace if this is desirable. In certain glassblowing operations, nitrogen, CO_2, *forming gas* (mixtures of hydrogen and nitrogen in various proportions), argon or helium can be introduced into the glass vessel in order to protect oxidizable metal parts during torching. (See FURNACE BRAZING, pp. 35 *et seq.* and OVENS AND HEATERS, p. 417.)

Atom, metastable. Ionized atoms, produced by collision with electrons, usually can exist for only a very short time (e.g., of the order of 10^{-8} second for neon). The transition to a stable state results in the emission of light. A few ionized atoms, however, exist at a special energy-level for a much longer time (0.1 second or more for neon) and are consequently able to ionize other atoms, thus making a large contribution to the ionization of the gas. This special energy level (16.6 ev for neon) is called the metastable state. It is thought that the pumping of the noble gases by getter-ion pumps is accomplished partially by exciting the gas atoms into this metastable state, during which the metastable ion can diffuse into the getter metal in a manner analogous to the diffusion of hydrogen into metals. When the metastable ion returns to the stable or ground state, it is thus already trapped and cannot diffuse back into the vacuum chamber. (See F. M. Penning, *Electrical Discharges in Gases,* pp. 14, 15. Macmillan Co., New York, New York.)

Austenitic stainless steels. This group of alloys takes its name from the presence of austenite, a solid solution of carbon in gamma iron. Austenite is relatively soft and ductile. Austenitic stainless steels [the so-called 18 (Cr) – 8 (Ni) types] are essentially nonmagnetic when annealed, although some magnetism may exist in cold-worked specimens. It is a very useful alloy in vacuum-tube work. The AISI (American Steel and Iron Institute) types 200 and 300 are austenitic (see **Stainless steels,** pp. 499 *et seq.*)

Avogadro's principle (see GAS LAWS, p. 265).

Back-diffusion. Same as backstreaming.

Backstreaming.[1] In a vacuum system employing a diffusion pump, a small number of the fluid-pump vapor molecules move in a contrary direction and may actually enter the tube or vessel being evacuated. This effect is minimized by cold-trapping, baffling, or gettering, or a combination of all these. In the case of oil-vapor molecules, decomposition occurs when the particles strike a hot surface (cathodes, filaments, anodes, etc.) to form carbon and various carbon compounds, some of which may be injurious to tube components, especially oxide-coated cathodes. (*Cf.* COLD CAP and COLD FINGER, p. 209; and COLD TRAP, p. 211. Also see pp. 75, 99, 110.)

Baffle, vacuum. A device to prevent the straight-line flow of gases and vapors but with a minimum of impedance to such flow. Oil particles (see BACKSTREAMING), for example, will strike the baffle plates, fins, or other surfaces and be retained there. If such a baffle is cooled or refrigerated, condensible materials are largely prevented from moving past its cooled surfaces. (See also COLD TRAP, p. 211 and *cf.* CHEVRON BAFFLE, p. 199.)

Bake-out. Tubes or vessels undergoing exhaust are heated one or more times during the process to drive out water vapor and other adsorbed gases from tube-component surfaces. The vessel is baked during initial exhaust and, if an oxide-cathode is present, again after conversion (activation or breakdown). (See pp. 98, 101.) Vacuum vessels are baked at temperatures which will be safely endured by the materials present; e.g. Pyrex glass at 500°C, nonex glass at 450°C, all-stainless steel (heliarc-welded or hydrogen-brazed copper-gold joints—no glass) at 800° to 1000°C.

Bakelite. A generic trade name for plastic products of the Bakelite Corp. Popularly, and more specifically, the word refers to phenolic insulating materials, with paper, cloth, or other types of filler-bases. Phenolics are not suitable for use in vacuum systems because of the continuously volatile nature of one or more of their ingredients.

Ballast pump, gas. At low pressures, certain vapors and gases (e.g., water vapor) condense and can thus mix with and contaminate the pump oil. The emulsion or mixture thus formed has a higher vapor pressure than clean oil and consequently reduces the degree of ultimate attainable pressure. To overcome this effect, some means, such as a valve, is provided to admit a controlled and timed amount of air into the exhaust or compression stage of the pump. Because pressure is increasing, the contaminating vapors are less apt to condense, since they are diluted by the air ballast, which provides a vehicle for carrying the unwanted vapors through the exhaust port into the atmosphere. Gas-ballast pumps are generally provided with a hand-valve to regulate the flow of air, so that as the vapors are removed, the air flow may gradually be reduced and eventually shut off entirely. Such pumps operate

---

[1] For a discussion of the measurement of backstreaming of diffusion pump oil tagged with a radioactive isotope, see "How Vacuum Tube Problems Are Solved by the Use of Radioisotopes," H. A. Stern, *Vacuum,* **11,** 2, 60, 1961.

at somewhat higher temperatures than those without gas-ballast because of the additional work performed by the mechanism in compressing the air.

Ballast tank. In a vacuum system comprising mechanical pumps, it is sometimes necessary to shut down these pumps temporarily; for example, to stop vibration while observations are made on sensitive devices, while at the same time maintaining the pumping via the diffusion pumps. This can be achieved by having a relatively large chamber or vessel between the forepump stopcock (or valve) and the diffusion pump which, when pumped down to forevacuum pressure, acts as a reservoir to back up the diffusion pump for a length of time dependent on the forevacuum pressure and the volume of the vessel. When such a vessel or tank is installed in a vacuum system, the pump-down time will, of course, be increased. A thermocouple or other type of forepressure gauge is placed in or near the ballast tank, and this can be arranged to restart the forepump automatically when the pressure rises to a predetermined value.

Barium. A soft, silvery-white metallic element of the alkaline earth group, atomic number 56, atomic weight 137.37, melting point 850°C, boiling point 1140°C, specific gravity 3.78 or 0.136 lb/in^3. It is slightly paramagnetic, having a susceptibility of 0.9×10^6 cgs.

Barium has two uses of importance in electron tube technology: (a) as barium oxide (plus strontium and sometimes calcium oxides), widely used in the so-called oxide-coated cathode, a substance with low work function and therefore a copious emitter of electrons at relatively low temperatures (see pp. 96 *et seq.*); and (b) as metallic barium for use as a getter material which aids in the removal of residual gases[1] (see pp. 105 *et seq.*).

Barium getters (see pp. 105 *et seq.*).

Barium pumps[1] (see above).

Bases for tubes. Most experimental tubes are not fitted with bases because there is such a great variety of sizes and shapes, many of which are not standard. This operation for tubes, requiring some kind of basing, is usually done after seal-off. For a listing of commonly used bases, the reader is referred to manufacturers' literature, such as the *RCA Tube Handbook,* HB-3, Vol. 1–2. Bases and caps having from 1 to 35 pins or terminals are listed.

Bayard-Alpert gauge. The commonly used ionization gauge consists of an emitter (tungsten or other material), an electron collector (grid), and an ion collector (plate) arranged concentrically with the emitter in the approximate center. The electron collector grid is made positive and the ion collector negative with respect to the emitter so that gas molecules are bombarded by electrons accelerated by the grid. These become ionized as a result and migrate to the ion collector plate, giving rise to a small current which is thus a measure of the concentration of gas molecules present. It has been found that at pressures below about 10^{-8} torr, the very small ion current is obscured by a background current which is caused largely by a minute X-ray effect within the tube. This effect appears to be roughly proportional to the surface area of the ion collector, which in the conventional ionization gauge is quite large. Bayard and Alpert[2] radically altered the configuration of the ioniza-

---

[1] See "Barium Absorption Pumps for High Vacuum Systems," R. W. Cloud, L. Beckman, and J. G. Trump, *Rev. Sci. Instr.,* **28,** 889–892, 1957.

[2] R. Bayard and D. Alpert, *Rev. Sci. Instr.,* **21,** 571, 1950.

tion gauge by (a) moving the emitter to the outside of the other elements, so that its electron effect on the grid and ion collector is reduced, and (b) reducing the surface area of the ion collector by making it a thin wire in the center, so that the number of electrons it "sees" is enormously reduced. The sensitivity is compensated for by amplification. Because the X-ray effect is thus greatly minimized, pressures down to 10^{-11} torr[1] can be indicated. (See also p. 303.)

Beading of glass. The sealing of wires into glass presses and vessels is greatly facilitated by applying a small bead of glass to the wire at the site of sealing. This is usually done by slipping a short length of light-wall tubing, of the same glass or a close match, onto the wire and heating to fuse the glass onto the wire.

Bellows, metal (see pp. 124, 127, 383–385).

Benzene. A volatile, flammable solvent used for degreasing. Because of the high toxicity and flammability of benzene, trichlorethylene (p. 545) or perchlorethylene is much preferred as a degreasing solvent.

Beryllium copper (from data furnished by The Beryllium Corp., Reading, Pennsylvania).

A hardenable copper-rich alloy having the properties listed in the table on p. 164.

Besides its use in making springs, bellows, electrical contacts, diaphragms, etc., beryllium copper is used as a dynode material in electron multipliers because it is easily made to release secondary electrons. The most expedient procedure is to form the dynodes of clean, bright metal to shape, assemble the multiplier, and heat-treat the assembly *in vacuo* at 600°C. Radio-frequency heating (see pp. 45, 51, 221, 222) is used. The beryllium content of the alloy is very sensitive to small amounts of oxygen and/or water vapor which might be present in tank hydrogen used in furnaces.

Beryllium copper is easily machined and formed by conventional methods. The recommended age-hardening procedures to produce maximum hardness and strength are as follows. For solution-annealed material, the time for age-hardening, at the temperatures given below, is 3 hours. For cold-worked material, the time is 2 hours.

ALLOY	TEMPERATURE °F	TEMPERATURE °C
Berylco 25	600	316
Berylco 165	600	316
Berylco 10	850–900	454–482
Berylco 50	850–900	454–482

The alloy is cooled by any convenient method and at any rate.

[1] See also: Y. Mizushima and Z. Oda, *Rev. Sci. Instr.*, **30,** 1037, 1959. G. J. Schulz, *J. Appl. Phys.*, **28,** 1149, 1957. E. K. Jaycox and H. W. Weinhart, *Rev. Sci. Instr.*, **2,** 401, 1931. C. G. Mongomery and D. D. Montgomery, *Rev. Sci. Instr.*, **9,** 58, 1938. F. A. Baker, *ibid.*, **31,** 911, 1960. S. Dushman, *Scientific Foundations of Vacuum Technique,* second edition, p. 330, John Wiley & Sons, Inc., New York, 1962. P. A. Redhead, *Rev. Sci. Instr.*, **31,** 343, 1960. J. P. Hobson, *Vacuum* (Br), **11,** 16, 1961. W. H. Hayward, R. L. Jepsen, and P. A. Redhead, *Trans. Am. Vacuum Soc.*, 10th Ann. Symp., pp. 228–233. The Macmillan Co., New York, 1963.

PROPERTIES OF BERYLLIUM COPPER

		BERYLCO 25	BERYLCO 165	BERYLCO 10	BERYLCO 50
Nominal composition (%)	Be	1.8–2.05	1.6–1.8	0.4–0.7	0.25–0.5
	Co	0.18–0.30	0.18–0.30	2.35–2.70	1.4–1.7
	Cu	bal.	bal.	bal.	bal.
Specific gravity		8.26	8.26	8.75	8.75
Density (lb/in^3)		0.298	0.298	0.316	0.316
Melting point:					
°F		1600–1800	1600–1800	1885–1955	1850–1930
°C		871–982	871–982	1030–1068	1010–1054
Coefficient of thermal expansion:					
20–100° in/°C $\times 10^{-6}$		16.7	16.7	—	—
20–200° in/°C		17.0	17.0	17.6	17.6
20–300° in/°C		17.8	17.8	—	—
68–212° in/°F $\times 10^{-6}$		9.3	9.3	—	—
68–392° in/°F		9.4	9.4	9.8	9.8
68–572° in/°F		9.9	9.9	—	—
Thermal conductivity:					
$Btu/ft^2/in/hr/°F$:					
68°F		750–900	750–900	1450–1800	1500–1700
392°F		900–1100	900–1100	—	—
Cgs:					
20°C		0.26–0.31	0.26–0.31	0.50–0.62	0.52–0.59
200°C		0.32–0.38	0.32–0.38	—	—
Electrical conductivity % IACS at 20°C:		22–30	22–30	48–60	50–55
Resistivity (microhm-cm):					
20°C		7.8–5.7	7.8–5.7	3.8–2.9	3.4–3.1
200°C		9.4–6.8	9.4–6.8	—	—
Temperature coefficient resistivity:					
20–200°C		0.0009	0.0009	—	—
Specific heat (cal/gm):					
30–100°C		0.10	—	—	—
100–300°C		0.11	—	—	—
Density increase on heat treatment (%)		0.6	—	—	—
Length decrease on heat treatment (%)		0.2	—	—	—
Poisson's ratio		0.30	—	—	—
Application		Standard BeCu	Lower cost	Current carrying. No heat treat. required	Resistance welding electrodes

Beryllium copper is solution-annealed for cold-working 1 hour per inch, or fraction of an inch, of section thickness at the following temperatures:

ALLOY	TEMPERATURE °F	TEMPERATURE °C
Berylco 25	1450	788
Berylco 165	1450	788
Berylco 10	1700	927
Berylco 50	1700	927

This heat-treatment is followed by a water quench.

Beryllium oxide (Beryllia).[1]

High-purity-grade beryllia (BeO) has the following properties:

Molecular weight 25.02

Composition, %, Si—0.01, Fe—0.01, Al—0.01, Ca—not detected, Mg—0.005, Mn—0.0005, Na—not detected, F—none, $H_2O \times$ vol—0.25, BeO—balance. Beryllium content: 36.05%

Melting point . . . . 2570°C, 4658°F
Specific gravity 3.025
Specific heat (gm-cal/gm) at
  100°C 0.229
  900°C 0.497
Heat of formation (cal/gm) 141.2
Hardness
  Mohs' scale . . . . 9 (= garnet)
  Knoop scale 1250
Maximum efficient operating temperature
  in high vacuum . . . . 2000°C, 3630°F
Coefficient of thermal expansion
  68–2550°F per °F $\times 10^{-6}$ 5.1–5.2
  20–1400°C per °C $\times 10^{-6}$ 9.2–9.4
Thermal conductivity, (cgs)[2]
  at 20°C 0.58
  at 500°C 0.15
Thermal shock resistance . . . . excellent (superior to quartz)
Vapor pressure at 3775°F (2080°C) . . . . 1.8×10^{-3} torr
Electrical resistivity at 2200°F (1204°) . . . . 100 ohm cm.
Load-bearing at 2200°F (1204°C) . . . . good

It is to be noted that the thermal conductivity of beryllium oxide is very high, comparing favorably with metals (almost as high as some brasses, and better than steel). It also has high dielectric strength, resistance to sudden thermal shock, low vapor pressure, and low thermal expansion. These properties make it useful for thermocouple tubes and ultrahigh frequency insulators for use inside vacuum tubes.

[1] Data from the Beryllium Corp., Reading, Pennsylvania.
[2] See page 520 for a definition and conversion to British units.

It is unaffected at 2000°C by carbon, carbon monoxide, and hydrogen. It is also gas-tight at 2200°C.

Beryllium oxide dust is toxic both by inhalation and by skin contact so that in machining or grinding, coolants should be used, and also efficient air exhaust systems. Tungsten carbide tools of the best quality should be used in machining.

Since BeO readily absorbs CO_2 and water vapor from the air, it should be stored in airtight containers. It is insoluble in water, but soluble in dilute or concentrated acids.

Beryllium, vapor pressure of (see pp. 143, 146).

Binders and binder removal. An adhesive constituent is added to (a) oxide cathode (pp. 97–100, 397) and (b) aluminum oxide materials (pp. 82, 100). It is usually nitrocellulose in an appropriate solvent or mixture of solvents. This constituent gives the sprayed coating a cohesive property which lasts long enough to operate until activation in the case of (a) and firing in the case of (b). At a temperature probably in the neighborhood of 300°C, the nitrocellulose decomposes, the solvents having evaporated earlier. In the case of (a), the binder is mostly eliminated during the first 450°C bake-out *in vacuo,* the decomposition products being removed as gases. Any remaining binder products are removed during the early stages of activation when heat is applied to the cathode (pp. 98 *et seq.*). In the case of (b), decomposition and elimination of the binder products are accomplished during the high-temperature hydrogen firing (p. 84), when the ceramic coating is sintered onto the metal.

Bismuth. This metal and its alloys have a high vapor pressure (see pp. 143, 146) and therefore cannot normally be used in high-vacuum devices which are to be heated. However, bismuth has some unique properties which make it of interest in the electronic field. The following data are taken from *Ductile Bismuth Wire,* third edition, I. E. Aske and Karl W. Fitzpatrick, Fitzpatrick Electric Supply Company, Muskegon, Michigan.

1. Most diamagnetic of all metals (susceptibility -1.35×10^6 cgs).
2. Highest Hall coefficient for ductile metals.
3. Greatest resistance change in a magnetic field.
4. Greatest resistivity of pure ductile metals.
5. Greatest temperature coefficient of resistivity.
6. Lowest thermal capacity of all metals, which makes it useful for low-temperature thermocouples where rapid response is required.
7. Lowest thermal conductivity of all pure ductile metals (0.0194 cgs at 18°C).
8. Highest negative thermocouple voltage per degree change in temperature.

The contraction and expansion of alloys containing bismuth can be controlled. Alloys having 55% or more bismuth expand on solidifying; those having less than 48% contract on solidifying. Those which expand on cooling are useful for making molds of intricate shape.

Black body (see p. 405).

Black vacuum (see p. 135). In a glass vacuum system, the color and character of the fluorescence produced by a sparker (Tesla coil) are a rough indication of the pressure. At high pressure, above 10^{-2} torr, the glow is bright, with a "snaky" character and a pink or violet color, indicating the presence of air. A greenish-gray tinge denotes the presence of decomposed oil vapors. With falling pressure, as pumping continues, the glow becomes more diffuse, paler, and more blue (less red). The blue color, becoming fainter and more transparent as the pressure is reduced, is generally attributed to carbon dioxide and water vapor in or on glass and metal parts which have not been thoroughly baked or outgassed. At pressures in the neighborhood of 10^{-4} torr, only a faint local fluorescence may be seen, and at 10^{-5} the glow has practically disappeared. This is called a "black" vacuum.

Bleeder valve. In any vacuum system, a small valve or stopcock is provided near the forepump. This valve has a dual purpose. In a demountable system (see Valve D in Fig. 18, p. 76), such as might be used for vacuum testing, vacuum firing, leak testing, etc., the valve allows air to be admitted (bled) into the vessel after the tests are completed and the pumps shut down, so that the bell-jar or container can be opened. In a vacuum system used for exhausting glass tubes (Fig. 22, p. 99), a small stopcock next to the forepump allows glassblowing operations to be carried out by providing a connection for the blow tube.

Blind holes in vacuum systems and vessels (see pp. 133, 134).

Bombarding. This term refers to two distinct operations in vacuum technology. One is the heating of metal structures *in vacuo,* or in a protective atmosphere, by means of a coil outside the glass vessel which is energized with radio-frequency power at around 450 kc. This is discussed on pp. 51 *et seq.* Another use of the terms is in electron bombardment (see p. 101), in which an anode or other structure in a tube to which a positive emf is applied is heated by being in the path of a stream of electrons from a cathode or emitter. In some instances this phenomenon is utilized to produce electrons from a relatively large surface S (see Fig. 44) which is positive with respect to a filament or emitter F in close proximity to it, but which itself is less positive (hence negative) with respect to another anode or target P. With the emitter F as a source of electrons, the element S (in the form of a disc or cup), being positive with respect to F, will heat by the action of the electron stream, and at a certain temperature will acually emit many times the electrons emitted by F. The electrons emitted by S will then be attracted to the anode P at a still higher positive emf. This is called emission by electron bombardment.

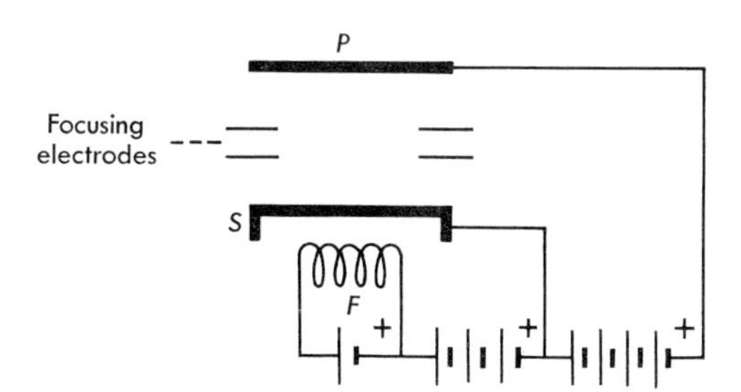

FIG. 44. Electron bombardment.

There is also a type of bombardment by *positive ions* (see p. 192) which may occur at pressures higher than 10^{-6} torr. This effect is produced when gas molecules, ionized by collision with electrons, and thus assuming a positive charge, migrate toward the cathode, which is negative, in quantities sufficient to produce heat and possible damage. This phenomenon is accompanied by a glow discharge of a color and intensity depending on (a) the potential difference across the space, (b) the nature, and (c) the pressure of the residual gases. Sometimes, in tubes which have not been sufficiently baked and outgassed during processing, overheating of the elements by electron bombardment (that is, overloading of the tube) causes gases to be released which then can give rise to positive ion bombardment. Such a tube is said to have become "gassy." (See also CATHODE SPUTTERING, p. 194.)

Booster pump. This is usually some type of diffusion or vapor pump which is designed to operate with its high-pressure end at forepump pressure, to back up a high-vacuum, single-stage diffusion pump. The tendency today is to use multistage diffusion or ultrahigh vacuum pumps in which, in a manner of speaking, the booster stage is incorporated integrally with the diffusion stages within a single package.

Borax flux. Borax, sodium tetraborate, $Na_2B_4O_7 \cdot 10H_2O$, is used as a flux in some types of high-temperature brazing. The borax fuses and flows over the surfaces, cleaning to some extent and protecting the heated metal from oxidation at the site of brazing. Some of the proprietary commercial fluxes for silver soldering contain borax.

Boron, vapor pressure of (see p. 146).

Boron nitride (data courtesy of the Carborundum Company, Research and Development Division, Niagara Falls, New York).

Boron nitride, in both solid and powder forms, has a hexagonal crystalline structure similar to that of graphite. The solid form is a dense, strong, self-bonded body whose properties are directional because of partial orientation of the plate-like crystals during formation. This property suggests boron nitride's use as a lubricant or mold-release agent in metal-melting operations. Following are typical analyses of the solid and powder forms:

CONSTITUENT	PERCENT IN SOLID FORM	PERCENT IN POWDER FORM
Boron nitride (BN)	97.0	99.50
Boric oxide	2.40	0.05
Alkaline earth oxides	0.10	0.10
Alumina and silica	0.20	0.20
Carbon	0.008	0.005

Boron nitride is not wetted or attacked by many molten metals and salts such as iron, silicon, aluminum, cryolite (sodium fluoaluminate, Na_3AlF_6), copper, and zinc, and resists the attack of many corrosive chemicals, including chlorine at 1300°F. It has excellent oxidation resistance up to 1300°F (704°C).

Although a semisoft material, the solid form's resistance to sandblasting erosion is equivalent to that of plate glass. It is considerably less brittle than most ceramic bodies and has a compressive strength of 45,000 psi measured parallel, and 34,000 psi measured perpendicular to the molding pressure, at room temperature.

Boron nitride's solid and powder forms consist of flat platelet-type crystals that easily slip over one another. This interesting property suggests possible uses in lubrication. Thin sections of solid boron nitride exhibit a slight resiliency, thus suggesting possible use in gasket and seal applications.

The material can be easily machined with standard steel cutting tools to precise tolerances and a high surface finish. (*Note:* Clean holes and fine threads can be cut in it without difficulty.)

Boron nitride is an excellent electrical insulating material having high electrical resistivity and high dielectric strength even at elevated temperatures. At low and moderate temperatures, its resistivity approximates that of electrical porcelains. In conditions of very high relative humidity, its resistivity is somewhat lower (see tables that follow). Its dielectric strength is in excess of 1000 volts per mil at high frequency. At high frequencies, the dielectric constant does not vary in the temperature range between 75°F and 900°F (24° to 482°C). When in contact with water and water-bearing compounds, boron nitride has a tendency to hydrolize very slowly. This rate is very low in cold water but increases somewhat at higher temperatures. The solid form retains its chemical and mechanical stability up to 3000°F (1650°C) in an inert atmosphere, and up to 1800°F (982°C) in an oxidizing atmosphere.

Boron nitride in solid form has excellent thermal conductivity and high thermal shock resistance. (*Note:* Unlike other ceramic materials it does not have to be fired after machining, except for purposes of outgassing, and it remains dimensionally stable after firing up to 900°C in hydrogen or vacuum.)

Its thermal expansion perpendicular to its molding direction is low (see the tables).

OXIDATION IN AIR

Hours	Weight loss (mg/cm^2)	
	700°C	980°C
2	0.014	0.35
10	0.062	0.85
30	0.138	4.80
60	0.235	10.00

RESISTANCE TO CHLORINE

Hours	Weight loss (mg/cm^2)	
	700°C	980°C
3	—	2.7
20	0.25	17.0
40	0.55	—

MODULUS OF RUPTURE

Temp. (°C)	Psi	
	Direction A†	Direction B†
24	15,880	7280
300	15,140	7030
700	3,840	1900
980	2,180	1080

MODULUS OF ELASTICITY

Temp. (°C)	Psi $\times 10^6$	
	Direction A†	Direction B†
24	12.36	4.91
300	8.79	3.47
700	1.54	0.51
980	1.65	—

DIELECTRIC STRENGTH

Sample diameter	thickness	Breakdown volts/mil
1 inch	0.010 inch	1450
2 inch	0.040 inch	925
2 inch	0.050 inch	940

† Direction A: measured parallel to molding pressure. Direction B: measured perpendicular to molding pressure.

Dissipation Factor

Frequency (cps)	Dissipation factor 24°C	350°C	480°C
	Direction A†		
10^2	0.00103	0.032	1.0
10^4	0.00042	0.0043	0.1
10^6	0.00020	0.0012	0.0056
10^8	0.000095	—	—
	Direction B†		
10^{10}	0.0003	0.0004	0.0005

Coefficient of Friction

Temp. (°C)	Boron nitride versus Boron nitride	Boron nitride versus stainless steel
20	0.70	0.20
200	0.70	0.60
700	0.62	—
920	0.39	—

Thermal Conductivity

Temp. (°C)	Cgs units* Direction A†	Direction B†
316	0.044	0.087
437	0.042	0.085
557	0.041	0.082
710	0.039	0.077
978	0.037	0.074

Thermal Expansion Coefficient

Temp. range (°C)	Coefficient (in/in/°C $\times 10^{-6}$) Direction A†	Direction B†
24–350	10.1	0.59
24–700	8.05	0.88
24–980	7.5	0.77

Specific Heat

Temperature °C	Specific Heat
182	0.278
265	0.312
455	0.303
682	0.373
857	0.355
1060	0.383

Reflectivity Values at Room Temperature

Wavelength (millimicrons)	Reflectivity (percent)
400	77.5
440	80.0
480	81.0
520	81.5
560	82.0
600	82.0
700	82.0

† Direction A: measured parallel to molding pressure. Direction B: measured perpendicular to molding pressure.

* See p. 520 for definition and conversion to British units.

RESISTIVITY VERSUS TEMPERATURE

Temp. (°C)	Direction A† ohms/in	Direction B† ohms/in
25	7.5×10^{12}	3.9×10^{12}
420	1.7×10^{11}	1.9×10^{10}
550	8.3×10^{8}	1.9×10^{8}
660	3.4×10^{7}	1.6×10^{7}
770	3.9×10^{6}	1.9×10^{6}
860	8.3×10^{5}	5.5×10^{5}
920	3.11×10^{5}	3.2×10^{5}

RESISTIVITY VERSUS HUMIDITY

Relative Humidity (%)	Resistivity at room temperature (ohm/in)
20	3.9×10^{11}
50	2.8×10^{10}
90	1.9×10^{9}

Other properties:

Density .... 2.10 (min.) gm/cc
Dielectric Constant .... 4+
Thermal shock resistance ..... Excellent
Hardness, Mohs' Scale 2

† Direction A: measured parallel to molding pressure. Direction B: measured perpendicular to molding pressure.

Boron nitride is available from the Carborundum Company, Refractories & Electronics Division, Latrobe, Pennsylvania, and from National Carbon Co., division of Union Carbide Corp., New York 17, N.Y.

Summary of properties of boron nitride:

Density .... 2.1 gm/cc
Working temperature,
  inert atmosphere
    solid .... 1650°C
    powder .... 2980°C
  oxidizing atmosphere
    solid .... 980°C
    powder .... 700°C
Dielectric constant .... 4+

Dielectric strength .... high
Electric resistivity .... high
Coefficient of friction ..... low
Thermal shock resistance .. excellent
Permeability .... surface only
Flexural strength .... good
Hardness, Mohs' 2
Mechanical shock
  resistance .... good

Note: Because of the tendency of boron nitride to absorb water on its surface, insulators for use in electron tubes should be thoroughly outgassed before use. The parts should be placed in a tantalum or molybdenum bucket and heated, *in vacuo,* by induction. The temperature is to be raised slowly to 900°C.[1] After being fired, the boron nitride parts are to be handled by the most "aseptic" technique available, and either assembled into the tube immediately in a "clean" room with very low humidity, or stored in an efficient vacuum desiccator.

Parts that have been handled, or have become discolored, should be cleaned with #320 Aloxite cloth and then subjected to the vacuum-firing treatment outlined above. Under no circumstances should boron nitride be cleaned in water or aqueous chem-

[1] Finished boron nitride parts may be vacuum-fired in a glass vessel sealed to the normal tube exhaust station and baked at 450°C until the gauge pressure shows complete outgassing.

icals. Clean acetone or alcohol can be used with caution, followed by an overnight bake in an air oven at 110°C. The parts are then to be vacuum-fired as described above.

Pyrolytic boron nitride (Boralloy) is available from the National Carbon division of Union Carbide Corporation. Although this is a harder material than regular BN, it can be machined. It is impervious to water, and its electrical properties are excellent.

A boron nitride coating from a water suspension is obtainable from the Carborundum Company. The good electrical insulating and heat conducting properties of this material make it very suitable for coating thermocouples, electric heating elements, and the like. To obtain these properties the coating must be heat treated.

Borosilicate glass (see table on p. 270).

Bottle brazing (see pp. 39–41).

Boyle's law (see GAS LAWS, p. 265).

Brass and bronze. Most of the commercial brasses and bronzes contain zinc and therefore are unsuitable for use in bakable vacuum systems. Brass may be used in demountable systems where elevated temperatures will not be encountered. (See p. 38.)

Brazing (see also pp. 35, 41, 67, 133).

The term "brazing" generally refers to a method of joining metals in which another metal or alloy is used to make the joint, and in which this brazing metal or alloy has a melting point lower than that of either of the metals being joined, yet considerably above the range of soft solders (i.e., tin-lead alloys—see pp. 250, 342).

The distinction between brazing and soldering materials is not too clear. The latter usually (but not always) contain lead-tin alloys of a much lower melting point than brazing materials have, and sometimes, as in the case of aluminum solders, contain zinc, cadmium, aluminum, and copper. The word "soldering" is sometimes used in the sense of high-temperature brazing, although the term "brazing" never indicates low-temperature soldering.

In CONTROLLED-ATMOSPHERE BRAZING, the parts are placed in a furnace or muffle (see pp. 35–41, and pp. 41–51), from which the air or oxygen is excluded by filling the chamber with one, or a mixture of various, inert or chemically reducing gases, such as endothermic, and exothermic[1] gases, hydrogen (wet or dry), dissociated ammonia (p. 156), or forming gas (p. 160).

---

[1] Endothermic gas is the product of a complete reaction of city or fuel gas with air in the presence of a catalyst. It is high in hydrogen and carbon monoxide and very low in water vapor (i.e. dry). The carbon content can usually be predetermined so as to provide a nondecarburizing environment for the heat-treatment of any particular steel. This gas can also be used for treating nonferrous metals. By the addition of small quantities of propane or methane (for the purpose of adjusting the hydrocarbon content), this gas can be used for case-hardening.

Exothermic gas is produced by the partial combustion of city or fuel gas mixed with air in various proportions to produce a lean or rich gas. It is relatively inexpensive, since the amount of commercial gas used is low compared with the volume of exothermic gas produced. This gas can be used for heat-treating nonferrous metals, and for steels which are not usefully affected by a decarburizing atmosphere. For example, exothermic gas can be used for copper-brazing low-carbon steels, for annealing copper, and for silver-brazing copper and brass in industry.

Controlled atmosphere brazing (CAB) has many advantages over other brazing or joining methods, namely:

1. The finished work is bright and clean. Because of the uniform heating, there is only a small amount of distortion.
2. Stresses are relieved.
3. There is high and uniform strength throughout the joint, especially where a slight amount of alloying takes place.
4. Complex assemblies can be built up from simple individual parts with the consequent elimination of extensive machining and waste. The parts can be of different metals or alloys. Assemblies can be so designed that little or no finish-machining is required.[1]

In CAB, the parts of an assembly should be made to hold together by some mechanical method, if possible, including the utilization of gravity. Jigs or fixtures can be used but should be avoided if possible because of the likelihood of the braze material's sticking to the jig and also because of the difficulty and expense of making a jig for a complicated assembly. The following methods for fastening parts are worth exploring:

1. Crimping
2. Knurling
3. Peening
4. Pinning
5. Riveting
6. Screwing
7. Shouldering with tight fit (make deep enough to hold at brazing temperature)
8. Spot or tack welding
9. Staking
10. Swaging

In any of these methods, use enough braze material to eliminate voids or pockets (see p. 133).

In brazing some assemblies, such as closed cylinders or chambers, provision should be made for venting, not only to allow for expansion of the gases inside but also to allow free access for the protective atmosphere. Venting can usually be secured by the judicious placing of one or more holes, slots, or other shaped openings.

It is often useful to provide a step or chamfer to retain the braze material, although internal or external groove rings should not be employed, since a void might be left when the braze material runs out. Also, such grooves are more expensive to machine.

In many cases a slight interference fit (for copper and silver-copper eutectic brazing) is required. For brazing with other binary or tertiary alloys which tend to form fillets, a light press fit (metal-to-metal contact) is sufficient. Sharp edges and corners should be avoided. Simple deburring is sufficient for good practice. It should not be expected that the braze material will fill up the gaps and discontinuities of a poor fit.

All parts to be brazed in CAB should be exceptionally clean (see pp. 1–3 *et seq.*) Where press fits are to be used, no oil or other lubricant should be used.

Consideration should be given to joining metals of different expansion coefficients —from room temperature to brazing temperature.

If a finished brazed assembly is to be heat-treated, this can be done provided the heat-treating temperature is lower than the brazing temperature.

---

[1] Holes and threads which might be fouled by braze material are best machined after brazing.

In work pieces which have been severely cold-worked or heavily machined before brazing, the probability of some dimensional distortion due to stress-relief during exposure to the brazing temperature is always high. For this reason it is good practice to follow one of these two procedures:

1. Rough-machine or form the parts oversize and then stress-relieve or anneal. This is to be followed by finish-machining, which should be no more than light (0.010 in.). When parts treated in this manner are subsequently brazed, the degree of heat distortion will be small to negligible.
2. Rough-machine or form parts oversize, except mating surfaces for brazing, then braze. This is to be followed by light-finish machining.

The first procedure is preferable for vacuum components because, since the brazing is the last operation, the assemblies need no further handling and can be stored clean until use.

Consideration should be given to inspection of brazed joints, and this is especially important where more than one joint is to be brazed serially on an assembly. Parts that are to be brazed in a consecutive series should not all be assembled at once because it may then be difficult or impossible to inspect one or more of the brazed joints that might be hidden by other parts.

The standard method of inspection is visual examination. If the braze material is placed at one end of the joint before brazing, the presence of the braze material at the other end of the joint is evidence of complete penetration. Military Specification MIL-B-7883 requires the following procedure:

> **Examination of product:** Each joint shall be examined visually for penetration of the filler alloy into the interstice of the joint and smoothness of exposed edges or fillets formed by the filler metal. Complete penetration is evidenced by the appearance of filler metal at the edge of the joint opposite to that at which filler metal was introduced or of openings provided for inspection purposes. Joints having incomplete penetration shall be rejected.
>
> **Other tests:** In the event that the completeness of penetration cannot be ascertained by visual examination, radiographic or ultrasonic examination may be required, or the Government Inspector may require the joints to be peel-tested or sectioned and examined for voids and other defects.

Complete penetration of braze material is evidence of a strong joint, since the spreading of the braze material between the mating surfaces is what determines the strength of a joint. For this reason mating surfaces should be clean and free of grooves or other irregularities, although a high polish is not required. For flat surfaces, a grind to not finer than 125 microinches is suitable. Nonflat surfaces can be steel-grit-blasted. Sand or alumina should not be used for blasting unless all traces of the grit and powder can be removed because such residues might interfere with the flow of braze material.

Brazing alloys. Under proper conditions many metals and alloys may be used as brazing materials. For example, pure copper (OFHC-grade) can be used to braze steel, stainless steel, nickel, and other metals of higher melting point if done in a controlled atmosphere (see above). (Also see pp. 35, 41, *et seq.*). Such brazing can also be done in vacuum.

A comprehensive list of metals and alloys that can be used for brazing is given on pp. 176–187. This list has been carefully compiled by Walter H. Kohl[1] and appears in his book *Materials and Techniques for Electron Tubes,* 2nd edition, Reinhold Publishing Corporation, New York, N.Y., 1959.

Additional palladium brazing alloys: The following list of brazing alloys containing palladium[2] shows materials which are suitable for vacuum-tube work. They have good mechanical properties at elevated temperatures; improved wetting characteristics on molybdenum, tungsten, and nickel alloys; and low intergranular penetration. All these alloys have extremely low volatile-metal impurity content.

ALLOY	PALLADIUM (%) AND COMPOSITION	MELTING RANGE (°C)
Pallabraze 810	5 Pd-AgCu	807–810
Pallabraze 840	10 Pd-AgCu	830–840
Pallabraze 850	10 Pd-AgCu	824–850
Pallabraze 880	15 Pd-AgCu	856–880
Pallabraze 900	20 Pd-AgCu	876–900
Pallabraze 950	25 Pd-AgCu	910–950
Pallabraze 1010	5 Pd-Ag	970–1010
Pallabraze 1090	18 Pd-Cu	1080–1090
Pallabraze 1237	60 Pd-Ni	1237

Brazing, bottle (see pp. 39 *et seq.*).

Brazing, ceramic to metal (see pp. 67–73).

Brazing, serial (see p. 36). This is a multiple-brazing process in which several joints are brazed consecutively with fillers of different melting points, beginning with that of the highest melting point. For example, after the first pass through the furnace with pure copper (melting point 1083°C), a copper-gold alloy (62.5% copper, 37.5% gold; melting point 1015–1040°C) can be used for a second brazing operation. Another copper-gold alloy (copper 6%, gold 94%; melting point 990°C) can be used for a third brazing and a nickel-gold alloy (nickel 18%, gold 82%; melting point 950°C) for a fourth. A copper-silver alloy (copper 50%, silver 50%; melting point 875°C) can be used for a fifth and silver-copper eutectic (silver 72%, copper 28%; melting point 779°C) for a sixth, and so on. (See Table of Brazing Alloys on pp. 176–187.) Consideration must be given to expansion coefficients in serial brazing of dissimilar metals and also to the ability of the braze material to wet the parts to be joined (which may, in cases such as silver on copper and gold on copper, be excessive).

---

[1] Electronics consultant on materials and techniques, Los Altos, California.

[2] "High Purity Palladium Brazing Alloys," M. H. Sloboda, *Platinum Metals Rev.* (Johnson Matthey Group and J. Bishop & Co., Platinum Works, Malvern, Pennsylvania), **7,** 8, 1963. These alloys are supplied ready for use in the form of wire. They are especially suitable for brazing procedures in dry hydrogen (see pp. 41–51) or in a vacuum of 10^{-5} mm Hg or lower.

TABLE OF BRAZING FILLER METALS FOR ELECTRON TUBES*

NO.	LIQUID. (°C)	SOLID. (°C)	COMPOSITION IN WEIGHT %[1]	LIQUID. (°F)	SOLID. (°F)	NOTES	ALLOY DESIGNATIONS AND SUPPLIERS[2]	APPLICATIONS AND COMMENTS[3]
1	3180	3180	Rhenium	5756	5756		CBC; (GPD)	W
2	2996	2996	Tantalum	5425	5425	4b	FMC	W
3	2468	2468	Columbium (niobium)	4474	4474	4b	FMC	Mo; W
4	2480	2480	Tungsten carbide (W_2C)	4496	4496		CC	Mo; W, W_2C
5	2500	2500	Ruthenium	4532	4532		BPD; SCC; (GPD); (HH)	Mo; W
6	2450	2450	Iridium	4442	4442		BPD; SCC; (GPD); (HH)	Mo; W
7	2150	2120	Silicon-molybdenum 10 90	3902	3848		TMC; VMC	
8	2080	2000	Dimolybdenumboride	3776	3632		BC	Mo; W
9	1990	1950	Iridium-platinum 40 60	3614	3542		BPD; SCC; (GPD)	
10	1966	1966	Rhodium	3574	3574		BPD; SCC; (GPD); (HH)	Mo; W
11	1950	1935	Rhodium-platinum 40 60	3542	3515		BPD; SCC; (GPD)	Mo; W
12	1900	1900	Ruthenium-molybdenum 20 80	3452	3452		BPD; SCC	Mo; W
13	1852	1852	Zirconium	3366	3366	4b	CC; FMC	Mo; W
14	1769	1769	Platinum	3216	3216		APW†; BPD; HH Platinum VTG; INCO; SCC; WGP; (GPD)	Mo; W
15	1695	1645	Gold-palladium-platinum 5 20 bal.	3083	2993		HH Premabraze 205 VTG	Mo; W
16	1660	1660	Titanium	3320	3320		LFA et al	Ceramic seals
17	1552	1552	Palladium	2826	2826	4b	APW†; BPD; HH Palladium VTG; INCO; WGP; (GPD)	Mo; W
18	1445	1445	Nickel-iron 36 64	2651	2633		ASC Ascovar 36; DHC Nilvar; Inco Invar; SEP	(NAHg)
19	1453	1453	Nickel	2647	2647		DHC; INCO; WBD	Mo; W
20	1440	1427	Palladium-gold 35 65	2624	2601		ASC Ascobraze 65AC; JMN; (HH); (GPD); (WGP)	
21	1410	1380	Palladium-gold 25 75	2570	2516		HH Premabraze 201 VTG	Mo; W
22	1410	1210	Platinum-gold 25 75	2570	2210		ASC Ascovar 75AD; JMN; (GPD); (HH); (WGP)	Mo; W
23	1330	1330	Molybdenum-cobalt 37 63	2426	2426			Mo; W

24	1320	1320	Molybdenum-nickel 46.5 53.5	2408	2408			Mo; W; Ni; (NM)
25	1320	1290	Palladium-nickel 30 70	2408	2354		ASC Ascobraze 70EC; (BPD); (GPD); (HH)	SS
26	1305	1260	Palladium-gold 13 87	2381	2300		HH Premabraze 210 VTG	Mo; W
27	1300	1230	Nickel-copper 45 55	2372	2246		ASC Ascobraze 55FE; DHC Advance; WBD Cupron; Constantan, Eureka	Mo; W; (NM)
28	~1260	>1232	Chrome-nickel-palladium 10 36 bal.	2300	>2250		HH Premabraze 101; (GPD)	
29	1250	1200	Platinum-copper 40 60	2282	2192		ASC Ascobraze 60FD; WGP Cuplat; (GPD) (HH)	
30	1240	1190	Palladium-gold 8 92	2264	2174		ASC Ascobraze 92AC; WGP Paloro; (GPD) (HH)	Mo; W; SS
31	1240	1170	Iron-nickel-copper 0.6 30 bal.	2264	2138		ABC Cupro Nickel 30%-702; ASC Ascobraze 70FE	Mo; W; (NM); watch for Zn
32	1238	1238	Nickel-palladium 40 60	2260	2260		APW APW 129†; BPD Alloy No. 940; (GPD); (HH)	SS; Inconel
33	1200	1182	Manganese-palladium-silver 3 33 bal.	2190	2160		APW APW 441; BPD Alloy No. 1170; (GPD)	SS; Inconel
34	1220	1220	Cobalt-palladium 35 65	2228	2228		ASC Ascobraze 65CG; WGP Palco; (GPD); (HH)	Mo; W; SS; Inconel
35	1205	1150	Nickel-copper 25 75	2201	2102		ABC Cupro Nickel 25%-705; ASC Ascobraze 75FE; Coin Nickel	Mo; W; (NM)
36	1177	1070	Palladium-silver 20 80	2150	1958		(GPD); (HH); (WGP) APW VTG 447	
37	1160	995	Platinum-silver 27 73	2120	1823		ASC Ascobraze 73BD; (GPD); (HH); (WGP)	Mo; W
38	1160	971	Carbon-boron-silicon-iron- 0.45 max. 2 2.5 2.5 chromium-nickel 10 bal.	2120	1780	4a, b	APW; WCC Nicrobraz 160	SS; Inconel

(Continued)

* As revised 1964. Original table copyright 1954 by Walter H. Kohl, electronics consultant on materials and techniques, P.O. Box 426, Los Altos, California. Revised 1959 for *Materials and Techniques for Electron Tubes*, by W. H. Kohl, Reinhold Publishing Corporation, New York, New York. Separately printed copies of this table are available as wall charts or file copies from the author. Manufacturers of brazing materials have generously cooperated in the preparation of this table; their help is gratefully acknowledged. The data published in this table must, however, not be construed as committing the respective manufacturers in any way or form.

TABLE OF BRAZING FILLER METALS FOR ELECTRON TUBES (*Continued*)

NO.	LIQUID (°C)	SOLID (°C)	COMPOSITION IN WEIGHT %[1]	LIQUID (°F)	SOLID (°F)	NOTES	ALLOY DESIGNATIONS AND SUPPLIERS[2]	APPLICATIONS AND COMMENTS[3]
39	1150	1100	Iron-nickel-copper 1.3 10 bal.	2102	2012		Cupronickel 10%	(NM); Watch for Zn
40	1135	1080	Iron-silicon-chromium-nickel 3 10 19 bal.	2075	1975	4a, b, c	CM Alloy No. 60	SS; Inconel
41	1135	1080	Carbon-silicon-chromium-nickel 0.15 max. 10 19 bal.	2075	1975		APW; WCC Nicrobraz 30	SS; Inconel
42	1121	1000	Manganese-palladium-silver 5 20 bal.	2050	1830		APW APW 440; BPD Alloy No. 1795; (GPD)	SS; Inconel
43	1105	977	Carbon-boron-silicon-iron- 0.55 2.5 3.25 3.75 chromium-tungsten-nickel 11.5 16 bal.	2020	1790	4a, b	APW; WCC Nicrobraz 170	Mo; W; SS; Inconel
44	1105	1060	Manganese-nickel-palladium-copper 10 15 20 bal.	2020	1940		BPD Alloy No. 1804; (GPD)	
45	1094	971	Carbon-boron-silicon-iron- 0.15 max. 3 3.5 3.5 chromium-nickel 11.5 bal.	2000	1780	4a, b	APW; WCC WG Nicrobraz	SS; Inconel
46	1090		Manganese-nickel-palladium-copper 15 20 30 bal.	1994			BPD Alloy No. 1803; (GPD)	SS
47	1090	1080	Palladium-copper 18 82	1994	1976		BPD Alloy No. 1800; (GPD); (HH)	
48	1083	1083	Copper	1981	1981	4a	ABC OFHC Copper-120· ASC Ascobraze OFHC; EWA EutecRod 184	Fe; Kovar; Monel; Fe; SS
49	1083	1083	Nickel-copper-tungsten 3 35 bal.	1981	1981		MWP Runnot C	Fe; Kovar; Monel; contains W powder
50	1083	1083	Silicon-copper 0.3 bal.	1981	1981		ABC, RCB Silicon Copper-107; ASC Ascobraze 99FH	For Fe-Ni alloys
51	1077	971	Carbon-boron-silicon-iron- 0.15 max. 3.5 4.5 4.5 chromium-nickel 13.5 bal.	1970	1780	4a, b	APW; WCC LC Nicrobraz	Inconel; SS
52	1075	965	Nickel-gold 35 65	1967	1769	5	HH Premabraze 131 VTG; (GPD); (WGP)	
53	1070	1070	Tin-platinum 29 71	1958	1958		ASC Ascobraze 70DJ; (GPD)	

54	1065	1002	Palladium-silver 10 90	1950	1835	5	APW Alloy No. 431†; ASC Ascobraze 90BC; HH Premabraze 901 VTG; (GPD); (WPG)	Mo; Ni; SS; W
55	1065	974	Chromium-nickel-gold 6 22 bal.	1950	1785		APW Alloy No. 265; HH Premabraze 128; (WGP)	
56	1065	954	Boron-silicon-chromium- 3 max. 5 max. 20 max. manganese-nickel 30 max. 60–85	1950	1750		SAC Solobraze NXI	SS
57	1063	1063	Gold	1945	1945		APW Alloy No. 200†; ASC Ascobraze 99, 99A; HH Fine Gold VTG; WGP 24 Karat Gold; (GPD)	Diffusion seals; Cu; Mo
58	1060	1000	Silver-copper 5 95	1940	1832	5	ASC Ascobraze 95FB; HH Braze 052 VTG; (GPD); (WGP)	Cu
59	1055	1055	Carbon-boron-chromium-nickel 0.15 max. 3.5 15 bal.	1930	1930	4a, b	APW, WCC Nicrobraz 150	Inconel; SS
60	(1055)	1041	Boron-silicon-nickel 1.9 3.5 bal.	(1930)	1905	7	CM Alloy No. 50; HH Handy Hi-Temp 93	Inconel; SS
61	1050		Manganese-palladium-silver 5 20 bal.	1922			BPD No. 1168; (GPD)	
62	1050	1030	Nickel-manganese 30 70	1922	1886		HH Handy Hi-Temp 30	SS
63	1038	1027	Carbon-boron-silicon-nickel 0.15 max. 3 4.5 bal.	1900	1800	4a, b	APW; WCC Nicrobraz 130	Inconel; SS
64	1038	977	Carbon-boron-iron-silicon- 0.8 3.5 4.5 4.5 chromium-nickel 13.5 bal.	1900	1790		APW; WCC Nicrobraz 120	Differs in mesh size from standard
65	1038	971	Carbon-boron-iron-silicon- 0.60 3.85 4 4.5 chromium-nickel 16.5 bal.	1900	1780	4a, b	CM No. 56; CSC Rexweld 64; EMA EutecBor 9; WCC Standard Nicrobraz	Inconel; SS
66	1035	1015	Gold-copper 30 70	1895	1859	5	ACS Ascobraze 70FA; HH Premabraze 404 VTG; (GPD); (WGP)	Cu; Fe; Kovar; Ni; SS
67	1032	1010	Carbon-silicon-manganese-nickel 0.15 max. 8 17 bal.	1890	1850	4a, b, c	APW; WCC Nicrobraz 60	Inconel; SS
68	1030	975	Nickel-gold-copper 3 35 bal.	1886	1787	8	HH Premabraze 129 VTG	Cu; Kovar; Mo; Monel; Ni; W; SS

(Continued)

TABLE OF BRAZING FILLER METALS FOR ELECTRON TUBES (*Continued*)

NO.	LIQUID (°C)	SOLID (°C)	COMPOSITION IN WEIGHT %[1]	LIQUID (°F)	SOLID (°F)	NOTES	ALLOY DESIGNATIONS AND SUPPLIERS[2]	APPLICATIONS AND COMMENTS[3]
69	1025	970	Silicon-copper 3 97	1877	1778		EWA EutecRod 182; RCB	Cu
70	1021	1005	Boron-nickel-cobalt-manganese 1 16 16 bal.	1870	1840		CM Alloy No. 62	SS
71	1020	1000	Gold-copper 35 65	1868	1832	5, 8	APW Alloy No. 260†; ASC Ascobraze 65FA; HH Premabraze 406 VTG; WGP Wesgo; (GPD)	Cu; Fe; Kovar; Ni; SS
72	1025	990	Nickel-gold-copper 3 35 bal.	1877	1814	5, 8	APW Alloy No. 243; ASC Ascobraze 62FAE; WGP Nicoro; (GPD)	Cu; Inconei; Kovar; Mo; Ni; Steel; W; SS
73	1019	950	Manganese-silicon-copper 1.1 3.1 bal.	1866	1742		ABC Everdur-1010	
74	1018	1018	Nickel-manganese 40 60	1864	1864			SS
75	1015	990	Gold-copper 37.5 62.5	1859	1814	5; 9 karat red gold 8	APW alloy No. 242; ASC Ascobraze 62FA; HH Premabraze 401 VTG; WGP; (GPD)	Cu; Fe; Kovar; Ni; SS
76	1015	970	Indium-gold-copper 3 20 bal.	1859	1778		ASC Ascobraze 77FAK; WGP Incuro 20	Cu; Kovar; Ni
77	1010	985	Gold-copper 40 60	1850	1805	8	ASC Ascobraze 60FA; WGP Wesgo; (HH); (GPD)	Cu; Fe; Kovar; Ni
78	1010	970	Palladium-silver 5 95	1850	1778		BPD Alloy No. 868; (HH) APW VTG 428	
79	(1005)	996	Boron-silicon-chromium-nickel-iron 3.50 5 16 72.50 bal.	(1840)	1825	7	HH Handy Hi-Temp 72	Inconel; SS
80	999	971	Carbon-iron-boron-silicon; 0.15 max. 2.5 3 4.5 chromium-nickel 6.5 bal.	1830	1780	4a, b	APW; WCC LM Nicrobraz	Inconel; SS
81	(996)	979	Boron-silicon-chromium-nickel-iron 2.90 4.50 7.00 82 bal.	(1825)	1795	7	CM Alloy No. 53; HH Handy Hi-Temp 82	SS
82	(993)	979	Boron-silicon-nickel-iron 2.90 4.50 91.25 bal.	(1820)	1795	7	CM Alloy No. 52; HH Handy Hi-Temp 91	Cu; SS
83	993	979	Titanium-boron-silicon-iron 0.75 3 4.5 bal.	1820	1795		CM Alloy No. 59	

84	990	965	Copper-gold 6 94	1814	1769		APW Alloy No. 259; ASC Ascobraze 94AF; (HH); (GPD); (WGP)	
85	985	664	Silver-tin-copper 7 8 bal.	1805	1225	5	APW D-275; ASC Ascobraze 85FJB; GSR GB07; HH Braze 071 VTG; UWS Sil-7T; WEC Co-Silver 7T; (GPD)	
86	975	950	Copper-gold 50 50	1787	1742	5, 8	APW Alloy No. 241; ASC Ascobraze 50AF; HH Premabraze 402 VTG; WGP Wesgo	Cu; Kovar; Ni
87	971	960	Manganese-silver 15 85	1780	1760		APW Silvaloy 850; ASC Ascobraze 85BL; ARS Aircosil P; EWA EutecRod 1807; GSR GB No. 85; HH Braze 852; UWS Sil 85 M; WEC Co-Silver 85; (GPD)	Inconel; SS
88	963	924	Silver-gold-copper 2.8 41.7 bal.	1765	1695	5	ASC Ascobraze 55FAB; HH Premabraze 031 VTG; (GPD)	Cu; Kovar
89	962		Nickel-silver-tungsten 3 35 bal.		1764		MVP Runnot S	Contains W powder
90	961	961	Manganese-silver 4 96	1762	1762		ASC Ascobraze 96BL; (HH); (GPD)	
91	960.5	960.5	Silver	1761	1761		APW†; ASC Ascobraze 99.9B; HH Fine Silver VTG; WGP; (GPD)	Very ductile
92	950	950	Nickel-gold 18 82	1742	1742	5 19.8 karat white gold	APW Alloy No. 255†; ASC Ascobraze 82AE; HH Premabraze 130 VTG; WGP Nioro; (GPD)	Cu; Inconel; Kovar; Mo; Ni; W; SS
93	950	779	Silver-copper 30 70	1742	1434		ASC Ascobraze 70FB; (GPD); (HH); (WGP)	
94	950		Palladium-copper-silver 10 22.5 bal.	1742			BPD Alloy No. 1802; (GPD); (HH)	
95	950	901	Copper-palladium-silver 21 25 bal.	1742	1654		BPD Alloy No. 1799; (GPD); (HH) APW VTG 492	
96	942	942	Nickel-titanium 28.5 71.5	1728	1728		LFA Ni-clad-Ti	Ceramic seals; (NM)
97	921	905	Silver-copper-gold 2.1 39.6 bal.	1690	1660	5	ASC Ascobraze 59AFB; HH Premabraze 032 VTG; (GPD); (WGP)	Ferrous and nonferrous alloys

(*Continued*)

Table of Brazing Filler Metals for Electron Tubes (*Continued*)

NO.	LIQUID (°C)	SOLID (°C)	COMPOSITION IN WEIGHT %[1]	LIQUID (°F)	SOLID (°F)	NOTES	ALLOY DESIGNATIONS AND SUPPLIES[2]	APPLICATIONS AND COMMENTS[3]
98	913	871	Copper-cobalt-phosphorus; 5 7.5 11 nickel-iron 42 bal.	1675	1600		CM Alloy No. 57	
99	910	900	Nickel-copper-gold 3.0 15.5 bal.	1670	1652		ASC Ascobraze 82AFE; WGP Nicoro 80; HH Premabraze 409 VTG; (GPD)	Cu; Kovar; Mo; Ni; W; steel
100	910	779	Silver-copper 40 60	1670	1434	5	ASC Ascobraze 60FB; HH Braze 401 VTG; (GPD); (WGP); (German BTL)	Ferrous and nonferrous alloys
101	900	860	Indium-copper-gold 3.0 37 bal.	1652	1580		ASC Ascobraze 60AFK; WGP Incuro; (GPD)	Cu; Fe; Kovar; Ni
102	900	850	Palladium-copper-silver 15 20 bal.	1652	1562		BPD Alloy No. 1798; (GPD); (HH) APW VTG 490	
103	900	714	Phosphorus-copper 5 95	1653	1317		ARS, WEC Phos Copper Strip; BSR Belmont BCuP-1	Ag; Cu; Mo; W; not for Fe or Ni alloys
104	898	879	Palladium-copper-silver 20 28 bal.	1648	1614		BPD Alloy No. 1801; (GPD); (HH) APW	
105	896	885	Silver-copper-gold 5 20 bal.	1645	1625	5	APW Alloy No. 261†; ASC Ascobraze 75AFB; HH Premabraze 050 VTG; WGP Silcoro 75; (GPD)	
106	888	888	Carbon-phosphorus-chromium-nickel 0.15 max. 10 13 bal.	1630	1630	4a, b, c	APW, WCC Nicrobraz 50	Inconel; SS
107	890	810	Copper-silver 7.5 92.5	1634	1490	5	ASC Ascobraze 92BF; HH Sterling Silver VTG; (GPD); (WGP)	
108	890	780	Lithium-copper-silver 0.2 7.3 bal.	1635	1435		APW, ARS AE 100; ASC Ascobraze 92BFN; HH Lithobraze 925; (GPD)	Inconel; SS; extremely fluid
109	889	889	Copper-gold 20 80	1632	1632	5; 19.2K red gold	APW Alloy No. 238†; ASC Ascobraze 80AF; HH Premabraze 403 VTG; JMN .800 Fine; (GPD)	
110	885	779	Nickel-copper-silver 5 32.5 bal.	1625	1435		APW Silvaloy T 50; (GPD); (HH)	Inconel; SS

111		800	Manganese-silver-copper 10 40 bal.		1472		(GPD), (HH); (German Kusiman)	Ag; Fe; Steel
112	877	877	Carbon-phosphorus-nickel 0.15 max 11 bal.	1610	1610	4a, b, c, d	APW, WCC Nicrobraz 10; INCO Niphos (German)	Cu; Fe; Inconel; Kovar; Mo; Ni; W; SS
113	875	779	Copper-silver 50 50	1607	1434	5	ASC Ascobraze 50BF; HH Braze 502 VTG; (GPD); (WGP)	
114	870	779	Copper-silver 10 90	1598	1434	5	ASC Ascobraze 90BF; HH Coin Silver VTG; (GPD); (WGP)	SS
115	852	827	Palladium-copper-silver 10 31.5 bal.	1566	1520		BPD Alloy No. 1797; (GPD); (HH) APW VTG 491	
116	849	752	Nickel-manganese-copper-silver 2 5 28 bal.	1560	1385		ASC Ascobraze 65BF LE; GSR 65 Mn; HH Braze 655; (GPD)	Stellites, carbides, and refractory metals containing W
117	845	835	Silver-copper-gold 20 20 bal.	1553	1535	5	ASC Ascobraze 60AFB; HH Premabraze 408 VTG; WGP Silcoro 60; (GPD)	Cu; Fe; Ni; very short melting range
118	843	815	Copper-silver-gold 17.7 24 bal.	1550	1500		ASC Ascobraze 58ABF; (HH); (WGP)	Cu; Fe; Ni
119	830	779	Nickel-copper-silver 2 21 bal.	1525	1435		APW Silvaloy T 52; (GPD); (HH)	Inconel; SS
120	824	794	Copper-silver-gold 23.5 27.5 bal.	1515	1460	12 Karat Gold	ASC Ascobraze 49ABF; (GPD); (HH); (WGP)	Cu; Fe; Ni
121	827	805	Copper-silver-gold 23.5 23.5 bal.	1520	1480		JMN No. 5087; (GPD); (HH); (WGP)	Cu; Fe; Ni
122	821	794	Copper-silver-gold 20.5 29.5 bal.	1510	1460	5	ASC Ascobraze 50 ABF; HH Premabraze 202 VTG; (GPD); (WGP)	Cu; Fe; Ni
123	815	641	Phosphorus-silver-copper 5 15 bal.	1500	1185	6	APW Silvaloy 15; ARS Aircosil 15; ASW S-115; EWA EutecRod 1803; GSR 15; HH Sil-Fos; UWS Phoson 15; WEC Phos Silver 15 M	Not for Fe or Ni alloys. Wide melting range.
124	805	644	Silver-phosphorus-copper 5 6.25 bal.	1480	1190	6	APW Silvaloy 5; ARS Aircosil 5; ASC Ascobraze FOS-5; HH Sil-Fos 5; UWS Phoson 6; WEC Phos-Silver 6M	Ag; Cu; Mo; W; not for Fe or Ni alloys
125	810	805	Palladium-copper-silver 5 26.6 bal.	1490	1480		BPD Alloy No. 1796; (GPD); (HH) APW VTG 478	
126	802	719	Nickel-tin-copper-silver 2.5 6 28.5 bal.	1475	1325	5	ASC Ascobraze 63 BFJE; HH Braze 630 VTG; (GPD)	Inconel; SS 430
127	795	780	Nickel-copper-silver 0.75 28.1 bal.	1463	1436	5	ASC Ascobraze 71BFE; HH Braze 720 VTG; WGP Nicusil 3; (GPD)	Inconel; Mo; SS; W; better wetting than Cu/Ag

(Continued)

TABLE OF BRAZING FILLER METALS FOR ELECTRON TUBES (*Continued*)

NO.	LIQUID (°C)	SOLID (°C)	COMPOSITION IN WEIGHT %[1]	LIQUID (°F)	SOLID (°F)	NOTES	ALLOY DESIGNATIONS AND SUPPLIERS[2]	APPLICATIONS AND COMMENTS[3]
128	788	640	Silver-phosphorus-copper 2 7 bal.	1450	1185		ARS Phos-Silver 2; ASW 23; GBS 02	For nonferrous metals and alloys
129	780	660	Indium-copper-silver 10 27 bal.	1436	1220	5, 8	ASC Ascobraze 63 BFK; HH Premabraze 630 VTG; WGP Incusil 10; (GPD)	
130	779	779	Copper-silver (Eutectic) 28 72	1435	1435		APW Silvaloy 301†; ARS Aircosil M; ASC Ascobraze 72BF; EWA EutecRod 1806; GPD ML; GSR 72; HH Braze BT VTG; SC_C Nu Braze; UWS Sil-72; WEC Co-Silver 72-28; WGP Cusil-Decarbonized; (GPD)	Cu; Inconel; Kovar; SS
131	770	714	Phosphorus-copper 7 93	1418	1317	6	ASW 21; ARS, WEC Phos Copper Rod; BSR Belmont BCuP-2; CLA Lo-Melt Copper; EWA EutecRod 800; UWS Phoson 0	Ag; Cu; Mo; W; Very free flowing; not for Fe or Ni alloys
132	760	743	Tin-copper-silver 5 27 bal.	1400	1370		ASC Ascobraze 68 BFJ; GPD SI-1; (HH)	
133	730	604	Manganese-tin-copper-silver 3 7 32.7 bal.	1345	1120		ASC Ascobraze 57BFJL; EWA EutecRod 1602; HH Braze 580; (GPD)	Chrome carbides
134	721	640	Silver-phosphorus-copper 5.5 7.25 bal.	1330	1190	6	ARS Phos-Silver 6; GSR 06; WEC Phos Silver	Ag; Cu; Mo; W; not for Fe or Ni alloys
135	718	602	Tin-copper-silver 10 30 bal.	1325	1115	5	APW Silvaloy 60; ASC Ascobraze 60BFJ; GSR 160; HH Braze 603 VTG; UWS Sil-60T; WEC Co-Silver 60T	
136	705	635	Indium-copper-silver 13 27 bal.	1300	1175		ASC Ascobraze 60BFK; GSR 260; (GPD); (HH)	

137	685	630	Indium-copper-silver 15 24 bal.	1265	1166	5	ASC Ascobraze 61BFK; HH Premabraze 615 VTG; WGP Incusil 15; (GPD)	
138	485	473	Indium-gold 20 80	905	883		ASC Ascobraze 80AK; ICA 19.2K	Cu; Fe; Ni; hard, brittle joints
139	425	425	Indium-gold 25 75	797	797		ASC Ascobraze 75AK; ICA 18K	Hard, brittle joints
140	232	232	Tin	450	450			Rarely used, poor wetting
141	230	166	Silver-Indium 10 90	446	331		ICA Indalloy No. 3	
142	157	157	Indium	315	315		ICA Indalloy No. 4	
143	117	117	Indium-Tin 50 50	225	225		ICA Indalloy No. 1	
144	980	760		1795	1400	4b or He	FMC Fannite “N”	For Fansteel #42 alloy and Cu
145	800	780	Nickel-copper-silver 0.5 24.5 bal.	1475	1435		APW T-51	
146	779	779	Titanium-cored silver-copper eutectic: Cu 28 — Ag 72, + Ti.	1435	1435	4a, b	HH Ti-Cored BT	For ceramic-to-metal seals
147	1230	1160	Palladium-silver 30 70	2250	2120	9	APW	SS, Steels
148	1120	1120	Palladium-manganese- 21 31 nickel (with 0.05 boron bal. and 0.02 lithium)	2050	2050	9	APW	High-temperature strength
149	1210	1210	Nickel-palladium 40 bal.	2210	2210	9	APW	Good wettability
150	860	770	Lithium-palladium-indium- 0.02 2.2 5.5 copper-silver 7.5 bal.	1580	1415	9	APW	SS. Low thermal conductivity

(Continued)

TABLE OF BRAZING FILLER METALS FOR ELECTRON TUBES (*Continued*)

NOTES

[1]—Alloy constituents are given in this sequence: the smallest additive first, others in increasing order, with the bulk constituent last, as balance.

[2]—Code letters signify suppliers and are listed below. Names following code letters are registered trademarks of the supplier. Code letters in parentheses signify that the alloy is not a stock item but can be custom-made. Omission of a supplier does not imply that the quality of his products is inferior. Alloys marked by (†) are being offered by APW in vacuum tube grade.

[3]—The chemical symbols for metals (Mo = molybdenum, W = tungsten, W_2C = tungsten carbide, Ni = nickel, Fe = iron, Cu = copper, Ag = silver) and the names of alloys, or abbreviations (SS = stainless steel), suggest parent metals which may be joined by the filler metal in question. (NM) = nonmagnetic; (NAHg) = not attacked by mercury.

[4]—Brazing operations for electron devices must be performed in inert or reducing atmospheres, or in vacuum: (a) Pure dry hydrogen or inert gases, (b) Vacuum, (c) Dissociated ammonia (see p. 156) (—60°F dew point or better), (d) Exothermic; rich, unpurified 6:1 air to gas ratio, or purified and dried.

[5]—Handy & Harman alloys marked "VTG" are produced as "Vacuum Tube Grade" with specially controlled, low impurity content, if so ordered. Items not marked VTG are not available from HH at this controlled level but as commercial alloys only. It might be well to emphasize Vacuum Tube Application when ordering alloys from other suppliers and to watch impurity content in all cases.

[6]—The liquidus temperatures of the Ag-Cu-P alloys Numbers 123 and 144 are 1480–1500°F; their working temperatures are near 1300°F.

[7]—The temperatures listed as liquidus temperatures for B-Si alloys No.'s 60, 81, and 82 are working temperatures rather than liquidus temperatures.

[8]—Alloys No. 68 and No. 72 are a duplication, and different values are given for liquidus and solidus. Entry No. 68 presents data recently released by Handy & Harman (HH), while No. 72 is close to values published by Western Gold & Platinum Company (WGP). Similarly, the HH values for alloys Nos. 71, 75, 77, 86, 129 are higher than those given by WGP, who believe, on the basis of their own extensive tests, substantiated by others, that their data are correct. The author of this chart does not intend to discriminate against these claims. Similar discrepancies may exist in other cases. Double entries contained in the original manuscript were eliminated to avoid confusion.

[9]—"New Era Brazing Turns to Filler Metals with Palladium," A. S. Cross, Jr., and J. B. Adamec, *Welding Journal*, Aug. 1963.

SUPPLIERS

ABC American Brass Company
414 Meadow Street
Waterbury 20, Conn.

APW American Platinum & Silver Division
Engelhard Industries, Inc.
231 New Jersey Railroad Avenue
Newark 5, N. J.

ARS Air Reduction Sales Company
150 East 42nd Street
New York 17, N. Y.

ASC American Silver Company, Inc.
36–07 Prince Street
Flushing 54, N. Y.

ASW All-State Welding Alloys Company, Inc.
249–55 Ferris Avenue
White Plains, N. Y.

BC The Borolite Corporation
Box 337
Niagara Falls, N. Y.

BPD Baker Platinum Division
Engelhard Industries, Inc.
113 Astor Street
Newark 5, N. J.

BSR Belmont Smelting & Refining Works, Inc.
330 Belmont Avenue
Brooklyn 7, N. Y.

CBC Chase Brass & Copper Company
236 Grand Street
Waterbury 20, Conn.

CC The Carborundum Company
P. O. Box 337
Niagara Falls, N. Y.

CLA Canadian Liquid Air Company Limited
1111 Beaver Hall Hill
Montreal, P. Q.

CM Coast Metals, Inc.
199 Rednick Avenue
Little Ferry, N. J.

CSC Crucible Steel Company of America
Oliver Bldg., Mellon Square
Pittsburgh 22, Pa.

DHC Driver-Harris Company
201 Middlesex Street
Harrison, N. J.

EWA Eutectic Welding Alloys Corporation
40–40 172nd St.
Flushing 58, N. Y.

FM Foote Mineral Company
18 W. Chelten Avenue
Philadelphia 44, Pa.

FMC Fansteel Metallurgical Corporation
2200 Sheridan Road
North Chicago, Ill.

GPD General Plate Division
Metals and Controls Division
Texas Instruments Incorporated
34 Forest Street
Attleboro, Mass.

GSR Goldsmith Bros. Smelting & Refining Co.
1300 W. 59th Street
Chicago 36, Ill.

HH Handy & Harman
850 Third Ave.
New York 22, N. Y.

ICA The Indium Corporation of America
1676 Lincoln Avenue
Utica 4, N. Y.

INCO The International Nickel Co., Inc.
67 Wall Street
New York 5, N. Y.

JMC Johnson, Matthey & Company, Inc.
608 5th Avenue
New York, N. Y.

JMN J. M. Ney Company
P. O. Box 990
Hartford 1, Conn.

LFA Little Falls Alloys, Inc.
189 Caldwell Avenue
Paterson 1, N. J.

MWP Metallwerk Plansee
Reutte, Tirol
Austria

RCB Revere Copper and Brass Incorporated
230 Park Avenue
New York 17, N. Y.

SAC Solar Aircraft Company
2200 Pacific Highway
San Diego 12, Calif.

SCC Sigmund Cohn Corporation
121 S. Columbus Avenue
Mt. Vernon, N. Y.

SEP Sylvania Electric Products, Inc.
Chemical and Metallurgical Division
Towanda, Pa.

TMC Temescal Metallurgical Corporation
1201 S. 47th Street
Richmond, Calif.

UWS United Wire & Supply Corporation
Providence 1, R. I.

VMC Vacuum Metals Corporation
Div. of Crucible Steel Co. of America
P. O. Box 977
Syracuse 1, N. Y.

WBD Wilbur B. Driver Company
1875 McCarter Highway
Newark 4, N. J.

WCC Wall Colmonoy Corporation
19345 John R Street
Detroit 3, Mich.

WEC Westinghouse Electric Corporation
P. O. Box 868
Pittsburgh 30, Pa.

WGP Western Gold & Platinum Company
525 Harbor Boulevard
Belmont, Calif.

Brazing stainless steel (see pp. 41–51).

Brazing, torch. Most torch-brazing procedures involve the use of a mixture of gases such as (1) air and city-gas, (2) oxygen and city-gas, (3) oxygen and acetylene, (4) propane or other fuel gases with air, (5) oxygen with hydrogen. Also, in most cases the use of a chemical flux is required. Its function is to fuse at a temperature lower than that at which the brazing alloy melts, and by flowing over the surfaces to be joined (and adjacent parts), it protects these parts from oxidation and/or exercises some cleaning action. The flux should not be called upon, however, to clean dirty or oxidized metal; parts to be joined by any type of brazing should be as clean as possible to begin with. For so-called silver soldering, a chemical mixture of borax, fluorides, and other materials is used. There are various proprietary fluxes on the market for different kinds of torch-brazing and for some kinds of controlled atmosphere-brazing.

Braze alloys or filler metals for torch brazing usually have lower melting points than the alloys used for controlled atmosphere-brazing without fluxes (see pp. 172 *et seq.*). Also, it is desirable in many cases of torch-brazing that the filler metal have a melting range resulting in a plastic stage, rather than the sharp melting point and free flow of simple metals and alloys. Poor fits and discontinuities can be filled or filleted with braze materials of this character. These effects are often obtained by alloying zinc, cadmium, and other low-melting, high-vapor-pressure elements with silver, copper, etc. Alloys containing easily vaporizable constituents should not be used for critical electron tube work (see pp. 36, 78) since the evaporated materials are likely to condense and deposit on surfaces where they are unwanted or where they might produce a deleterious poisoning effect, such as on oxide-coated cathodes.

Breakdown of cathode. This term is synonymous with **Activation of Cathodes** (see pp. 98 *et seq.*, p. 149). In the activation process, the original material, a mixture of barium, strontium, and sometimes calcium carbonates, is decomposed or broken down into the respective oxides with the liberation of carbon dioxide.

Breakdown voltage.[1] In a tube containing two electrodes and a gas at atmospheric pressure, at zero (dc) voltage between the two electrodes, the gas is practically a perfect insulator (e.g., two electrodes in dry air) and will remain so up to a certain voltage value, which is a function of both the kind of gas and the pressure.[2] At the critical value for a given set of conditions, called the breakdown voltage, the gas suddenly becomes conductive, an effect which is manifested as a spark of very short duration. The original very high resistance of the gas is lowered to the order of a few ohms under the action of the spark. Intermediate values of resistance cannot be realized in durable form.

If, however, the pressure in the tube is now reduced, self-sustaining currents of microamperes may flow when the gas changes from insulator to conductor. These are called Townsend Discharges. For example, in neon at a pressure of about 10 torr, with electrodes 1 cm apart, a current of a few microamperes is maintained by a dc potential of several hundred volts in series with a resistor of 100,000 ohms.

As stated, different gases have different breakdown or *ionization* voltages, and sometimes mixtures of gases have still other breakdown properties. For example,

---

[1] From *Electrical Discharges in Gases,* F. M. Penning, Macmillan Co., New York, New York, 1957.

[2] See PASCHEN LAW, p. 427.

small amounts of argon (0.1% to 5×10^{-4}%) added to neon cause the latter to ionize at a lower breakdown voltage than would be required for pure neon.

Breakdown may occur as a result of high-frequency fields, with consequences similar to those discussed above. This is the principle upon which the Tesla coil or sparker (pp. 134, 493) operates, and also that which causes the glow discharge seen in high-frequency induction heating (see p. 77). *Ionization* of the gas in the vessel causes a glow discharge over a certain pressure range. When the pressure is high, electron activity is restricted because of the closeness of the gas molecules (the mean free path is very short), so that at atmospheric pressure no glow discharge occurs. At very low pressures (below 10^{-5} torr), little or no glow discharge occurs because of the scarcity of gas molecules that can be ionized. When a piece of metal is heated, it gives off gases and, depending upon its work function, electrons, both of which interact to produce ionization.

Ionization is utilized in the gas-filled rectifier tube having a hot cathode and an anode. If an alternating voltage is applied to the tube, a heavy current will pass through the tube when the cathode is negative, but when the anode is negative, no current will pass because the anode is not emitting electrons. If, however, the voltage is made very high (greater than the Peak Inverse Anode Voltage), a gas discharge can start and an excessive current can flow in the other direction, which would be injurious to the tube. This is called a "flashback" and is a type of self-sustaining discharge which can occur in high-vacuum tubes.

For rectifying heavy current at low voltage, therefore, a hot-cathode, gas-filled tube is used. High-vacuum, hot-cathode tubes are used for rectifying high voltages at low current.

Additional References

"High Frequency Gas-Discharge Breakdown," S. C. Brown, *Proc. I. R. E.*, **39**, 1493, 1951.

"High Frequency Breakdown in Air at High Altitudes," A. D. MacDonald, *Proc. I. R. E.*, **47**, 436, 1959.

"Vacuum as an Insulator," R. Hawley, *Vacuum*, (Br) **10**, 310, 1960.

"Experimental Test of the Clump Hypothesis of Vacuum Breakdown for Low Voltages," M. Raether, Report R-148, Coordinated Science Laboratory, University of Illinois, Urbana, Illinois, July, 1962.

Breakoff seal (Breakoffsky) (see pp. 120, 123).

Bright dip for brass and copper (see p. 6).

Bronzes (see Brass and Bronze, pp. 38, 172).

BT braze material. This is a trade designation for the silver-copper eutectic (72% Ag, 28% Cu, melting point 779°C) as manufactured by Handy & Harman Co., New York. (See p. 184, No. 130.)

Bypass valve. A valve which allows the forepump to be directly connected to the vessel being pumped, bypassing the diffusion pump, so that rapid cycling is accomplished. The valve C in Fig. 18 (p. 76) is used as a bypass valve.

Cadmium. This metallic element is a constituent of some intermediate melting-point brazing alloys and has a high vapor pressure (see the table on p. 146); therefore, its use in electron tubes should be restricted. Cadmium is also used as a rust-protective plating for steel. Tube technicians should watch for cadmium-plated screws and nuts which sometimes get into places where stainless steel parts are stored. Cadmium plating can be stripped by the processes described on pp. 33, 34.

Carbon, activated (see ACTIVATED CARBON and CHARCOAL, p. 149).

Carbon, graphite. Graphite carbon is sometimes used for anodes in power tubes. It is difficult to outgas; the minimum temperature for the removal of most sorbed gases appears to be in the neighborhood of 2150°C. When carbon is used as a crucible for melting or evaporating metals *in vacuo,* some contamination of the metal by carbon should be expected. This is especially true of sensitive metals such as titanium.

Colloidal carbon in distilled water or alcohol is useful for coating the inside of vacuum tubes as an electrostatic shielding electrode, with subsequent heating or baking at 350°C. (See pp. 157, 199 *et seq.*)

Carbon is frequently used in the making of glassblowing jigs and tools (paddles, etc.) and is also employed in the making of jigs for torch- or induction-brazing.

Carbon, thin films. Thin films of unattached pure carbon can be made by firing in a hydrogen furnace a good-quality filter paper (lowest ash content[1]) between two fine-ground plates of preoxidized type 304 stainless steel. The temperature of firing is about 800°C in dry hydrogen. This process can also be done in vacuum by means of induction or radiation heating.

Carbon blacks (see ACTIVATED CARBON, p. 149).

Carbon dioxide (CO_2). An odorless, colorless gas, at room temperature, having a molecular weight of 44.01, a density of 1.98 gm/liter at 0°C, and solidifying at −78.5°C to form CO_2 snow (dry ice). The solid sublimes directly into the gaseous form without a liquid phase at atmospheric pressure. Carbon dioxide gas is very soluble in cold water (171.3 gm/100 ml of water at 0°C), also in alcohol and acetone. As "dry ice," it is a useful refrigerant for vacuum-cold traps either alone or mixed with acetone or alcohol. Such mixtures form a lower-temperature refrigerant than CO_2 snow alone.

Tank carbon dioxide bubbled through isopropyl alcohol is useful as a protective atmosphere for the inside of copper vacuum vessels during torch-brazing or heat-treating in muffles. The alcohol-saturated gas is fed at a small positive pressure through a small opening in the vessel that is to be protected. When this vapor mixture comes in contact with a hot surface, there are decomposition products including carbon monoxide and hydrogen, both of which have a strong reducing effect on the oxides of copper.

Carbon dioxide is the major gas evolved during the activation of oxide-coated cathodes.

Carbon dioxide glow discharge colors (see pp. 135, 213).

Carbon dioxide ice (dry ice) (see CARBON DIOXIDE, above).

Carbonization of thoriated filaments (see p. 92).

Carpenter alloys.[2] Certain nickel-iron alloys used for glass-sealing are made by the Carpenter Steel Company, Reading, Pennsylvania. Alloys with similar properties

---

[1] Examples are Whatman No. 41H or No. 44 manufactured by W. & R. Balston, Ltd., London, and distributed by laboratory supply houses in the United States.

[2] See "Carpenter Alloys for Electronic, Magnetic, and Electrical Applications," 1962.

and compositions are made by Sylvania, Driver-Harris, Allegheny-Ludlum, American Steel, Wilbur B. Driver, and others.

Cataphoresis. In electron tube technology, this term indicates a method of depositing materials by electrolysis. Tungsten and tantalum filaments can be coated with the oxides of thorium, lanthanum, and other rare-earth metals,[1,2,3] and with the hexaborides of thorium, alkaline earth, and rare-earth metals[4] for purposes of enhancing their electron emission. Tungsten filaments can also be coated with aluminum oxide (Alundum, alumina) by cataphoresis for electrical insulating purposes at high temperatures (see p. 85).

Cataphoretic deposition of aluminum oxide (see p. 85).

Cataphoretic deposition of thoria, etc. (see above).

Cathaloys (see pp. 93–94).

Cathodes, general.[5,6] The element in an electron tube which is connected to a negative potential and serves as a source of electrons is called a cathode. This may be either a cold cathode (see p. 192) or a thermionic (hot) cathode consisting of tungsten, molybdenum, platinum, or other bare metal in the form of wire, coil, strip, disc, tube (sleeve), etc., and heated to a temperature at which primary electrons are emitted, depending on the work function (see pp. 235, 432–4, 570–1) of the metal (p. 88 *et seq.*). Sometimes alloys or mixed materials are used, for example, as thoriated tungsten (pp. 89–92).

Oxide-coated cathodes, on the other hand, are those in which a base metal, normally nickel, although other bases have been used, is coated with a chemical mixture of materials which have a very low work function; i.e., they emit electrons at temperatures lower than those mentioned above (pp. 96–102).

There are still other types of electron-tube cathodes which have been developed to have certain enhanced characteristics. Examples of such developments are the Philips dispenser cathodes (pp. 103–104).

Cathode is also used to designate that part of an electroplating or electropolishing system which is connected to the negative pole of the power source. In normal plating with nickel, silver, copper, gold, chromium, platinum, rhodium, cadmium, zinc, and other metals, the article to be plated is made the cathode. The anode is usually a piece of the pure metal which replenishes the ions of that metal in the

---

[1] "Some Experiments on Thorium Oxide Cathodes," (in French), O. A. Weinrich, *Rev. Gen. d'Electr.*, **54,** 243, 1945.

[2] "Spectral Emissivity and Electron Emission Constants of Thoria Cathodes," T. E. Hanley, *J. Appl. Phys.*, **19,** 583, 1948.

[3] "Cataphoretic Deposition of Thoria on Tantalum," C. P. Hadley, *Rev. Sci. Instr.*, **27,** 177, 1956.

[4] "Boride Cathodes," J. M. Lafferty, *Phys. Rev.*, **79,** 1012, 1950; also same author, *J. Appl. Phys.*, **22,** 299, 1951. See also "The Magnesium Oxide Cold Cathode and Its Application in Vacuum Tubes," A. M. Skellett, B. G. Firth, and D. W. Mayer, *Proc. I. R. E.*, **47,** 1704, 1959.

[5] See OTS Selective Bibliography: "Thermionics and Cathodes," SB-431, Office of Technical Services, U.S. Dept. of Commerce, Washington, D.C., September, 1960.

[6] See "Thermionic Electron Sources," G. A. Haas, NRL Report 5657, U.S. Naval Research Laboratory, Washington, D.C., October 6, 1961.

See also bibliography on p. 102.

solution which migrate to the work. In some types of electropolishing, the work is made the anode, and a process of *deplating* takes place.

Cathodes, cold.[1, 2] It is possible to secure conduction through a gas-filled tube with a cold cathode. If the gas pressure in such a tube is within certain limits and the voltage between its electrodes is gradually increased, a point is reached where current flow through the tube increases abruptly (see BREAKDOWN VOLTAGE, p. 188) and the tube is filled with a glow, the color of which is characteristic of the gas used.

If no electrons were present in the gas before application of the voltage, conduction could not take place. However, some ionized particles always exist in any gas, and thus positive ions are attracted to the negative electrode and negative electrons to the positive electrode. The electrons will collide with atoms of gas and, if they reach a sufficiently high velocity before collision, will produce ionization; i.e., ionization will result if they fall through a difference in potential at least equal to the ionizing potential of the gas. Thus, the possibility of a self-sustained discharge appearing must depend in large part upon two things: (1) the mean free path (p. 363) of the electron, and (2) the potential applied between the electrodes. At atmospheric pressure the mean free path is so short that practical potentials will not give the electrons sufficient velocity between collisions to produce ionization. Reducing the pressure will then lengthen the mean free path until ionization results. If the pressure is still further reduced, however, a point is reached where the potential must again be raised to produce ionization, until finally no ionization is possible (as in a near-perfect vacuum). At these low pressures the length of the mean free path exceeds the dimensions of the tube so that most electrons travel the entire distance from cathode to anode without colliding with a gas atom.

The foregoing explanation alone is not sufficient to make the appearance of a self-sustained discharge understandable, since each electron is traveling toward the anode, and each new electron that it frees by ionization must lie still nearer to the anode. Thus, each new electron will produce less ionization than its predecessor, and the ionization process would, of necessity, decrease as all electrons are drawn to the anode. Eventually, all free electrons would be removed from the tube, and conduction would cease.

Apparently the positive ions also produce ionization as they travel to the cathode. This they do by collision with other atoms of gas, by positive-ion bombardment of the cathode, or by both. Thus, new electrons are freed at points close to the cathode, and will, in traveling to the anode, collide with and ionize other atoms. If a sufficient number of electrons is freed by positive-ion collisions and bombardment, the action becomes cumulative and a glow discharge is established.

Since neither cathode nor anode is heated in a cold-cathode tube, either electrode may serve as the cathode, depending on the polarity of the applied emf. Cold-cathode tubes are therefore inherently bilateral conductors; i.e., they will pass current equally in either direction. Examples of such tubes are the small neon lamps that are used as pilot lights or indicators of live circuits.

---

[1] Excerpted from *Fundamentals of Vacuum Tubes*, by A. V. Eastman, with the permission of the publisher, McGraw-Hill Book Company, Inc., New York. The material is taken from both the second and third editions (1941 and 1949).

[2] See "The Magnesium Oxide Cold Cathode and its Application in Vacuum Tubes," A. M. Skellett, B. G. Firth and D. W. Mayer, *Proc. I. R. E.*, **47**, 1704, 1959.

It is possible to make cold-cathode tubes conduct more readily in one direction than in the other by constructing the electrodes with different cross-sectional areas. For example, if one electrode consists of a small wire and the other is of relatively large cross section, the current flow will be greatest when the small electrode is positive. Apparently the tube drop is nearly independent of the magnitude of the current flowing, so long as the current density on the surface of the cathode does not exceed a given amount. However, if the current required by the load is such as to cause the current density to exceed this critical value on the small electrode but not on the large one, a much higher voltage would have to be applied in one direction than in the other to cause the same current to flow on both polarities of the supply. Since the voltage of both halves of the ac supply is normally the same, the current flow in one direction is much greater than in the other, and a net direct, or rectified, current results.

Cold-cathode tubes are commonly used as voltage regulators in circuits where the voltage across the load will be maintained at the rated voltage of the tube, provided the supply voltage is appreciably higher. If the load current increases, tending to reduce the voltage, the tube will immediately draw less current in order to satisfy the current-voltage relationship, so that the total current through a resistance in the circuit remains essentially constant regardless of the magnitude of the load current. A reduction is, of course, accompanied by an increase in the current flowing through the tube. On the other hand, an increase in the supply voltage will tend to raise the output voltage, but the current through the tube will immediately rise until the increased drop through the resistance again leaves the same output voltage across the tube and load.

Regulator circuits may be designed using cold-cathode tubes which will maintain the output potential constant to within a fraction of a volt. (See Chapter 8, third edition, of reference (1) above.)

Some gas molecules can be ionized by ultraviolet rays (e.g., the Heaviside Layer, about 60 miles above the earth's surface, is ionized by radiation from the sun); by X-rays (see BAYARD-ALPERT GAUGE in this connection, p. 162); by the alpha or gamma rays emitted by radioactive materials (e.g., the Alphatron vacuum gauge, a cold-cathode ionization gauge in which the source of ionizing energy comes from a small amount of radioactive material within the tube); and by cosmic rays striking the earth's surface and atmosphere, as in the Geiger-Muller tube. In addition to these phenomena in which gas molecules are ionized, electrons can be released from the surfaces of certain metals by the action of various kinds of radiation, including those mentioned above. For example, visible and infrared light rays can liberate electrons from cesium on cesium oxide, while ultraviolet radiation can release electrons from platinum and tungsten. It is upon this effect that the operation of gas-filled photoelectric cells is based. *Cf.* Penning, Philips gauge, p. 431.

Cathodes, dispenser (see p. 103).

Cathodes, electroplating (see p. 191).

Cathodes, oxide-coated (see pp. 96 *et seq.*).

Cathodes, Philips (see pp. 103 *et seq.*).

Cathode bases (see pp. 93–96).

Cathode coating (see p. 97).

Cathode nickels (see pp. 93, 293).

Cathode ray tube (see pp. 130, 131).

Cathode ray tubes, conductive coating for (see pp. 157, 199).

Cathode sputtering.[1] In electron tubes in which some gas is present, whether by design or outgassing of the tube elements due to overheating, the application of excessive positive voltage to the anode gives rise to positive ions resulting from the collision of electrons with the gas molecules. Since the cathode is negative, these positive ions travel toward it with sufficient velocity to eject atoms from the cathode material itself. This is evidenced by the fact that in the spectrum of the glow discharge around the cathode, lines of the cathode material are strongly exhibited. This effect is turned to use in the spectroscopy of metals where the metal to be examined is formed into a hollow cathode. Such cathode-sputtering is also useful, for example, in coating small mirrors with silver. In this work the pressure must be kept low in order that the sputtering will be as efficient as possible, and also so that contaminating gases, which might dull the sputtered surface by chemical action (e.g., oxides) are reduced to a minimum. In addition, at higher pressures the atoms of metal tend to form in clumps or aggregates before deposition, and this causes the deposited surface to appear discolored or black.

However, in electron tubes in general, sputtering due to ion bombardment is to be avoided because it may result in destruction or shortening the life of the cathode. (See p. 101.)

Cements and adhesives. Most commercial adhesives and cements are unsuitable for vacuum work because they contain volatile organic ingredients or solvents and/or have too low an operating temperature. However, for room-temperature application in demountable systems, etc., many products find some use.

The EPOXY or EPOXIDE resins, in general, consist of a two- or three-component system: (1) the uncured resin, (2) the curing agent (hardener or catalyst), and (3) a filler. Cured epoxy resins containing inorganic fillers have a fairly low vapor pressure at room temperature and can be used up to about 100°C in demountable systems. The curing agent is usually volatile to some degree so that a complete heat-curing is required for the epoxies to be used in vacuum work.[2,3] Properly applied according to the manufacturers' instructions, the epoxies are vacuum-tight and have high strength when applied to clean surfaces. Except for those epoxy-bonding materials which have metallic or conductive fillers, such as carbon, aluminum, etc., these products have good electrical properties. The epoxies are water- and solvent-resistant when thoroughly cured, and also resist the action of weak acids, alkalies, and other chemical reagents. In addition to their uses as bonding agents for many materials, including metals, glass, ceramics, and some plastics (except possibly Teflon, Kel-F, and other fluorocarbons, which can sometimes be specially treated for improved adhesion), the epoxies can be used as potting, encapsulating and molding compounds. The hardness or elasticity of the epoxies can sometimes be controlled by the ratio of curing agent added; the data on formulation is given by the various suppliers.

SILICATE CEMENTS. These are inorganic cements which have as a vehicle sodium silicate (water glass) or potassium silicate in water and as fillers various ceramic or glass powders, powdered mica, metallic powders, or mixtures of these. These cements adhere well to clean glass and metal surfaces, but are not vacuum-tight, water-

---

[1] See also pp. 224, 498.

[2] See the table on p. 141.

[3] J. F. Sayers, *Jour. Sci. Instr.* (Br), **37**, 203, 1960.

resistant, or flexible. They are sometimes used in small amounts or thin layers to bond components inside vacuum tubes. Heavy layers should be avoided because the cement tends to harden on the surface, and in subsequent evacuation, the water trapped beneath this skin ruptures it to form bubbles or blowholes which may cause failure of the cement. Silicate cements will withstand moderate heating (up to about 500°C) but tend to be gassy *in vacuo*. They should not be used near oxide-coated cathodes.

Sodium or potassium silicate solutions in water can be used to cement well-fitting glass or ceramic parts where only a small amount of the liquid is required. These solutions are also useful in low concentrations as a binder for graphite-conductive coatings (see AQUADAG, pp. 157, 199) and fluorescent screens on glass (see pp. 250 *et seq.*).

These cements have a vapor pressure of about 10^{-5} torr at 500°C or 2×10^{-7} at room temperature after baking.

Sodium silicate-base cements are marketed by The Sauereisen Cement Co. (Pittsburgh 15, Pennsylvania) as Sauereisen and by Central Scientific Company (Chicago 13, Illinois) as Insalute, or they can be formulated by the user.

PHOSPHATE-BASE CEMENTS. These are similar to the silicate-base cements in that they will withstand moderately high temperatures (maximum in the neighborhood of 500°C). Unlike the silicate cements, the phosphate cements consist of two separate components which are mixed just before use, and the mixture is cured at 315°C for 1 hour. They are more water-resistant than the silicate cements. The electrical properties are fair at room temperature, gradually deteriorating as heat is increased. There are no data as to the porosity or vapor pressure. The phosphate cements can be obtained from High Temperature Instruments Corporation, 1 Highland Avenue, Bala-Cynwyd, Pennsylvania, under the trade names Allen P-1 and Allen PBX Ceramic Cement.

DEKHOTINSKY CEMENTS.[1] These shellac-base cements somewhat resemble sealing wax and are useful for making temporary joints. The cement is applied by heating it until fluid and applying to clean, hot surfaces, which are then pressed together until cool. The cement has a vapor pressure of about 10^{-6} torr at room temperature, and about 10^{-4} at 73°C, which limits its usefulness to not much higher than room temperatures. Good adhesion and strength can be obtained with this cement if properly applied. There are several grades, of different melting points and degrees of hardness. They are slowly soluble in alcohols.

EASTMAN 910 ADHESIVE. This material forms very strong bonds on porous surfaces and on a number of different types of materials, including metals, ceramics, glass, and rubber. The setting time is very fast, being 10 to 30 seconds for nonporous materials such as glass and metal, to 3 to 8 minutes for wood. The maximum bond strength is achieved in about 48 hours, at which time the tensile strength has been measured at 5030 psi, and the shear strength at 2200 psi on metal-to-metal bonds.

The constituents are approximately 90% monomer, 7% polymeric thickening agent, and 3% plasticizer. These ingredients come mixed ready for use. The bonds are very slowly affected by humidity, but the cement is resistant to alcohol, benzene, and acetone, and somewhat resistant to acids and alkalies. The material can be used as a vacuum seal at room temperatures, but it is not to be used above 85°C,

[1] Central Scientific Company, Chicago 13, Illinois.

although short exposures to temperatures up to 100°C might be tolerated for short periods.

SILICONE RESINS. Some of these may be useful in vacuum work. J. R. Young[1] has described one which can be used as a permanent leak sealer with baking temperatures up to 300°C.

Ceramics[2] (see ALUMINUM OXIDE, p. 153; BORON NITRIDE, pp. 168 *et seq.;* LAVA, pp. 340 *et seq.;* also CERAMIC-TO-METAL SEALS, pp. 67–75).

The use of ceramics in the construction of experimental electron tubes is subject to certain limitations. The hard, fired ceramic bodies, such as alumina, zirconia, steatite, beryllia, porcelain, etc., cannot be machined by conventional methods, but can be formed by grinding operations which are usually expensive and difficult. In mass-production tube manufacture, however, it becomes economically feasible to mold or slip-cast such ceramic parts, but this is prohibitive for small laboratory operations. For some applications either Lava in one of its forms or boron nitride can be used to advantage. Both these materials are machinable by conventional methods; the latter is somewhat more amenable to very fine detail—threads, clean holes, and very close tolerances—and requires no firing except to outgas. The Lavas must be fired to develop their properties and are not machinable after firing.

Boron nitride is somewhat porous and therefore precautions must be taken to avoid absorption of water, gases, and other contaminants. Cleaning is to be done dry; i.e., freshly machined surfaces should not be handled with bare fingers, and unmachined surfaces should be cleaned with very fine abrasive cloth (aluminum oxide-coated Aloxite) and then not handled. No water, solvents, or chemicals should be used. The finished pieces are to be placed in an air-oven at 110°–150°C for several hours and then vacuum-fired in a glass bulb at 500°C or in a tantalum container at 900°C, after which they should be immediately assembled in a dust-free, low-humidity area, or remain sealed in vacuum until use.

The Lavas are much less porous after firing (see pp. 341–342 for firing schedule and additional data), but there is some evidence that these materials should not be used too close to hot oxide-coated cathodes.

In the use of any ceramic material of construction, consideration should be given to its expansion characteristics. This applies particularly to those instances in which metal bonds are to be made, and also to places where the ceramics are close fits with unbonded metal parts, or where screws and nuts are used to fasten parts together. The ceramics, in general, are very strong in compression but weak in tension and torsion, and their expansion *rates* are likely to be different from those of metals.

---

[1] "An Ultrahigh Vacuum Leak-Sealing Material," J. R. Young, *Rev. Sci. Instr.*, **35,** 116, 1964.

[2] See also "Investigation for the Development of Ceramic Bodies for Electron Tubes," H. R. Wisely, for U.S. Air Force Cambridge Research Laboratories, AFCRL 344, Cambridge, Massachusetts, May, 1961; "High Temperature Dielectric Materials," D. A. Lupfer, for AFCRL. Final Report, Contract No. AF 19(604)–5730, August 31, 1961. Available from Office of Tech. Services, U.S. Dept. of Commerce, Washington 25, D.C.; "Ceramics as Insulators and Dielectrics," F. J. Oliver, *Elec. Mfg.*, p. 10, May 1950; "Design Limitations for Ceramic Parts," N. H. Snyder and J. H. Koenig, *ibid.*, p. 90, December 1950; *Ultrahigh Vacuum and its Applications,* R. W. Roberts and T. A. Vanderslice, pp. 95, 105, Prentice-Hall, Inc., Englewood Cliffs, N.J., 1963; *Dielectric Materials and Applications,* A. R. von Hippel, John Wiley & Sons, New York, 1954.

Such very porous materials as firebrick, although highly refractory, should not be used either in vacuum tubes or as furniture in the hydrogen furnace. Semirefractory materials not classified as ceramics, such as Transite (asbestos-portland cement mixtures), asbestos, and bonded mica materials, should not be used in vacuum systems because they are either likely to be very gassy and/or contain organic or easily volatilized constituents.

Ceramic-to-metal seals (see pp. 67 *et seq.*).

Ceramvar. An iron-nickel-cobalt alloy suitable for ceramic-to-metal seals, especially for sealing to high alumina. Its properties are given below (W. B. Driver Co.).

Composition:	Fe, 48%; Ni, 27%; Co, 25%
Density (lb/in.^{3})	0.295
Specific gravity (gm/cc)	8.17
Melting point (°C)	1421

Specific heat (calculated), (gm-cal/gm/°C)

−100	0	+20	100	200	300	400	500
0.095	0.111	0.112	0.119	0.125	0.131	0.136	0.141

Thermal conductivity (cgs) 20°C	0.040
600	0.057
Electrical resistivity at 20°C (microhm-cm)	36.9
ohm-mil-ft	222
Electrical conductivity (20°C % IACS)	4.679
Thermal emf versus Cu (0°–100°C)	−0.039 mv/°C

Temperature coefficient of resistivity from 20°C to temperature (°C)

−80	0	100	200	300	400	500	600
0.003	0.003	0.0038	0.0039	0.0039	0.0037	0.0034	0.0030

Curie temperature (°C)	525–550
Modulus of elasticity (psi × 10^6)	19
Modulus of rigidity (psi × 10^6)	7.1
Transformation temperature (°C)	below −80

Average coefficient of thermal expansion from 20°C to temperature (°C)

Temperature (°C)	100	200	300	400	500	600	700	800	900	1000
Coefficient $\times 10^{-6}$ per °C	8.80	8.70	8.39	7.96	7.65	8.32	9.46	10.47	11.34	12.12

Ceramvar machines much like R-Monel (Monel Alloy R-405; see p. 382). High-speed steel, Stellite, or cemented carbide tools having smaller cutting angles than for steel are used.

Ceramvar can be cleaned by methods used for Kovar (p. 337).

The alloy can be brazed to metallized ceramics (see pp. 67 *et seq.*) with commercial brazing alloys. The following conditions must be met for making successful seals:

1. The components to be joined must be absolutely clean.

2. The joint must be designed to have a high mechanical strength prior to bonding. Ceramic should be in compression rather than in tension.

3. If possible, the thermal expansion of the brazing alloy should be close to that of the components.

4. Brazing time and temperature must be accurately controlled.

5. Ceramvar is to be annealed or stress-relieved before seals are made. Procedures similar to those for Kovar (p. 330) can be used.

6. Copper-plating Ceramvar diminishes intergranular penetration. Gold-copper alloys are less apt to penetrate than copper-silver alloys.

7. Do not use fluxes. Atmosphere-brazing (in hydrogen or vacuum) is preferred. Uniform heating is required.

Cermets. These are combinations of ceramic and metals in various proportions, applied by chemical, flame-spray, or plasma-arc processes, for the purpose of protecting metals, etc., against high temperatures.

Cesium, preparation of, in the laboratory. Distilled metallic cesium can be prepared in the laboratory for subsequent introduction into vacuum tubes by the following method (Fig. 45).

The apparatus, of Pyrex glass, is to be evacuated and baked at 450° to 500°C before the tantalum container is loaded into the bulb. After cooling, the bulb is cracked open at *A*——*A* (see the figure), and the tantalum container (previously vacuum-outgassed) is loaded with the materials given below and suspended as shown in the figure. For a 20-gm yield of cesium, place in the container 25.2 gm of cesium chloride, reagent-grade, and 8 gm of calcium metal, reagent grade, freshly chipped or scraped so as to have a minimum of oxide present. Thorough mixing is not necessary. After the bomb is sealed together, the system is pumped down, with the cold-trap in place, and while pumping is going on, the tantalum container is heated by induction. Reaction of the two ingredients will take place at or below red heat, and the metallic cesium will condense on the cooler parts of the system in the region *B*——*B*. A Bunsen burner is used to heat this part of the tubing to make the metal run successively into the ampoules 1, 2, 3, 4, etc. When the ampoules are one-half to two-thirds full, they can be sealed off at the constriction.

Since cesium metal is highly reactive, the apparatus should be sealed off at the constriction beyond the cold trap and not reused. Disposal should be made according to existing safety standards.

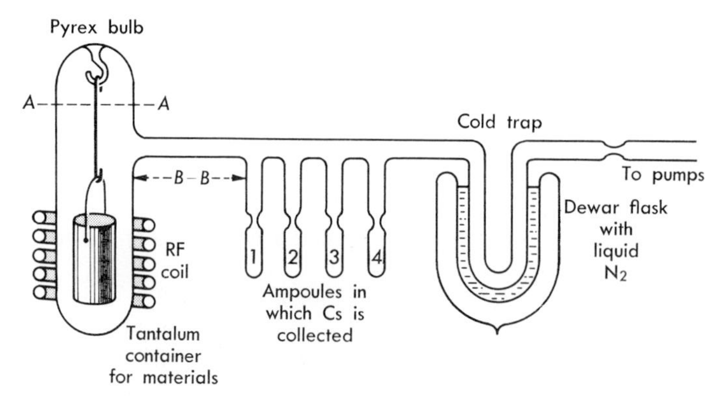

FIG. 45. Preparation of cesium in the laboratory.

Cesium, vapor pressure of (see p. 146).

Ceto getters. An alloy of thorium, mischmetal, and aluminum.[1]

Characteristics of tubes, variation of, with geometry. (see p. 132).

Charcoal, activated (see ACTIVATED CHARCOAL, p. 149).

Charles' law (see GAS LAWS, p. 265).

Chemical procedures (see pp. 3–35).

Chemisorption (or Chemosorption)[2]. In vacuum technology, these terms are used to describe the removal of gases by chemical reaction, with some substance or mixture of substances in the vessel. Most ordinary gettering procedures (e.g., the absorption of oxygen and water vapor by barium) are examples of simple chemisorption. A typical two-stage chemisorption is that in which the oxides of iron, copper, chromium, tungsten, molybdenum, and other metals are removed by heating to appropriate temperatures in hydrogen; the subsequent removal of the water vapor thus formed is by evacuation.

For precisely controlled chemisorption, the nature of the contaminants must be known and the active gas or absorber must be dry and of high purity. (*Cf.* PHYSISORPTION, p. 435, and DESORPTION, p. 224.)

Chevron baffle. This is a type of vacuum baffle in which there is no line-of-sight optical path between the pump and the vessel being evacuated, this being accomplished by a series of chevron-shaped fins fixed at an angle, and which can be water- or refrigerant-cooled. The chevron baffle has a conductance which compares favorably with that of other types.

Chrome iron. This is an alloy of 72% iron and 28% chromium used as a glass-sealing metal with certain soft glasses such as Corning #8160 and #001. (See p. 56.)

Chromium, vapor pressure of (see p. 146).

Chromium oxide on stainless steel (see pp. 37, 41).

Chromium plating (see p. 25).

Cleaning fluid, chromic-sulfuric (see p. 5).

Cleaning procedures for tube components (see pp. 1–23).

Cleaning solution for glass and tantalum (see pp. 7, 16).

Closed spaces, avoidance of in vacuum components (see pp. 134, 173).

Coatings, conductive. Various materials are used to provide electrically conductive coatings on electron-tube wall surfaces. In wide use are the Aquadag colloidal carbon dispersions.[3] Instructions for using these are given by the manufacturer as follows:

> There are two methods commonly used for coating the walls of cathode-ray tubes with CRT Interior Wall Coating. Both these methods give satisfactory results, and the choice of the method depends primarily upon the technique employed by the user.
>
> The first method of coating a cathode-ray tube is to coat the walls of the tube and the upper portion of the neck with CRT Interior Wall Coating as it is supplied. Before using material from the jar, stir with a clean paddle to ensure a uniform dispersion. This is particularly true if the material in the jar has stood

---

[1] See note on p. 107.

[2] See "Molecular Sieve Pumping," R. R. Bannock, *Vacuum* (Br), **12,** 101, 1962. See also Zeolites, p. 572.

[3] Data on Aquadag Colloidal Carbon Dispersions courtesy of the Acheson Colloids Corp., Port Huron, Michigan.

for any length of time before being used. If your judgment indicates that the material is a little too heavy for proper application, sufficient distilled water should be added to bring it to the viscosity desired. The portion of the neck which the gun contacts should be coated with a mixture of CRT Interior Wall Coating containing approximately 20% Kasil #1 (potassium silicate solution, 28%). Sodium silicate may be substituted for the potassium silicate if desired, but we recommend sodium silicate of a low alkaline ratio. Since Kasil #1 contains 28% solids, substitution should take into consideration the solids content of the material substituted. The addition of the silicate binder to CRT Interior Wall Coating for this portion of the tube is necessary tò prevent scratching of the film by the friction prongs on the gun and also to prevent the prongs from burning through the film when the tube is operated.

The second method is to use the mixture of CRT Interior Wall Coating and approximately 20% Kasil #1 for the wall of the tube as well as for the neck. This gives the graphite film greater adhesion throughout the tube. This method requires greater care to ensure proper drying because the silicate binder retains approximately 6% moisture in normal atmospheric conditions.

In both methods the long-handled brush is used for application as the tube (inclined at an angle) is rotated. (*Note:* A glass-blowing lathe can be used to advantage.) The brush should have relatively short bristles and they should be sable or camel hair. A daub of the coating is smeared on the button, and then the wall is coated in the usual manner, starting at the top of the tube and working down toward the neck. Normally, one brushful is sufficient to coat a 5-inch tube. The coating should not be applied so heavily that ridges are formed or that the material runs. A quantity of the dispersion may be transferred to a flat, open container, preferably one equipped with a rotating wheel with paddles. This will keep the dispersion uniform throughout the day and will prevent the material from drying or caking. The brush used in coating the tube may be filled by holding it on the rotating wheel.

The neck of the tube may be coated with the same brush or with a special brush having a stiff handle and stiffer bristles. This will depend upon the technique of the operators. A sharp boundary on the lower edge of the coating can be obtained by the brush itself, or by holding a rag-covered stick on the edge as the tube rotates.

After the tube is coated, it should be dried for 15 to 30 minutes by forcing a current of *dry* air through the tube. (*Note:* Rotation of the tube may continue during the drying.) The length of time required will vary with the technique employed, but it is very important that the tube be thoroughly dried. Some manufacturers employ a lehr oven for prebaking the tubes before evacuation. If such a prebaking period is used, it is important that air be circulated through the tube during this operation as well, to remove any moisture or gases that may be driven from the film inside the tube. If prebaking ovens are used, the tubes should be heated at a temperature of 360°C, or above, for a period of at least 30 minutes. Other manufacturers have found that prebaking is not necessary. It is their practice to heat the tubes at temperatures in the vicinity of 385° to 400°C for 20 to 30 minutes while the tubes are being evacuated.

When adding sodium silicate or potassium silicate to this dispersion, it is merely necessary to pour the silicate into the CRT Interior Wall Coating and stir with a clean paddle until the mixture appears uniform. Vigorous shaking or high-speed mixing will thin the dispersion. Therefore, unless a lower viscosity mix is desired, agitation by either of these methods is not recommended.

Conductive coatings containing metallic silver are manufactured by E. I. du Pont de Nemours & Co., Inc., and by Engelhard Industries, Inc., East Newark, New Jersey.

Du Pont[1] Conductive Silver Preparations are classified into six groups which represent the major applications:

Group 1—for direct soldering: Application and firing on ceramic bodies for use as capacitors or printed circuits with direct solderability. Firing temperature 1400°F (760°C). Parts are placed in cool oven and temperature is raised to about 350°C in about 9 minutes, then to 760°C in another 3 minutes. Parts can be removed from oven when temperature has dropped to about 350°C.

Group 2—for use prior to electroplating: Application and firing on ceramic bodies (steatite, porcelain, alumina), as well as on soft and high-temperature glasses, where the fired coating is to be nickel- or copper-plated and tinned for hermetic seal or similar use. Firing temperature 1250°F (677°C). Heating schedule same as for Group 1.

Group 3—for application on mica: Application and firing on mica for capacitor use. Firing temperature 1100°F (593°C). Parts are placed in cool oven (40°C) and temperature is raised rapidly to 593°C, held for about 1 minute, and then allowed to cool rapidly. Parts can be removed from oven at about 350°C.

Group 4—as electrodes on special ceramic materials: Electrode coatings for piezoelectric ceramic and thermistor bodies. Firing temperature range 1100°–1300°F (593°–704°C). Firing schedule same as for Groups 1 and 2.

Group 5—thermosetting type for conductive cements: Low-temperature, thermosetting compositions for application on nonceramic bases (e.g., epoxy resin boards or metallic diodes) which will not withstand the elevated temperatures required for fired-on silvers. Coatings are usually cured at temperatures of 150°–260°C.

Group 6—air-dry type for static shielding: Air-dry compositions on nonceramic base materials, such as Lucite acrylic resin and polystyrene resins, which will not withstand temperatures above the 80°–100°C range.

Typical silver preparations[2] and suggested thinners:

Group 1—for direct soldering (not suitable for electroplating).

Silver	*Method of application*	*Suggested thinner*
#6730	Squeegee	Butyl Carbitol acetate
#6337	Banding wheel	Butyl Cellosolve
#7167	Dip or spray	Toluene or xylene

[1] From their bulletin, "Ceramic Products CP 2–361" (1962), Electrochemicals Dept., E. I. du Pont de Nemours & Co., Wilmington 98, Delaware.

[2] Examples have been chosen from each group to illustrate the wide variety of Du Pont Conductive Silver Preparations. Many others, varying in metal content, viscosity, specific gravity, and thinners, are available for specific requirements.

Group 2—for use prior to electroplating (the acid copper bath CuP-7 on p. 28 is suitable).

#6216	Brush	Toluene
#6980	Squeegee	Butyl Carbitol acetate

Group 3—for application on mica.

#6831	Squeegee	Butyl Carbitol acetate

Group 4—as electrodes on special ceramic materials

#7095 (for use on Pb-Zr-Ti piezoelectric crystals)

	Squeegee	Butyl Carbitol acetate

#4731 (for use on Ba-Ti piezoelectric ceramic materials)

	Dip or spray	Toluene

#7345 (for use on thermistor bodies)

	Squeegee	Butyl Carbitol acetate

#7313 (for use on thermistor bodies)

	Dip or spray	Toluene

#7713 (for use on soft glasses)

	Squeegee	Butyl Carbitol acetate or toluene

Group 5—for nonceramic materials; nonsolderable. Should be kept in refrigerator for extended shelf-life.

#5504A	Squeegee	Butyl Cellosolve acetate
#5815	Dip or brush	Methyl Cellosolve

Group 5—for nonceramic materials; solderable (for use on phenolic board, etc.). A two-step process is used to obtain a direct-soldering silver coating. Primer #7106 is applied to the phenolic board by brushing or spraying and cured at 160°C for 10–12 minutes. Silver #4929 is then applied over the primer by squeegee and cured at 160°C for 30–35 minutes. The silver coating applied in the two-step process can be directly soldered.

#7106 (primer)	Brush or spray	Methyl ethyl ketone
#4929	Squeegee	Butyl Cellosolve acetate

Group 6—air-dry type for nonceramic materials. These will dry in 24 hours at room temperature, but drying can be expedited by heating to 80°–100°C for 50–60 minutes. These coatings may be copper-plated, but they are relatively soft and do not have as good adhesion or abrasion resistance as do the silvers in Group 5.

#4817	Brush or spray	Butyl acetate
#4922	Brush or spray	Butyl acetate
#4929	Squeegee	Butyl Cellosolve acetate

(*Note:* Butyl Carbitol acetate, butyl Cellosolve, butyl Cellosolve acetate, and methyl Cellosolve are registered trademark names for thinners manufactured by the Union Carbide Corporation.)

Metallic silver conductive coatings are supplied by Handy & Harman, 850 Third Avenue, New York 22, New York. Two types are produced: (a) the fire-on types for mineral-base materials that can withstand heating to temperatures in the range 480°–930°C, and (b) the air-dry types for organic base or other materials that must usually be dried in the range of room temperature to 260°C.

With the fire-on types, the coating is predried at low temperatures to drive off volatile solvents and then fired in an oxidizing atmosphere (air) at the designated temperature to burn off the organic residues and fuse the glass. This bonds the silver in a tight, adherent, highly conductive layer to the mica, ceramic, or other mineral-base surface. The coating then has electrical conductivity ranging from 50% to 75% of the conductivity of the equivalent weight and shape of solid silver. Some compositions may be electroplated; others may be soldered to directly.

With the air-dry or low-bake type of formulations, the bonding agent is an organic resin and may be either thermoplastic or thermosetting. The viscosity and drying rate are adjusted for designated methods of application, as in the fire-on types. Some may be dried in air or force-dried at higher temperatures. Thermosetting types require baking at temperatures of 150°–200°C, and in special cases, up to 430°C. Hardness and flexibility are regulated by resin and plasticizer choice.

The conductivity of air-dry coatings will vary from about 5% to 25% of the conductivity of the equivalent weight and shape of solid silver. Baking increases the conductivity of room-temperature dried coatings.

These coatings are used as terminal strips for resistors, printed circuits, and electrostatic shielding, and they may be electroplated. A partial list of the conductive coatings supplied by Handy & Harman will be found on p. 208.

Engelhard Industries, Inc. (Hanovia Liquid Gold Division), 1 West Central Avenue, East Newark, New Jersey, gives information on its metallic conductive coatings as follows:

Hanovia Ceramic Silver Coatings for use in the electrical and communications industries.

Hanovia Ceramic Silver Coatings are made in powder, paste, and liquid forms, all of which find their special applications for coating refractory nonconductors such as porcelain, steatite, Alsimag, Isolantite, glass, Pyrex, quartz crystals, mica, Mycalex, graphite, titanates, etc. When fired to maturing temperature, they form thin but dense films of very fine texture which are used for bonding metal to glass or ceramics, and for current-carrying purposes.

Silver paste is a viscous suspension of finely divided, precipitated or flake silver in organic vehicles. To prepare silver paste for brushing, mix it with a sufficient amount (10–15%) of oil of turpentine to form a paint that will level out without "running" if applied with a camel-hair brush. For accurate results the pieces to be coated should be kept revolving (on a banding wheel or lathe) while the paint is being applied, either by hand or automatically. Where the banding method cannot be employed on account of the shape of the objects, free-hand application must be resorted to unless one of the methods quoted in the next paragraph is applicable.

Liquid silver is fundamentally the same as the silver paste, except that it is supplied in ready-mixed form. Before use, liquid silver preparations need only be thoroughly shaken or stirred so that the solids are uniformly dispersed throughout the vehicle. Liquid silver coatings are available in various consistencies appropriate to the method of their intended use. The usual methods of application are: dipping, spotting, spraying, machine-banding, and screen-printing. For screen-printing it is recommended that a 230-mesh stainless steel, or a No. 16 silk screen, be used.

After a silver coating has been applied by any of the above-mentioned methods, it must be fired in a muffle-type or continuous furnace. It is of greatest importance that the firing chamber be well-ventilated in order to create and maintain an oxidizing atmosphere until the organic matter contained in the coating is completely destroyed, which will be accomplished at the approach of red heat (approximately 450°C or 850°F). All ceramic silver coatings contain certain fluxes which cause them to adhere firmly to the coated surfaces when fired to maturing temperatures. These fluxes and the degrees of maturity vary according to the refractoriness of the material to be coated. The following list gives the principal silicate products, together with the temperatures required for firing silver coatings to maturity:

	°C	°F
Mica	540	1004
Quartz crystals	550	1022
Soft glass	580	1076
Lime glass	600	1112
Pyrex and quartz glass	650–680	1202–1256
Ceramics	750–800	1382–1472

The various Hanovia silver preparations are listed below:

METHOD OF APPLICATION	CERAMICS. FOR ELECTRICALLY CONDUCTIVE FILMS	CERAMICS. BASE FOR PLATING AND SOLDERING	GLASS, QUARTZ, MICA
Brushing	Liquid silver #228, #521	Liquid silver #321, #543	Liquid silver #467, #108-AS
Spraying	Liquid silver #613	Liquid silver #132-A	Liquid silver #138, 421
Spotting			Liquid silver #122-A, #150
Screen Printing	Liquid silver #228, 545	Liquid silver #232	Liquid silver #220, 467, #108-AS

Bright platinum films on ceramic and glass: Hanovia Liquid Bright Platinum is essentially a solution, in volatile oils and other solvents, of organic platinum and gold compounds of resinous character. When painted on a glazed ceramic surface and heated to maturing, it yields, without further treatment, a film of high mirror polish. The fired film has the color of platinum metal. Besides the precious metals, Bright Platinum contains some base metal-organic compounds which serve as fluxes to fix the metal firmly on glass or ceramics.

Bright Platinum is made in different degrees of fluidity, ranging from the consistency of a thin varnish to that of heavy molasses. The types preferably used by the electrical and electronics industries are those with lower viscosity. Among these the Liquid Bright Platinum #05 has come to be regarded as a standard product which is used widely for producing thin conductive films on porcelain, glass, and other ceramic materials. It lends itself particularly well to application by means of a camel-hair brush and, if properly thinned, may also be applied by spraying. The area to be covered must be clean and dry, and no more liquid platinum should be applied to it than is necessary to make the coating level out evenly. At room temperature the coating dries within an hour sufficiently to be handled with care. To speed up production, the drying time may be reduced by passing the coated objects through a warm zone. The recommended firing temperatures are:

	°C	°F
Mica	540	1004
Quartz crystals	550	1022
Soft glass	580	1076
Lime glass	600	1112
Pyrex and quartz glass	650–680	1202–1256
Ceramics	750–800	1382–1472

Platinum preparations for solder seals: When applied and fired on glass or ceramics, organic platinum and gold solutions (Liquid Platinums) produce thin metallic films which can be soft-soldered to form hermetic seals.

These preparations offer the following advantages over other soldering bases currently in use.

1. Formation of a strong, hermetic-soldered adjoinment.
2. Moderate cost.
3. Ease of application.
4. Can be screen-printed directly on glass or ceramic surfaces.
5. Can be machine-banded directly on glass or ceramic surfaces.
6. Firing can be carried out in an oxidizing atmosphere.
7. No copper electroplating is necessary prior to tinning.
8. These liquid platinums contain no silver; therefore, the many problems caused by silver migration into the glass or ceramic substrate are avoided.

Platinum preparations: The following Liquid Platinums have been developed specifically for solder seals.

1. For application to soda-lime glasses:

   by brushing—Liquid Matt Platinum #6923.

2. For application to borosilicate glass, quartz, and glazed and unglazed ceramics:

   by brushing—Liquid Bright Platinum #6857

   by screen-printing or machine-banding; Squeegee Bright Platinum #6844.

Application: Matt Platinum #6923 contains finely divided solids in suspension. Before using, shake the bottle thoroughly until all solids are dispersed uniformly throughout the liquid. The Matt Platinum should be reshaken at intervals to assure continued dispersion. Bright Platinums #6857 and #6844 contain no suspended matter and therefore do not require shaking or stirring before use.

The glass or ceramic must be clean—free of moisture, dust, grease, etc.—before being coated.

When brushing, apply a *thin* coating, just sufficient so that brush marks flow out. The unfired coating should be transparent and light brown in color.

Screen-printing: For application by screen-printing, use a 238 Nitex screen for glass and glazed ceramics. For unglazed ceramics, such as alumina, use a #10 silk screen. (*Note:* Swiss silk bolting cloth is available from dealers in silk-screen painting supplies.) This will deposit sufficient material to form a continuous metallic film on the uneven surface of this type of substrate.

Firing: Place the coated ware in a furnace at room temperature and heat to the maturing temperature over a period of about one hour. Leave the furnace door wide open until a temperature of 400°C (750°F) is reached. This will ensure the presence of an oxidizing atmosphere which is necessary to burn away all organic matter. When the furnace temperature has reached 400°C, close the door and continue heating to the maturing temperature. It is important to hold the furnace at this temperature for a minimum of 15 minutes to ensure thorough bonding of the precious metal film to the substrate. The following maturing temperatures are recommended:

	°C	°F
Soda-lime (window) glass	566–599	1050–1110
Borosilicate (Pyrex) glass	649–677	1200–1250
Quartz (Vycor, etc.) glass (includes fused quartz)	677–732	1250–1350
Glazed and unglazed ceramics	732–816	1350–1500

Properties of the fired precious metal film: On firing these Liquid Platinum Preparations, a semitransparent platinum-gold film is produced having a thickness of the order of 0.1 micron (5 microinches = 0.000005 inch). When applied and fired properly on glass or glazed ceramics, Bright Platinum #6857 and #6844 produce mirror-bright, specular films. If the fired film is hazy or scummed, this is caused by either too heavy an application or insufficient ventilation in firing. Matt Platinum #6923 produces a film with a semimatt appearance when fired on glass and glazed ceramics.

On unglazed ceramics, all three Liquid Platinums fire out with a matt appearance, and the degree of mattness corresponds to the roughness of the substrate surface.

Soldering: No copper plating is required prior to soldering. The usual tin-lead solders, soldering fluxes, and heating methods can be used. It is not necessary to use silver-bearing solders. Flux for solder dipping is usually ammonium chloride in glycerin. For soldering with an iron, zinc chloride and ammonium chloride salts dissolved in water are recommended.

While these Liquid Platinums produce metallic films which have good burn-through resistance, overheating should be avoided because the molten solder will eventually dissolve the precious metal film.

When a correctly fabricated adjoinment is pulled apart, the break will occur in the glass or ceramic part. Bond failures between the platinum film and the glass or ceramic substrate are usually due to insufficient firing temperature and time or poor ventilation during the firing process.

Material cost (at the present writing): 100 grams of these Liquid Platinums will completely cover approximately 55 square feet. This is equivalent to a material cost of $0.70 to $0.95 per square foot. Due to the fluctuations in the price of platinum metal, Engelhard Industries quote on these materials on request.

Transparent conductive coating for hard glass.[1] This is a tin oxide coating which is very hard and almost completely transparent. The procedure for application is as follows:

Materials required—stannic chloride, anhydrous, fuming; deionized water; kaolin paste; Paasche spray-gun or airbrush; low temperature oven (under 100°C) or radiant heat with circulating air; high temperature oven under efficient hood (575°C maximum).

Procedure—dilute the stannic chloride 68% by weight to 32% by weight of deionized water. Pour the stannic chloride into the water slowly, under a hood to remove fumes.

The glass to which the material is to be applied must be thoroughly cleaned in fresh chromic-sulfuric cleaning fluid (p. 5) and rinsed well first in running tap water, then in three final rinses of deionized water.

Mix the kaolin with deionized water to the consistency of thick cream. This is to be used as a mask to protect the parts of the glass where the coating is not wanted, or where subsequent glassblowing is to be done. Apply the kaolin mix to a thickness of about $\frac{1}{8}$ inch. Several coats may be required, with drying under infrared lamps after each.

Allow the coated glass to dry thoroughly in a low-temperature oven or under a heat lamp with circulating air blast. When dry, place the work in a high-temperature oven at *room temperature* and bring the temperature up to 575°C. Hold this temperature for 5 to 10 minutes, depending on the size of the work. Turn off the oven current. Remove the work from the oven and while it is hot, spray with the stannic chloride solution *under a hood*. Noxious fumes are produced during this operation. Return the work piece to the oven and allow it to come to room temperature before removing.

This coating has a slight opalescence which interferes only slightly with transparency. The resistance is from several hundred to several thousand ohms per square inch, providing excellent static shielding.[2]

Glasses with integral transparent coatings are supplied by the Libby-Owens-Ford Glass Company, Liberty Mirror Division, Breckenridge, Pennsylvania.

Coiled-coil heaters. This term is used to designate tungsten wire heaters or filaments which are made from standard incandescent-lamp filament material. The tungsten wire, of small size, is close-wound helically on a molybdenum wire of considerably larger size, called the mandrel, and comes in continuous lengths. Various sizes are manufactured by lamp makers, and are designated according to the wattage of the lamps for which they are designed.

---

[1] J. Palermo, Lincoln Laboratory, M.I.T., private communication.

[2] A stannic oxide coating for lead glass is described by R. H. Goodall in *Rev. Sci. Instr.*, **31**, 344, 1960.

PARTIAL LIST OF CONDUCTIVE COATING MATERIALS*

TYPE	NO.	METHOD OF APPLICATION	PERCENT SILVER	RECOMMENDED USES AND CHARACTERISTICS	THINNERS
1	672	Brush	65	General-purpose brush paint, excellent adherence and solderability on most ceramics. Fire temperature 650°–815°C. High Q for titanate ceramics.	Butyl Cellosolve
1	542	Brush	50	Low silver tube paint; for direct-soldering ceramics; fire temperature 650°–815°C. High Q for titanate ceramics.	Xylol, turpentine
1	452	Spray, dip	50	Excellent for spray production. High Q for mica capacitors. Fire temperature 430°–540°C.	Xylol, turpentine
1	545	Dip, spray	65	Glass and metals; excellent adherence and solderability. For direct-soldering to glass, quartz, and semiconductor bodies. Fire temperature 430°–540°C.	Butyl Cellosolve
1	461	Brush	65	Soft glass. Excellent adherence and solderability. For direct soldering to glass, quartz, etc. Fire temperature 430°–540°C.	Solvesso 150
1	548	Dip, spray	65	Excellent adherence to quartz crystals. Fire temperature 430°–540°C.	Xylol, turpentine
1	485	Brush	65	Plateable paint for alumina, porcelain (glazed or bisque), hard and soft glass. Fire at 870°–930°C for plating on ceramics.	Butyl carbitol acetate
1	601	Brush	70	Same as No. 485 except fire at 650°–700°C.	Toluol
2	357	Brush	50	Air-dry, low bake. For plastics, glass, metals and paper. Thermosetting; high-temperature bake at 200°–430°C.	Xylol
2	378†	Brush	60	Air-dry, low bake. For plastics, glass, metals, and paper. Excellent conductivity; can be force-dried at 100°–180°C.	Cellosolve; ethyl alcohol
2	489	Brush	45	For plastics, glass, metals, paper. Excellent electrical conductivity; excellent for coating Nylon, plastics.	Water, isopropyl alcohol
2	659	Spray	30	For plastics, glass, metals, paper. Low silver-shielding paint.	Ethyl alcohol

* Courtesy of Handy & Harman Co., 850 Third Ave., New York 22, New York
† This coating may be copper-plated in an acid copper plating bath (see p. 28).

For use as indirect cathode heaters in electron tubes, the wire is first cleaned by process T-2 (p. 17), then wound on a clean oxidized stainless steel mandrel of the shape desired, and fired in hydrogen at 1100°C for 30 minutes. After removal from the mandrel, the coiled-coil is treated by process Mo-4 (p. 12) and is then coated with Alundum in the manner described on pp. 80 *et seq.*

If the coil, when treated chemically to dissolve the molybdenum mandrel as described above, shows a tendency to distort out of its formed shape, this indicates that the temperature of firing was too low, the temperature of chemical treatment was too high, or both (see p. 88).

Coils, inductive, for use in vacuum. Fiberglas-insulated wire, commercially available, can be machine-wound, bound with Fiberglas tape, and fired at 400°–500°C in air to burn out the plastic binder.[1] After the first firing, the coil may be coated by brushing it with solder-glass (pp. 486 *et seq.*) and then mounting it inside the vacuum vessel. During evacuation the coil is baked at a temperature appropriate to the type of solder-glass used.

Coils for induction (RF) heating (see pp. 51 *et seq.* and 221).

Coin silver (see SILVER ALLOYS, p. 480).

Cold cap. A metal baffle or plate, water- or refrigerant-cooled, attached to, but thermally insulated from, the upper jet of a metal diffusion pump. The more volatile molecules are condensed on this cap and thus do not migrate into the high-vacuum system (thus reducing backstreaming, p. 161). The design requires that the supply of cooling fluid for the cold cap enter and leave through brazed or welded vacuum-tight fittings on the pump body.

Cold cathode (see CATHODE, COLD, p. 192).

Cold cathode gauge (see PENNING GAUGE, p. 431).

Cold emission (see CATHODE, COLD, p. 192).

Cold finger.[2] A type of cold trap (p. 211) in which the refrigerant container protrudes into the vacuum plumbing for condensation of oil vapors, etc. (*Cf.* COLD CAP, above.)

Cold-rolled steel. This term is misleading since many kinds of steel can be obtained in a cold-rolled or cold-drawn condition. As popularly used, the term generally refers to the low-carbon steels such as SAE types 1010, 1020, 1022, and 1112 (see table on p. 210.[3]

(*Note:* The low sulfur content of the first four steels in the table make them the choice where it is necessary or desirable to use cold-rolled steel for electron tube parts. These steels cannot be hardened to any extent, as shown in the table, by cold-working or by heat-treating, except that surface hardening can be done by case-hardening or carburizing processes which add carbon to the skin of the metal. Hot-rolled steels often have a heavy scale which should be completely removed before machining.)

---

[1] "Multiturn Coils for Use in Vacuum," F. H. Nicoll, *I. R. E. Trans. Prof. Group on Electron Devices,* **ED-4,** April, 1957.

[2] "Means for Attaining Vacua without the Use of Pump Fluids," I. Ames, R. L. Christensen, and J. Teale, *Rev. Sci. Instr.,* **29,** 736, 1958.

[3] *Metals and Alloys Data Book,* S. L. Hoyt, Reinhold Publishing Corp., New York, 1943.

MECHANICAL PROPERTIES OF A FEW REPRESENTATIVE LOW-CARBON STEELS

SAE NUMBER	CONDITION	COMPOSITION %				TENSILE STRENGTH (psi × 10^3)	YIELD STRENGTH (psi × 10^3)	ELONGATION IN 2 IN. (%)	HARDNESS (BRINELL)	MACHINABILITY*
		C	Mn	P_{max}	S_{max}					
1010	HR	0.08 to 0.13	0.3 to 0.5	0.04	0.05	51–65	29–40	38–32	101–137	40–50
	CD					56–76	33–43	35–30	113–143	45–50
1019	HR	0.15 to 0.20	0.7 to 1.0	0.04 to 0.05	0.05	68–69	45–47	32–30	143	55–62
	CD					72–78	50–53	29–23	149–163	65–70
1020	HR	0.18 to 0.23	0.3 to 0.5	0.04	0.05	67–70	41–45	32–31	130–137	52–58
	CD					69–80	48–67	30–18	143–162	60–65
1022	HR	0.18 to 0.23	0.7 to 1.0	0.04	0.05	69	47	30	143	62
	CD					78	53	23	163	70
1022	1-inch round, carburized 8 hours at 927°C in box, reheated to 885°C, water-quenched. Core properties:					109	85	7	225	—
1112	CD	0.1 to 0.16	1.0 to 1.3	0.045	0.08 to 0.13	80	62.5	16	170	100

* The basis of comparison is SAE 1112 steel shown on the last line of the table.

Cold trap. A portion of the vacuum plumbing usually situated between the diffusion pump and the vessel which is being evacuated (with associated ionization gauge) is given as large a surface as possible in contact with the refrigerant, compatible with pumping speed (see below), i.e. conductance of flow, and is refrigerated to cause condensation of water, mercury, oil, and other condensible vapors. Various refrigerants can be used, some of which are shown in the table below:

Refrigerant	Temperature
Running tap water	4 to 15°C
Solid CO_2 (dry ice) (may be mixed with acetone or alcohol to lower temperature)	−80°C
Freon (in a closed circulatory system—refrigerator compressor unit)	110°C (approx.)
Liquid nitrogen (preferable to liquid air because the N_2 evaporates first, leaving a high concentration of O_2 which could be a fire or explosion hazard)	−196°C
Liquid helium	−269°C

The conventional type of cold trap has a shape as shown in Fig. 46, which includes a set of curves for calculating the conductance of such shapes. The technique of cold-trapping is also called *cryotrapping* or *cryopumping.*

(*Note:* Because the function of the cold trap is to catch and hold condensible vapors, which thus tend to accumulate in the trap, some means must be provided for removing them; otherwise, when the trap is brought back to room temperature, these condensed materials will return to the system as vapors. It is customary to bake out the trap at whatever temperature it can withstand while pumping (450°–550° for glass; higher for steel or stainless steel traps). Where a trap is used in conjunction with an oil-diffusion pump, most of the oil vapor is returned to the pump during the baking. However, a small amount of oil-decomposition products is present, together with extraneous material picked up from the vessel, tube, or manifold being evacuated, and this will necessitate a cleaning-out of the trap at intervals, depending on the frequency of use and the quantity and quality of the air pumped through the system. The cleaning of a trap is done by one or a combination of techniques to be found on pp. 1–23, depending on the materials of construction. See also pp. 161, 199.)

References

Saul Dushman, *Scientific Foundations of Vacuum Technique,* second edition, John Wiley & Sons, New York, New York, 1962.

R. W. Roberts and T. A. Vanderslice, *Ultra-high Vacuum and its Applications,* p. 12, Prentice-Hall, Inc., Englewood Cliffs, New Jersey, 1963.

Cold welding (also Diffusion welding). Certain metals, under strict conditions of cleanliness and fit, can be joined together by extreme pressure applied at room temperature, or at temperatures below the melting points of the metals. Platinum, gold, silver, aluminum, and various alloys of these metals can be thus joined. Aluminum can be cold-welded together by applying pressure immediately after shearing,

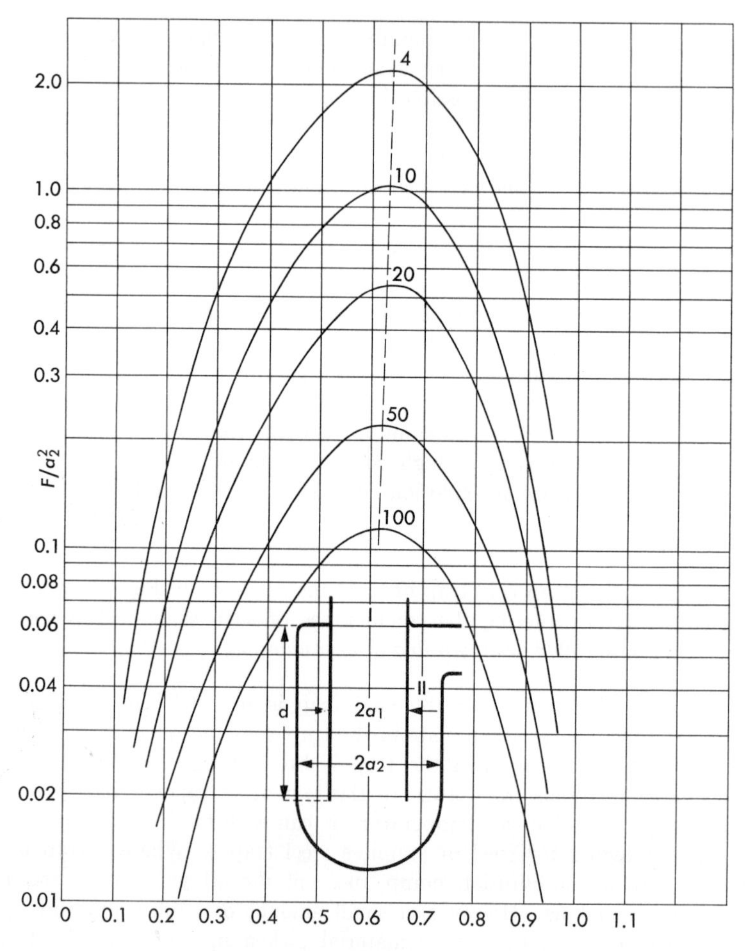

FIG. 46. Curves for calculating conductance of vacuum-cold traps. F is conductance in liters/sec, a_2 denotes the inside *radius* in cm of outer tube II, a_1 denotes the inside *radius* in cm of inner tube I. Each curve corresponds to the indicated value of d/a_2, where d is total length in cm of trap. For large values of d/a_2, the maxima (dashed line) occur at $a_1 = 0.62a_2$.

so as to present a fresh, oxide-free surface. Special tools and methods have been developed for this process,[1, 2] which can be applied to metals other than aluminum.

One of the oldest examples of this phenomenon is that in which two pieces of pure and clean gold or platinum can be welded together at room temperature by a single smart blow with a hammer.

---

[1] The General Electric Co. Ltd. of England (London), "G. E. C. Cold-Pressure Welding, Particularly as Applied to Aluminum," 1948.

[2] Utica Drop Forge & Tool Corp., Utica 4, New York, "Utica Koldweld Process"; also "Electrical Joints by Pressure Welding," Aluminum Co. of America, Sales Development Division, New Kensington, Pennsylvania, 1954.

Two pieces of copper can be bonded by interposing pure gold. The parts must be accurately machined and polished, and held together under pressure, with the gold (as foil, wire, or electroplate) making intimate contact. In this method the gold will diffuse into the copper if it is held sufficiently long under pressure, at a temperature well below the melting point of gold. Temperatures as low as 500°C have been used. If the pressure fixture is made of metal having a lower coefficient of expansion, advantage is taken of the fact that higher pressure will develop during heating (see third reference below).

REFERENCES

P. B. Aitken, *Nucleonics,* November, 1952.
P. P. Cioffi, *Bell Laboratories Record,* **36,** 172, 1958.
D. K. Das, *Rev. Sci. Instr.,* **29,** 70, 1958.
Also refer to footnotes on p. 212.

Colors of discharges (see also p. 135).

ELECTRICAL DISCHARGE COLORS OF VARIOUS GASES

GAS	CATHODE GLOW[1]	NEGATIVE GLOW[2]	POSITIVE COLUMN[3]
Air	Rose	Blue-pink	Pink at higher pressures, blue at lower
Argon	Rose	—	Violet
Ammonia	Blue	Green-yellow	Blue
Carbon dioxide	—	—	Blue-green
Carbon monoxide	—	—	White
Helium	Rose	Pale green	Violet-red to yellow-pink
Hydrogen	Brown-pink	Light blue	Reddish-pink to orange
Mercury vapor	Whitish-blue	Blue	Whitish-blue
Neon	Brick-red	Yellow	Blood red
Nitrogen	Reddish-pink	Blue or violet	Orange or yellowish-red
Oxygen	Red	Violet	Yellow with reddish core
Water vapor	Whitish-blue	Blue	Whitish-blue

[1] *The Cathode glow* is due to excitation of atoms of the gas by positive ions close to the cathode (see pp. 167, 192).

[2] *The Negative glow* is due to excitation of atoms by the electrons which have escaped from the space charge around the cathode.

[3] *The Positive column* consists of positive ions and electrons in equal number (*plasma*), the glow resulting from the ionization of collision and recombination into neutral atoms. The concentration of electrons is greatest at the tube axis and falls off radially because of the loss by collision with the tube wall. (See Fig. 47 and also p. 286.)

Color scale of temperatures (from C. J. Smithells, *Metals Reference Handbook,* Interscience Publishers, Inc., New York, New York, 1949). Various color-temperature charts have been suggested, and four such charts are compared in Fig. 48. The differences emphasize the danger of using color as more than a rough guide to estimating the temperature of incandescent bodies (see also OPTICAL PYROMETER, pp. 244, 405).

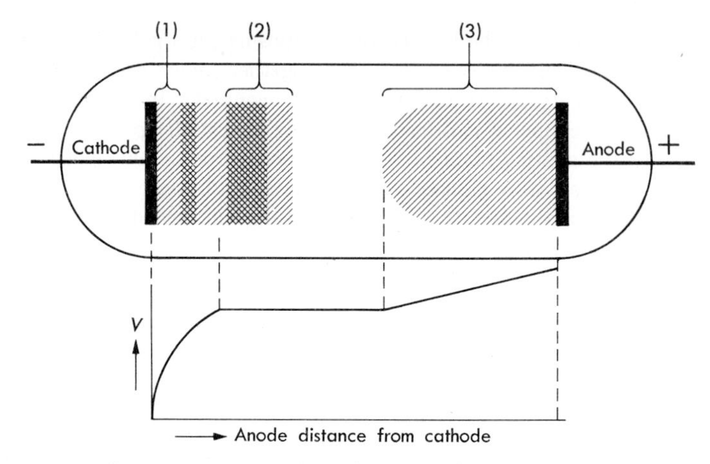

FIG. 47. Different types of glow discharge between anode and cathode. The diagram shows the appearance of the glow, luminous intensity being indicated by the density of crosshatching. At the bottom is shown the potential distribution (voltage versus cathode-anode distance). (After Penning.)

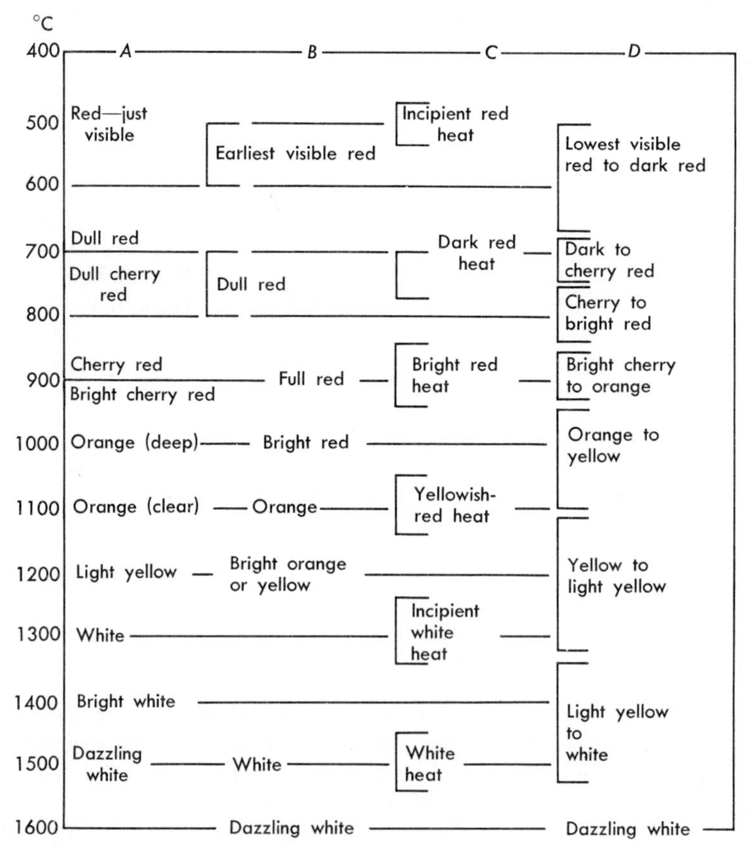

FIG. 48. Comparison of four color-temperature charts.

Columbium (niobium)—Cb or Nb.

Columbium metal has some properties in common with tantalum. It has a coefficient of thermal expansion of $7.2 \times 10^{-6}/°C$, a specific heat of 0.065, and electrical resistivity of 13 microhm-cm at 18°C, or 13.3% IACS (copper).

A summary of some of the physical properties of columbium is given in the table below.* This metal has some properties in common with tantalum.

Atomic number	41
Atomic weight	92.91
Atomic volume	10.83
Lattice type	Body-centered cube
Lattice constant at 20°C (A)	3.3004
Isotope (natural)	93
Density at 20°C:	
gm/cc	8.57
lb/in^3	0.31
Melting point (°C)	2415
Boiling point (°C)	4930
Linear coefficient of expansion/°C (in./in.)	7.2×10^{-6}
Thermal conductivity at 20°C ($cal/cm^2/cm/°C/sec$	0.13
Specific heat at 20°C (gm-cal/gm/°C)	0.065
Electrical conductivity (%) IACS (copper)	12
Electrical resistivity at 20°C (microhm-cm)	14.1
Temperature coefficient of electrical resistivity per°C (0–100°C)	0.00395
Tensile strength (psi $\times 10^3$):	
at 20°C	75–150
at 500°C	35
at 1000°C	13–17
Young's modulus of elasticity (psi $\times 10^6$) at:	
20°C	12–15
500°C	6.5
1000°C	—
Poisson's ratio	0.38
Thermionic work function (ev)	4.0
Magnetic susceptibility (10^{-6} cgs)	1.5
Spectral emissivity (wavelength approximately 0.65μ)	0.49 ($<$ melting point)
Total emissivity at 1500°C	0.19
Total emissivity at 2000°C	0.24
Working temperature	room
Recrystallization temperature	900–1300°C
Stress-relieving temperature	800°C
Nuclear cross section, thermal neutrons (barns/atom)	1.1
Metallography—polishing	emery to 000 levigated alumina to finish
Metallography—etchant	$HF\text{-}NH_4F$ solution

Etch and polish repeatedly until grain boundaries appear

* From Fansteel Metallurgical Corporation, North Chicago, Illinois, 1960.

Columbium is made by a powder-metallurgy process, compacted and sintered in the same manner as that used for tungsten, tantalum, and molybdenum. A vacuum-arc melting method in recent use produces these metals with higher purity. Columbium is available in the form of sheet, rod, wire, powder, and fabricated parts. It is nonmagnetic.

The metal is only slightly less resistant to corrosion in air at room temperature than tantalum, and is only very slightly attacked by most organic and mineral acids, but is less resistant to alkalies. Hydrofluoric acid or a mixture of HF and HNO_3 attacks it vigorously. It is more easily attacked than tantalum by other acids above 100°C.

Columbium has a high affinity for oxygen, and at moderately elevated temperatures, nitrogen penetrates more easily than oxygen. At higher temperatures columbium reacts with chlorine, bromine, and iodine, and with practically all gases except the noble gases. It is consequently useful as a getter in vacuum tubes.

Columbium work hardens slowly and can be drawn, stamped, and spun into various shapes. These operations are to be done at room temperature. Reductions as high as 60% can be made in one pass. It can be machined with the tools used for steel. Carbon tetrachloride is useful as a cutting fluid.

Columbium is annealed at temperatures above 1070°C in high vacuum.[1] This can be done by induction-heating.

The metal can be spot-welded. Arc-welding is difficult and gas-welding is not suitable because of the large absorption of gases. Electron-beam welding is applicable to this metal.

Small amounts of columbium (or tantalum or both) are alloyed with certain grades of stainless steel to prevent intergranular corrosion by a mechanism of bonding with the carbon. This is especially useful in stainless steels used at temperatures from 430°C to 900°C. Thus stainless steel types 347 and 347F (free-machining) contain 0.8% (minimum) Cb-Ta, or about 10 times the carbon content, and type 348 contains 0.8% (minimum) Cb, or about 10 times the carbon content, plus 0.1% tantalum. The columbium (or tantalum) acts in this use as a stabilizer.

Columbium has been used as a cathode material in an ion source,[2] and also as a braze material for tungsten, tantalum, or molybdenum.

Column, positive (see GLOW DISCHARGE, etc., pp. 188, 213, 286).

Concentrator (induction heating coil) (see pp. 222, 579).

Conductance of vacuum system components (molecular gas flow)[3, 4] (see p. 376).

Assuming that (a) the mean free path of the molecules is large compared to the diameter of the tubing, (b) that Lambert's cosine law holds for reflection from any impact with the walls, (c) that the velocity distribution is Maxwellian, and (d) that

---

[1] Must *not* be hydrogen-fired.

[2] "Ion Source for Production of Heavy Ions," C. E. Anderson, *Rev. Sci. Instr.*, **27**, 809, 1956.

[3, 4] For a fuller discussion of this subject, see Section 2 in *Scientific Foundations of Vacuum Technique*, second edition, revised, S. Dushman (J. M. Lafferty, editor), John Wiley & Sons, Inc., New York, New York, 1962; and "Vacuum Flow of Gases through Channels with Circular, Annular, and Rectangular Cross Sections," Vol. 2, p. 1116, W. Dong and L. A. Bromley, 8th National Vacuum Symposium, 1961 Transactions, American Vacuum Society, Pergamon Press, New York, New York, 1962.

the number of molecules striking any area is proportional to the pressure, then

$$G = \frac{r^3}{L} \cdot \frac{1}{\left(1 + \frac{8r}{3L}\right)} \cdot \sqrt{\frac{T}{300} \cdot \frac{29}{M}} \text{ liters/sec},$$

where G means conductance, r means radius in mm, L means length in mm, T means temperature in °K, M means molecular weight of the gas (air = 29). For air at room temperature, and if inches are used,

$$G = 80 \frac{d^3}{H + 4d/3} \text{ liters/sec},$$

where d means diameter in inches and H means length in inches.

Conductances in series will have a total conductance of

$$G_{tot} = \frac{G_1 G_2}{G_1 + G_2}.$$

For the conductance of a cold trap, see pp. 211, 212.

The rate of flow of gas through a capillary is

$$Q_m = \frac{4}{3}\left(\frac{2\pi}{RT}\right)^{1/2} \frac{a^3}{L} (P_1 - P_2)$$

for cases in which the mean free path is much greater than the diameter of the tube; and

$$Q_m = \frac{\pi}{8} \frac{a^4}{L} \frac{1}{\eta RT} \left[\frac{1}{2} (P_1^2 - P_2^2)\right]$$

for cases in which the mean free path is much smaller than the diameter of the tube, where Q_m means mass/sec (gas flow), a means radius of tube, L means length of tube, R means gas constant, T means temperature °K, P_1 means high pressure, P_2 means low pressure, and η (the viscosity as a function of temperature) $= \eta_0 f(T)$, $f(T) \simeq (T/T_0)^{0.69}$ (for air), $\eta = \eta_0$ at $T = T_0$.

Conductive coatings (see COATINGS, CONDUCTIVE, pp. 199–207).

Constantan alloy (see ADVANCE ALLOY, p. 150).

Contamination (see pp. 1–3, 113).

Controlled-atmosphere brazing (CAB) (see BRAZING, pp. 35, 39, 41, 45, 133, 172).

Conversion of pressure units (see the table on p. 218).

Conversion of oxide-coated cathodes (see pp. 98–101).

Conversion temperature for stainless steel (reduction of chrome oxide) (see p. 41).

Cooling on vacuum systems (see COLD TRAPS, p. 211).

Vacuum-diffusion pumps are cooled either by circulating water or by air blasts. Metal diffusion pumps are cooled either with integral water-jackets or by means of copper tubing soldered helically to the outer wall.[1] Glass diffusion pumps are made

[1] L. Riddiford, "Cooling of Diffusion Pumps," *Vacuum* (Br) **III**, 49, 1953. See also S. Dushman, *Scientific Foundations of Vacuum Technique*, Chapter 3, second edition, John Wiley & Sons, Inc., New York, New York, 1962.

CONVERSION OF PRESSURE UNITS

	ATMOSPHERE	BAR	DYNES/CM^2	INCH/Hg AT 0°C	MM Hg AT 0°C*	LB/IN^2	GM/CM^2
Atmosphere	1	1.0133	1.01320×10^6	29.921	760	14.696	1033.3
Bar	0.98692	1	1.000×10^6	29.530	750.1	14.504	
Dynes/cm^2	9.8692×10^{-7}	1×10^{-6}	1	2.9530×10^{-5}	7.5006×10^{-4}	1.4504×10^{-5}	1.0198×10^{-3}
Inch/Hg at 0°C	0.033421	0.339	3.38639×10^4	1	25.4	0.49116	
mm Hg at 0°C*	0.0013158	0.001333	1333.22	0.394	1	0.019337	1.3595
lb/in^2	0.068046	0.068947	6.8947×10^{-4}	2.0360	51.715	1	70.308
gm/cm^2	9.6777×10^{-4}		980.6		0.73551	0.014223	1

* See Torr, page 545; the unit torr = mm Hg.

with integral glass water-jackets, or they can be air-cooled by small blowers. Mercury-in-glass diffusion pumps are usually water-cooled with integral glass jackets.

Commercial power tubes are cooled by convection, forced air, or water.[1] When the high-voltage anode is water-cooled, some provision must be made for electrically isolating the anode from the grounded water main. One method of accomplishing this is with a helical cast-ceramic pipe of sufficient length so that the voltage drop between ground and anode can be maintained.

Commercial nonelectrolytic coolants with very high specific volume resistivities[2] can be used in a closed system with a circulating pump and a heat exchanger.

Water cooling on small metal tubes can be carried out by designing appropriate water-jacketing.[1,3] Experimental glass tubes should be cooled with small blowers whenever metal structures inside the tube and close to the glass walls are heated in operation.

Copper (see pp. 35, 89, 119, and below).

Copper, brazing of (see pp. 35 *et seq.*).

Copper, welding of. Copper can be welded by the use of the inert-gas-shielded *non-consumable*-electrode arc-welding method (Heliarc), with pure or alloy copper as a filler material, or by the inert-gas-shielded *consumable*-electrode *process* (Aircomatic), using Anaconda #372, a proprietary alloy of 98.85% copper, with the balance tin, manganese, and silicon. The shielding gas may be either helium or argon, the latter being preferable because it is cheaper and reduces the spatter of the filler material.[4]

Copper foil trap (see reference on p. 110).

Copper gasket seals (see pp. 117, 118).

Copper-to-glass seals (HOUSEKEEPER SEALS) (see p. 63, also *cf* p. 282).

Copper OFHC. This is the designation for oxygen-free, high-conductivity copper which is to be used for electron-tube envelopes and structures in place of ordinary electrolytic copper (see p. 35).

The ASTM designation for regular-grade OFHC copper is B170–47 for wire, bars, billets, and cakes. This grade has a minimum content (Cu plus Ag) of 99.92%, and the resistivity is not to exceed 0.15328 international ohms per meter gram[5] at 20°C in the annealed state, equivalent to a conductivity of 100% I.A.C.S. (International Annealed Copper Standard).

The metal must appear free from cuprous oxide at a magnification of 75 diameters. An embrittlement test is specified as follows: After being annealed in hydrogen at 800°C for 20 minutes, the sample shall withstand a minimum of four bends at 90°, two one way and two the other. As a rough test to identify OFHC copper, twist the piece of wire in a torsion machine until it breaks, then if the broken piece will bend and loop without breaking, it is OFHC copper. Ordinary electrolytic copper will break.

---

[1] See "Review of Industrial Applications of Heat Transfer to Electronics," J. Kaye, *Proc. I. R. E.*, **44**, 977, 1956.

[2] "Coolanol-45," Monsanto Chemical Co., St. Louis, Missouri.

[3] "Water-Cooling of Low-power Klystrons Used in the Laboratory," E. Niesen, R. W. Beatty, and W. J. Anson, *Rev. Sci. Instr.*, **29**, 791, 1958.

[4] E. F. McLaughlin, *Rev. Sci. Instr.*, **30**, 372, 1959.

[5] This is equivalent to the resistance of a uniform round wire 1 m long weighing 1 gm, 1.7241 microhm-cm, or 10.371 ohm-mil-ft, all at 20°C.

A typical analysis of OFHC copper is as follows:

	Percent		Percent		Percent
Antimony	0.0006	Lead	0.0006	Silicon	0.0004
Arsenic	0.0004	Manganese	0.0005	Silver	0.002
Bismuth	trace	Nickel	0.0006	Sulfur	0.0025
Chromium	nil	Oxygen	nil	Tin	0.0001
Copper	balance	Phosphorus	nil	Tellurium	0.0009
Iron	0.0015	Selenium	0.0005		

A grade of OFHC copper with stricter specifications is designated as Certified OFHC. This is especially suitable for copper-to-glass seals (see pp. 63–64). It conforms to the specifications for regular OFHC grade except as follows:

Embrittlement: Two 7-inch pieces of 0.081-inch wire annealed in hydrogen at 850°C for 30 minutes and quenched in water must withstand 10 bends of 90° in opposite directions.

This grade should appear free of cuprous oxide at magnifications of 200 diameters. The impurity maxima are as follows: phosphorus 0.0003%, sulfur 0.004%, zinc 0.0003%, mercury 0.0001%.

As a test for excessive phosphorus content in copper, the sample is first degreased, then heated in air for one-half hour at 850°C, and then quenched in water. If the black oxide flakes off the surface, phosphorus is present in deleterious amounts. If the black oxide is very adherent, this is an indication that the phosphorus content is very low.

Other properties of copper are given below.

Properties of Copper

Atomic weight	63.54
Melting point (°C)	1083
Boiling point (°C)	2336
Coefficient of linear expansion ($in/in/°C \times 10^{-6}$) at °C:	
−190 to +16	14.09
+ 25 to 100	16.8
25 to 300	17.8
0 to 625	16.07
Electrical resistivity microhm-cm, annealed:	
−258.6°C	0.014
−150	0.567
−100	0.904
+20	1.73
100	2.28
200	2.96
599	5.08
1000	9.42
1500 (liquid)	24.62

Temperature coefficient of electrical resistivity, annealed:	
20°C	0.00393
Hard-drawn	
20	0.00382
100	0.0038
400	0.0042
1000	0.0062
Pure, annealed:	
0–100°C	0.00433
Thermal conductivity (cgs units):	
−160°C	1.097
+18	0.918
100	0.908
100–541	0.902
100–837	0.858
Specific heat (cal/gm):	
−253°C	0.0031
−100	0.0783
0	0.0910

+20 .... 0.0921	Thermionic work function 3.85–4.55
100 .... 0.0939	Photoelectric work function 4.07–5.61
200 .... 0.0963	Ultimate tensile strength,
900 .... 0.1259	annealed, room temperature
1084 (liquid) 0.101	22.5–24.6 × 10^3 psi

Copper tubing seal (see p. 119; also the following references—H. V. Neher and A. R. Johnston, *Rev. Sci. Instr.*, **25,** 517, 1954; and H. V. Neher, *ibid.*, **28,** 267, 1957.

Corning glasses (see p. 267 *et seq.*).

Coupling of RF induction coils. Induction heating is a process by which the temperature of a metal part is raised by the electrical generation of heat within the material, a result of eddy currents flowing in the material. (In magnetic metals, there is heating, up to the curie point, by hysteresis, in addition to eddy currents.) Generating heat in the work piece, therefore, requires a current-carrying conductor, the heating coil, as illustrated in Fig. 49. This coil surrounds or is adjacent to the surface to be heated. The high-frequency current enters at one end of the coil and passes out through the other, as indicated by the arrows. This current sets up a magnetic field, which flows around the surface of the work. Magnetic fields occur in the entire area within and surrounding the heating coil, their strength varying inversely as the square of the distance from the coil. What takes place is a transfer of electrical energy from the coil into the work piece, where it is converted into heat. For maximum heating, therefore, the current-carrying coil should be arranged as close to the work as possible. The *coupling* of the coil to the work is said to be close or tight when the distance between them is small. When slower heating is desired, the coupling is loosened (decreased) by making the coil diameter larger in the case of cylindrical work, or by moving the coil away in the case of flat work pieces. (See p. 51, also CURRENT TRANSFORMER below.)

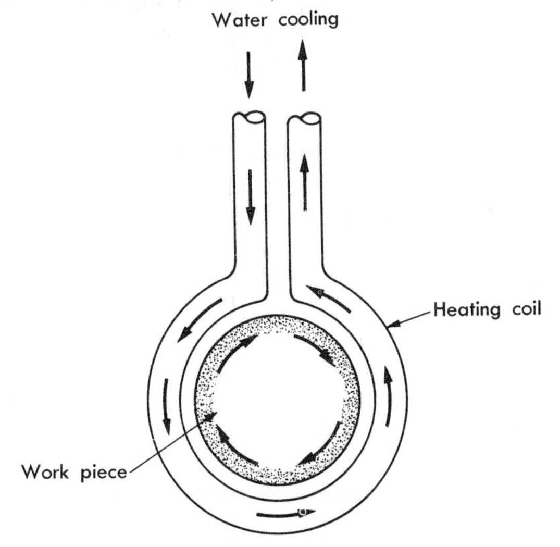

FIG. 49. RF-induction heating coil showing how magnetic flux flows around the work piece in a direction opposite to that in the coil. Eddy currents and hysteresis effects (in magnetic materials) produce the heating. (See text.)

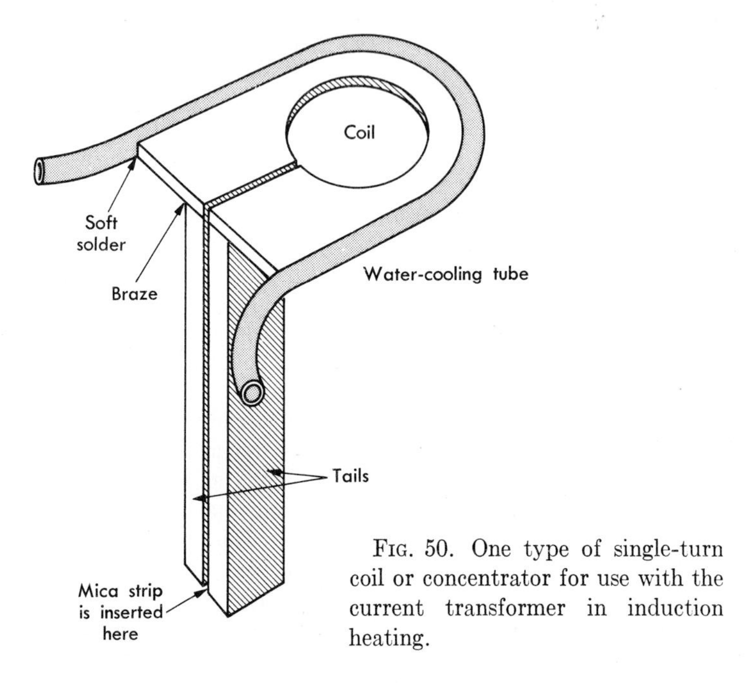

FIG. 50. One type of single-turn coil or concentrator for use with the current transformer in induction heating.

Cryopumping (see p. 110, also COLD TRAP, p. 211).

Crypts in vacuum system, avoidance of (see p. 134).

Curie temperature or **curie point** (see p. 231).

Current transformer for RF induction-heating. The current transformer, as used for induction heating (see p. 51 *et seq.*), is a device which allows the efficient use of a coil of only a few turns, or even of a single turn (concentrator), which would normally be a gross mismatch for the oscillating tank circuit of the RF generator. Simply stated, the device is a step-down transformer in which the primary, connected to the generator in place of the regular multiturn work coil, has the proper number of turns to match the tank circuit, while the secondary consists of a single turn, usually of heavy copper sheet with copper tubing soldered to it for water cooling. The water supply for the secondary turn must be brought in from a separate line. Since the voltage induced in this secondary turn is low, the water inlet and outlet are essentially at ground potential. The secondary turn or coil is provided with integral wide copper straps, closely spaced to give low impedance, and as near a continuous field as possible.

The secondary straps are clamped to the tails of a single-turn work coil by means of an insulated clamp or a piece of insulating material under one jaw so as not to short-circuit the coil. A strip of mica can be used to insulate the work-coil tails. One type of work coil is illustrated in Fig. 50. Note that the spacing at the discontinuity is very small.

The current transformer is sometimes called a load coil.

Cutting oils for use in machining tube parts.[1] The following list of cutting oils has been prepared with the cooperation of some of the manufacturers of electron tubes.

---

[1] *Cf.* LUBRICANTS FOR DEEP DRAWING, p. 329.

Each of the oils has been examined on tube parts both chemically and experimentally to determine their effects on oxide-coated cathodes. The oils are of the nonsulfonated type, or have the sulfur so bound chemically as not to break down and affect emission even at elevated temperatures.

1. Sinclair Refining Company
   (a) **Sinclair Solvent**
   (b) **Cadet Oil**
2. Esso-Humble Oil Company
   (a) **Rust Ban #392**
   (b) **Fanax #46**
3. Sun Oil Company
   (a) **Sunicut #4**
   (b) **Sunicut #2B**
4. Gulf Oil Company
   (a) **E. P. Lubricant #65**
   (b) **Cut Aid**
5. Union Carbide Corporation
   Butyl Carbitol Acetate
6. Shell Refining Company
   Shell Macron #27

Demountable vacuum system. When it is required to open and close a vacuum system rapidly and/or frequently, some means must be provided, such as bolted and gasketed flanges, doors, covers, bell-jars, ground joints, etc.

In many applications, such as vacuum-metallizing, chemical procedures, food processing, vacuum metallurgy, and heat treating, it is suitable to use rubber (Neoprene)[1] or Silicone O-rings (see pp. 407–409 and 410) or gaskets, greased ground joints, or Pyrex pipe components[2, 9] with Neoprene gaskets (see below). Such joints cannot, of course, be outgassed by heating beyond whatever temperature the gasket or grease can stand. Teflon gaskets, O-rings, or special seals, such as *V*-packings, will take somewhat higher temperatures, but where bake-out at 450°C or higher is required, some kind of metal gasket is to be used (see pp. 117, 118), usually of OFHC copper[3, 4, 5, 6, 7] or type 1100 aluminum.[8] Both metals are to be fully annealed for use. OFHC copper can be annealed by firing in tank hydrogen at 800°C.

Pyrex glass pipe,[2, 9] which is useful in many vacuum applications (see Fig. 51), is made from heavy-wall tubing uniformly machine-made. Corning Glass Works Corning, New York, and its agents market the following sizes: 1 inch, $1\frac{1}{2}$ inches, 2 inches, 3 inches and 4 inches. Fischer and Porter Company, Hatboro, Pennsylvania, supply the pipe in the following sizes: $\frac{1}{4}$, $\frac{3}{8}$, $\frac{1}{2}$, $\frac{3}{4}$ and 1 inch. These sizes correspond closely to the inside diameter of the tubing. Various fittings and accessories are available, including 90° and 45° elbows, reducers, reducer elbows, caps, tees, reducer tees, crosses, reducer crosses, U-bends, spacers, slip-joints, stopcocks, metal flanges and coupling devices, and Neoprene and Teflon gaskets.

---

[1] H. R. Moore, *Rev. Sci. Instr.*, **29**, 737, 1958.
[2] C. E. Cohn, *ibid.*, **31**, 1165, 1960.
[3] H. H. Pattee, Jr., *ibid.*, **25**, 1132, 1954.
[4] P. J. van Heerden, *ibid.*, **26**, 1130, 1955.
[5] N. T. Williams, *ibid.*, **26**, 1207, 1955.
[6] P. J. van Heerden, *ibid.*, **27**, 410, 1956.
[7] W. J. Lange and D. Alpert, *ibid.*, **28**, 726, 1957.
[8] T. Foote and D. B. Harrington, *ibid.*, **28**, 585, 1957.
[9] L. Holland, *Trans. Am. Vacuum Soc.*, 7th Ann. Symp., p. 172, Pergamon Press, New York, 1961. Experimental vacuum components for classroom use are outlined by J. G. King, *Amer. J. Physics.*, **31**, 4, p. xiii, 1963.

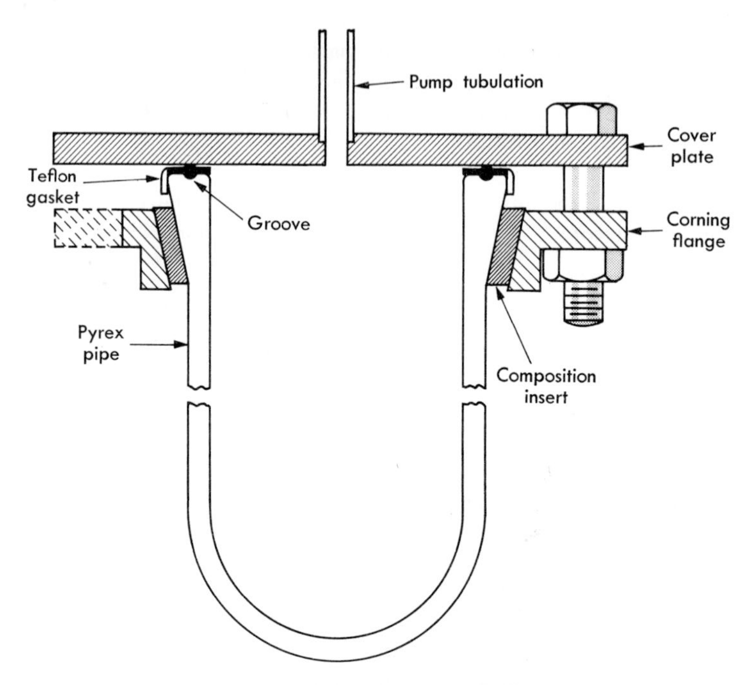

FIG. 51. Demountable vacuum vessel made from Pyrex pipe. The cover plate is metal with a copper tubulation which can be pinched off. Electronic structure can be mounted on underside of metal plate. Pyrex pipe can be any length and can be joined to another length of pipe, or to any of the fittings supplied by Corning.

The groove indicated in Fig. 51 is not to be used for an O-ring (see reference 2 p. 223) but to provide a method of obtaining additional sealing safety when a Neoprene gasket is used. The Teflon gaskets supplied by Corning are molded to seat in the grooves, and are also fitted with external metal clips to hold the gasket in place during assembly.

Deposition is the application of a thin layer of material, usually metal, to a base of another material, called the substrate, by vacuum evaporation or sputtering.[1] Metals such as aluminum, silver, gold, etc., are heated to the melting point, or beyond, on tungsten filaments. At such elevated temperatures *in vacuo,* the metal evaporates and condenses on any cooler surface in the line of sight.[2]

Design of tubes and tube components (see pp. 80, 112, 128, 132).

Desorption is the liberation of gas from the surface of a (solid) body. In ordinary terrestrial environments, it is normal for solids to hold varying amounts of common gases (including water-vapor), whether on the surface (adsorption) or below the surface (absorption), or both.

---

[1] See pp. 194, 247, 498.

[2] A method of protecting bell-jars and reducing evaporation is given by P. R. Nelson, Jr., and J. E. Slawek, Jr., in *Rev. Sci. Instr.,* **29,** 253, 1958.

Desorption, the reverse of adsorption and absorption, can be brought about in many instances by heating *in vacuo* and by ion and electron bombardment. *Cf.* CHEMISORPTION, p. 199 and PHYSISORPTION, p. 435.[1]

Dewar flask. A double-walled vessel with the intervening space evacuated to minimize conduction of heat. If the flask is made of glass, the outer surface of the inner chamber and the inner surface of the outer chamber are silvered to reflect heat. If the flask is made of metal (stainless steel), welded or brazed, the surfaces are to be highly polished for maximum efficiency The ordinary Thermos bottle is a Dewar flask.

Dewars are commonly used in vacuum systems to contain refrigerants around cold traps (see pp. 211, 212) and in procedures in cryogenics. Pyrex glass is somewhat permeable to hydrogen and helium, soft glass much less so. Monax glass (British) is hydrogen-tight.

Dew point is the temperature at which condensation of water vapor in a gas takes place. The percent of moisture by volume in air versus the dew point temperature, for temperatures below 0°C, is given in the table on the next page.[2]

The vapor pressure in atmospheres at various dew point-temperatures can be obtained by dividing the values in the "percent by volume" column in the table by 100.

Dew point of hydrogen for brazing stainless steel (see p. 42).

Diamond. A pure form of crystalline carbon. Diamonds can be brazed or bonded to metals by the titanium hydride (active metal) process (see pp. 67, 68), as described by Hall.[3] Synthetic diamonds for industrial uses are manufactured by General Electric Company, Metallurgical Products Division, Detroit, Michigan, from essentially pure graphite, carbon black, sugar charcoal, or carburizing compound, in a device for producing high pressures and temperatures such as that described by Hall.[4, 5]

Dielectric constant. A factor or coefficient to which the electrical *capacity* of a substance is proportional. In most materials this factor is dependent on the frequency and the temperature of measurement. The dielectric constant ϵ of a vacuum is unity.

---

[1] "Kinetic and Experimental Basis of Flash Desorption," G. Ehrlich, *J. Appl. Phys.*, **32,** 4, 1961. See also "Sorption and Desorption of Gas in a Hot-Cathode Ion-Gauge," F. E. Baker, *J. Appl. Phys.*, (Br) **11,** 435, 1960; "Reactions of Oxygen with Pure Tungsten," J. A. Becker, E. J. Becker, and R. G. Brandes, *J. Appl. Phys.*, **32,** 411, 1961; "Thermal Degassing of Tube Materials," R. H. Collins and J. C. Turnbull, *Vacuum* (Br) **11,** 119, 1961; "Attainment of Ultra-high Vacua, etc.," A. L. Hunt, C. C. Damm, and E. C. Popp, *J. Appl. Phys.*, **32,** 1937, 1961; "Pumping of Argon, Nitrogen, and Hydrogen in a Bayard-Alpert Gauge," B. Cobic, G. Carter, and J. H. Leck, *J. Appl. Phys.* (Br), **12,** 384, 1961; "Adsorption of Molecular Gases on Surfaces and its Effect on Pressure Measurement," D. Lee, H. Tomaschke, and D. Alpert, *Trans. Am. Vacuum Soc.*, 8th Ann. Symp., pp. 151–159, Pergamon Press, Inc., New York, 1962.

[2] Courtesy of General Electric Company; from Bulletin GEC 588, September, 1950.

[3] H. T. Hall, *Rev. Sci. Instr.*, **25,** 1035, 1954.

[4] H. T. Hall, *ibid.*, **31,** 125, 1960.

[5] "New Materials and Components," *ibid.*, **31,** 230, 1960.

MOISTURE BY VOLUME IN AIR VS. DEW POINT TEMPERATURE

DEW POINT TEMPERATURE		MOISTURE CONTENT	
°F	°C	MG/LITER	PERCENT BY VOLUME
32	0	4.88	0.602
30	—1.11	4.50	0.553
28	—2.22	4.15	0.511
26	—3.33	3.84	0.384
24	—4.44	3.55	0.434
22	—5.56	3.28	0.398
20	—6.67	3.02	0.367
18	—7.78	2.79	0.337
16	—8.89	2.56	0.308
14	—10.0	2.35	0.282
12	—11.1	2.16	0.258
10	—12.2	1.99	0.236
8	—13.3	1.83	0.216
6	—14.4	1.68	0.198
2	—16.7	1.41	0.165
0	—17.8	1.30	0.150
—4	—20.0	1.08	0.124
—8	—22.2	0.896	0.102
—10	—23.4	0.815	0.093
—14	—25.6	0.674	0.076
—18	—27.8	0.555	0.062
—20	—28.9	0.505	0.056
—24	—31.1	0.410	0.045
—28	—33.4	0.336	0.036
—30	—34.5	0.303	0.033
—34	—36.6	0.245	0.026
—38	—38.9	0.197	0.021
—40*	—40.0*	0.177	0.019
—44	—42.2	0.141	0.015
—48	—44.5	0.112	0.012
—50	—45.6	0.101	0.010
—54	—47.7	0.080	0.008
—58	—50.0	0.063	0.0063
—60	—51.2	0.054	0.0056
—65	—53.9	0.040	0.0041
—70	—56.7	0.029	0.0029
—75	—59.5	0.021	0.0021
—80	—62.2	0.014	0.0015
—85	—65.0	0.011	0.0010
—90	—67.8	0.008	0.0007
—95	—70.5	0.005	0.0005
—100	—73.3	0.003	0.0003

* Note that C and F temperature values coincide at —40°.

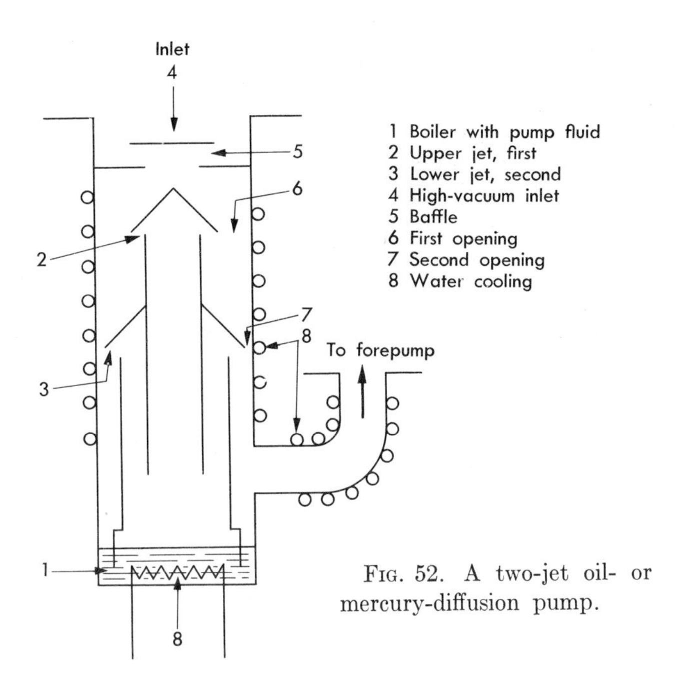

FIG. 52. A two-jet oil- or mercury-diffusion pump.

Diffusion pump.[1] This is a pump with no moving mechanical parts. Molecules of gas, by virtue of their random motion, are caught up in a stream of vapor moving from a liquid-containing boiler through a jet or orifice and compressed into a space where they can be exhausted by a mechanical pump. Diffusion pumps are often compound or otherwise designed so that the gas molecules being pumped can be compressed to a value at which the connected mechanical or forepump can operate efficiently. The walls of the pump are continuously cooled so that the pump vapor is eventually condensed and returned to the boiler(s) as a liquid.

For many years mercury was the only pump fluid used in diffusion pumps, and it is still widely used for many applications. Today a number of organic and semi-organic oils of very low vapor pressure (see pp. 400, 401) are used, and diffusion pumps have been improved to obtain high pumping speeds, low ultimate pressures, and large volume.

A two-jet metal diffusion pump is outlined in Fig. 52. The fluid in the boiler (1), either oil or mercury, is evaporated rapidly by means of the electric heating element (8). Vapor streams up the chimneys through jets (2) and (3), which direct the flow downward and fill the annular openings (6) and (7) with vapor molecules moving downward at high velocity. A gas molecule entering the pump at (4) will, through its normal impacts with other gas molecules and the walls of the pump,

[1] See "Testing Performance of Diffusion Pumps," M. H. Hablanian and H. A. Steinherz, *Trans. Am. Vacuum Soc.*, 8th Ann. Symp. (1961), **1**, 333–341, Pergamon Press, Inc., 1962; "Development of Diffusion Pumps," W. Bächler, R. Clary, and H. Forth, *ibid.*, 10th Ann. Symp., 147–152, Macmillan Co., New York, 1963; "Scientific Foundations of Vacuum Technique," S. Dushman, 2nd Edition, pp. 141, 678, John Wiley & Sons, Inc., New York, 1962.

enter the opening (6), and through impacts with the vapor stream be moved downward through the pump. The vapor stream strikes the (water) cooled outer walls of the pump, condenses, and returns to the boiler. The downward motion given the gas molecules crowds them together.

The pressure to which the first jet (2) can compress the gas may be too low for efficient operation of a forepump, and additional jets may be required to compress the gas further. The speed of the pump is roughly proportional to the area around the first jet through which air can enter the vapor stream. It is customary to use a pump casing of uniform cross section and to decrease the area around the second and third jets progressively by decreasing the jet clearance, i.e., the distance to the wall.

As the jet clearance is decreased, the speed is decreased, but in general the pressure differential and maximum exhaust pressure are increased because the vapor stream is confined to a smaller working area (less expansion after leaving the nozzle). Thus, by using several jets in series, the highest pump speed obtainable from a casing of given size can be combined with a high maximum exhaust pressure.[1]

Fractionating and multistage diffusion pumps are illustrated in Figs. 56 and 57 on p. 232.

Diffusion welding (see COLD WELDING, p. 211).

Diode. A vacuum electron tube consisting only of a cathode and an anode. (Also, a solid-state device with only two terminals.) The electron-tube diode has the ability to rectify alternating currents by reason of the unilateral flow of electrons from cathode to anode, so that an externally applied current will flow only when the anode is relatively positive and electron emission is present. In a thermionic diode, the flow of electrons (i.e., current) from cathode to anode can be controlled by the voltage on the anode (plate) and the temperature of the filament or cathode. Figure 53 gives the variation of anode current I_p with anode voltage E_p for three values of cathode temperature. Current through the diode increases approximately as the square of the voltage across it for low values of current, a relation which becomes more linear in the middle section of the curve. As the anode voltage is further increased, the curve tends to flatten out, due to the limited number of electrons being emitted for the given cathode temperature. If the temperature of the cathode is raised to a higher value, an increased number of electrons becomes available and the anode current for any given anode voltage is greater. The flattening of the current-voltage characteristic is called *saturation*. In Fig. 53 the saturation effect at point X is caused by limited electron emission.

Note that the current increases slightly with increasing voltage, above the bend or *knee* in the curve. This is called the *Schottky* effect and is caused by field emission (p. 249) of electrons from the cathode, i.e., a result of the increasing electrostatic field which mechanically pulls electrons from the cathode and thus slightly increases the anode current.

If the positively charged anode were not present, the electrons would form in a cloud around and close to the cathode and would eventually fall back on the cathode. This cloud of electrons is called the *space-charge*. With the introduction of the positively charged anode, the space-charge is partially neutralized, i.e., the electrons are drawn away from the cathode, up to the capability of the anode voltage. If the

[1] H. M. Sullivan, *Rev. Sci. Instr.*, **19**, 1948.

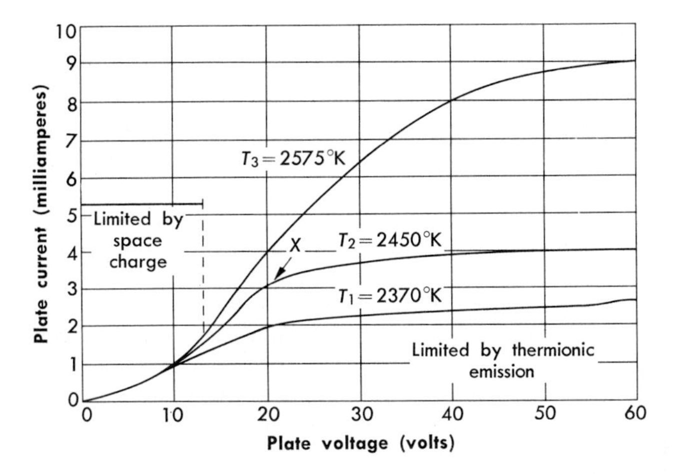

FIG. 53. Variation of anode current for three values of tungsten filament (cathode) temperature.

number of electrons being emitted from the cathode is greater than can be drawn away by the anode, some electrons remain near the cathode and the tube is said to be *space-charge-limited*. The curves in Fig. 54 show this effect in which the 8-volt and 15-volt anode potentials are not sufficient to overcome the space charge, while the 32-volt value overcomes the space charge. Increasing the cathode temperature will increase the space charge. (*Cf.* p. 132.)

Diode, test (see p. 98).

Discharge (see BREAKDOWN VOLTAGE, p. 188, and PASCHEN'S LAW, p. 427).

Drill rod. A tool steel having a carbon content of about 1%, susceptible of hardening by heat treatment, suitable for making drills and other tools. Drill rod is ferromagnetic and can be used for small permanent magnets in the hardened condition.

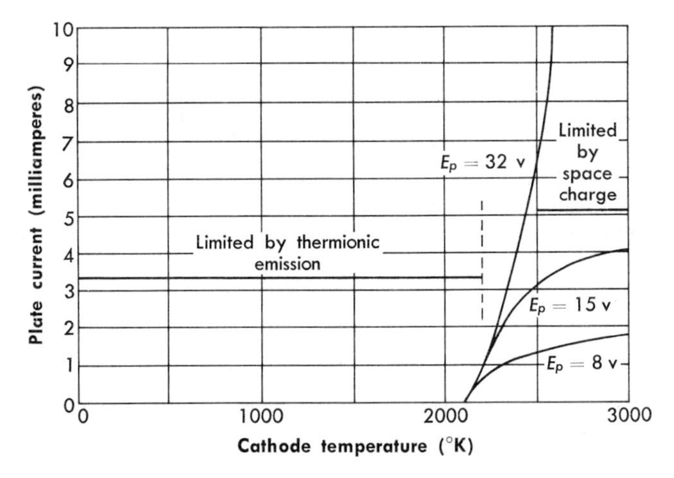

FIG. 54. Variation of plate current-cathode temperature characteristics for three values of anode voltage.

Dry box. A leak-tight chamber made of glass, plastic, or welded metal (with gas-tight windows), in which work can be done on assemblies or components which must be protected from the air and/or contamination. In unsophisticated form, the dry box has an opening through which the operator inserts his hands protected by suitable gloves. A positive pressure of a filtered and dried inert gas, such as nitrogen, argon, etc., is piped into the box.

More complex arrangements consist of special gas-tight iris-glove fittings through which the hands are inserted, microscopes and lighting for working on small or delicate components, and heating and cooling if required. In some models, means for evacuating the chamber with pumps and gauges are provided. Accessories comprising mechanical-electrical controls for manipulation, without inserting the hands, are available.

In a dry box means should be provided for working on electron tube structures, for receiving and delivering parts, and also for storage of parts.

Dry ice (solid carbon dioxide, CO_2) (see CARBON DIOXIDE, pp. 190, 211).

Drying agents for removal of water. The table below shows the ability of various drying agents to remove water from air and gases.

DRYING AGENT	RESIDUAL WATER AT 25°C (MG/LITER)
Charcoal trap	1.6×10^{-23}
Phosphorus pentoxide	2.0×10^{-5}
Barium oxide	8.0×10^{-4}
Magnesium chlorate	5.0×10^{-4}
Melted potassium hydroxide	2.0×10^{-3}
Activated alumina (see p. 151)	1.0×10^{-3}
Silica gel	3.0×10^{-2}
Zinc chloride	8.0×10^{-1}
Calcium chloride, anhydrous	3.6×10^{-1}
Sulfuric acid, concentrate, anhydrous	3.0×10^{-1}
Calcium oxide	2.0×10^{-1}
Copper sulfate, anhydrous	1.4

Synthetic metal-aluminosilicates (artificial zeolites)[1] are also efficient drying agents for use in vacuum and gas systems (see p. 572).

At low temperatures, solid CO_2 (dry ice), liquid nitrogen, and liquid helium are used in vacuum systems to remove water vapor by condensation and freezing.

Drying of plated articles (see p. 24).

Dumet. This is the name of an alloy composite, commonly in the form of wire, of 42% nickel, 58% iron, with a cladding of OFHC copper (p. 219) to the extent of 18–28% by weight. The copper is bonded in hydrogen with a thin intermediate layer of brass, bronze, or silver braze. Dumet is widely used in lamps and electron tubes as electrical lead-wires and feedthroughs.

The copper surface of the Dumet wire must be smooth and free from scratches. Fine alumina powder in distilled water is used for polishing. The copper is then oxidized to a light straw color and beaded with glass (see **Beading,** p. 163).

---

[1] See MOLECULAR SIEVES, p. 377.

A type of Dumet known as Multilayer[1] does not have the intermediate layer of brass, bronze, or silver braze and is made by a direct bonding process. This product can be obtained with a borated coating, which facilitates sealing, or as unborated wire. The borated wire must be stored in a dry atmosphere (below 50% rh) to prevent a whitish cast known as blooming. (See table of glass-to-metal seals, p. 56.)

Eddy current heating (*Cf.* pp. 51–53, 221, 222).

In RF heating, the work acts as the secondary of a transformer, the work-coil being the primary, inducing currents into the work due to the difference of potential at various points. The work piece may be thought of as a single short-circuited turn. Because the induced currents are at high frequency, the heating effect does not penetrate much below the surface of the work, the interior of which, in the case of a solid piece, is heated largely by thermal conduction from the surface. In nonmagnetic materials, these induced currents are known as *eddy currents* and are the sole source of heating, which is approximately proportional to the square of the frequency and the field strength.

In magnetic materials, in addition to eddy current heating, there is also heating by *hysteresis* losses in which the magnetic molecules "vibrate" in trying to align themselves in resonance with the frequency, thus producing friction. Hysteresis heating is directly proportional to the frequency of the magnetic field and the magnetic field strength.

All magnetic materials lose their magnetic properties at a temperature characteristic of each material. This point is called the *curie temperature.* In induction heating, magnetic materials therefore heat by both eddy currents and hysteresis losses up to the curie temperature, above which the heating is by eddy current losses alone.

Materials of low resistivity (i.e. smaller voltage drop), such as copper, require more power to heat than metals of higher resistivity.

Ejector pump. This is a type of vacuum pump used largely in industrial processes and little used in laboratory-scale operations. It will discharge gas against atmospheric pressure, using steam or oil vapor which moves at high velocity through a Venturi-type jet, thus drawing the gas being pumped into the stream. The fast-moving flow of steam or oil vapor A (Fig. 55) passes through the Venturi jet J, reducing the pressure in the space X-X and thus drawing gas from the vessel being evacuated. The gas is then exhausted and the steam or oil vapor is condensed and returned to the boiler.

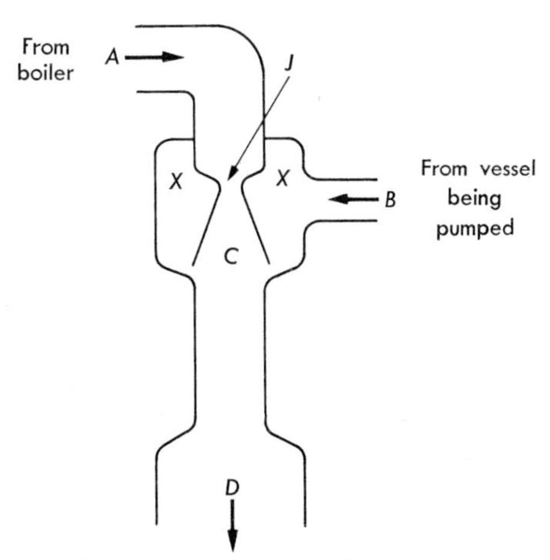

FIG. 55. Ejector pump.

Ejector pumps can be used in cascade; pressures as low as 0.03 mm Hg may be attained with a five-stage steam

[1] Metals & Controls, Inc., Wire and Tubing Department, Attleboro, Massachusetts.

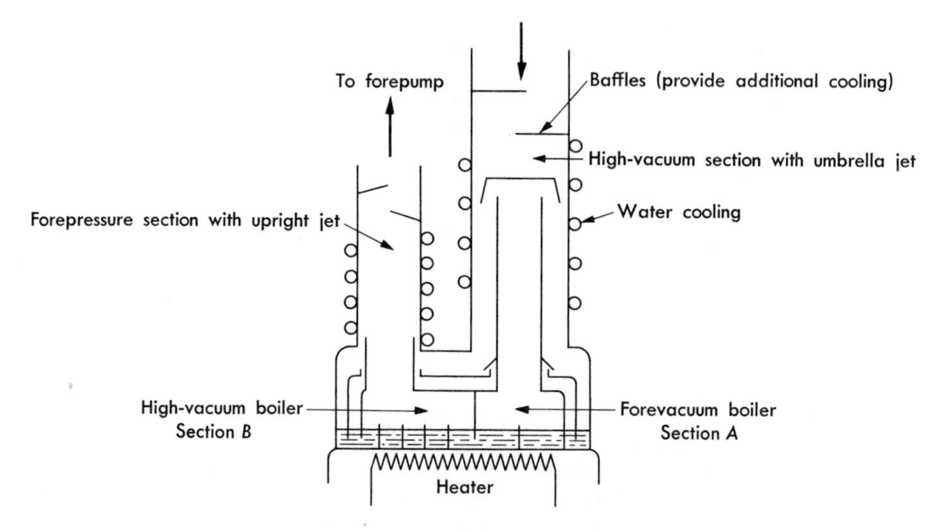

FIG. 56. Fractionating oil-diffusion pump. Section B has small dams which make the oil pass over a longer path, enabling the more volatile constituents to evaporate in this boiler. All return oil enters Section B. The less volatile constituents flow over to Section A. Some larger pumps have a third jet added to the high-vacuum section.

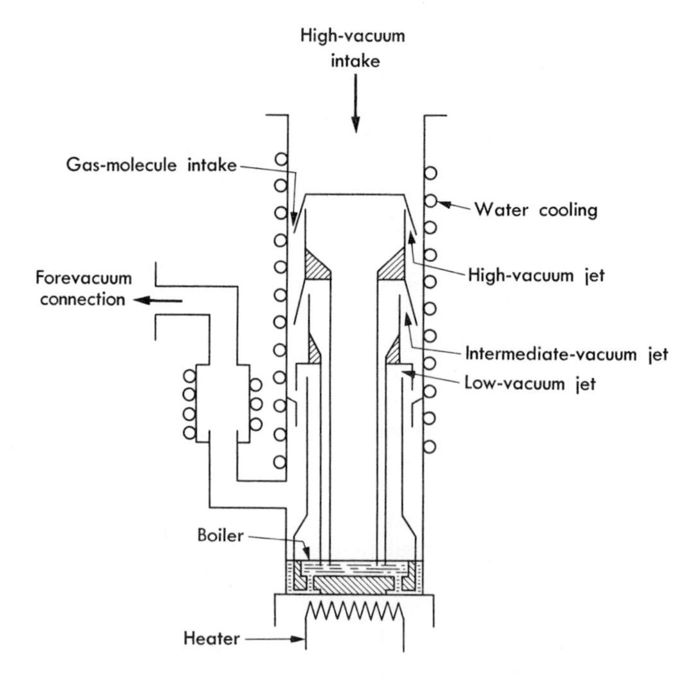

FIG. 57. Vertical fractionating oil-diffusion pump with three-stage jet.

ejector in which there are interstage vapor condensers. Very large volumes of gas can be pumped with this type of pump, which is sometimes used as a forepump for diffusion pumps. (See Figs. 56 and 57.)

Electroforming. This is a process of forming metal objects by heavy deposits of electroplate. Intricate shapes and high accuracy can be obtained which would be impossible or prohibitively expensive by ordinary machining methods.

Electroluminescence; Electrophotoluminescence. Certain crystals have the property of emitting visible light upon the passage of electric currents through them. These substances include barium titanate, $BaTiO_3$; strontium titanate, $SrTiO_3$; titanium dioxide, TiO_2; zinc sulfide, ZnS; potassium niobiate, $KNbO_3$; silicon carbide, SiC; and, to some extent, all the common phosphors used to make cathode ray screens.[1]

The electroluminescent lamp[2] is a flat-plate luminous capacitor activated by alternating current. It may be made either on a glass-base sheet or on a metal base. The glass-base sheet usually requires the application of a thin transparent conductive film. The next layer contains the electroluminescent material or phosphor embedded in a ceramic dielectric. The ceramic material offers protection against moisture. Finally, the top conductor is applied, using either a transparent conductive film or a metallic film, depending upon the application. The thicknesses of all the coatings applied to the glass backing amounts to less than one-hundredth of an inch.

It should be pointed out that light is emitted where and only where there is capacitive coupling. Thus, by patterning the top or bottom conductive films in given areas, it is possible to arrive at any shape, configuration, or group of areas capable of lighting individually or in unison, so that the device can be used for a wide range of display purposes.

Electrolytic cleaning; electropolishing. (See IRON, STEEL, KOVAR, p. 8; KOVAR, STAINLESS STEEL, and NICKEL, p. 9; NICKEL, p. 14; STAINLESS STEEL, p. 16; TUNGSTEN and MOLYBDENUM, p. 17).

Electrometer tubes. Ordinary electron tubes used for voltage amplification where small voltages and currents of milliamperes are encountered are not suitable for the detection and measurement of very small currents, down to 10^{-15} amp. The limiting causes are leakage from grid to cathode, ionization of residual gas within the tube, and the presence of undesired currents from other sources that include (a) positive ion emission from a hot cathode, (b) photoelectric emission from the grid due to light from the filament or from external sources, and (c) soft x-rays produced by the impact of electrons on the space-charge grid and anode.

Steps can be taken to overcome these effects, namely: (1) greatly increasing the leakage path from grid to cathode (use of reentrant-fused quartz insulators within the tube, extreme care in assembling the tube under hyperclean conditions, careful cleaning of the outside of the tube, and sometimes coating with a wax to reduce moisture adsorption); (2) obtaining a very "hard" tube by ultrahigh vacuum con-

---

[1] "Observation of Electroluminescence Excited by DC Fields in Cathode-Ray Tubes," F. H. Nicoll and B. Kazan, *Proc. I. R. E.*, **43,** 1012, 1955.

[2] "Sylvania Electroluminescent Display Devices," Sylvania Electric Products, Inc., 1740 Broadway, New York 19, New York, 1960.

See also: (a) "Transfluxor Controlled Electroluminescent Display Panels," J. A. Rajchman, G. R. Briggs, and A. W. Lo, *Proc. I. R. E.*, **46,** 1808, 1958; (b) "Photoelectronic Circuit Applications," S. K. Ghandhi, *Proc. I. R. E.*, **47,** 4, 1959.

ditions, baking, pretreatment of tube elements. The effects of (a), (b), and (c) above can be minimized by operating the cathode at a very low temperature (less than 1200°C for a thoriated tungsten filament), installing the tube in a light-tight housing which could also be gas-tight and either evacuated or provided with a moisture-absorbent to enhance (1) above, and operating the tube with low space-charge grid and anode voltages to reduce soft x-ray effects. The space-charge grid is provided to repel the positive ions emitted by the cathode.

Such a tube can be used in place of the far more delicate, temperamental, and expensive vane electrometer for the measurement of currents emanating from photocells exposed to light from stars, cosmic rays, chemical procedures (e.g., pH with glass electrodes), ionization in ultrahigh vacuum gauges, and nuclear particles (see references below).

It is feasible to couple the electrometer tube, which is essentially a current amplifier, to a conventional dc amplifier for indication with an ordinary micro-ammeter or milliammeter.

References

W. B. Nottingham, J. Franklin Institute, **208,** 469, 1929; **209,** 287, 1930.

F. A. Firestone, *Rev. Sci. Instr.*, August, 1932.

C. Morton, *J. Sci. Instr.*, September, 1932.

L. A. Turner, C. O. Siegelin, *Rev. Sci. Instr.*, August, 1933.

F. Rosebury, *Ind. Eng. Chem.*, Anal. Ed. **4,** 398, 1932.

L. A. DuBridge, *Phys. Rev.*, **37,** 392, 1931; L. A. DuBridge and H. Brown, *Rev. Sci. Instr.*, October, 1933.

P. A. Macdonald and J. T. Macpherson, *Phil. Mag.*, and *J. Sci.*, **15,** 72, 1933.

A. H. Taylor and G. P. Kerr, *Rev. Sci. Instr.*, **4,** 28, 1933.

C. E. Nielsen, *ibid.*, **18,** 18, 1947.

I. Pelchowitch and J. J. Zaalberg van Zelst, *ibid.*, **23,** 73, 1952.

R. M. Dowben, *ibid.*, **23,** 506, 1952.

W. P. Senett and R. W. Pierce, *ibid.*, **23,** 534, 1952.

W. T. Hughes and J. J. Lander, *ibid.*, **24,** 331, 1953.

S. K. Chao, *ibid.*, **30,** 1087, 1959.

G. F. Vanderschmidt, *ibid.*, **31,** 1004, 1960.

Electron. A fundamental particle of matter having mass, charge, and spin, but no measurable structure.[1]

Electron beam process. A high-power electron gun (see pp. 435 *et seq.*), having a magnetic focusing coil to concentrate the beam on a small spot of high intensity, is mounted in a vacuum chamber so that the beam impinges on a piece of metal or other material. This electron beam has sufficient intensity so that even the most refractory materials can be melted, evaporated, vacuum-refined. If the work is arranged on a platform to which either linear or rotary automatic motion can be imparted from outside through a suitable vacuum seal (see p. 383), it is possible to weld refractory metals or those difficult to weld by other processes (such as Ta, Ti, Be, and Cb). Fast and efficient pumping is required because the local intense heat-

---

[1] An interesting and readable discussion of electrons will be found in "On the Nature of the Electron," J. L. Salpeter, *Proc. I. R. E.*, **45,** 1588, 1957.

ing liberates gases. If a good vacuum is maintained, ductile welds can be produced free of gases and other contamination.

The emitter used in the electron gun for this purpose is usually tungsten, and so arranged that it can easily be replaced.

Because anode ("ultor") voltages of up to 30,000 (sometimes even higher) are commonly used, adequate shielding must be provided, since these voltages are capable of producing x-rays injurious to personnel.

The fast-pumping system used in this procedure can be set up in a manner similar to that shown in Fig. 18, p. 76, where the bypass arrangement allows (a) the chamber to be opened for rapid cycling without shutting down the pumps, and (b) fast pump-down when a new job is set up.

Because it is possible, with proper design of the electron gun, to focus the beam to a spot of 0.010 inch or better, welding on thin sheet metals and other delicate structures is feasible.

REFERENCES

L. McD. Schetky, *Research & Development,* **12,** 40, 1961.

T. H. Crane, American Welding Society Symposium presented at the Hotel Bostonian, Boston, Massachusetts, April 13, 1959.

"Airco Announces Electron Beam Welding," Air Reduction Corp., New York 17, New York, 1960.

Third Annual Electron Beam Symposium, March 23–24, 1961, at Sheraton-Plaza Hotel, Boston, Massachusetts, sponsored by the Alloyd Electronics Corporation, Cambridge 42, Massachusetts.

See also:

"Magnetic Focusing of Electron Beams," J. T. Mendel, *Proc. I. R. E.* **43,** 327, 1955.

"Pinhole Camera Investigation of Electron Beams," C. C. Cutler and J. A. Saloom, *Proc. I. R. E.,* **43,** 299, 1955; also "Thermal Velocity Effects in Electron Guns," C. C. Cutler and M. E. Hines, *ibid.,* p. 307.

"Electron Beam Focusing with Periodic Permanent Magnet Fields," J. T. Mendel, C. F. Quate, and W. H. Yocom, *Proc. I. R. E.,* **42,** 800, 1954.

"The Annular Geometry Electron Gun," J. W. Schwartz, *Proc. I. R. E.,* **46,** 1864, 1958.

"Progress in Electron Emission at High Fields," W. P. Dyke, *Proc. I. R. E.,* **43,** 1955.

"A Study of Electron-Beam Welding," S. S. White, H. J. Lander, W. T. Hess, and R. Bakish, *Welding J.,* June, July, 1962; "Electron-Beam Welding Techniques," R. Bakish, S. A. E. National Aeronautical Meeting, Paper No. 514A, New York, N.Y., April, 1962; "Electron Beam Design for Melting, Welding, Evaporation, and Drilling," E. B. Bas, G. Cremosnik, and H. Lerch, *Trans. Am. Vacuum Soc.,* 8th Ann. Symp. (1961), pp. 817–829, Pergamon Press, Inc., New York, 1962.

Electron bombardment (see pp. 101, 167).

Electron emission. When metals and other substances are heated, electrons are given off in amounts dependent on the *work function* of the material, a characteristic property which is expressed as the quantity of energy, in *electron volts,* which must be applied to the substance in order to liberate an electron. Numerically, the range is roughly from 10^{-12} to 10^{-11} erg for materials used in practice.

A low work function means, therefore, that the substance will give off electrons at a lower temperature than one with a higher work function. A table of work function values for the more common materials used in electron tubes is given below.

SUBSTANCE	ELECTRON WORK FUNCTION	SUBSTANCE	ELECTRON WORK FUNCTION
Barium, Ba	2.1[1]	Nickel, Ni	4.50–5.24[4]
Barium on barium oxide	1.0[1]	Palladium, Pd	4.99[4]
Barium boride, BaB_6	3.45[2]	Platinum	6.27[4]
BaSr carbonate	1.0–1.5[3]	Rhenium, Re	4.74–5.1[4]
Carbon, C	4.0–4.84[4]	Silicon, Si	3.59–4.02[4]
Calcium, Ca	2.24[4]	Strontium boride, SrB_6	2.67[2]
Calcium boride, CaB_6	2.86[2]	Tantalum, Ta	4.03–4.19[4]
Cerium boride, CeB_6	2.59[2]	Thorium, Th	3.35[4]
Cobalt, Co	4.4[4]	Thorium boride, ThB_6	2.92[2]
Cesium, Cs	1.81[1]	Thoriated tungsten	2.5–2.6[2]
Copper, Cu	3.85–4.55[4]	Titanium, Ti	3.95[4]
Iron, Fe	4.04–4.76[4]	Uranium, U	3.27[4]
L Cathode (Philips)	1.6–2.0[5]	Tungsten, W	4.25[1]
Lanthanum boride, LaB_6	2.66[2]	Zirconium, Zr	4.12–4.21[4]
Molybdenum, Mo	4.15–4.44[4]		

See curves in Fig. 58, p. 237.

[1] F. M. Penning, "Electrical Discharges in Gases," Macmillan Co., New York, 1957.

[2] *Materials Technology for Electron Tubes,* second edition. W. H. Kohl, Reinhold Publishing Corp., N.Y., 1959.

[3] Converted to oxides; the conventional oxide cathode.

[4] *Handbook of Chemistry and Physics,* edited by C. D. Hodgman, Chemical Rubber Publishing Co., Cleveland, Ohio, 41st edition, 1959–60.

[5] See p. 103 *et seq.*

Electron emission formulas

When a pure metal surface is heated to a temperature T°K, whose work function is ϕ_0 volts, a certain number of electrons will be emitted per second from each square centimeter of the metal surface. For practical purposes the emission is given in amperes ($1 \text{ amp} = 0.624 \times 10^{19}$ electrons per second). The formula is[1]

$$I_s = AT^2 \epsilon^{-\phi_0/kT}$$

where I_s means emission in amp/cm^2, A means a constant which has the theoretical value of 60.2 for all pure metals, k means Boltzmann's constant (0.863×10^{-4} v/°K).

[1] Richardson's equation; D. G. Fink, *Engineering Electronics,* 1st edition, p. 38, McGraw-Hill Book Co., New York, 1938; O. W. Richardson, *Phil. Mag.,* **28,** 633–647, 1914.

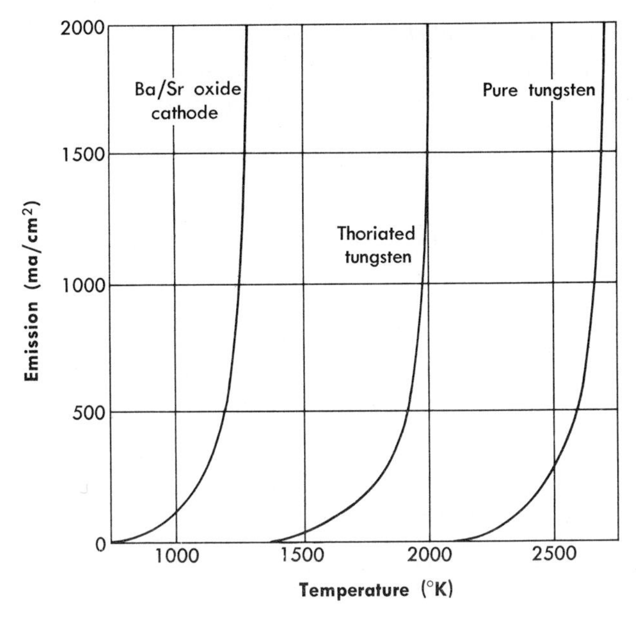

FIG. 58. Curves showing relative emission of three types of thermionic cathodes.

This equation consists of three separate factors:

(a) The constant A—for impure metals the value is much higher than 60.2. For example, platinum, which is usually associated with oxygen, has a value of 17,000.

(b) T^2 is the temperature in °K squared. This factor shows that the number of electrons emitted increases as the temperature rises. So far as this factor is concerned, the emission quadruples when the temperature is doubled, increases ninefold when the temperature is tripled, etc. Actually, the emission may increase by several millionfold when the temperature is doubled because the effect of the third factor (below) is much greater than that of the second.

(c) The third factor, $\epsilon^{-\phi_0/kT}$, is the number $e = 2.718$ (the base of natural logarithms) raised to the power indicated. To evaluate the effect of this factor, we choose tungsten as an example. At a temperature of $T = 1600$°K (slightly above red heat), the value of the exponent is:

$$\frac{\phi_0}{kT} = \frac{4.52}{0.863 \times 10^{-4} \times 1600} = 32.8.$$

The value of the factor is then $e^{-32.8}$. When the temperature is changed to 3300°K, the exponent is decreased to a value of 15.8, which means an enormous increase in the value of the third factor, or approximately 24×10^6 times. Thus, comparatively small changes in temperature produce large changes in the electron emission.

In pure tungsten the emission is about 10^{-6} amp/cm² at 1600°K, and about 100 amp/cm² at 3300°K.

Illustrations of the use of the Richardson equation.

Problem 1. Calculate the total emission, in amperes, available from a pure tungsten emitter wire 5 cm (2 in) long and 0.01 cm (0.004 in) in diameter, operated at a temperature of 2500°K.

Given:

$$A = 60.2, \quad T = 2500, \quad e = 2.718, \quad b_0 = \frac{\phi_0}{kT} = 52{,}400, \quad l = 5 \text{ cm}, \quad d = 0.01 \text{ cm}.$$

To find:

$$\begin{aligned} I_s &= AT^2\epsilon^{-b_0/T} \text{ amp/cm}^2 \\ &= 60.2 \times (2500)^2 \times 2.718^{-52400/2500} \\ &= 3.76 \times 10^8 \times (2.718)^{-20.9} \\ &= 3.76 \times 10^8 \times 0.795 \times 10^{-9} \\ &= 0.299 \text{ amp/cm}^2. \end{aligned}$$

The area of the surface of the wire is $\pi dl = 3.1416 \times 0.01 \times 5 = 0.157$ cm². The emission from the surface is therefore

$$0.299 \times 0.157 = 0.047 \text{ amp. total.}$$

Problem 2. Calculate the emission from a barium-strontium oxide surface whose area is 0.157 cm² at a temperature of 1100°K.

Given:

$$A = 10^{-2}, \quad T = 1100, \quad \epsilon = 2.718, \quad b_0 = 12{,}000, \quad \text{area} = 0.157.$$

To find:

$$\begin{aligned} I_s &= AT^2\epsilon^{-b_0/T} \text{ amp/cm}^2 \\ &= 10^{-2}\,(1100)^2 \times 2.718^{-12000/1100} \\ &= 1.21 \times 10^4 \times 2.718^{-10.9} \\ &= 1.21 \times 1.85 \times 10^{-1} \\ &= 0.224 \text{ amp/cm}^2. \end{aligned}$$

$$I_{\text{tot}} = \text{area} \times I_s = 0.224 \times 0.157 = 0.0352 \text{ amp}.$$

The Three-halves Power Law for Electron Emission:

$$I = \frac{2.34 \times 10^6 E^{3/2}}{S^2} \text{ amp/cm}^2,$$

where I means current in amp/cm² (of each plate) flowing between two large parallel plates separated by S cm and with voltage E volts applied between them.

When the voltage is doubled, the current increases 2.8 times ($2^{3/2}$). When the voltage is tripled, the current increases $3^{3/2}$ times, or 5.2 times. If the separation between the plates is doubled, the current becomes $\frac{1}{4}$, etc.

For coaxial cylinders, the three-halves power law becomes:

$$I = \frac{14.68 \times 10^{-6} E^{3/2}}{rB^2} \text{ amp/cm length,}$$

where r means radius of outer cylinder, and B means a quantity depending on the ratio of the outer cylinder to that of the inner. For most cases it is usually sufficient to take a value of $B^2 = 1$.

Both the above formulas postulate an infinite or ample supply of electrons, i.e., saturation (see p. 228). Figure 58 shows the relative emission of three types of thermionic cathodes.)

Electron gun. The structure of an electron tube, which comprises the cathode (with heater, if indirectly heated) and auxiliary electrodes for focusing and deflecting the beam of electrons, is called an electron gun. Referring to Fig. 35, p. 130, the components K_h, K, G, H, F, O, A, B, and C constitute an electron gun, and, in the case of a cathode-ray tube, are mounted together as a unitary assembly, together with getters, if required, for ease in assembly. (See ELECTRON OPTICS below; also PIERCE GUN, p. 435 *et seq.*)

Electron multiplier (photomultiplier).[1] This is an electron tube in which an initial entering electron, ion, or other moving particle, in striking the first electrode, liberates *secondary electrons* from it, which are then attracted to a second more positive electrode, in turn liberating a larger number of secondary electrons, and so on for a number of stages. Since the action is cumulative, after nine stages the electron amplification may be as much as 2.5×10^6 for 150 volts per stage. The electrodes are called *dynodes* and the metal used for them is chosen and processed so as to have as high a secondary emission as possible.

Dynodes are commonly made of beryllium copper, and the assembled structure is heated for processing in a vacuum to about 650°C, which apparently produces a high beryllium concentration on the surface.

According to Penning[2] the secondary emission coefficient for the alkali and alkali earth metals is higher than for the metals in subsequent columns of the periodic table. Since the beryllium in the alloy beryllium-copper is a stable and easily available element (Group II), it is a natural choice. Other less common alloys, such as silver-magnesium, have been used.

Electron optics.[3] The electrons emitted by a thermionic cathode can be channeled and focused in a manner analogous to light. The "lenses" in this case are either electrostatic or magnetic fields. Practically all cathode-ray and television picture tubes commercially available today use electrostatic focusing. (See pp. 130, 131.)

If the shapes of the electrodes are such as to form a field which extends only a limited distance along the axis of the electron beam (i.e., substantially a radial field),

---

[1] See *The Electronic Engineering Handbook*, R. R. Batcher and W. Moulic, Electronic Development Associates, New York, 1944; also *Gaseous Conductors*, J. D. Cobine, p. 112, Dover Publications, Inc., New York, 1958; "Reference Data for Radio Engineers," fourth edition, p. 408, H. P. Westman, International Telephone & Telegraph Corp., New York, 1956; "Fundamentals of Secondary Electron Emission," M. A. Pomerantz and J. F. Marshall, *Proc. I. R. E.*, **39,** 1367, 1951.

[2] F. M. Penning, *Electrical Discharges in Gases,* Macmillan Co., New York, New York, 1957.

[3] See PIERCE GUN, p. 435 *et seq.*

the result is a "thin" lens. If the contour and spacing of the electrodes are such that the field is not entirely radial, a more gradual bending of the ray is produced, and a "thick" lens results. A single lens or several in tandem may be found necessary to give the desired concentration.

In Fig. 35, p. 130, it will be seen that a number of electrodes, either cylinders or circular plates with central openings (G, H, F), are arranged axially and symmetrically in the space between the cathode K and the anode A. A radial electrostatic field, or the radial component of such a field, introduces restorative forces that alter the direction of all the electrons that diverge away from the true axial direction. For perfect focusing it is necessary that the electrostatic potential at each point along any radius, starting from the axis of the beam, have a restorative force proportional to the distance of that point from the axis, so as to give those electrons that stray the greatest amount, i.e., the greatest restorative force.

A definite voltage relation is always maintained between the anode voltage and that applied to the focusing electrode F, so that lines of force are set up between them. The radial components of this field, if all the parts are accurately aligned, are zero at the axis, steadily increasing as the distance from the axis is increased.[1]

The principles of electron optics are utilized in the *electron microscope* in which a very thin section of the material to be examined is placed in the beam and its shadow is refocused on a very fine-grained fluorescent screen.

Electrons, secondary (see ELECTRON MULTIPLIER, above).

Electron volt. A quantity which represents the energy of an electron which has gone through a change of potential of one volt in a vacuum. It is equivalent to approximately 1.6×10^{-12} erg. The velocity of an electron which has passed through a one-volt potential difference is 600 km/sec. For comparison, the velocity of a neon ion in the same condition is only 3 km/sec.

Electrophotoluminescence (see ELECTROLUMINESCENCE, p. 233).

Electroplating (see pp. 23–33; also Chromium plating, p. 25; Nickel plating, pp. 29–31; copper plating, pp. 25–28; Silver plating, pp. 32, 33; Gold plating, p. 28; Platinum plating, p. 32; Electroplating nickel on molybdenum, p. 31).

Electropolishing. This is a cleaning process for metals involving an electrolytic method in which a surface layer of the metal, acting as the anode, is plated out and removed. (See pp. 9–22.)

Emission (see ELECTRON EMISSION above).

Emission, cold (see CATHODES, COLD, p. 192).

Emission formulas (see ELECTRON EMISSION FORMULAS).

Emission of tungsten (see ELECTRON EMISSION above).

Emissivity of metals. When a metal (or other) surface is heated, it radiates energy to the surroundings, since it is usually not isolated in space. The energy thus radiated from unit area in unit time for unit difference in temperature between the surface and surrounding bodies is called the *emissivity* or *emissive power*.

The emissivity of a surface is a function of the material of which the surface is composed, the condition of that surface, and the wavelength of light radiated. An oxidized surface, or one which is roughened, has a higher emissivity than a brightly polished and clean surface of the same material.

---

[1] R. R. Batcher and W. Moulic, *Electronic Engineering Handbook,* Electronic Development Association, New York, New York, 1945.

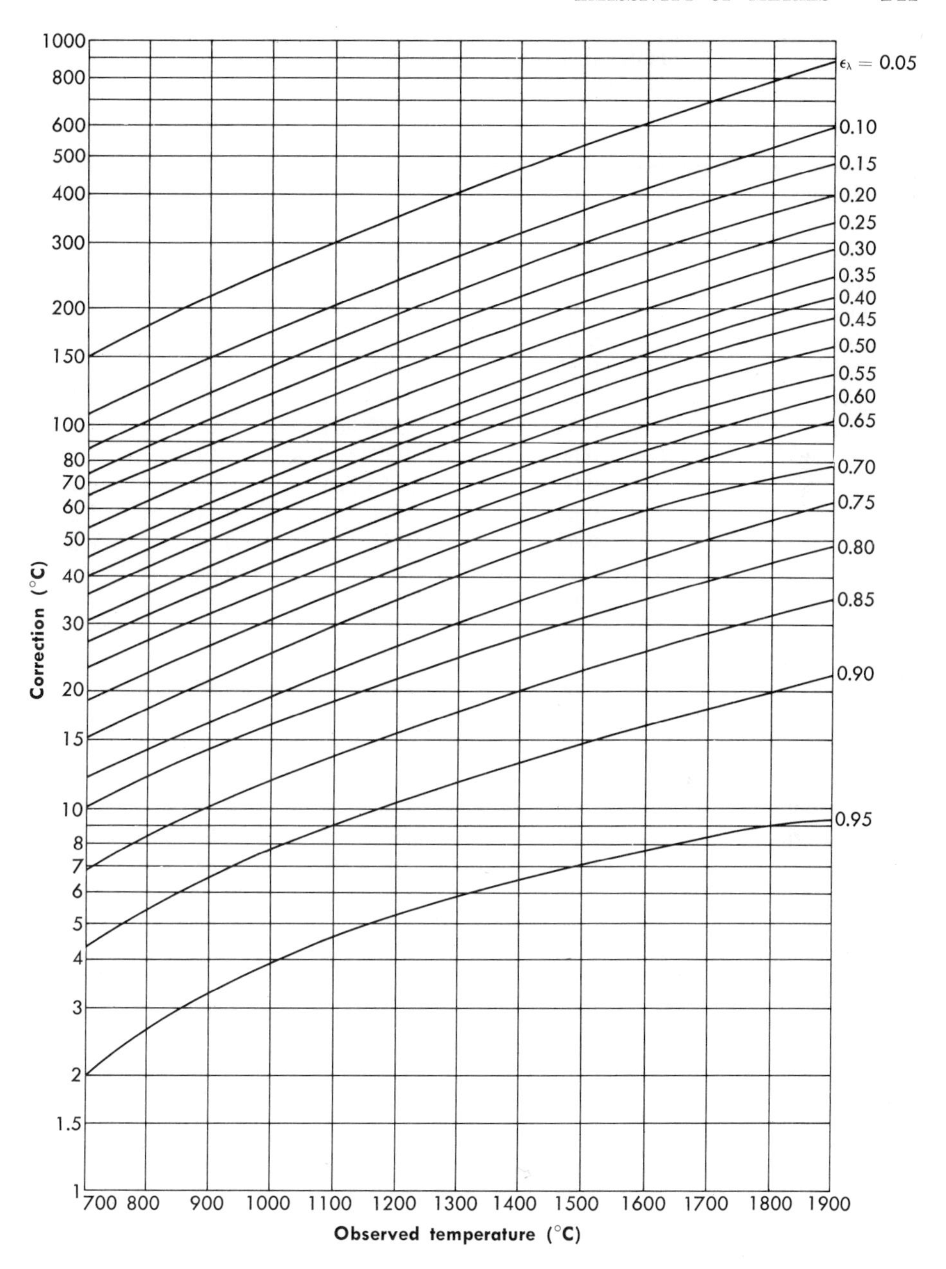

FIG. 59. Corrections to optical pyrometer readings for spectral emissivity.

SPECTRAL EMISSIVITIES OF SOME METALS[1]

METAL	WAVE-LENGTH (μ)	TEMPERATURE (°C)	SPECTRAL EMISSIVITY	SOURCE[2]
Chromium	0.65	1460	0.39	1
Chromium	0.55	1460	0.53	1
Copper	0.66	1000	0.105	1
Copper	0.66	1080	0.12	1
Copper	0.66	1100(liq)	0.15	1
Copper	0.66	1225(liq)	0.13	1A
Copper	0.55	1080	0.38	1A
Copper	0.55	1100(liq)	0.36	1
Copper	0.55	1225(liq)	0.28	1A
Gold	0.66	1063(mp)	0.145	1
Gold	0.66	1063(liq)	0.22	1
Gold	0.66	1000	0.140	2
Gold	0.55	1000	0.45	2
Gold	0.46	1000	0.63	2
Iridium	0.65	1750	0.30	1
Iron	0.66	1050	0.39	3, 1
Iron	0.66	1350	0.38	3, 1
Iron	0.66	1450	0.37	3, 1
Iron	0.66	1530	0.36	3, 1
Iron	0.66	1535(liq)	0.367	1
Molybdenum	0.66	1000	0.378	2
Molybdenum	0.66	1700	0.353	2
Molybdenum	0.66	2500	0.332	2
Molybdenum	0.667	1000–1800	0.382	4
Molybdenum	0.467	1000	0.395	2
Molybdenum	0.467	1700	0.380	2
Molybdenum	0.467	2500	0.365	2
Nickel	0.66	950–1400	0.375	2
Nickel	0.55	950–1400	0.425	2
Nickel	0.46	950–1400	0.450	2
Niobium (Columbium)	0.65	<mp	0.49	1
Niobium	0.65	>mp (liq)	0.40	1
Niobium	0.667	1300–2200	0.374	4
Niobium	0.55	<mp	0.61	1
Palladium	0.66	1000	0.35	5
Palladium	0.66	1450	0.31	5
Palladium	0.66	1530	0.33	1
Palladium	0.66	1555(liq)	0.37	1
Palladium	0.55	1530	0.38	1
Platinum	0.66	900	0.29	2
Platinum	0.66	1100	0.30	2

[1] From C. J. Smithells, *Metals Reference Handbook,* Interscience Publishers, Inc. New York, New York, 1949.

[2] See next page.

SPECTRAL EMISSIVITIES OF METALS (CONTINUED)

METAL	WAVE-LENGTH (μ)	TEMPERATURE (°C)	SPECTRAL EMISSIVITY	SOURCE (see below)
Platinum	0.66	1300	0.30	2
Platinum	0.66	1500	0.31	2
Platinum	0.66	1100	0.285	6
Platinum	0.66	1300	0.29	6
Platinum	0.66	1500	0.295	6
Platinum	0.463	1300	0.37	2
Platinum	0.463	1500	0.385	2
Platinum	0.463	1600	0.39	2
Rhodium	0.667	1000–1700	0.242	4
Rhodium	0.65	<mp	0.29	1
Rhodium	0.65	>mp(liq)	0.30	1
Rhodium	0.55	<mp	0.29	1
Silver	0.66	700–1400(liq)	0.055	3
Silver	0.66	940	0.044	1
Silver	0.55	980(liq)	0.072	1
Tantalum	0.66	900	0.459	2, 7
Tantalum	0.66	1100	0.442	2, 7
Tantalum	0.66	1800	0.416	7
Tantalum	0.66	2500	0.392	7
Tantalum	0.467	1100	0.505	2
Tantalum	0.467	1800	0.460	2
Titanium	0.65	1550	0.63	1
Titanium	0.65	1800(liq)	0.65	1
Titanium	0.55	1550	0.75	1
Titanium	0.55	1880(liq)	0.75	1
Tungsten	0.665	20	0.470	8
Tungsten	—	900	0.452	8
Tungsten	—	1900	0.431	8
Tungsten	—	2900	0.411	8
Tungsten	0.650	20	0.453	9
Tungsten	0.650	900	0.444	9
Tungsten	0.650	1700	0.436	9
Zirconium	0.65	<mp	0.32	—
Zirconium	0.65	>mp(liq)	0.30	—
Steel	0.65	<mp	0.35	—
Steel	0.65	>mp(liq)	0.37	—
Constantan	0.65	<mp	0.35	—
Nichrome	0.65	<mp	0.35	—

Sources:

1. Burgess & Waltenberg, 1915.
1A. Burgess, 1909.
2. Worthing, 1926.
3. Bidwell, 1914.
4. Whitney, 1935.
5. Waldner and Burgess, 1907.
6. Stephens, 1939.
7. Malter and Langmuir, 1939.
8. Worthing, 1917, 1924.
9. Hamaker, 1934.

The *optical pyrometer* (see pp. 405–407) measures an apparent temperature T_s, which is related to the true temperature T by the equation

$$\frac{1}{T} - \frac{1}{T_s} = \frac{\lambda \log_\epsilon E_\lambda}{1.438 \text{ (cm degrees)}},$$

where E_λ = spectral emissivity, ϵ = base of natural logarithms (2.718), and T and T_s are in °C (See Fig. 59).

The corrections to be applied to the optical pyrometer for various spectral emissivities are shown in Fig. 59. In the chart the spectral emissivities E_λ are given by the curves for a wavelength of 0.65μ. At the point where the temperature observed (optical pyrometer) (verticals) intersects the curve nearest that of the spectral emissivity of the metal under observation (see table, pp. 242, 243), the correction to be added is read on the left (horizontals).

Smithells[1] notes that, "The ability of a surface to radiate energy is governed by the material of which the surface is composed and its physical condition. Any attempt therefore to place a numerical value on this radiating ability should be related to a definition of the surface condition. It is usual to choose smooth, polished surfaces for this purpose and thus arrive at values which are comparable from one metal to another."

When an optical pyrometer is used to measure the temperature of hot surfaces within tubes with glass envelopes,[2] errors due to the absorption of the glass must be considered, also the angle of observation with respect to the glass.[3] If there has been even a small (almost invisible) amount of deposited (evaporated) material on the glass, the error arising from transmission and reflection must be added.

Emitter, thermionic. A source of electrons given off by a heated surface; a hot cathode. An anode which is heated by electron bombardment becomes a thermionic emitter when there is a second anode beyond it which is more positive. The arrangement is as follows: a thermionic emitter, the cathode, is heated directly (tungsten filament) or indirectly (oxide-coated cathode). The first anode, positively charged with respect to the cathode, draws electrons to it in quantities large enough to heat the first anode to incandescence. This anode now becomes a cathode with respect to a second anode, to which a still higher positive emf is applied. As this voltage is increased, the number of electrons increases (up to saturation), producing a current capable of melting the second anode. (See ELECTRON EMISSION, p. 235, and ELECTRON BEAM PROCESS, p. 234.)

Environment for tube assembly (see pp. 1–3 and footnotes).

Epoxy resins (see p. 194).

Equipotential cathode (see UNIPOTENTIAL CATHODE, p. 562).

Equipotential lines. In a diode (see p. 228) consisting of two similarly shaped and parallel plates, one of which is the cathode and the other the anode (positive), the potential gradient from cathode to anode is uniform; that is, all points at the same distance between them will have the same potential. In other words, there are

---

[1] C. J. Smithells, *Metals Reference Handbook,* Interscience Publishers Inc., New York, New York, 1949.

[2] P. P. Coppola, *Rev. Sci. Instr.,* **31**, 137, 1960.

[3] "Pyrometric Practice," Technical Paper No. 170, of National Bureau of Standards, p. 117, 1921.

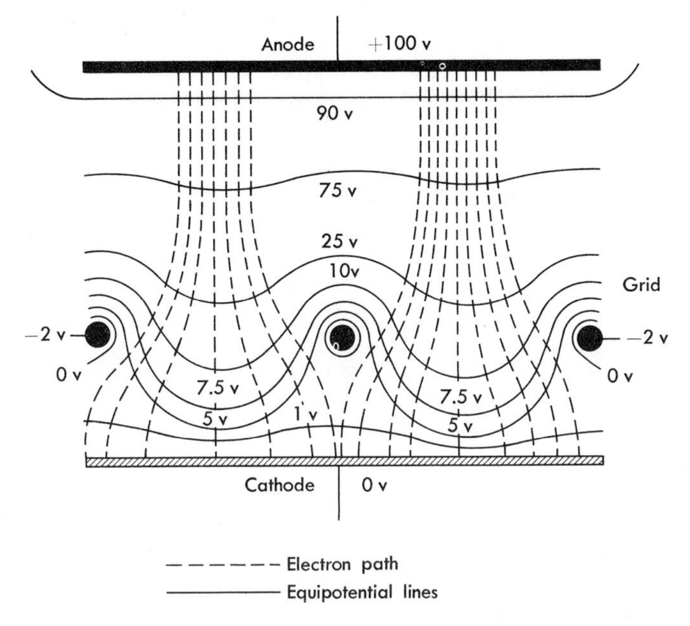

FIG. 60. Electron paths from cathode to anode of a triode are located at right angles to the imaginary surfaces having equal voltage with respect to the cathode. Cross-sectional views of these surfaces are shown as the equipotential lines.

imaginary planes parallel to the plates where the potential is the same at every point over the entire plane. If a cross section of this is considered, the lines denoting these planes will be *equipotential lines*.[1]

The introduction of a third electrode, or grid, negatively charged, changes the configuration of the equipotential lines in a complex way, which is shown in Figs. 60 and 61. If the equipotential lines (solid) extend past the grid or third electrode almost to the cathode, the electrons in the space charge (p. 228) will be partially neutralized and electron current will flow to the anode. This condition is shown in Fig. 60, where there is still a small positive potential close to the cathode despite the negatively charged grid (−2v). If, however, the grid is made more negative (to −10v), as shown in Fig. 61, the equipotential lines change polarity near the grid and the resulting negative field prevents the escape of electrons from the space-charge region. This condition is known as *cut-off*. (See also Fig. 38 on p. 132 for the effect of cathode-grid-anode spacing on tube characteristics.

Etching metal to form (see p. 434).

Ethyl alcohol (see p. 150).

Eutectic. In metallurgy, an alloy of lowest melting point. The melting temperature of a binary (two elements) eutectic alloy is usually lower than that of either constituent. As an illustration, the constitution diagram of the silver-copper alloys is shown in Fig. 62. These two metals alloy in all proportions, and the melting point of any combination of these two metals can be read from the curve. A eutectic is

[1] The electrons moving toward the anode always do so in a direction perpendicular to these equipotential lines; thus in the simple diode we have postulated, the electrons travel in straight lines perpendicular to both electrodes and thus parallel to each other.

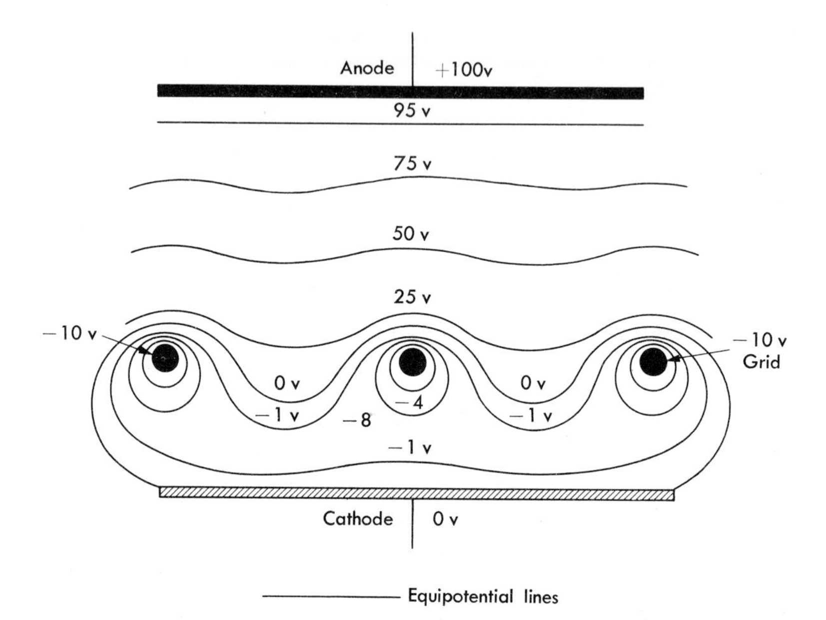

FIG. 61. Condition of plate-current cutoff, in which no part of the electrostatic field, having a positive potential, extends near enough to the cathode to attract electrons. The effect of the anode voltage is entirely neutralized.

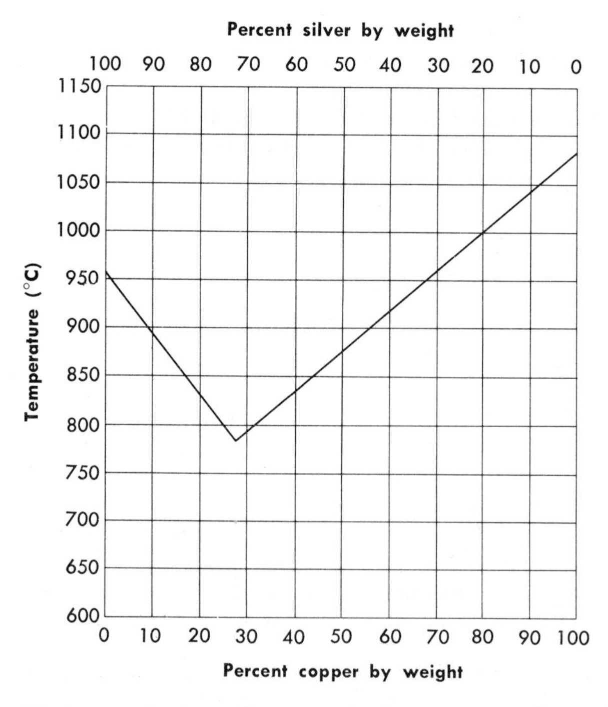

FIG. 62. Simplified constitution diagram of silver-copper alloys, illustrating a eutectic.

formed with 72% silver (Ag melting point 960°C) and 28% copper (Cu melting point 1083°C).

Many of the metals used in electron tube construction are likely to form eutectic alloys with each other, and this is to be taken into consideration when spot-welding or brazing parts of dissimilar metals. For example, where it is necessary to join heavy tungsten filaments to leads of another metal (e.g., nickel), it is always preferable to attach by crimping or clamping rather than by welding, since at high temperatures, even though the nickel leads are adequate by themselves to carry a heavy current without undue heating, a eutectic-like alloy could be formed at the weld which might have a melting point lower than that of nickel, and therefore constitute a source of failure.

Evacuation (see EXHAUST on p. 249).

Evaporation, vacuum (see DEPOSITION on p. 224). The table below gives the evaporation temperatures of various metals *in vacuo*.

METAL	REMARKS	MELTING POINT (°C)
Cesium	Evaporates readily at 433°C	28.5
Rubidium	Evaporates readily at 450°C	38.5
Potassium	Evaporates readily at 480°C	62.3
Cadmium	Evaporates readily at 541°C	320.9
Sodium	Evaporates readily at 565°C	97.5
Zinc	Evaporates readily at 623°C	419.5
Magnesium	Evaporates readily at 712°C	651
Strontium	Evaporates readily at 811°C	770
Lithium	Evaporates readily at 821°C	186
Calcium	Evaporates readily at 878°C	850
Barium	Evaporates readily at 905°C	710
Bismuth	Evaporates readily at 913°C	271.3
Antimony	Evaporates readily at 973°C	630.5
Lead	Evaporates readily at 1000°C	327.4
Tin	Evaporates readily at 1148°C	231.9
Chromium	Evaporates with difficulty at 1190°C	1550
Silver	Evaporates readily at 1319°C	960.5
Gold	Evaporates readily at 1445°C	1063
Aluminum	Evaporates readily at 1461°C	660
Copper	Evaporates readily at 1542°C	1083
Iron	Evaporates readily at 1694°C	1540
Nickel	Evaporates readily at 1717°C	1455
Platinum	Very difficult to evaporate at 2332°C	1773
Iridium and Rhodium[1]		
Molybdenum	Very difficult to evaporate at 2755°C	2622
Tungsten	Very difficult to evaporate at 3505°C	3400

(See also p. 564, *et seq.*)

[1] "Vaporization of Iridium and Rhodium," M. B. Panish and L. Reif, *J. Chem. Phys.*, **34**, 1915, 1961.

Notes: Zinc, aluminum, and other metals: tungsten heater used. Chromium evaporates with difficulty; does not liquefy; use Cr-plated spiral. Molybdenum and tungsten: only thin films of these metals evaporated in long periods.

REFERENCES TO EVAPORATION AND DEPOSITION

L. Holland, *The Vacuum Deposition of Thin Films,* W. Edwards & Co.; John Wiley & Sons, New York, New York, 1956.

E. Kafig, "Reproduction of Printed Patterns by Vacuum Evaporation," *Rev. Sci. Instr.,* **23,** 54, 1952.

"Vacuum Distillation of Zinc," M. J. Spendlove and H. W. St. Clair, *ibid.,* **23,** 471, 1952.

"Detection of Molecular Beams," W. E. Quinn, A. Pery, J. M. Baker, H. R. Lewis, N. F. Ramsey, and T. LaTourette, *ibid.,* **29,** 935, 1958.

"High Temperature Evaporation of Metals and Oxides," J. T. Krause, *ibid.,* **31,** 907, 1960.

"Evaporation Source," E. M. DaSilva, *ibid.,* **31,** 959, 1960.

Scientific Foundations of Vacuum Technique, S. Dushman, 2nd edition, chapter 10; John Wiley & Sons, Inc., New York, 1962.

For evaporation of nonmetallic materials, see K. Blodgett, *Phys. Rev.,* **55,** 391, 1939.

Evaporation of metals in vacuum firing (see pp. 52, 224).

Evaporation of volatile metals (see pp. 36, 38, 39, 78).

Evapor-ion pump (see also TITANIUM-ION PUMPING, p. 106).

The following abstract is from a paper by Davis and Divatia. *Rev. Sci. Instr.,* **25,** 1193, 1954.

A type of high-vacuum pump has been developed which makes possible the elimination of organic vapors and high-vapor pressure materials from vacuum systems without using coolant traps or baffles. This pump utilizes the gettering action of continuously evaporated titanium in conjunction with ion pumping. Some pumping speeds are: 7000–8000 liters/sec at 3×10^{-6} mm Hg for hydrogen, 6500–7500 liters/sec at 1.5×10^{-6} mm Hg for nitrogen and oxygen, approximately 9 liters/sec at 4×10^{-6} mm Hg for argon, and approximately 4 liters/sec at 3×10^{-5} mm Hg for helium. The lowest pressure obtainable is about 2×10^{-7} mm Hg. Dependence of pumping speed on the temperature of the gettering surface, the pressure, and the rate of evaporation of titanium are given.

REFERENCES

A. S. Divatia, R. H. Davis, and R. G. Herb, *Phys. Rev.,* **93,** 926, 1953.

Herb, Davis, Divatia, and Saxon, *ibid.,* **89,** 897, 1953.

J. Plücker, *Pogg. Ann.,* **105,** 84, 1858.

H. Schwarz, *Z. Physik,* **117,** 23, 1940; *Z. tech. Physik,* **21,** 381, 1940; *Rev. Sci. Instr.,* **24,** 371, 1953.

W. Lumpe and R. Seeliger, *Z. Physik,* **121,** 546, 1943.

F. M. Penning, *Physica,* **4,** 71, 1937.

A. T. Finkelstein, *Rev. Sci. Instr.,* **11,** 94, 1940.

D. Alpert, *J. Appl. Phys.,* **24,** 860, 1953.

J. S. Foster, E. O. Lawrence and E. J. Lofgren, *Rev. Sci. Instr.,* **24,** 388, 1953.

H. Schwarz, *ibid.,* **24,** 371, 1953.

Excitation. In electron-tube parlance, excitation refers to the *state* of an atom which is ionized, i.e., which has lost or gained one or more electrons by collision with other particles, and is thus in an unstable condition. Excitation of gas atoms within a certain pressure range below atmospheric is often manifested as a glow discharge. (See BREAKDOWN VOLTAGE, p. 188.)

Exhaust, exhaust procedure. The removal of gases from a vessel by some form of pumping is called exhausting or evacuating. See pp. 77, 78.

Farvitron (see OMEGATRON, pp. 402–404).

Feed-through, passthrough. Electrical leads are brought into a vacuum vessel through some type of sealed conductor. In conventional glass or glass-metal vacuum tubes, the leads are Dumet (pp. 56, 230), Kovar (pp. 55, 58, 61, 322), tungsten (pp. 58, 61, 62), or other metals. Fixed or demountable terminals for low and high voltages can be made from glass-metal seals or headers commercially available or formed from ceramic-to-metal seals (see pp. 67–73). For demountable seals, O-rings (pp. 223, 407–409) of Neoprene, silicone rubber, Teflon, or other materials can be used.[1,2]

Fernico. This is a glass-sealing alloy made by General Electric Company which is similar but not identical to Kovar (see pp. 322 *et seq.*). The following tabulation gives some of the differences.

	FERNICO	KOVAR
Composition (percent)	Fe 54 Ni 31 Co 15	Fe 53.7 Ni 29 Co 17 Mn 0.3
Tensile strength (psi)	72,000–80,000	89,700
Modulus of elasticity (psi)	18×10^6	20×10^6
Melting point (°C)	1460	1450 (approximately)
Density (gm/cc)	8.24	8.35
Electrical resistivity (microhm-cm)	43.8	49
Curie point (°C)	—	435
Hardness Rockwell B (approximate)	75	78–84 at 760°C (annealed) 93–100 (unannealed)
Thermal conductivity (cgs)	—	0.046
Thermal expansion 25°–300°C	4.95×10^{-6}	$4.41\text{–}5.30 \times 10^{-6}$
Yield point (psi)	55,000	50,500

Fernico is sintered by a powder-metallurgy technique in hydrogen, and is ductile and free from embrittlement under conditions of ordinary use including heating and annealing in air, hydrogen, or gas, as well as soldering, brazing, and welding.

Ferrovac (see VACUUM-MELTED METALS, pp. 366–368).

Field emission (auto-electronic emission, cold emission). In an electron tube in which the cathode is nonthermionic, or is operating at saturation (p. 228), an increase of

[1] J. W. L. DeVilliers, *Rev. Sci. Instr.*, **29**, 527, 1958.
[2] H. Wieder and A. W. Smith, *ibid.*, **29**, 794, 1958.

the anode potential causes electrons, which have insufficient energy of their own to leave the cathode, to "leak" through the threshold of the cathode due to the "pulling" effect of the intense electric field. This accounts for the gradual increase of plate current in the curves of Figs. 53 and 54, p. 229, and is called the *Schottky effect.* (See also CATHODES, COLD, p. 192.)

Fifty-fifty solder (soft solder). Also known as common solder, it nominally contains 50% lead and 50% tin, with small admixtures of antimony (0.12–0.5%). Fifty-fifty solder begins to melt at 181°C and is completely liquid at 213°C.

Filaments and heaters. The term *filament* usually designates a directly heated cathode or emitter, e.g., a tungsten wire or ribbon operated at about 2500°K or a thoriated tungsten wire or ribbon operated at about 2000°K. A *heater,* in electron-tube terminology, is a tungsten or molybdenum (or other suitable metal) wire placed inside or close to an oxide-coated or dispenser-type cathode, and operated in the neighborhood of 1700°K. (See pp. 80, 86.)

Fine silver. This is the designation of a high-purity silver (99.9+%) having a melting point of 960.5°C. (See p. 478 and item 91, p. 181.)

Finger (cold) trap. In contrast to the conventional form of cold trap (see Fig. 46, p. 212), in which the refrigerant surrounds the vacuum duct in a Dewar flask, the "cold finger" is a tube with a closed bottom which is inserted concentrically into a widened part of the vacuum duct so that the gas flows around it. The finger can, if desired, be provided with fins or other devices to increase the area of cold surface.

Finishing valve. A valve inserted between the forepump (p. 253) or mechanical pump and the high pressure port of the diffusion pump (p. 227). Valve B in Fig. 18, p. 76 is an example.

Firebrick. This is an insulating and refractory material that is used in the construction of bake-out and glass-annealing ovens. It also has many other uses in the laboratory. It is *not* suitable for use inside vacuum devices because of its extremely high porosity. It should not be used in hydrogen or other atmosphere furnaces for the same reason.

One type of firebrick in common use is supplied in various standard shapes by the Babcock and Wilcox Company.[1] The approximate composition is alumina 45% and silica 52%, with small amounts of titania, iron oxide, calcium oxide, magnesia, and sulfur trioxide. This firebrick is produced in several different grades, as outlined in the table on p. 251, reproduced by courtesy of the Babcock and Wilcox Company.

It will be noted that the higher temperature brick (e.g., K-30) has in general a higher heat conductivity and density. For most efficient designing, where several layers of brick are required, as in the oven described on pp. 46 and 47, the higher temperature brick is used in a single layer on the interior of the oven or furnace, backed up with the lower temperature types. For example, in a furnace which is to operate at 1300°C, one layer of type K-26 or K-28 brick is used as an inner lining, then a layer of K-20 brick, and if a third layer is needed, K-16 would be used outside. The bricks can be cemented if necessary with refractory cements supplied by the Babcock and Wilcox Company.

Flashing of cathodes and emitter (see pp. 89, 100).

Flow of gases in vacuum (see PUMPING SPEED, p. 455; also GAS LAWS, p. 265).

Fluorescence in vacuum (see pp. 134, 166, 213).

Fluorescent materials (phosphors). Certain chemical materials glow under the action of an electron beam. These materials are commonly applied in the form of a fine

---

[1] Refractories Division, 161 East 42nd Street, New York 17, New York. (Data from their Bulletin R-38, 1961.)

PROPERTIES OF BABCOCK AND WILCOX FIREBRICK

PROPERTIES	BABCOCK AND WILCOX INSULATING FIREBRICK K-1620	K-20	K-23	K-26	K-28	K-30
Service temperature (°C)						
Exposed	871	1093	1260	1427	1538	1593
Backup	1093	1093	1260	1427	1538	1593
Density (lb/9″ straight*)	1.29	1.70	1.85	2.60	2.70	3.06
(lb/ft³)	21.8	29.1	31.6	44.5	46.2	52.3
Fusion temperature (°C)	1482	1510	1510	1704	1754	1754
Heat conductivity (ASTM C 182-47) at mean temperature of						
260°C	0.78	0.97	1.07	1.70	1.82	2.04
538°C	1.00	1.25	1.32	2.10	2.16	2.36
816°C	1.28	1.55	1.59	2.71	2.64	2.96
1093°C	—	—	1.91	3.43	3.20	3.80
Hot-load strength (%), deformation under load of 10 lb/in², 1½ hrs at						
871°C	0	—	—	—	—	—
1093°C	0	0	—	—	—	—
1204°C	—	—	0.1	0.3	0.3	0.2
Reheat shrinkage† at temperature (°C) of	843	1066	1232	1399	1510	1538
K-1620, K-20, K-23, K-26 (ASTM C 210–46) K-28, K-30 (ASTM C 113-46), %	0	0	0	0.2	0.6	0.5
Cold-crushing strength, (lb/in²) (ASTM C 93–54)	70	110	145	195	190	295
Modulus of rupture (lb/in²) (ASTM C 93-54)	75	110	150	200	200	280

* This designates a standard brick, 9″ × 4½″ × 2½″. Other sizes and shapes are available.

† Repeated cycling at the temperatures given resulted in the shrinkages noted in the line below.

powder out of an aqueous suspension to form a thin, uniform, adherent layer on the inner faces of cathode-ray tubes, television picture tubes, and other devices.

The aqueous suspension contains, in addition to the phosphor, potassium silicate as a binder and a small percentage of barium acetate, an electrolyte which effects the gelation of the phosphor particles with the potassium silicate. Barium acetate is used on glass, quartz, and other nonconductors but *not* when phosphors are being deposited on metallic substrates.

There are a number of phosphors available in various colors. In the table on p. 254[1] coumn 1 gives the designation numbers agreed upon by the radio and elec-

[1] Sylvania Electric Products, Inc., Tungsten & Chemical Division, Towanda, Pennsylvania.

tronics industry. Column 3 gives the composition of the material in which, for example, $(Zn,Mg)F_2{:}Mn$ means that the phosphor consists of mixed zinc and magnesium fluorides, with manganese as an activator.

In columns 4 and 5 the differences are mainly of degree. The fluorescent effect is produced by a beam of electrons or other radiation and disappears almost immediately after the beam is removed, while the phosphorescence may persist for a considerable interval, although it is relatively weak.

Under the heading "Persistence," column 6, the times given refer to the fluorescence, and in no case are they more than a few seconds. For television picture tubes, a short or medium persistence is required, of the order of a millisecond or less for the fluorescence to have diminished in brightness to 1% of its initial intensity. For radar presentation, a fluorescent screen of long persistence is usually required.

One of the most widely used phosphors for laboratory-type tubes is *willemite* (see p. 569) which fluoresces a brilliant green, and corresponds to Phosphor P-1 in the table (Sylvania types 160, 161, 221).

Of the various methods for applying screens to glass or other bases, only settling-out of an aqueous suspension will be described here. (In making television color-picture tubes, "dots" of several different phosphors can be applied by a photoresist or printing method in such a way that one phosphor does not contaminate another.)

The optimum *screen weight* (amount of phosphor per unit area) varies somewhat with the kind of phosphor used, but for any given phosphor it is not a significant factor with respect to beam current. The beam current does, however, fortunately influence the visual brightness, which for any given phosphor reaches a maximum at about the same screen weight. The range of screen weights for some of the materials is shown in column 9 of the table.

The sequence of steps in making a screen by settling are given below. The steps marked with an asterisk are optional and need not be followed for laboratory-scale operations: (1) transfer of the suspension to the bulb, (2) settling, (3) decanting, (4) air-drying, (5)* rewetting, (6)* lacquering, (7)* decanting, (8)* air drying, (9) evacuating, (10)* aluminizing, (11) baking.

For a five-inch-diameter screen (approximately 125 cm^2), the following procedure may be used for settling a fluorescent coating on a laboratory scale. For larger or smaller screens, proportionate amounts of the materials are used.

(a) The bulb or screen base is to be thoroughly cleaned by one of the methods given in the section on cleaning (formula C-1, or chromic-sulfuric fluid, p. 5) followed by thorough rinsing and drying. For flat glass, Vycor, quartz or ceramic screens not part of the bulb or envelope, the screen or plate is placed face up and level in the bottom of a clean vessel of adequate size, e.g., a Pyrex beaker.

(b) Pour in about 950 ml of deionized water and add 60 ml of a 1% solution of barium acetate, electronic grade. Stir thoroughly and allow to come to rest. This constitutes the "cushion."

(c) In a separate vessel, make up a suspension or slurry of 45 gm of the phosphor, with 24 ml of a 35% solution of potassium silicate (Sylvania PS-6), in about 100 to 200 ml of deionized water. This should be made fresh for each application (or each day).

(d) Dilute the slurry of step (c) with 800 to 900 ml of deionized water and *stir thoroughly*.

(e) To the bulb or vessel containing the screen, add through a dispensing funnel the well-mixed phosphor plus potassium silicate slurry of step (d). The dispensing funnel is a device to sprinkle the slurry gently onto the water cushion in the bulb or vessel, so as to spread the materials evenly.

(f) Allow to settle free of movement and vibration for one-half to three-quarters of an hour.

(g) Slowly decant as much of the supernatant water as possible, being careful to avoid shocks or jarring. (A mechanical tilt-table is useful where large tubes are handled or where the volume of work warrants the expense. This is a heavy motor-driven device which holds the bulb firmly and tilts it for decanting at a slow, uniform rate.) The bulb or vessel is then returned to its original position with the screen face up.

(h) The screen is dried by the use of a gentle stream of filtered, warm air introduced through the neck of the bulb. Do not use too small an air nozzle and do not position it too close to the screen during drying.

(i) When the screen appears to be thoroughly dry, the bulb is placed in an air-oven at room temperature and the heat is slowly raised to 350°C. This temperature is maintained for two hours.

(j) After removal from the oven, the neck of the bulb is covered with clean aluminum foil, free of pinholes, until ready for seal-in.

Note: See "Phosphor Characteristics for Cathode-Ray Tubes," Electronic Industries Association, Joint Electron Device Engineering Council. A reprint of this paper is available from Sylvania Electric Products Co., a subsidiary of General Telephone & Electronics, Towanda, Pennsylvania. Also see the technical information bulletins, "Sylvania Phosphors," and "Sylvania Screening Materials."

Flux, fluxes (see also pp. 87, 116). In spot-welding metals such as tungsten and molybdenum to themselves or to each other (p. 493), an operation which is sometimes difficult, the interposition of a thin foil of some other metal, such as nickel, tantalum, platinum, etc., facilitates the operation. The interposed metal is called a *flux* and it should be chosen on the basis of the operating temperature.

Forepump. Any type of vacuum pump used to provide a pressure below atmospheric that is low enough for the operation of a diffusion or getter-ion pump, which does not work at atmospheric pressures. It can be an oil-sealed mechanical pump in which an eccentric rotor with some kind of sliding vanes or valves compresses and discharges the gas, or some type of ejector pump (see p. 231). Even a water-aspirator (p. 453) can be used in some applications. The operation of various types of mechanical forepumps is shown in Figs. 63 and 64.

The rotor rotates inside a stator X. Line or area of contact G, between rotor and stator, and contact K, between vane V and stator, divide the volume between rotor and stator into two chambers. (In pumps with two vanes instead of one, this volume is divided into three chambers.) Due to the motion of the rotor, one chamber is expanding while the other is contracting. The expansion chamber is connected to the intake I of the pump and the contracting chamber to the exhaust E. Oil films at G and K seal the pump. A springloaded, oil-sealed valve D (in most but not in all pumps) seals the contracting chamber against a flow of gas inward.

The free-air displacement of a rotary oil-sealed pump is a function of the volume between the rotor and the stator and the number of revolutions the rotor makes in

Phosphors

1 NO.	2 SYLVANIA NO.	3 MATERIAL	4 FLUORESCENT COLOR	5 PHOSPHORESCENT COLOR	6 PERSISTENCE	7 APPROX. AVE. PARTICLE SIZE (MICRONS)	8 REMARKS	9 SCREEN WEIGHT (mg/cm^2)	10 APPLICATION
P-1	160	Zn_2SiO_4: Mn	Green	Green	Medium	2	Small particle size		Oscilloscopes and radar
P-1	161	Zn_2SiO_4: Mn	Green	Green	Medium	5		4–6	Oscilloscopes
P-1	221	Zn_2SiO_4: Mn	Green	Green	Medium	10	Large particle size		Oscilloscopes
P-2	145	ZnS: Cu	Blue-green	Green	Long	30			Oscilloscopes and radar
P-4	CR-40 & 401	ZnS: Ag & (Zn, Cd)S: Ag	White	Blue-white	Medium-short	10			Television receivers
P-4	CR-421 & 422	ZnS: Ag & (Zn, Cd)S: Ag	White	Blue-white	Medium-short	10	Silica-coated		Television receivers
P-5	135	$CaWO_4$	Blue	Blue	Very short	8			Special oscilloscopes (fast photography)
P-7	130 140	ZnS: Ag (Zn, Cd)S: Ag	Blue Yellow	— Yellow	Medium-short Long	15 30	Two-layer (cascade) screen		Radar
P-11	132	ZnS: Ag	Blue	Blue	Short	5			Oscilloscopes for visual or photo observation
P-12	144	(Zn, Mg)F_2: Mn	Orange	Orange	Medium-long	6			Radar
P-13	211	$MgSiO_3$: Mn	Red	Red	Medium	2			
P-14	130 146	ZnS: Ag (Zn, Cd)S: Cu	Blue Orange	— Orange	Medium-short Long	15 30	Two-layer (cascade) screen		Radar
P-15	137	ZnO: Zn	Blue-green	Blue-green	Very short	4			Flying spot scanners
P-22	151	$Zn_3(PO_4)$: Mn	Red	Red	Medium	3–6		4–5	Color-television receivers
P-22	161	Zn_2SiO_4: Mn	Green	Green	Medium	3–6		4–6	Color-television receivers
P-22	131	ZnS: Ag	Blue	Blue	Medium-short	4–8		4–6	Color-television receivers
P-22	110	(Zn, Cd)S: Ag	Red	Red	Medium-short	10–20		7–10	Color-television receivers
P-22	170	$CaMg(SiO_3)_2$: Ti	Blue	Blue	Medium-short	3–5		4–5	Color-television receivers

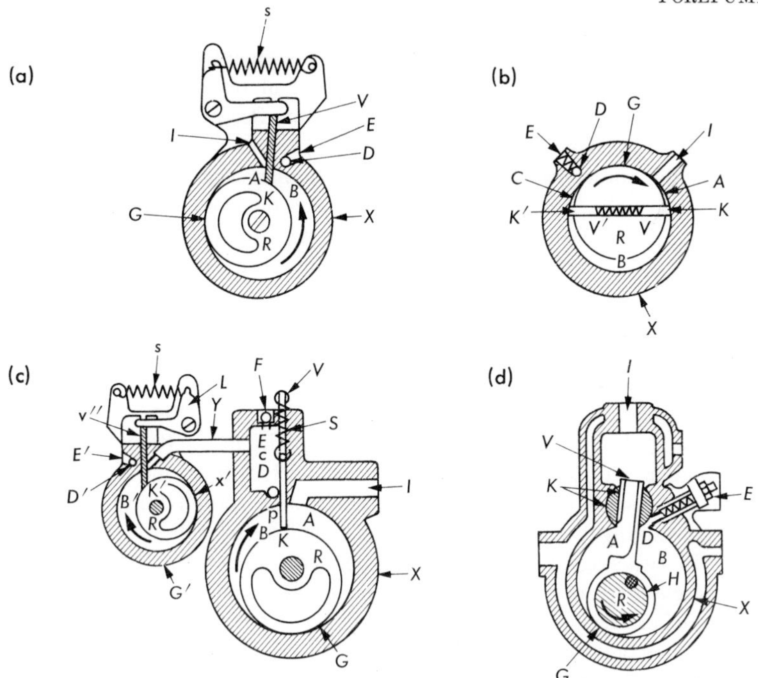

Fig. 63. Four types of mechanical pumps or forepumps: (a) Cenco hyvac pump; (b) Welch duo-seal pump; (c) Cenco hypervac pump; (d) Kinney high-vacuum pump.

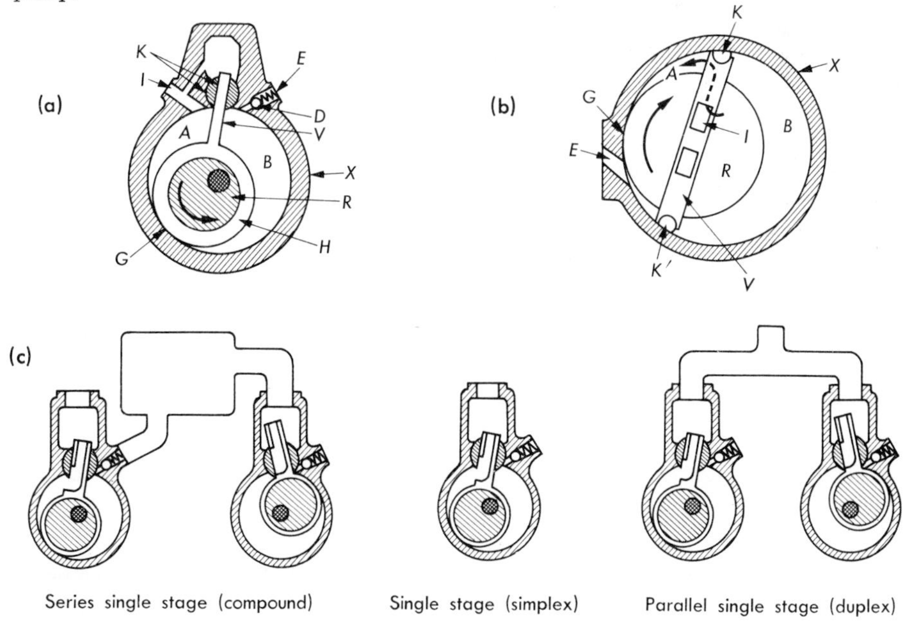

Fig. 64. Various types of mechanical pumps: (a) Stokes microvac; (b) Beach-Russ-type RP pump; (c) Single-stage arrangements.

unit time. In single-vane pumps, the free-air displacement, expressed in liters/sec, liters/min, or ft^3/min, is the product of the number of revolutions of the rotor per time unit and the volume between the rotor and stator. See Fig. 64(a).

The free-air displacement of a double-vane pump is the product of the number of revolutions of the rotor per time unit, and twice that volume contained between rotor, stator, and vanes, just as the volume is sealed off from the intake [volume *B* in Fig. 64(b)]. In Fig. 63(a), (b), and (c), the vanes are held in contact by springs, whereas in Fig. 64(a) and (c) the rotor rotates inside a housing *H* with the vane rigidly attached to the housing. A sliding, oscillating seal is provided for the vane in the top section of the stator. The high-vacuum intake *I* is through the vane in Figs. 63(d) and 64(b). The stator in Fig. 64(b) is machined elliptically to keep the vane a fixed length as the rotor rotates.

Single-stage pumps will produce a vacuum efficiently to 10^{-2} torr. To go below this, two-stage pumps are needed. These are efficient to 10^{-3} torr and below. The most common arrangement is to directly connect, with connections as short as possible, the exhaust of one unit into the intake of a second unit, with no valve between. The valving between the stages is handled through the phasing of the two rotors. In two-stage pumps of this type, both stages are the same size and handle all the gases at all pumping pressures. In Fig. 63(c) the second or backing stage has a smaller free-air displacement than the first stage. The exhaust valve *F* between the two stages permits gas to be exhausted from the pump when the pump is handling large volumes of gas, as in the roughing-down portion of the evacuating cycle. The second stage acts as a backing pump after the first stage has reduced the pressure at its intake considerably below atmospheric. The first stage is then a more effective pump and will reduce the pressure at *I* to 10^{-3} torr and below. This arrangement of stages permits larger capacity pumps to occupy smaller physical space. Figure 64(c) (single-stage arrangement) shows, besides a two-stage compounded pump, two arrangements of single-stage pumps: simplex and duplex. Pump capacity is increased by the duplex connection, and ultimate vacuum attained by the pump is enhanced by the compound connection.[1]

Formulas for calculating pumping speed will be found on pp. 455, 456.

Forevacuum. The below-atmospheric pressure condition which is produced by a forepump (see above) at the discharge or high-pressure port of a diffusion pump.[2]

Formex insulation, stripping of (see p. 35).

Forming gas (see ATMOSPHERE, PROTECTIVE, p. 160).

Formvar, vapor pressure of (see p. 140).

Forsterite. A ceramic which has the chemical name of magnesium orthosilicate ($2MgO \cdot SiO_2$). A dense, very low loss (electrical) material having the following properties:[3]

Water absorption	0–.02%	Safe temperature for continuous use	1000—1100°C
Specific gravity gm/cc	2.8		

[1] "Vacuum Pumping Equipment and Systems," H. M. Sullivan, *Rev. Sci. Instr.*, **19**, 1, 1948. By permission of the American Institute of Physics.

[2] An interesting article for the amateur vacuum technologist will be found under the title, "Concerning Homemade Vacuum Pumps and Some of the Things That Can be Done with Them," C. L. Stong, *Scientific American*, March, 1960, pp. 187–200.

[3] American Lava Corp., subsidiary of Minnesota Mining & Manufacturing Co., Chattanooga 5, Tennessee. (Alsimag #243).

PROPERTIES OF FORSTERITE (continued)

Temperature at which 1 cm^3 has resistance of 1 meg (Te value)	1000°C
Color	buff
Softening temp.	1440°C
Thermal expansion at 25–700°C	$10.0 = 11.2 \times 10^{-6}$ in.
Tensile strength	10,000 psi
Compressive strength	85,000 psi
Flexural strength	20,000 psi
Resistance to impact (Charpy)	4
Thermal conductivity (cgs)	0.008
Dielectric strength (volt/mil)	240
Volume resistivity (ohms) at:	
25°C	$>10^{14}$
300	7×10^{11}
700	1×10^{8}
900	3×10^{6}
Dielectric constant	
60 cycles	6.3
1 Mc	6.2
100 Mc	6.1
10,000 Mc	5.8
Power factor	
60 cycles	0.0014
1 Mc	0.0004
100 Mc	0.0003
10,000 Mc	0.001
Loss factor	
60 cycles	0.009
1 Mc	0.002
100 Mc	0.002
10,000 Mc	0.0058
Hardness (Mohs')	7.5

Forsterite can be machined by grinding with alumina, carborundum, or diamond. Metal-to-ceramic seals can be made between Alsimag 243 and 16% chrome-iron using the moly-manganese method (see p. 72 *et seq.*).

This ceramic is related to steatite ($MgO \cdot SiO_2$) but has a higher magnesia content, which lowers the electrical loss factor but increases the thermal expansion. Forsterite is thus less resistant than steatite to thermal shock. It has very low dielectric losses and is less permeable than glass to the diffusion of helium.

Forsterite may be fired in hydrogen or in vacuum without breakdown or reduction to free metal. Commercial forsterite may contain small amounts of MnO_2, Fe_2O_3, TiO_2, Al_2O_3, and small quantities of Na_2O and K_2O. It has relatively high firing shrinkage (up to 20%) which limits the precision of fired parts. It is vacuum tight after firing.

Forsterite outgasses during tube bake-out at 450°C. It can be heated to 1200°C without appreciable vaporization; however, such high temperatures should be avoided because of internal and seal stresses due to its high expansion coefficient.[1]

Fractionating pump. A diffusion pump in which the various fractions of the pump fluid (oil), slowly formed by thermal decomposition, are largely separated and discharged. The fractions, as a general rule, have lower molecular weights and lower boiling points, and to some extent act as pump fluids themselves. However, if sufficient quantities of these lower fractions accumulate, the speed of the pump will be reduced. A fractionating pump is one in which, by virtue of the jet design and/or number of stages, this accumulation is very slow, thus eliminating the necessity for frequent cleaning and oil changes.

[1] "A Manual of Materials for Microwave Tubes," D. L. Thornburg, E. S. Thall, and J. Brous, WADD Technical Report 60-325, AD 267327, Office of Technical Services, U.S. Department of Commerce, Washington 25, D.C., 1961.

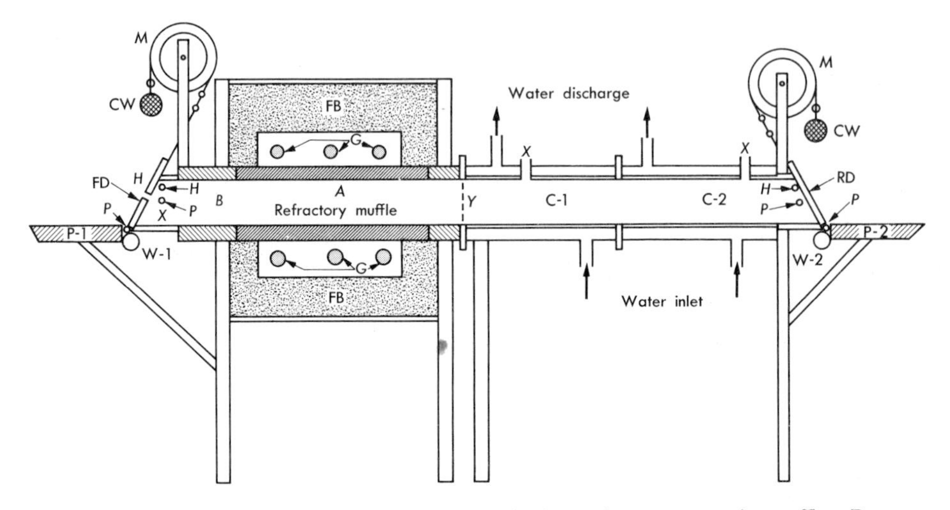

FIG. 65. Pusher-type atmosphere furnace. *A*—heated zone, ceramic muffle; *B*—preheat zone, ceramic; *C*-1, *C*-2—first and second water-cooled sections; *CW*—counterweights (see *M*); *FD, RD*—front and rear doors (slide up); *FB*—firebrick insulation; *G*—Globar radiant heaters; *H*—hydrogen discharge (burns off); *M*—mechanism for opening doors; *P*—illuminating gas pilots; *P*-1, *P*-2—loading and unloading platforms; *W*-1, *W*-2—flame curtains (air and gas); *Y*—movable gate; *X*—throat of preheat section. *H* is a tabulation through wall of *X*. *P, P* are outside of wall, so placed as to ignite exhaust hydrogen.

Free path, mean (see MEAN FREE PATH, pp. 136, 363).

Freon. DuPont's name for several chloro-fluoro compounds, existing either as gases or liquids. Some of them are used widely as refrigerants and some as solvents. They are relatively nontoxic, nonflammable, nonexplosive, and noncorrosive.

Furnaces (see also pp. 35, 417, 552). Atmosphere furnaces commonly used in processing and brazing electron tube parts are usually of a type outlined in Fig. 65.

Hydrogen (or other gas—see ATMOSPHERE, PROTECTIVE, p. 160) flows at a rate of about 5 to 15 liters per minute. This may vary widely with the various sizes and types of furnaces. The protective gas is admitted at the three points indicated at *X* in the figure. Hydrogen (and other flammable gases) burn off at the points shown at *H*, but the gas does not burn inside the furnace chambers. The doors of cast iron lie loosely against their guides by gravity so that no pressure can build up inside the chamber. A gas-air flame curtain ignites from the pilots (city or illuminating gas) at either end of the furnace when the doors are raised, so that outside air cannot enter when work is loaded or unloaded.

A typical schedule for starting and operating such a furnace is as follows:

Assuming that the muffle is up to temperature, and the gas pilots are on, the doors are opened and the hydrogen is admitted through a regulating valve and a flow-gauge. It will ignite with a slight "pop," whereupon the doors are closed and the hydrogen is allowed to flow until a clear hydrogen flame (pale blue) is seen at all the outlets. The work is loaded into nickel, stainless steel, Inconel, or Nichrome boxes, boats, or trays with smooth bottoms so as not to damage the muffle, and pushed into the preheat section *B*. The door is shut and the work is allowed to preheat for a length of time dependent on its size and mass—roughly about 10 minutes. This is done partly as a precaution to protect the ceramic muffle in the hot zone *A* against thermal shock.

The work is then pushed into the heated zone *A* and allowed to remain for the stated time. An optical pyrometer can be used to sight through the hole *H* in the front door. If brazing is being done, the work can be observed through this opening (see p. 39). At the end of the heating cycle, the work is pushed into the first cooling chamber *C*-1, which is a water-jacketed steel extension the same size as the muffle. The gate *Y* may be closed to protect the work from radiation, and thus hasten cooling. The cooling chambers are maintained at temperatures of about 180°F (*C*-1) and 100°F (*C*-2) by means of automatic thermostatic valves (not shown in the figure). For average work, 15 to 30 minutes in each chamber should provide cooling sufficient to allow exposure to the air upon unloading.

To shut down the furnace, open both doors, with the flame curtain burning, and shut off the hydrogen or other gas. After a few minutes, the illuminating gas supply can also be shut off. It is common practice to keep the electric power to the heaters on at all times. These heaters, *G,* are maintained at any desired temperature by means of a thermocouple-pyrometer-indicator-controller, (not shown). A temperature of 800°C is adequate to keep moisture and other contamination out of the furnace. A muffle which is allowed to cool to room temperature between runs does not have as long a service life as one which is kept hot continuously, probably because of thermal stresses.

Another type of atmosphere furnace for dry hydrogen processing of stainless steel is described on pp. 41–51. So-called "bottle" brazing is described on pp. 39–41.

Modifications of the pusher-type furnace are available industrially. One type has a Nichrome or Inconel-mesh conveyor belt driven by a motor at a controlled rate so that work can be fed and removed continuously. Another type has a metal muffle instead of a ceramic muffle, the latter's porosity being a disadvantage in certain kinds of work.

Gallium. This silvery-white metal melts at 29.78°C and remains fluid up to its boiling point of 2403°C. This property makes it useful for high-temperature thermometers. Its vapor pressure is low (see below). The surface tension of molten gallium at 30°C is 735 dynes/cm.

Due to its low vapor pressure and excellent wetting of almost all constructional materials, gallium is well suited for vacuum seals, especially when high environmental purity is needed or desirable. The melting point of gallium, being only 8° or 9°C higher than room temperature, makes it feasible to design joints which are demountable by the application of slight heat.

Gallium will alloy readily with many metals, including tin, indium, zinc, cadmium, aluminum, silver, magnesium, copper, and others. It will not combine with tantalum up to about 450°C or with tungsten up to 800°C. Graphite is not attacked at any temperature, and silica-base refractories resist combination up to about 1000°C. Pure gallium expands on freezing.

For mobile joints, it has been found practical to alloy gallium with other metals having equally low vapor pressures. Thus, by the addition of indium (pp. 297 *et seq.*), a binary eutectic alloy is obtained with a melting point of 15.7°C.[1] By the

---

[1] UG-2 Alloy, United Mineral & Chemical Corp., 16 Hudson St., New York 13, New York.

introduction of a third component, tin, a ternary eutectic is formed with a melting point of 10°C.[1] If the proportions of gallium, indium, and tin are varied, a eutectic alloy can be prepared with a melting temperature as low as 5°C. The vapor pressure of such eutectics remains below 10^{-8} torr, and the surface tension above 500 dynes/cm. The viscosity of the gallium-indium alloy is 3.2 centipoises at 20°C; the viscosity of the gallium-indium-tin alloy is 3.9 centipoises. The viscosity of pure gallium at 97.7°C is 1.61 cps.

Gallium is extremely anisotropic [i.e. the properties mentioned vary with axis of the (solid) metal] as to coefficient of electrical resistivity, which is very high, and as to coefficient of thermal expansion. Other properties of gallium are given below.

PHYSICAL PROPERTIES OF GALLIUM[2]

Atomic Number	31
Atomic Weight	69.72
Specific Gravity, (g/ml)	
Solid (29.6°C)	5.904
Liquid (29.8°C)	6.095
(32.38°C)	6.093
(301°C)	5.095
(600°C)	5.720
(806°C)	5.604
(1100°C)	5.445
Solidification Expansion	3.2%
Linear Coefficient of Thermal Expansion of Solid (/°C)	
Crystallographic Axis	
"c"	1.6×10^{-5}
"a"	1.1×10^{-5}
"b"	3.1×10^{-5}
Volume Coefficient of Thermal Expansion	
(0° to 30°C) Solid	5.8×10^{-5}
100°C Liquid	12.0×10^{-5}
900°C Liquid	9.7×10^{-5}
Vapor Pressure (mm Hg)	
600°C	4.4×10^{-9}
800°C	5.9×10^{-6}
1000°C	8.2×10^{-4}
1200°C	3.0×10^{-2}
1400°C	4.5×10^{-1}
1600°C	3.8mm
1800°C	21
2000°C	86
2200°C	280
2403°C	760
Hardness (MOHS Scale)	1.5–2.5

(Cont.)

[1] UG-1 Alloy, same source.

[2] "Gallium and Gallium Compounds," Aluminum Co. of America, Chemicals Division, Pittsburgh 19, Pennsylvania, 1961.

(*Cont.*)

Specific Heat (cal/gm°C)	
—268.9°C (solid)	0.0000291
—257.1°C (solid)	0.0046
—213.1°C (solid)	0.042
0° to 24°C (solid)	0.089
12.5°C to 200°C (liquid)	0.095
Latent Heat of Fusion (cal/gm)	19.16
Latent Heat of Vaporization at B.P. (cal/gm)	930.4
Viscosity, poises (cgs units)	
97.7°C	0.01612
1100°C	0.00578
Volume Resistivity of Liquid (microhms cm)	
0°C*	25.2
20°C	25.6
40°C	26.0

Volume Resistivity of Solid (microhms cm)

	"c" Axis	"a" Axis	"b" Axis
29.7°C	54.3	17.4	8.1
0°C	48.0	15.4	7.16
—195.6°C	10.1	3.08	1.43
—268.9°C†	0.00138	0.00068	0.00016
—272.06°C	Superconducting Transition Temp.		

Magnetic Susceptibility (cgs units)	
Solid (18°C)	-0.24×10^{-6}
Liquid (100°C)	-0.04×10^{-6}

* High-purity gallium supercools very greatly and can remain liquid below the freezing point indefinitely.

† Value for 99.9999% gallium; higher for less pure materials.

The eutectic alloys of gallium retain the excellent wetting properties for all metals, as well as glass, quartz, and ceramics, requiring no heat or flux. The application of a eutectic alloy is done by means of a glass pipette or a stick, and the alloy is rubbed on the previously degreased metal, glass, or ceramic so that it wets the adjacent parts and bridges the gap without a discontinuity. Ground glass joints should preferably be flame-polished. To treat a clean metal surface and to obtain proper wetting, rubbing the alloy onto the surface with a piece of stainless steel or Monel wool or mesh has been found useful in some cases.

Mild steel, stainless steels (such as the 14% chromium and the austenitic types), Monel, nickel, copper, and brass have been wetted with the gallium alloys and allowed to stand for six weeks at room temperature and at 100°C. All the metals were found intact, with the exception of copper and brass, which showed a slight corrosion at 100°C. At temperatures over 300°C all the above metals are attacked by gallium and its eutectics. Tantalum and columbium resist corrosion up to 450°C and beryllium up to 500°C. Tungsten and rhenium are completely unaffected at temperatures up to 800°C, as are graphite and zirconia. Beryllia, alumina, and silica resist temperatures of 1000°C and higher.

Gallium and its eutectic alloys can be used in valves, motion seals of various kinds, flanged joints, etc. Because of their good electrical conductivity, these alloys can be used to make electrical contacts between moving parts in a vacuum. The surface tension of the alloys can withstand atmospheric pressure across a 10^{-3} cm (0.0004 inch) gap between solids, provided the liquid metal wets and bridges the sides continuously. Such seals can withstand 10^{-7} torr pressure and 3 psi helium positive pressure.

Because the seals remain fluid, the metal can be used repeatedly. However, if the seals are to remain for a period of time, they should be protected against the accumulation of dust by suitable shields.[1]

Gallium and its alloys have also found application for bonding thermocouples into heated bodies,[2] where their low contact resistance and good thermal contact properties make them useful.

Gallium and its alloys are also available from Anchor Metal Company, Inc., 966 Meeker Avenue, Brooklyn 22, New York. See *Rev. Sci. Instr.*, **27**, 436, 1956.

Gases, admission to tubes (see pp. 119–124).

Gas ballast pump (see p. 161).

Gas discharge (see BREAKDOWN VOLTAGE, p. 188).

Gas discharge colors (see p. 213).

Gases in metals. A number of gases are likely to be associated with metals, not only as *adsorbed* layers on the surface, or in the form of oxides, nitrides, hydrides, etc., but *absorbed* in the body of the metal. Some permeation may also occur under certain conditions (see pp. 105, 121).

Oxygen, carbon monoxide and dioxide, nitrogen, water vapor, and hydrocarbon gases (e.g., methane, ethane, acetylene) may be evolved during evacuation and heating of electron tube and vacuum components. For example, in a tube containing an oxide-coated cathode, and in which organic pump-oil vapors have decomposed in contact with the hot cathode surface, carbides of the alkali-earth oxides are formed, which then react with any water-vapor present to form acetylene.

Most of the sorbed gases in metals can be removed by appropriate heat-treatment in a good vacuum. A method and apparatus are described on pp. 75–79.

The *inert gases* of group 0 (He, Ne, A, Kr, Xe, and Rn) do not dissolve in any metal, solid or liquid. Some of these gases can, however, be adsorbed on metal surfaces (see METASTABLE ATOMS, p. 160).

Since *hydrogen* is used in processing (heat-treating, annealing, brazing) many metals used in tube fabrication, this gas is almost certain to be present. In the case of nickel and high nickel alloys, heat-treatment in hydrogen generally reduces the total gas content. In any event, the hydrogen is fairly easy to eliminate by subsequent heat treatment as part of the vacuum processing.

Oxygen. Metals and alloys such as chromium, iron, aluminum, and stainless steels easily form protective (passive) layers of oxide, even at room temperature, although these layers may not be visible to the eye. In the cases of iron and stainless steel, this oxide layer can be removed by dissociation or reduction with hydrogen (see p. 41).

---

[1] United Mineral & Chemical Corporation, 16 Hudson Street, New York 13, New York.

[2] G. G. Harman, *Rev. Sci. Instr.*, **31**, 717, 1960.

BIBLIOGRAPHY

S. Dushman, *Scientific Foundations of Vacuum Technique,* second edition, p. 589, John Wiley & Sons, Inc., New York, 1962.

C. J. Smithells, *Gases in Metals,* Chapman & Hall, London, 1937.

F. J. Norton, *Trans. Am. Vacuum Soc.,* 8th Ann. Symposium (1961), p. 8, Pergamon Press, Inc., London, 1962.

P. F. Varadi, *ibid.,* p. 73.

G. D. Halsey, *ibid.,* p. 119.

J. P. Hobson, *ibid.,* p. 146.

J. L. Robins, *ibid.,* 9th Ann. Symposium, p. 510, The Macmillan Company, New York, New York, 1962.

R. W. Roberts, *J. Appl. Phys.* (Br), **14,** 485, 1963; also *ibid.,* p. 537.

P. A. Redhead, *Vacuum* (Br), **13,** 253, 1963.

J. P. Hobson and R. A. Armstrong, *J. Phys. Chem.,* **67,** 2000, 1963.

W. J. Grubbs, G. H. Snider, and F. I. Scott, "A Quantitative Study of the Evolution of Gases from Electron Tubes and Materials," 1st, 2nd, 3rd and 4th Scientific Reports prepared for AFCRL Electronics Research Directorate, 1961–1963, AF 19(628)-326. These four reports are obtainable from U.S. Department of Commerce, OTS, Washington, D.C.

Gases, noble. These are the nonreactive, or inert, gases found in small quantities in the atmosphere. They are argon, neon, helium, krypton, xenon and radon. Their molecular weight and fraction percent in the atmosphere are given in the table on p. 160 (ATMOSPHERE).

Gases, thermal conductivity of. The heat conductivity of gases determines the response of various types of vacuum gauges, including the Pirani and thermocouple types, which operate on the principle of the change in temperature of an electrical conductor carrying a constant current. The temperature of such a conductor decreases as the thermal conductivity of the gas increases, all other conditions being equal. The response of the gauge will change with the density of the gases present. At pressures above the range of molecular flow (see p. 376) the thermal conductivity of a gas is relatively independent of the pressure.

MIXTURES (PERCENT BY VOLUME OF GAS AT LEFT)	TEMPERATURE (°C)	k^*
H_2, 100	22	44.5
$O_2 + H_2$, 5.26	22	37.4
$O_2 + H_2$, 14.29	22	32.1
$O_2 + H_2$, 25	22	27.4
$O_2 + H_2$, 33.3	22	23.7
$O_2 + H_2$, 50	22	18.2
$O_2 + H_2$, 75	22	11.1
$O_2 + H_2$, 80	22	9.9
$O_2 + H_2$, 84.64	22	9.2
$O_2 + H_2$, 93.94	22	7.1
$O_2 + H_2$, 96.64	22	6.5
O_2 100	22	6.2
$N_2 + H_2$, 57.4	36	1.47

As can be seen from the table, the thermal conductivity of a gas increases (non-linearly) with temperature. For this reason, the calibration of a thermal vacuum gauge will hold only within a given range of ambient temperatures.

The thermal conductivities of some gases are given in the table below. Conductivity values are given in cgs units, 10^{-5} (cal/cm^2-sec)/(°C/cm) for various temperatures. (See p. 520.)

THERMAL CONDUCTIVITIES

GAS	TEMPERATURE (°C)						
	−180	−100	−50	0	20	100	200
Hydrogen	—	21.8	35.0	41.9	44.5	54.7	63.4
Oxygen	2.0	3.9	4.9	5.8	6.2	7.6	—
Nitrogen	2.1	3.9	4.9	5.7	6.1	7.3	8.5
Helium	16.3	24.6	29.6	34.3	36.1	40.8	—
Neon	4.9	8.2	10.9	—	—	13.3	—
Krypton	—	—	—	2.1	—	—	—
Argon	1.4	2.6	3.2	3.9	4.2	5.2	—
Xenon	—	—	—	1.2	—	1.6	—
Air (dry)	2.1	3.9	4.9	5.8	6.1	7.4	8.8
Deuterium	—	—	—	30.6	—	37.7	—
Carbon monoxide	—	—	—	5.3	—	—	—
Carbon dioxide	—	—	—	3.4	—	—	—
Nitric oxide, NO	—	—	—	4.6	—	—	—
Nitrous oxide, N_2O	—	—	—	3.6	—	—	—
Ammonia, NH_3	—	—	—	5.2	—	—	—
Hydrogen sulfide, H_2S	—	—	—	3.0	—	—	—
Sulfur dioxide, SO_2	—	—	—	2.0	—	—	—
Carbon disulfide, CS_2	—	—	—	1.6	—	—	—
Methane, CH_4	—	—	—	7.3	—	—	—
Ethane, CH_3CH_3	—	—	—	4.3	—	—	—
Propane, $CH_3CH_2CH_3$	—	—	—	3.6	—	—	—
n-Butane, $CH_3(CH_2)_2CH_3$	—	—	—	3.2	—	—	—
Acetylene, C_2H_2	—	—	—	4.4	—	—	—
Ethylene, C_2H_4	—	—	—	4.0	—	—	—
Carbon tetrachloride, CCl_4	—	—	—	1.9	—	—	—
Water vapor, H_2O	—	—	—	—	—	5.19	—
Ethanol, C_2H_6O	—	—	—	—	—	4.61	—
Acetone, C_3H_6O	—	—	—	2.17	—	—	—
Chlorine	—	—	—	1.72	—	—	—
Mercury	—	—	—	—	—	—	1.85
Ethyl ether, $C_4H_{10}O$	—	—	—	2.88	—	—	—
Benzene, C_6H_6	—	—	—	2.1	—	—	—
n-Pentane, C_5H_{12}	—	—	—	2.7	—	—	—
Isopentane, C_5H_{12}	—	—	—	2.69	—	—	—

GAS MIXTURES: $CO_2 + H_2$, PERCENT BY VOLUME

PERCENT CO_2	TEMPERATURE (°C)	k*
0.	36	45.0
5.705	36	36.0
16.55	36	28.0
39.32	36	17.2
63.02	36	10.3
82.99	36	6.1
90.6	36	4.8
92.5	36	4.5
100.	36	4.0

* k, the thermal conductivity, has the same value as in the table on p. 264.

Gas filling of tubes (see pp. 119–124).

Gas, illuminating, as hydrogen source (see p. 121).

Gas laws. The fundamental gas laws are as follows:

BOYLE'S LAW. The volume of a given quantity of any gas at a constant temperature is inversely proportional to the pressure:

$$pv = p_1v_1 = \text{a constant},$$

where p = pressure, v = volume.

DALTON'S LAW OF PARTIAL PRESSURES. The pressure exerted by a mixture of gases is equal to the sum of the separate pressures which each gas would exert if it alone occupied the whole volume:

$$pv = v(p_1 + p_2 + p_3, \text{etc.}).$$

GAY-LUSSAC'S LAW OR CHARLES' LAW. The volume of a given quantity of any gas at a constant pressure increases about 1/273 of its volume at 0°C for each rise of 1°C (within moderate ranges of temperature).

The pressure of a given quantity of any gas at constant volume increases about 1/273 of the pressure at 0°C for each 1°C rise in temperature:

$$\frac{p_1}{T} = \frac{p_2}{T} \text{ (constant volume)} \quad \text{and} \quad \frac{v_1}{T_1} = \frac{v_2}{T_2} \text{ (constant pressure).}$$

For an original volume v_0 at 0°C, the volume at T°C (at constant pressure) is $v_1 = v_0\,(1 + 0.00367T)$.

AVOGADRO'S PRINCIPLE. The molecules present in equal volumes of gases at the same temperature and pressure are equal in number.

GAS EXPANSION LAWS. Boyle's law and Avogadro's principle can be combined into a single law:

$$PV = RmT$$

where P = pressure in bars, V = volume in cm^3, R = a constant ($= 8.314 \times 10^7$), m = mass of the gas in moles,[1] T = °C + 273.

[1] One mole equals a gram molecular weight of gas which occupies a volume of 22.4 liters at STP; e.g., one mole of oxygen = 32 gm.

By the use of this equation and Avogadro's number ($= 6.023 \times 10^{23}$, which is the number of molecules in one mole of gas at STP[1]) it can be demonstrated that the number of molecules in 1 cm^3 at 10^6 bars (approximately atmospheric pressure) and at 0°C is 2.654×10^{19}. At a pressure of 10^{-7} mm Hg, the number of molecules per cm^3 of gas is approximately 3×10^9.

In general, the number of molecules of gas per cm^3 is

$$n = 7.244 \times 10^{15} \frac{p}{T} \text{ molecules,}$$

where p is pressure in bars, and T is absolute temperature (°K).

Gas pressure measurements (see VACUUM GAUGES).

Gas versus vapor. These two terms are often used interchangeably. In general, however, the word *gas* is applied to those substances which exist under usual conditions of temperature and pressure as gases, such as air, nitrogen, oxygen, carbon dioxide, etc., and the word *vapor* is used to describe the condition of substances at elevated temperatures or subnormal pressures which are normally solids or liquids at room temperature and atmospheric pressure, such as mercury, water, iodine, alcohol, etc.

Gases, equivalents of liquid and gas phases. The following table[2] compares the mass of gases liquefied by refrigeration to the volume of the gas phase at STP.[1]

Gas		Mass of liquid		Volume of gas produced at STP*		Heat of vaporization	
		gm	lb	Liters	Ft³	Cal	Btu
Helium	(He)	125.2	0.276	700	24.7	650	2.58
Hydrogen	(H_2)	70.8	0.156	780	27.5	7560	30.0
Deuterium	(D_2)	168	0.370	935	33.0	12,700	50.4
Nitrogen	(N_2)	808	1.78	650	23.0	38,600	153.2
Fluorine	(F_2)	1110	2.45	654	23.1	45,600	181.0
Argon	(A)	1410	3.11	770	27.2	53,500	212.4
Oxygen	(O_2)	1140	2.51	799	28.2	58,100	230.7
Carbon dioxide (solid)	(CO_2)	1630	3.59	829	29.3	223,000	885.3

Gaskets, general (see pp. 117, 309, 320).

Gaskets, O-rings (see O-RINGS, pp. 111, 407, 410).

Gaskets, metal (see pp. 117, 309, 408, 571).

Gassy materials. Those substances which by virtue of their porous or easily decomposed nature give off gases *in vacuo*. Examples of the former are firebrick, carbon, plaster of paris, asbestos in its various forms; examples of the latter are Bakelite (phenolic resin), animal or vegetable materials, many plastics, rubber, etc. There

[1] STP is the abbreviation for standard temperature and pressure: 0°C and 760 mm Hg or torr.

[2] Courtesy of Arthur D. Little, Inc., Cambridge, Massachusetts.

is some overlapping, as for example in commercial asbestos products, which have an organic binder which chars (decomposes) when heated.

All substances are likely to be gassy under certain conditions (see p. 138) and those used in electron and vacuum devices must be freed from as much of this gas as possible by heating to appropriate temperatures in as high a vacuum as can be obtained. (See GASES IN METALS, p. 262; also see pp. 113, 138.)

Certain metals have a high vapor pressure, i.e., they begin to vaporize *in vacuo* at relatively low elevated temperatures. For a list of the vapor pressures of metallic elements, see the table on pp. 146–148.

Gassy tube (see p. 168).

Gauges, vacuum (see VACUUM GAUGES in index).

Gay-Lussac's law (see GAS LAWS, p. 265).

Getter-ion pumps (see p. 108).

Getters (see p. 105).

Glass, cleaning of (see pp. 5, 7).

Glass.[1] This noncrystalline material has no regular internal structure. It is rigid at ordinary temperatures and soft or almost fluid at high temperatures. It has no definite freezing point, but becomes solid because its viscosity increases progressively to values which, for all practical purposes, are infinitely great.

Although silica sand (SiO_2) is a principal ingredient of most glasses, melting economy and flexibility of properties require the addition of other melting agents and modifiers. Thus, depending on the choice of these additional constituents, glasses can be classified into several groups with characteristic properties.

Soda lime glasses (or lime glasses), used for lamp envelopes, are melted from silica that has been fluxed with lime (CaO) and soda (Na_2O) plus small quantities of other oxides. A typical lime glass composition is approximately as follows:

Silica (SiO_2)	72%
Soda (Na_2O)	15%
Lime (CaO)	9%
Magnesia (Mg0)	3%
Alumina (Al_2O_3)	1%

Lime glasses are easily hot-worked and are usually specified for service where high heat resistance and chemical stability are not required.

Lead glasses are used for electric light bulb stems and neon sign tubing. A typical composition is given below:

Silica (SiO_2)	68%
Lead oxide (PbO)	15%
Soda (Na_2O)	10%
Potash ($K_2 0$)	6%
Lime (CaO)	1%

Lead glasses are useful because of their good hot-workability, high electrical resistivity, and high refractive index. Dense lead glasses serve as shields to cut off X-rays and gamma radiations.

[1] Courtesy of Corning Glass Works, Corning, New York, from their Bulletin B-83, "Properties of Selected Commercial Glasses," 1961.

Borosilicate glasses are used for hard glass tubes, chemical laboratory glassware, glass pipe, etc. Their compositions are usually similar to the following:

Silica (SiO_2)	80%
Boric oxide (B_2O_3)	14%
Soda (Na_2O)	4%
Alumina (Al_2O_3)	2%

High chemical stability, low coefficients of thermal expansion, high heat shock resistance, and excellent electrical resistivity make borosilicate glasses the best choice for most laboratory tube applications.

Glasses composed entirely of *silica* are made by chemically removing the flux from a borosilicate glass after it has been melted and formed to the desired shape. Since removal of the flux leaves voids in the glass, it is necessary to consolidate each piece by an additional firing operation. Considerably more expensive than the other three types of glass, its principal applications are at high temperatures, since it does not begin to soften until it reaches 1000°C and can be regularly used at temperatures as high as 800°C. The low thermal expansion coefficient of such high-silica glass enables it to withstand easily the most severe thermal shocks. Its chemical composition is:

Silica	96% at least
Boric oxide	3% at most
Other oxides	1% at most

MECHANICAL PROPERTIES OF GLASS. These properties are so different from those of metals that some discussion of their physical properties is necessary before the engineer can properly appreciate the data given in the table on p. 270. For example, shear strength means much when associated with metals but it has little significance in glasses. Similarly, hardness of glasses must be measured and reported in terms that rarely apply to ductile materials.

The following notes detail the properties of glass that require explanation before they can be correctly evaluated from tabulated data.

Strength. Glass, like other ceramics, is a brittle material. Thus, it does not plastically deform before failure and it fractures only from tensile stresses, never from shear or compression. The stress-strain curve for glass is a straight line up to the breaking point.

The intrinsic strength of all glasses is extremely high, possibly as much as 3×10^6 psi. Glass fibers have supported tensile stresses of over 10^6 psi. The useful strength of glass is a small fraction of the above figures because of stress concentrations due to surface imperfections. A rod of glass with perfect surfaces may be as strong as steel, but normal handling introduces surface imperfections that limit its ultimate strength to about 10^5 psi. Another consequence of surface faults is the introduction of a time factor—glass is stronger under momentary loading than under prolonged stresses.

When an adequate safety factor is provided, the prolonged working stress for annealed glass is taken at 10^3 psi, and for tempered, or thermally strengthened, glass as 2000 to 4000 psi, depending on the piece in question. It should be noted that the composition of glass has no practical effect on its strength, although most borosilicate glasses resist scratching and therefore usually give better mechanical service. The above figures can be used for all commercial glasses.

Elasticity. For all ordinary purposes it can be assumed that glass is perfectly elastic up to the point of fracture. The Young's modulus of elasticity varies from $6\text{–}13 \times 10^6$ psi, but most commercial glasses have values between 9 and 10×10^6 psi. Values are listed in the table.

Poisson's ratio (lateral deformation to longitudinal deformation) can be taken as 0.20, since it is seldom less than 0.18 or more than 0.22.

Hardness. This cannot be measured by the Brinell or Rockwell machines but is usually evaluated by scratch tests or impact abrasion tests.

On the Mohs' scale (diamond = 10) of scratch hardness, glasses lie between apatite (=5) and quartz (=7). Some common materials that are hard enough to scratch glass include agate, sand, carborundum (silicon carbide), hard steel, and emery. Glasses are harder than mica, mild steel, copper, aluminum, and marble.

Impact abrasion resistance of glasses is evaluated by measuring their resistance to sandblasting under standard conditions. Values recorded are relative only, showing resistance as compared to soda lime plate glass, which is arbitrarily given a value of unity. Data for various glasses are given in the table.

Thermal stresses. *Steady state thermal stresses.* Those stresses due to steady-state thermal gradients can be either innocuous or dangerous, depending entirely on the degree of constraint imposed by some parts of the item upon others or by the external mounting. Thus under minimum constraint and maximum uniformity of gradient through the thickness, very large temperature differences can be tolerated. Under complete constraint, the tensile stress on the cool side depends only on the temperature difference and on the glass properties (expansion, elastic and thermal) and can be calculated. The formula is

$$S = \frac{\alpha E \Delta T}{2(1 - \mu)},$$

where S = maximum stress (tension on cooler surface, compression on hotter surface),
α = coefficient of linear thermal expansion,
E = Young's modulus of elasticity,
μ = Poisson's ratio,
ΔT = temperature differential between the two surfaces.

When complete constraint is imposed, it is important to know the temperature difference that approaches the danger point of $S = 1000$ psi. This is

$$T_{1000} = \frac{2000(1 - \mu)}{E\alpha}.$$

It must be remembered that temperature differential means temperature difference between the two glass surfaces, exclusive of gradients across the surface itself. In air, particularly, an appreciable difference exists between surface temperature of the glass and the temperature of the air moving past it.

Transient thermal stresses. When glass is suddenly cooled, such as by removal from a hot oven, tensile stresses are introduced in the surfaces and compensating compressional stresses in the interior. Conversely, sudden heating leads to surface

Properties of Selected Commercial Glasses*

1	2	3	4	5	6			7	
Glass code	Type	Color	Principal use	Forms usually available	Corrosion resistance			Thermal expansion Coeff. 10^{-7}/in/°C.	
					Weathering	Water	Acid	0–300°C	Room temp.-setting point
0010	Potash Soda Lead	Clear	Lamp Tubing	T	2	2	2	91	100
0080	Soda Lime	Clear	Lamp Bulbs	B M T	3	2	2	92	103
0120	Potash Soda Lead	Clear	Lamp Tubing	T M	2	2	2	89	98
1720	Aluminosilicate	Clear	Ignition Tube	B T	1	1	3	42	52
1723	Aluminosilicate	Clear	Electron Tube	B T	1	1	3	46	54
1990	Potash Soda Lead	Clear	Iron Sealing	—	3	3	4	127	136
2405	Borosilicate	Red	General	B P U	–	–	–	43	51
2475	Soda Zinc	Red	Neon Signs	T	3	2	2	93	—
3320	Borosilicate (Uranium)	Canary	Tungsten Sealing	—	[3]1	[3]1	[3]2	40	43
6720	Soda Zinc	Opal	General	P	[2]–	1	2	80	92
6750	Soda Barium	Opal	Lighting Ware	B P R	[2]–	2	2	87	—
6810	Soda Zinc	Opal	Lighting Ware	B P R	[2]–	1	2	69	—
7040	Borosilicate	Clear	Kovar Sealing	B T	[3]3	[3]3	[3]4	48	54
7050	Borosilicate	Clear	Series Sealing	T	[3]3	[3]3	[3]4	46	51
7052	Borosilicate	Clear	Kovar Sealing	B M P T	[3]2	[3]2	[3]4	46	53
7056	Borosilicate	Clear	Kovar Sealing	B T P	2	2	4	51	57
7070	Borosilicate	Clear	Low Loss Electrical	B M P T	[3]2	[3]2	[3]2	32	39
7250	Borosilicate	Clear	Sealed Beam Lamps	P	[3]1	[3]2	[3]2	36	38
7570	High Lead	Clear	Solder Sealing	—	1	1	4	84	92
7720	Borosilicate (NONEX)	Clear	Tungsten Sealing	B P T	[3]2	[3]2	[3]2	36	47
7740	Borosilicate	Clear	General	B P S T U	[3]1	[3]1	[3]1	32.5	35
7760	Borosilicate	Clear	General	B P	2	2	2	34	37
7900[1]	96% Silica (VYCOR)	Clear	High Temp.	B P T U M	1	1	1	8	7
7913	96% Silica	Clear	High Temp.	B P R S T	1	1	1	8	7
7940	Fused Silica	Clear	Ultrasonic	U	1	1	1	5.6	7
8160	Potash Soda Lead	Clear	Electron Tubes	P T	2	2	3	91	100
8161	Potash Lead	Clear	Electron Tubes	P T	2	1	4	90	97
8363	High Lead	Clear	Radiation Shielding	L C	2	1	4	104	112
8871	Potash Lead	Clear	Capacitors	—	2	1	4	103	113
9010	Potash Soda Barium	Grey	TV Bulbs	P	2	2	2	89	102
9700	Borosilicate	Clear	u v Transmission	T U	[3]1	[3]1	[3]2	37	39
9741	Borosilicate	Clear	u v Transmission	B U T	[3]3	[3]3	[3]4	39	47

8				9			10	11			
Upper working temperatures (Mechanical considerations only)				Thermal shock res. Plates 6″ × 6″			Thermal stress resistance °C	Viscosity data			
Annealed		Tempered		Annealed							
Normal service °C	Extreme limit °C	Normal service °C	Extreme limit °C	1/8″ Thk. °C	1/4″ Thk. °C	1/2″ Thk. °C		Strain point °C	Annealing point °C	Softening point °C	Working point °C
110	380	—	—	65	50	35	19	395	430	625	970
110	460	220	250	65	50	35	17	470	510	695	1000
110	380	—	—	65	50	35	20	395	435	630	975
200	650	400	450	135	115	75	[4]29	670	715	915	1200
200	650	400	450	125	100	70	25	670	710	910	1175
100	310	—	—	45	35	25	14	330	360	500	755
200	480	—	—	135	115	75	[4]36	500	530	770	1085
110	440	—	—	65	50	35	[4]17	440	480	690	1040
200	480	—	—	145	110	80	[4]40	500	540	780	1155
110	480	220	275	70	60	40	19	510	550	775	1010
110	420	220	220	65	50	35	[4]18	440	475	670	1040
120	470	240	270	85	70	45	[4]23	490	530	770	1020
200	430	—	—	—	—	—	38	450	490	700	1080
200	440	235	235	125	100	70	39	460	500	705	1055
200	420	210	210	125	100	70	41	435	480	710	1130
200	460	—	—	—	—	—	34	475	510	720	—
230	430	230	230	180	150	100	66	455	495	—	1100
230	460	260	260	160	130	90	48	490	540	780	1180
100	300	—	—	—	—	—	—	340	365	440	560
230	460	260	260	160	130	90	49	485	525	755	1130
230	490	260	290	180	150	100	52	520	565	820	1240
230	450	250	250	160	130	90	[4]51	480	525	780	1210
800	1100	—	—	1250	1000	750	200	820	910	1500	—
900	1200	—	—	—	—	—	200	820	910	1500	—
900	1100	—	—	1250	1000	750	290	990	1050	1580	—
110	380	—	—	65	50	35	[4]18	395	435	630	975
110	390	—	—	—	—	—	—	400	435	600	860
100	200	—	—	—	—	—	19	300	315	380	460
125	300	—	—	55	45	35	17	350	385	525	770
110	380	—	—	—	—	—	18	410	445	650	1015
220	500	—	—	150	120	80	45	520	565	805	1195
200	390	—	—	150	120	80	[4]40	410	450	705	—

(Cont.)

PROPERTIES OF COMMERCIAL GLASSES (*cont.*)

1	12	13	14		15			16			17	18
Glass code	Impact abrasion	Density gm/cm³	Young's modulus psi × 10⁶	Poisson's ratio	Log₁₀ of volume resistivity			Dielectric properties at 1 Mc and 20°C			Refractive index Sod. D line (0.5893 microns)	Glass code
					25°C	250°C	350°C	Power factor %	Dielectric const.	Loss factor %		
0010	0.8	2.85	8.9	.21	17.+	8.9	7.0	.16	6.7	1.0	1.539	0010
0080	1.2	2.47	10.0	.24	12.4	6.4	5.1	.9	7.2	6.5	1.512	0080
0120	0.8	3.05	8.6	.22	17.+	10.1	8.0	.12	6.7	.8	1.560	0120
1720	2.0	2.53	—	—	—	11.4	9.5	.38	7.2	2.7	1.530	1720
1723	2.0	2.63	12.8	0.26	—	13.5	11.3	.16	6.3	1.0	1.547	1723
1990	—	3.47	8.4	.25	—	10.1	7.7	.04	8.3	.33	—	1990
2405	—	2.50	—	—	—	—	—	—	—	—	1.507	2405
2475	—	2.59	10.0	—	—	7.8	6.2	—	—	—	1.511	2475
3320	—	2.59	—	—	—	8.6	7.1	.30	4.9	1.5	1.481	3320
6720	—	2.58	10.2	.21	—	—	—	—	—	—	1.507	6720
6750	—	2.63	—	—	—	—	—	—	—	—	1.513	6750
6810	—	2.65	—	—	—	—	—	—	—	—	1.508	6810
7040	—	2.24	8.6	.23	—	9.6	7.8	.20	4.8	1.0	1.480	7040
7050	—	2.25	8.7	.22	16.	8.8	7.2	.33	4.9	1.6	1.479	7050
7052	—	2.28	8.2	.22	17.	9.2	7.4	.26	4.9	1.3	1.484	7052
7056	—	2.28	9.2	.21	—	10.2	8.3	.27	5.7	1.5	1.487	7056
7070	4.1	2.13	7.4	.22	17.+	11.2	9.1	.06	4.1	.25	1.469	7070
7250	3.2	2.24	9.2	.20	15.	8.2	6.7	.27	4.7	1.3	1.475	7250
7570	—	5.42	8.1	—	—	10.6	8.7	.22	15.	3.3	—	7570
7720	3.2	2.35	9.1	.20	16.	8.8	7.2	.27	4.7	1.3	1.487	7720
7740	3.1	2.23	9.5	.20	15.	8.1	6.6	.50	4.55	2.6	1.474	7740
7760	—	2.23	9.1	—	17.	9.4	7.7	.18	4.5	.79	1.473	7760
7900[1]	3.5	2.18	10.0	.19	17.	9.7	8.1	.05	3.8	.19	1.458	7900[1]
7913	3.5	2.18	9.6	.19	—	—	—	.04	3.8	0.15	1.458	7913
7940	3.6	2.20	10.5	.16	—	11.8	10.2	.001	3.8	.0038	1.459	7940
8160	—	2.98	—	—	—	10.6	8.4	.09	7.0	.63	1.553	8160
8161	—	4.00	—	—	—	12.0	9.9	.06	8.3	0.50	1.659	8161
8363	—	6.22	7.4	.27	—	9.2	7.5	.19	17.0	3.2	1.97	8363
8871	—	3.84	8.4	.26	—	11.1	8.8	.05	8.4	.42	—	8871
9010	—	2.64	9.8	.21	—	8.9	7.0	.17	6.3	1.1	1.507	9010
9700	—	2.26	9.6	.20	15.	8.0	6.5	—	—	—	1.478	9700
9741	—	2.16	—	—	17.+	9.4	7.6	—	—	—	1.468	9741

NOTES

COLUMN 1

[1] Glasses 7910, 7911 & 7905, for special U.V. and infrared applications.

COLUMN 5

B—Blown ware
M—Multiform
U—Panels
P—Pressed ware
R—Rolled sheet
LC—Large castings
S—Plate glass
T—Tubing and rod

COLUMN 6

[2] Since weathering is determined primarily by clouding which changes transmission, a rating for the opal glasses is omitted.

[3] These borosilicate glasses may rate differently if subjected to excessive heat treatment. See page 278.

COLUMN 7

See page 280, also Fig. 75.

COLUMN 8

Normal service: Freedom from excessive thermal shock is assumed.

Extreme limits: Glass will be very vulnerable to thermal shock. Recommendations in this range are based on mechanical considerations only. Tests should be made before adapting final designs.

These data approximate only.

COLUMN 9

These data approximate only. See page 269.

Based on plunging sample into cold water after oven heating. Resistance of 100°C means no breakage if heated to 110°C and plunged into water at 10°C. Tempered samples have over twice the resistance of annealed glass.

COLUMN 10

Resistance in °C is the temperature differential between the two surfaces of a tube or a constrained plate that will cause a tensile stress of 1000 psi on the cooler surface. See page 274.

[4] These data are estimated.

COLUMN 11

See page 279. These data subject to normal manufacturing variations.

COLUMN 12

Data show relative resistance to sandblasting.

COLUMN 15

Data at 25° extrapolated from high-temperature readings and are approximate only. See Figs. 67, 68.

COLUMN 16

See also Figs. 69, 72. For other electrical properties, see Figs. 67 through 72.

* All data subject to normal manufacturing variations.

Courtesy of Corning Glass Works, Corning, New York, 1961.

compression and internal tension. In either case the stresses are temporary (transient) and disappear on attainment of temperature uniformity. Since the strength of glass is greater under momentary stress than under prolonged load, thermal shock endurance cannot be directly calculated but is generally determined by empirical testing.

Since glass fails only in tension, and usually at the surface, the temporary stresses from sudden cooling are much more damaging than those resulting from sudden heating, assuming of course, that all surfaces are heated or cooled at the same time.

The transient thermal stresses increase directly with expansion coefficient and in a complex way with glass thickness. They also depend upon the shape of the article and on the method of chilling or heating. Thus, a complicated shape would be more severely stressed than a simple one. Sudden chilling by immersion in cold water is more rigorous than by blowing with cold air.

Column 9 of the table on p. 271 illustrates the most extreme case: direct plunging into cold water. Cooling into less severe media, such as air, permits much higher temperatures than those listed.

HEAT TRANSMISSION. *Thermal conductivity.*[1] At room temperature the thermal conductivity of glasses ranges from 0.0016 to 0.0029 cgs with the most common compositions near the upper end of the range. At a mean temperature of 200°C, the values are greater by 20 to 25%.

For code 7740 (Pyrex), a borosilicate glass used frequently in heat-transfer applications, the thermal constants are listed below.

Thermal conductivity at 25°C (cgs)	0.0023
(Btu/ft^2-hr)/(°F/in)	6.7
Mean specific heat (25°–175°C) (cgs or Btu)	0.20
Emissivity coefficient, radiant energy (see p. 240)	0.94

TRANSMISSION OF RADIANT HEAT. Many glasses effectively transmit heat radiation from incandescent tungsten filaments and similar sources. Transmission of heat energy increases with source temperature so that most of the energy from high temperature sources is transmitted through the glass by radiation rather than by conduction. Data for glasses 7740 and 7900 are shown in Fig. 66.

ELECTRICAL PROPERTIES. Some of these are shown graphically in Figs. 67 through 72.

Figure 67 shows the surface resistivity of borosilicate and soda-lime glasses versus relative humidity. The effect of treating the surface of borosilicate glass with silicone is given.

Figure 68 gives the breakdown voltage variation with thickness for glasses under varying conditions.

Figure 69 shows the variation of dielectric constant with temperature for various glasses.

Figure 70 shows the variation of volume resistivity with temperature for various soft and hard glasses.

Figure 71 shows breakdown voltage of several glasses as a function of temperature.

Figure 72 exhibits the variation of the loss tangent with temperature for various glasses.

---

[1] See p. 520.

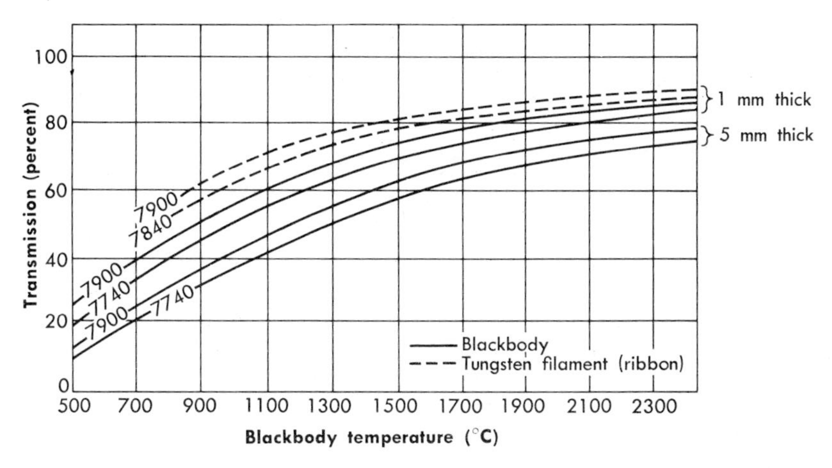

FIG. 66. Transmission of radiant energy in glasses 7740 and 7900 (Corning).

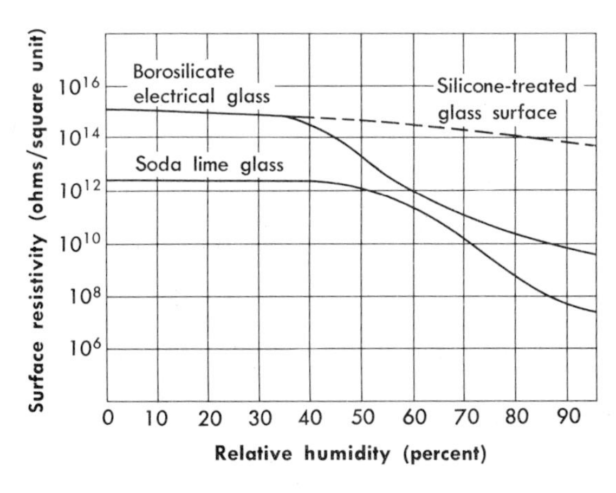

FIG. 67. Surface resistivity of glasses versus relative humidity. Values given are markedly affected by any contamination on the surface of the sample.

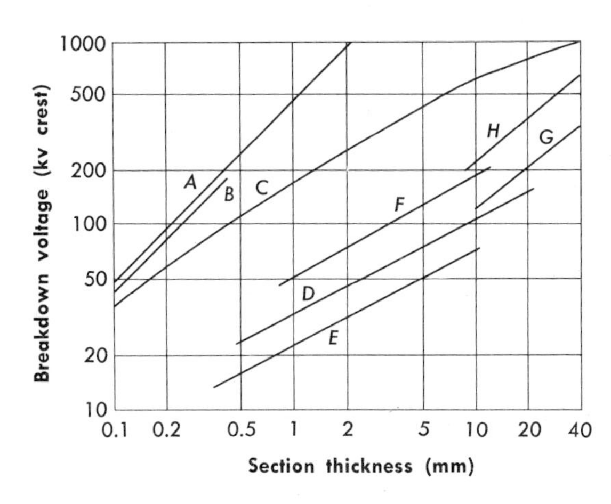

FIG. 68. Breakdown voltage versus thickness of glass for different conditions at room temperature. The 60-cycle voltage is raised continuously. *A*—intrinsic dielectric strength of borosilicate glass, *B*—intrinsic dielectric strength of soda-lime glass, *C*—highest test values available for borosilicate glass, *D*—borosilicate glass plate immersed in insulating oil, *E*—soda-lime glass plate immersed in insulating oil, *F*—borosilicate glass plate immersed in semiconducting oil, *G*—borosilicate glass power line insulator immersed in insulating oil, *H*—borosilicate glass power line insulator immersed in semiconducting oil.

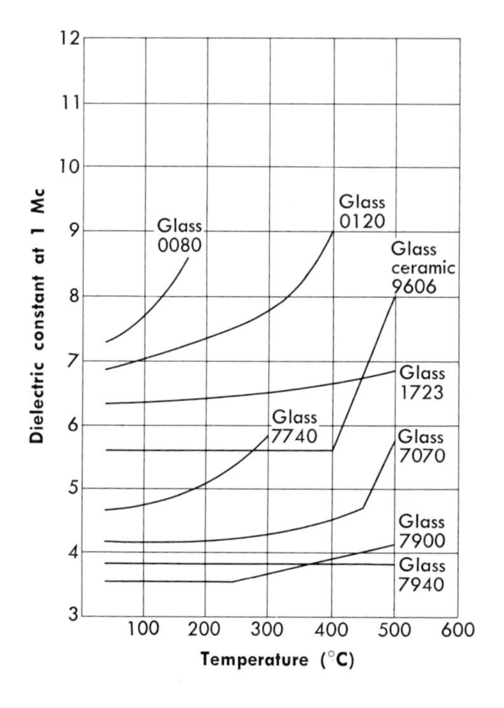

FIGURE 69

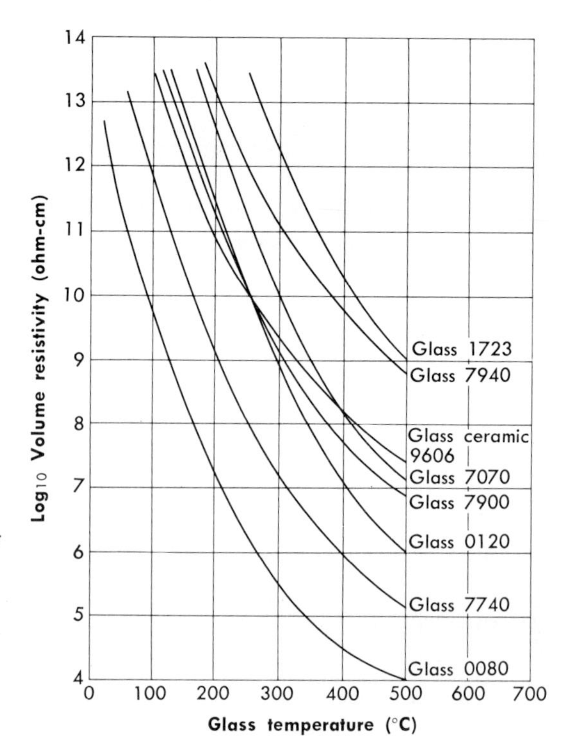

FIG. 70. Volume resistivity versus temperature.

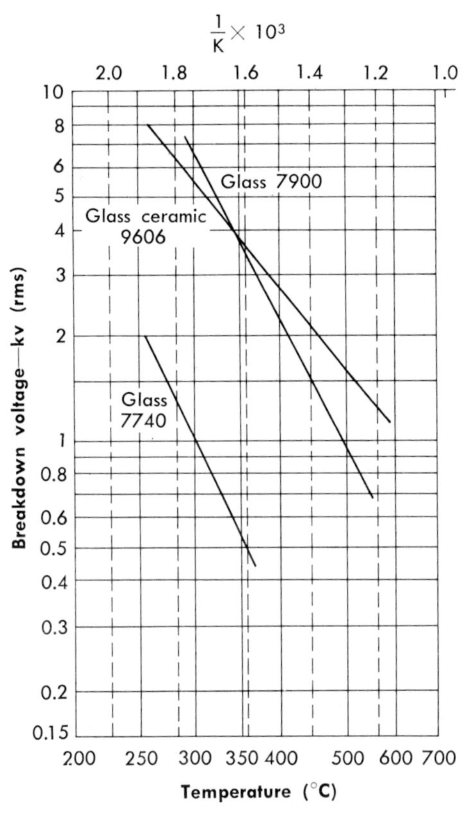

Fig. 71. Dielectric breakdown of glasses at high temperature (1-minute life for 2-mm thickness at 60 cycles).

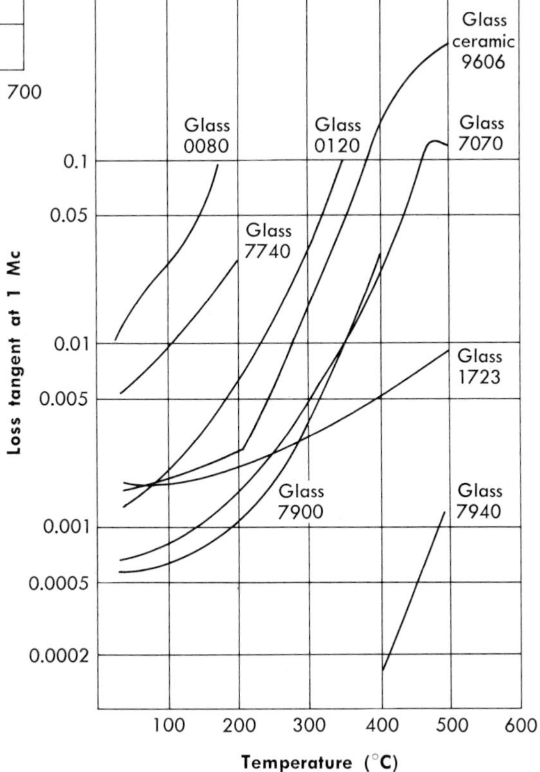

Figure 72

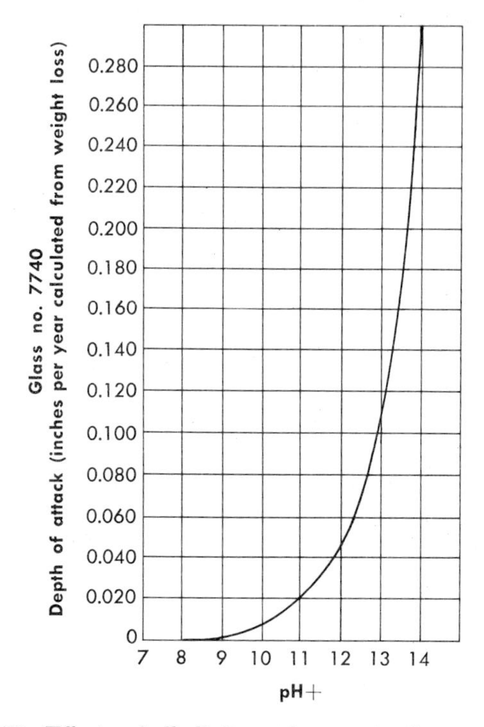

FIG. 73. Effects of alkalinity and concentration on corrosion of 7740 glass.

CORROSION RESISTANCE OF GLASS. For practical purposes a discussion of the chemical corrosion of glass can be very simple indeed. Glass is attacked by so few reagents that we can correctly say it is measurably affected only as follows:

(1) Hydrofluoric acid—serious corrosion.
(2) Hot concentrated phosphoric acid—serious corrosion.
(3) Alkaline solutions—see detailed data below.
(4) Superheated water—see details below.

Borosilicate glasses, especially 7740, and high silica glasses like 7900 are more resistant to most forms of chemical attack and, generally speaking, they should be used where this is a problem.

Alkaline attack. Cold alkaline solutions, dilute or concentrated, attack glasses very slowly, but as temperature is increased the rate of corrosion rises rapidly. See Figs. 73 and 74. The following points may be helpful in explaining this.

(1) Agitation of liquor in contact with the glass intensified attack since the products of decomposition are removed more rapidly and more corrosive liquor contacts the glass.

(2) For equal concentrations by weight, the attack of glass 7740 by other reagents compares with that of sodium hydroxide approximately as follows:

(a) Potassium hydroxide (KOH)—approximately the same.
(b) Lithium hydroxide (LiOH)—about 50% as severe.
(c) Sodium carbonate (Na_2CO_3)—less severe.
(d) Ammonium hydroxide (NH_4OH)—about 5% as severe.

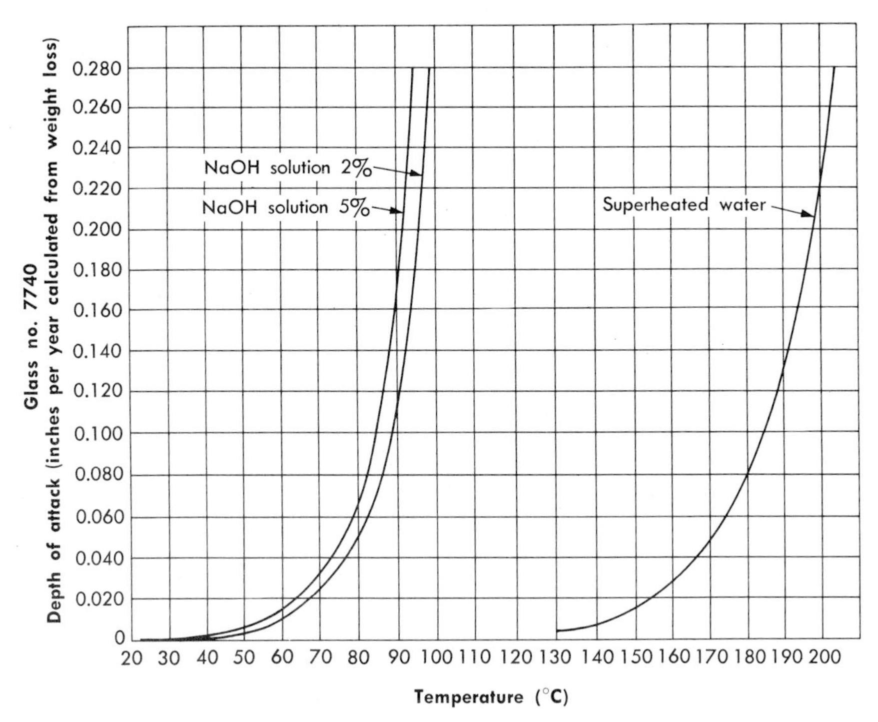

FIG. 74. Effects of alkaline solutions and superheated water in causing corrosion of glass at various temperatures.

VISCOSITY DATA. At ordinary temperatures the viscosity of glass is so high that it can be considered to be infinite. As the temperature is raised, however, the viscosity decreases and the glass gradually assumes the character of a liquid. Four points on the viscosity-temperature curve have been arbitrarily chosen to represent the softness of the glass at important points in its change from solid to liquid. These points, or reference temperatures, are listed in Column 11 of the table on p. 271.

The following definitions for strain and annealing and softening points are taken from those tentatively adopted by the American Society for Testing Materials (ASTM). The Working Point definition is employed by Corning Glass Works and corresponds to the upper end of the working range as defined by ASTM.

Strain point. The temperature, at the lower end of the annealing range, at which the internal stress is substantially removed in 4 hours. The strain point corresponds to a viscosity of $10^{14.5}$ poises when measured by the tentative method of test for annealing point and strain point of glass (ASTM Designation: C. 336).

In general the strain point represents the extreme upper limit of serviceability for annealed glass. (Tempered glasses are limited to a considerably lower absolute maximum temperature because they begin to lose their temper in the region below the strain point.

Annealing Point. The temperature, at the upper end of the annealing range, at which the internal stress is substantially relieved in 15 minutes. The annealing point corresponds to a viscosity of $10^{13.0}$ poises when measured by the tentative method of test for annealing point and strain point of glass (ASTM Designation: C. 336).

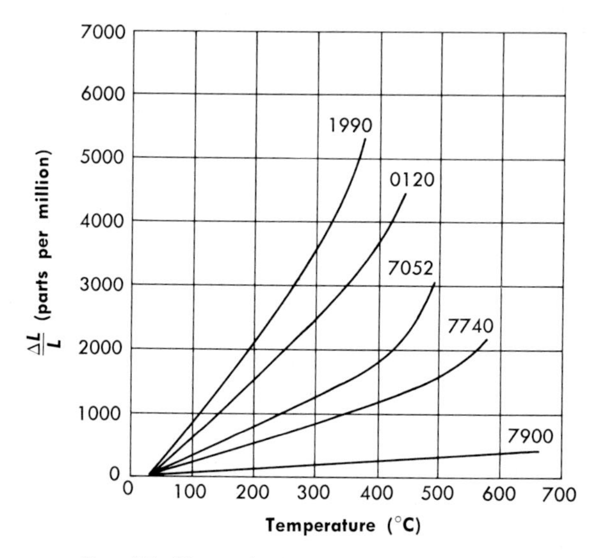

FIG. 75. Expansion-temperature curves.

In an annealing operation the glass is heated somewhat above the annealing point and slowly cooled to somewhat below the strain point. Distortion of the glass becomes a problem about 50°C above the annealing point.

Softening point. The temperature at which a uniform fiber, 0.55 to 0.75 mm in diameter and 23.5 cm in length, elongates under its own weight at a rate of 1 mm/min when the upper 10 cm of its length is heated in the manner prescribed in the Tentative Method of Test for Softening Point of Glass (ASTM Designation: C. 338) at a rate of approximately 5°C/min. For glass of density near 2.5 gm/cm^3 this temperature corresponds to a viscosity of $10^{7.6}$ poises.

At the softening point the glass deforms very rapidly and starts to adhere to other bodies.

Working point. The temperature at which the glass is soft enough for hot-working by most of the common methods. Viscosity at the working point is 10^4 poises.

THERMAL EXPANSION. As the temperature is raised, glasses tend to expand. In general the change is smaller than with most ordinary substances, but because of the brittle nature of glass, the expansion is often quite important in connection with heat-shock resistance and rigid seals to other materials, such as metals, ceramics, and other glasses.

Figure 75 shows some typical glass "expansion curves" in which the change in length-per-unit-length ($\Delta L/L$) is plotted against the temperature (T) in °C. It will be noted that the curves are initially linear but that they swing upward, indicating a higher rate of expansion, as we approach the annealing zone. The quantity which we usually refer to by the term "expansion," and which we list in the table as "Thermal Expansion Coefficient," is the slope of the initial, linear portion of this curve. To be more precise, it is the average change of length-per-unit-length per °C between 0°C and 300°C. This figure gives a good indication of the ability of the glass to withstand heat shock. It also gives a general indication of sealing compatibility. However, to make a precise prediction of the expansion match between two materials for sealing purposes, we need to know the complete expansion curves of both up to the setting point of the combination. Complete expansion curves have been determined by the Corning Glass Works for most of the glasses that are of interest for sealing applications.

The expansion of glass is affected to some extent by its thermal history, and for this reason our measurements of this property are always made on well-annealed samples.

Optical properties. Absence of physical imperfections and availability of more than one glass type are basic requirements of optical glass. Optical glasses are made of a variety of compositions, including soda-lime, lead, and borosilicate, as well as some compositions that do not contain silica.

The optical properties of glass are important in applications where transmission, refraction, or absorption of light rays is essential. Glasses are now available which transmit and control radiation through a broad portion of the spectrum.

Some of the optical properties of glass which can be controlled are: refraction—the bending of light rays passing through a piece of glass; dispersion—differences in the refraction at various wavelengths; reflection—the amount of light returned from a glass surface; and absorption and transmission—controlling the amount of light which passes through glass.

Optical glasses are used for lenses, prisms, and mirrors in microscopes, cameras, binoculars, and range-finders. They are also used in a wide variety of scientific and photographic equipment, including infrared-detecting missile domes. Glass windows (e.g., for visual observation, radiation transmission, such as pyrometry, etc.) can be sealed into glass or metal vacuum vessels. It is normally required that these windows be of good optical quality (see p. 55, and Fig. 10).

Bibliography

ASTM Standards for Glass and Glass Products, April, 1955, p. 74.

Properties of Glass, G. W. Morey, Reinhold Publishing Corp., New York, 1938.

Glass, the Miracle Maker, C. J. Phillips, Pitman Publishing Corp., 1948.

"Vycor Brand Industrial Glassware," Corning Glass Works Bulletin B-91.

"Laboratory Glassware," Corning Glass Works Bulletin LG-2.

"Designing with Glass for Industrial, Commercial, and Consumer Applications," Corning Glass Works Bulletin IZ-1.

Glass Engineering Handbook, E. B. Shand, McGraw-Hill Book Company, 1958.

Glass, aluminosilicate. Corning lists a hard glass under this name (Code 1720); see the table on p. 270. This glass can be baked for outgassing up to 700°C and can be used for making disc-type and coaxial seals with molybdenum.[1,2] There is also a calcium aluminosilicate glass (Corning, Code 1723, see p. 270) which can be sealed to "chromallized" molybdenum. The chromallizing process is done commercially by the Chromalloy Corp., 450 Tarrytown Road, White Plains, New York.

---

[1] J. F. Margiotta, *Electron-Devices Techniques Bulletin,* No. 102, Stanford University Electronics Laboratory, September 1, 1959. U.S. Government Contract NONR 225(24). See also L. Bell and M. Hillier, "High-Melting-Point Aluminosilicate Glasses in Microwave Valves," *Services Electronics Research Laboratory Tech. Jour.* (Br), **4,** No. 1, February, 1954; and same authors, *J. Appl. Phys.* (Br), **9,** 94, 1958.

[2] G. W. Hees and K. D. Early, *Sylvania Technologist,* **13,** 148, 1960.

The aluminosilicate glasses are less permeable to helium than borosilicate glass such as Corning Code 7740 (Pyrex).[1]

Glass, borosilicate (see table of Corning glasses on p. 270). This is the general designation for "Pyrex" glass, a trade name of the Corning Glass Works.

Glass, copper sealing (Corning Glass Works, Code No. 7295). This glass can be fused to commercial-grade copper using known sealing techniques (see below). This glass has a high expansion coefficient (154×10^{-7} in/in/°C) which closely matches that of copper. It is currently available in Multiform shapes. Other properties of this glass are as follows:

Working point	655°C
Softening point	465°C
Annealing point	366°C
Strain point	344°C
Density	2.56 gm/cc
Log_{10}resistivity, 250°C	6.78[2]
Log_{10}resistivity, 350°C	5.01[2]
Durability in water	0.05[3]

7295 Glass-sealing recommendations[4]

A. Preparation of parts prior to sealing

1. Cleaning: Heavily oxidized copper should not be used. Both the copper and the Multiform glass beads can be cleaned in dilute nitric acid (10–30%). Roughening of the copper leads in the sealing area by sandblasting or scoring improves adherence.

2. Firing: The glass beads can be heated in an air oven at 400°C to drive off surface moisture. Fire the copper parts (use OFHC copper only, see p. 219, and *cf.* p. 172) in hydrogen or in a forming gas of the composition, 8% H_2 and 92% N_2. The latter is more effective in cleaning up surface oxides.

B. Sealing

1. Best results are obtained with continuous ovens or furnaces using an atmosphere of forming gas or hydrogen. This type of oven is recommended because sudden cooling sometimes checks the glass around the copper leads when hot assemblies are transferred from a sealing oven to an annealing oven.

2. Do not exceed sealing temperatures of 600–700°C. Higher temperatures cause bloating or blistering of the very high-expansion Multiform glass.

Glass, evolution of gas and water vapor from.[5] It is well known that most glasses accumulate a film of water and other contamination on the surface, due largely to the relative humidity and condition of the prevailing atmosphere. Temperature and

---

[1] F. J. Norton, *J. Appl. Phys.*, **28**, 34, 1957.

[2] See Column 15 in the table on p. 272.

[3] About like 0080 glass (see p. 270).

[4] Courtesy of Corning Glass Works, Corning, New York. Bulletin of December 26, 1958.

[5] *Scientific Foundations of Vacuum Technique*, S. Dushman, 2nd edition, Sec. 7.7, John Wiley & Sons, Inc., New York, 1962.

pressure also have some bearing on the surface condition of glasses. Kohl[1] quotes several authorities in citation of these effects. Of several glasses tested, the surface resistivity decreased with increasing ambient humidity, the hard glasses (see above) being somewhat less affected than the soft glasses. Even glass which has been chemically cleaned and vacuum-outgassed at an elevated temperature will adsorb moisture and other contaminants if left exposed to room air.

Where glass is exposed to high humidities, there are certain surface treatments which can be applied to reduce the effect. One of these is dimethyldichlorosilane (a silicone) $(CH_3)_2SiCl_2$. Such a film, in a very thin layer, reacts with the water-film on the glass to evolve hydrochloric acid, which is evaporated, and a final residue of dimethyl siloxane, which presents a layer of methyl groups to the outer surface of the glass.[2]

For room-temperature work, when the glass is not to be baked or heated in any way, glass vessels can be coated with one of the water-repellent waxes of good electrical properties, such as Picein,[3] a black wax of low vapor pressure (10^{-6} torr Hg at 20°C). This wax is soluble in benzol and turpentine but is unaffected by alcohol and water. It also resists a short immersion in chromic-sulfuric cleaning fluid (p. 5).

Glass, hard versus soft. The so-called hard glasses, in general, have the (lower) range of thermal expansion coefficients from 5 to 67×10^{-7} in/°C; the so-called soft glasses have expansion coefficients of 69×10^{-7} in/°C and higher. (*Cf.* table on p. 270.)

Glass-to-metal seals (see p. 54).

Glass, Nonex. A borosilicate glass (Corning 7720, see table p. 270) suitable for sealing to tungsten.

Glass-to-sapphire seals. Tubing seals of glass to sapphire can be made by the technique described by Spindler.[4]

The procedure involves *adhesion* of the glass to the sapphire, since the latter has a sharp melting point (2000°C) and therefore cannot be "worked" like glass. The seals are of the graded type (p. 289). A graded seal has the following transitions: Corning 7280, 3320, 7740 (Pyrex) (see below). Tungsten can be sealed to the Pyrex in the usual manner. This grade is then sealed to the sapphire tube with Corning 1826 glass powder (300 mesh), which is applied to the sapphire tube in a $2\frac{1}{2}\%$ solution of nitrocellulose in amyl acetate. Several coats are brushed onto the end of the sapphire tube, each coat dried before the next is applied. Sapphire windows can be sealed to glass tubing in a similar manner.

The sealing is done in a laboratory furnace, resistance-wound to obtain two temperatures in different zones, 700 and 900°C. The sapphire can be supported on alumina blocks or in a fused silica holder. When silica is used, the sapphire must be

---

[1] *Materials Technology for Electron Tubes,* second edition, W. H. Kohl, Reinhold Publishing Corp., New York, 1959.

[2] *Physical Properties of Glass,* J. E. Stanworth, Clarendon Press, Oxford, 1950.

[3] Also see p. 140.

[4] "Technique of Sealing Glass to Sapphire," paper presented by G. P. Spindler at the 4th Symposium of the American Glassblowers' Society, Corning, New York, May, 1959. Reprints of Mr. Spindler's paper may be obtained from the Adolf Meller Company, Sapphire Products Division, P.O. Box 702, Providence 1, Rhode Island.

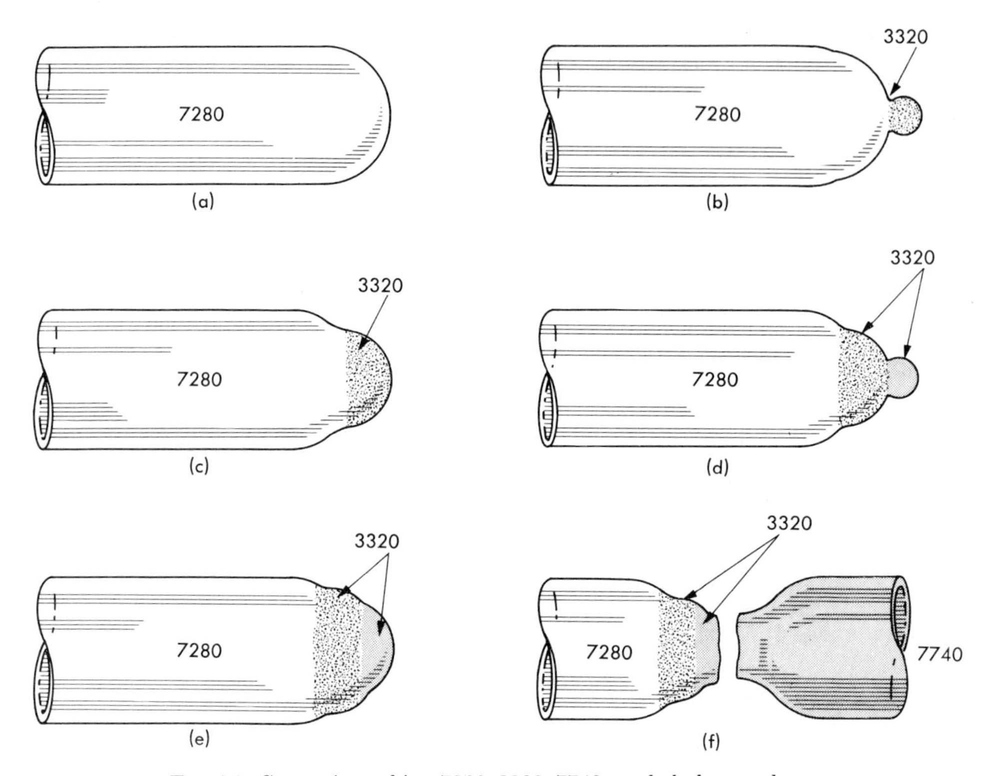

Fig. 76. Stages in making 7280–3320–7740 graded glass seal.

separated from the silica with asbestos paper, since sapphire reacts with silica at the temperatures used.

Sealing glass to high-alumina ceramic (Coors AD-99, AD-995—see p. 154) can be accomplished in the same manner.

Figure 76 shows the stages in making the graded seal. A tube of 7280 glass is buttoned-off (test-tube end), as at (a). With a hydrogen flame, a 3-mm ball of 3320 glass is fused to the end under oxidizing conditions, as at (b). This ball is then carefully melted by strongly applying the flame only to the ball, so that it diffuses into the 7280 glass. Under close observation, a small ring of light-green color will appear between the 7280 and 3320 glass. This green ring is an indication that good diffusion has occurred. The tube is then blown out slightly, as at (c). For strength, another 3-mm ball of 3320 glass is added to the area blown out, as at (d). This in turn is strongly heated with the hydrogen flame under oxidizing conditions, and the tube blown out a second time, as at (e). With a sharp flame the tube is opened, as at (f), and is now ready to be sealed onto the 7740 glass; this is done with the hydrogen flame. Standard glass-blowing procedure is used to make the seal come out to the original diameter of the two tubes. The 7280 glass must be at least $\frac{3}{4}$ inch from the grade, where it can be cut off and flared slightly. After a slight roughening on a carborundum wheel, it is ready for making the sapphire seal.

Glass sealing alloys. The following metals can be used for making glass-to-metal seals, which are described on the pages indicated.

Alloy designation or number	*Page numbers*	*Alloy designation or number*	*Page numbers*
Allegheny 42	58	Fernichrome	—
Allegheny 4750	56	Fernico	58, 249
Allegheny 55	See chrome iron	Kovar	58, 322
Carpenter 27	See chrome iron	Molybdenum	58, 377
Carpenter 42	See Allegheny 42	Platinum	56, 445
Carpenter 49	—	Rodar	58, 465
Carpenter 426	56	Sealmet	—
Chrome iron	56, 199	Sealvac-A	58
Cold-rolled steel	56, 209	Stainless steel Type 304	58, 64, 499
Copper, OFHC	58, 63, 219	Sylvania 4	56
Driver-Harris 14	56	Therlo	58
Dumet	56, 230	Tungsten	58, 62, 559

Glass, solder (see SOLDER GLASS, pp. 486 *et seq.*).

Glass, strains in and detection of. All glass that has been worked by the conventional methods of glass blowing (i.e. heating to and manipulation at the working temperature range) is subject to strains, and this is especially true when glass-to-metal seals are present because of the small departures from identical expansion coefficients of the glass and metal members. The common practice is to place the piece of work in a glass-annealing oven (see p. 417), which is maintained at a temperature appropriate to the type of glass, *immediately* after working and while the glass is still hot. This should be done as quickly as possible, and the work should be protected from drafts. Industrially, continuous ovens are used in which the glass-working and annealing are done in a conveyor-belt or other type of oven from which the work is not removed until near room temperature.

Under column 10, subhead "Annealing Point," in the table on p. 271 will be found the temperatures suitable for various Corning glasses.[1] The length of time the work is to remain in the annealing oven will vary with the size and complexity of the piece. For satisfactory annealing, the glass should remain at the annealing temperature about 30 minutes (more or less), after which the temperature of the oven can be slowly reduced to room temperature.

If, after annealing is done, it is to be determined whether or not there are strains still present in a piece of work, a simple device can be used. Figure 77 shows an easily constructed strain detector, consisting of two sheets of "Polaroid"[2] mounted in a box with a light source which can be an ordinary incandescent lamp (100-watt size is convenient) with or without a reflector.

The piece of work is rotated into as many positions as possible. The field of view at G (Fig. 77) is normally dark, and if strains are present in the work piece, these will appear as a bright interference pattern in certain positions.[3]

---

[1] Temperatures 50°–100° above those given are recommended.

[2] Polaroid Corporation, Cambridge, Massachusetts. Polaroid is available in sheets up to several square feet in area.

[3] For a full treatment of the annealing and strain detection in glass, see W. H. Kohl, *Materials Technology for Electron Tubes,* second edition, Reinhold Publishing Corp., New York, New York, 1959.

Glass, uranium. A uranium glass is available from the Corning Glass Works, designated Code No. 3320. It has the following properties:

Type of glass	borosilicate
Color	canary
Principal use	tungsten sealing
Forms usually available	tubing only
Thermal expansion coefficient (°C)	40×10^{-7}
Upper working temperatures (°C) (mechanical considerations only)	
annealed, normal service	200
annealed, extreme limit	480
Thermal shock resistance (°C), plates 6 inch × 6 inch annealed:	
1/8 inch thick	145
1/4 inch thick	110
1/2 inch thick	80
Thermal stress resistance (°C)	40
Viscosity data (all °C):	
strain point	495
annealing point	540
softening point	780
working point	1155
Specific gravity	2.29
Log_{10} volume resistivity at 250°C	8.6
at 350°C	7.1
Dielectric properties at 1 Mc and 20°C:	
power factor	0.30
dielectric constant	4.9
loss factor	1.5
Refractive index, Na D line (0.5893 micron)	1.481

Corning 3320 glass is sometimes used for beading (p. 163) tungsten rods and wires which are then sealed into flares or bulbs of Corning 7720 (Pyrex) glass. (See the table on p. 270.)

Glass, Vycor. Several glasses bear this registered trademark of the Corning Glass Works. These have code numbers 7900, 7910, 7911 (see the table on p. 270 for properties). They contain 96% silica, and are designed for service at temperatures over 250°C and up to 800°C, or where ultrasevere thermal shocks will be encountered.

Glow discharge column (see BREAKDOWN VOLTAGE, pp. 188 *et seq.* and pp. 166, 213). That portion of the discharge in Fig. 47, p. 214 indicated at (3) is called the **Positive column,** or simply the column, and occurs in a gas tube when the cathode and anode are sufficiently far apart. The appearance of this column takes many different forms, but is the same throughout the length of the tube. A *striated* column exhibits light and dark layers which may either remain stationary or, in the

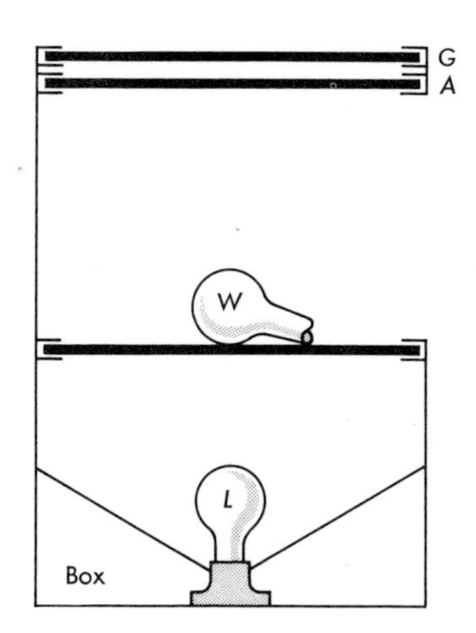

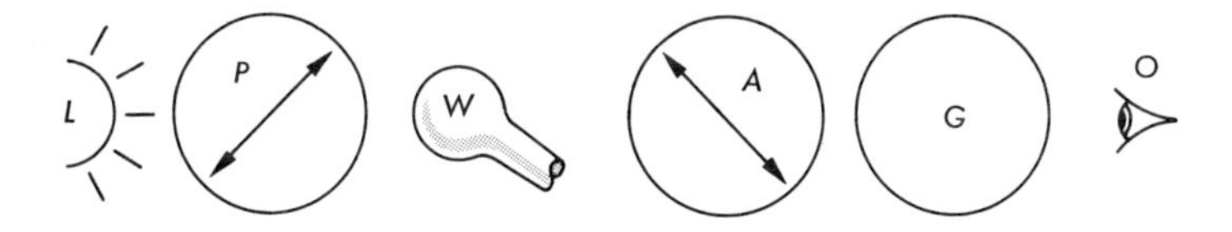

FIG. 77. Construction and operation of a single-strain detector for glass: *L*—light source, *P*—Polaroid screen (polarizer), *W*—work piece, *A*—Polaroid screen (analyzer), *G*—ground glass diffuser; *P* and *A* are oriented at right angles to each other for maximum extinction.

case of the noble gases (p. 160), move along the tube. Sometimes the column occupies only a small part of the tube diameter (at certain pressures) and wriggles about in an erratic, snaky manner.

The homogeneous part of the column is distinguished by the fact that its condition is exactly the same at various distances from the cathode. In a tube arranged with a movable anode so that the length of the column can be varied while keeping the current constant, it can be shown that under these conditions the rest of the discharge is not changed in any way. By determining how the cathode-anode voltage increases as the distance is shortened, we can find the potential difference per unit length of the column and thus the strength and gradient of the electric field. In the homogeneous part of the column, the field strength is constant, which indicates that the gas of the column contains an equal number of positive ions and electrons per unit volume. This is an example of a **plasma.**[1] (See p. 442.)

Glow tube (or GLOW LAMP). A tube having two metal electrodes is evacuated and then filled with a gas to a certain pressure. Up to a critical voltage across the two electrodes, practically no current flows, but when this voltage is reached (see BREAKDOWN VOLTAGE, p. 188) a *discharge* occurs and the voltage across the tube

[1] F. M. Penning, *Electrical Discharges in Gases,* Macmillan Co., New York, 1957.

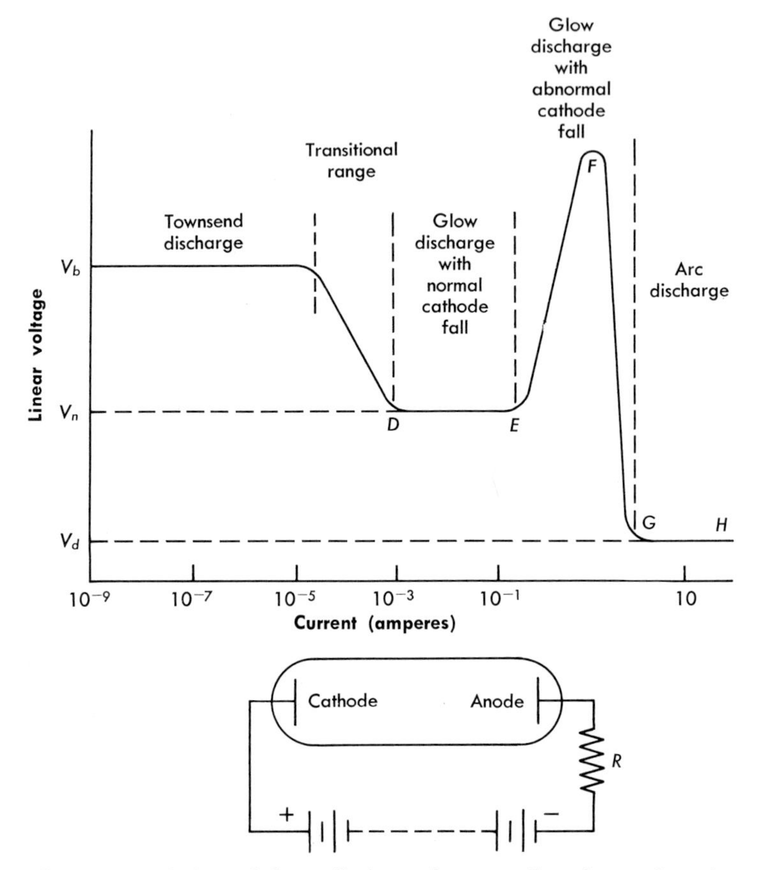

FIG. 78. Stages passed through by a discharge between flat plates when the current is made to increase, as, for example, by reducing the ballast resistor R. (After F. M. Penning.) Breakdown voltage is V_b, V_n is normal cathode fall of potential, V_d is arc discharge.

drops and becomes quite constant regardless of current fluctuations over a considerable range ($D-E$ in Fig. 78).

This effect is employed in electronic circuits. The glow tube is connected across a dc voltage supply, where it holds the voltage constant over a considerable range of currents drawn by the load.

Glow tubes must always be used with a current-limiting or *ballast* resistor (R in Fig. 78) to prevent the condition of arc discharge ($G-H$), which would destroy the tube.

Glyptal. A trade name for a resin with an alkyd or glycol-phthalate base that is manufactured by General Electric Company, Plastics Department, Pittsfield, Massachusetts. It is supplied either clear or with a pigment. The cured resin, when freed from solvent (toluene), has a fairly low vapor pressure (clear—2.4×10^{-6} torr at 25°C; red—6.8×10^{-7} at 28°C). (See p. 140.) Glyptal is sometimes used as a semipermanent sealant for small leaks in vacuum systems. For this purpose the material is to be applied when the vacuum vessel is at atmospheric pressure, then allowed to dry either at room temperature or higher until hard. If Glyptal is applied to a vessel under vacuum, it is drawn into the leak and is thereby rendered ineffective.

Grade A nickel (Electronic).[1] This is a selected grade of commercial purity-wrought nickel produced by melting and deoxidizing electrolytic nickel. It is easily drawn and can be readily worked and welded, and brazed with silver or copper (and alloys of the two). It has a high resistance to corrosion; oxidation at elevated temperatures is low, and any oxide scale formed is tightly adherent. Sufficient strength is retained at normal bombarding (outgassing) temperatures to prevent deformation. Its modulus of elasticity and damping factor are high, minimizing vibrational and microphonic effects.

The electrical resistivity of Grade A nickel is about 57 ohm-mil-ft at 32°F (9.5 microhm-cm^3 at 0°C), with a temperature coefficient of resistivity of 0.0041–0.0051 per °C. Its thermal conductivity is 0.142 (cgs) at 18°C, 0.088 (cgs) at 600°C, and 0.058 (cgs) at 1200°C.

Grade A nickel is easily spot-welded and heated by induction. The electrical conductivity at moderate temperatures is high enough to render it suitable as a current-carrying lead.

The high magnetostriction coefficient of nickel makes it useful in devices employing this principle. Nickel is magnetic at room temperature, and becomes non-magnetic near 360°C (the curie point).

Electronic Grade A nickel has the following limiting composition (percent):

Nickel and cobalt	99.00 min.	Carbon	0.35 max.
Copper	0.15 max.	Magnesium	0.15 max.
Iron	0.20 max.	Titanium	0.01–0.05
Manganese	0.35 max.	Silicon	0.15 max.
Sulfur	0.008 max.		

Graded seal, glass. In sealing together two kinds of glass whose expansion coefficients are different enough to produce serious stresses, a graded seal is employed in which one or more different glasses with intermediate expansion coefficients are interposed so as to minimize the stress at any one junction. In the table on p. 61, as explained on p. 62, stress values of less than 1 kg/mm^2 indicate a satisfactory match, while stresses up to 3 kg/mm^2 can be tolerated under ideal conditions. For example glass No. 7720 (a borosilicate glass), which closely matches tungsten, and is thus used for beading this metal (p. 163), will have a stress of only +0.5 kg/mm^2 when sealed to glass No. 3320 (a uranium glass) used as an intermediate. The uranium glass (p. 286) can then, in turn, be sealed to Pyrex glass 7740 with a tolerable stress of −1.6 kg/mm^2. The 7720 glass would have a stress of +1.9 kg/mm^2 if sealed directly to Pyrex 7740, and a higher value of −3.5 kg/mm^2 if sealed directly to tungsten.

[1] "Inco Nickel Alloys for Electronic Uses," International Nickel Company, Inc., 67 Wall Street, New York 5, New York, 1959. See also p. 94. Grade A nickel is now called "Nickel 205" under the Huntington Alloy Numbering System. *Cf.* p. 388.

Graded seals in tubing form (see below) are commercially available from the Corning Glass Works, Corning, New York.

GLASS NUMBER	SEALS TO		EXPANSION $\times 10^{-7}$	SOFTENING POINT (°C)
	HARDER	SOFTER		
7750	7740	7510	40.5	704
7510	7750	7520	50	705
7520	7510	7530	60	755
7530	7520	7550	71	728
7550	7530	7560	79	716
7560	7550	Most lime glasses[1]	86	702

Approximate O.D.: 12 mm; Approximate length: 12 inches

Graphite (see CARBON pp. 149, 157, 190). Graphite is a black crystalline form of carbon having a density of 2.25 gm/cc. It sublimes at 3652°–3697°C and boils at approximately 4200°C.

Greases, stopcock (see APIEZON, pp. 157, 158; also the table on p. 141: Lubriseal, Celvacene).

Stopcocks lubricated with the greases described should not be subjected to temperatures higher than those indicated in the tables. A minimal quantity of grease should be used so as not to plug the openings by repeated rotations. When a glass stopcock becomes noticeably stiff to turn, the grease should be thoroughly cleaned out, using trichlorethylene, acetone, etc. (see DEGREASING, p. 7) and replaced with fresh grease.

In addition to the greases described, there are several silicone vacuum greases which can be used at higher temperatures than some of the organic greases. The silicone greases, however, require special solvents for cleaning, about which the manufacturer should be consulted.

Grid. In an electron tube, an electrode, which has a loose structure, is normally negatively charged and has the function of controlling the flow of electrons from the cathode to the anode, between which it is interposed. This element in the tube receives the incoming signal, which, by its fluctuation in strength or polarity, produces like changes in the grid potential and thus produces corresponding but amplified variations in the anode current (see pp. 546–548, EQUIPOTENTIAL LINES, pp. 244–245). Some tubes have two or more grids.

Grid emission (see p. 445).

Gun, electron (see ELECTRON GUN, p. 239).

Hard soldering (see BRAZING, pp. 172, 492).

Hard vacuum. Roughly speaking, any pressure below about 1×10^{-6} mm Hg. The term is rather vague, however, and the value may vary over wide limits depending upon application and circumstances.

Headgate valve. In Fig. 18, p. 76, Valve *A*, which closes off the diffusion pump from the bell-jar (or manifold), is sometimes called a headgate valve. This valve allows

[1] See the table on p. 270.

the bell-jar to be opened at atmospheric pressure for rapid cycling. For this purpose, Valve *C* is also closed while the pumps continue to run. After the ionization gauge has been shut off, Valve *D* is slowly opened, allowing air to enter the bell-jar. After a new setup is made, Valve *D* is closed and Valve *C* is opened, which immediately begins the evacuation cycle. When the pressure has dropped sufficiently, the head-gate valve (*A*) is opened, whereupon the diffusion pump takes hold at once.

Such a valve must be of a construction that will allow the lowest pressures required in the system, i.e. the gaskets or seals must have a low-vapor pressure.

Heat conductivity (see THERMAL CONDUCTIVITY, p. 520).

Heaters—filaments (see pp. 80–92, 250, 548).

Heaters, annealing of (see pp. 82, 87).

Heater coating (see pp. 81, 552).

Heater design (see p. 80).

Heater design nomogram (see pp. 80, 554).

Heater design volt/ampere table (see p. 81).

Heating, RF-induction (see pp. 45, 51–53, 221, 222).

Heat shields. In a vacuum, heat losses from filaments and emitters are mainly by radiation. In designing a tube where either (a) the power requirements for heating the emitter are limited and must be conserved, or (b) structures in proximity to the emitter must be protected from high temperatures, resort is had to the use of heat shields, i.e., one or more metal plates or cylinders which must satisfy the requirements of being highly reflective and of being able to withstand the temperatures to be encountered. The greater the number of heat shields used, the more protection and/or conservation of heat is afforded. For very high temperatures, highly polished molybdenum or tungsten is indicated; for lower temperatures, nickel is used, or austenitic stainless steel if a nonmagnetic structure is required.

Heat treatment of metals for glass sealing (see the tables on pp. 56–59).

Heat treatment for bright-annealing stainless steel (see pp. 41–51).

Helium. One of the noble or rare gases. It is a colorless, odorless, inert gas having a molecular weight of 4.003. Its melting point is −272.2°C, or only 0.8° absolute, at 26 atmospheres pressure. Its boiling point is −268.9°C. It is slightly soluble in water, as follows:

WATER TEMPERATURE (°C)	SOLUBILITY (cm^3 IN 100 ML OF WATER)
0	0.94
25	0.94
50	1.05
75	1.21

Helium is somewhat absorbable by platinum but is insoluble in alcohol. It is nonflammable, nonexplosive, and nontoxic. Its lightness and inertness make it a useful substitute for hydrogen in many laboratory and industrial procedures, but precautions should be taken to free tank helium from contaminants such as water vapor, oxygen, etc. It is used widely in mass-spectrometer-type leak detectors (pp. 137, 359) because of its ability to penetrate minute leaks. Helium is also used in the liquid state as a refrigerant in vacuum work.

Helium leak detector (see MASS SPECTROMETER, p. 358).

High vacuum. In industrial parlance, pressures from 10^{-3} to 10^{-7} mm Hg are considered to be high vacuum. Pressures lower than 10^{-7} are thought of as ultrahigh vacuum. (See p. 110.)

Ho factor.[1,2] An empirical quantity, sometimes called the *speed factor,* as applying to diffusion pumps, and dependent upon the kind of vapor, its temperature, the shape of jets or nozzles, the vapor density distribution below the diffusion annulus of the pump, and probably other factors.

Housekeeper seal for copper-to-glass (see p. 63).

Housekeeper seal for stainless steel-to-glass (see p. 64).

Hydrochloric acid, inhibited. The specifications for this cleaning agent used for removal of oxides and scale from iron, steel, nickel, Kovar, etc., call for the addition of ½% by volume of Rodine to 50% hydrochloric acid. The Rodine, a proprietary additive (see formula K-4, p. 9), minimizes pitting or etching of the metal.

Hydrofluoric acid. This is a strong mineral acid used in dilute solutions for cleaning aluminum (p. 5), glass (p. 7), molybdenum (p. 10), stainless steel (p. 15), titanium (p. 16), and other metals. It should be used with caution in an efficiently ventilated hood because the vapor is extremely irritating to the skin, eyes, and mucous membrane.

Hydrogen. A very active gas, the lightest of all the elements, highly flammable and explosive when mixed with air or oxygen. Hydrogen is not soluble in water but unites with many elements and is a usual constituent of organic materials. It is a strong *reducing* agent; i.e., it combines under proper conditions with the oxygen in oxides, converting them to water vapor and the metal. This is the basis of the bright heat-treatment of metals in hydrogen-atmosphere furnaces (see pp. 35, 41–51, 258, 259, 552), in atmosphere furnaces using dissociated ammonia (75% hydrogen, 25% nitrogen; see p. 156), and other high-hydrogen-content gas mixtures (see p. 172).

The limits of flammability of hydrogen in air at atmospheric pressure are 4.0 to 74.2% by volume. The ignition temperature (or flash point) is 580 to 590°C.

Hydrogen, admission to tubes (see pp. 119–123).

Hydrogen, ignition temperature of (see above).

Hydrogen, methods of diffusion (see HYDROGEN, ADMISSION TO TUBES, above).

Hydrogen, purifying and drying (see HYDROGEN, DRY, above).

Hydrogen, dry (see pp. 41–51).

Hydrogen, safe operation with (see pp. 40, 51 (reference), 258).

Hydrogen brazing (see HYDROGEN above).

Hysteresis heating (see EDDY CURRENT HEATING, p. 231).

Ignition temperature of hydrogen (see above).

Inco cathode alloys. The table on the next page gives the composition and properties of some nickels manufactured by the Huntington Alloy Products Division of the International Nickel Company, for use as cathode base materials.

Inconel (Inconel 600). A corrosion-resistant, work-hardenable alloy sometimes used as springs and spring parts in electronic tubes where other materials show higher

---

[1] T. L. Ho, *Physics,* **2,** 386 (1932).

[2] S. Dushman, *Scientific Foundations of Vacuum Technique,* second edition revised, John Wiley & Sons, Inc., New York, 1962.

Inco Cathode Alloys

INCO TYPES		COMPOSITION (PERCENT)												AVAILABLE FORMS[2]	CATHODE TYPE	REMARKS
NEW DESIGNATION[1]	PREVIOUS DESIGNATION	Ni MIN.	C MAX.	Mn MAX.	Fe MAX.	S MAX.	Si	Cu MAX.	Ti	Mg	W	Co MAX.	Cr MAX.			
Nickel 205	Grade A Nickel (Electronic)	99.0	0.15	0.35	0.20	0.008	0.15 max.	0.15	0.01 to 0.05	0.01 to 0.08	—	—	—	All forms, wrought.	Passive	High corrosion resistance, high thermal and electrical conductivity; low gas content and low vapor pressure; good formability.
Nickel 202	202 Nickel	93.7	0.10	0.02	0.02	0.008	0.06 max.	0.02	0.02 max.	0.01 to 0.10	3.5 to 4.5	—	—	CR strip and ribbon tubing, seamless, welded, and drawn. Lockseam and disc.	Active	Tungsten-bearing; high strength at elevated temperatures. Good shock resistance.
Nickel 220	220 Nickel	99.0	0.08	0.20	0.10	0.008	0.01 to 0.05	0.10	0.01 to 0.05	0.01 to 0.08	—	—	—	CR strip and ribbon. Tubing, seamless, welded, and drawn. Disc, lockseam, and lapseam cathodes.	Active	Easy activation without liberation of excessive amounts of Ba.
Nickel 225	225 Nickel	99.0	0.08	0.20	0.10	0.008	0.15 to 0.25	0.10	0.01 to 0.05	0.01 to 0.08	—	—	—	CR strip and ribbon. Tubing, seamless, welded, and drawn. Disc, lockseam, and lapseam cathodes.	Active	High silicon content makes for greater activity than Nickel 220 has, where activation under adverse conditions is required. The high reducing agent content tends to liberate appreciable Ba.
Nickel 230	230 Nickel	99.0	0.10	0.15	0.10	0.008	0.01 to 0.035	0.10	0.005 max.	0.04 to 0.08	—	—	—	CR strip and ribbon.	Active	Closely controlled product.
Nickel 233	330 Nickel	99.0	0.10	0.30	0.10	0.008	0.10 max.	0.10	0.005 max.	0.01 to 0.10	—	—	—	CR strip and ribbon, tubing, welded, and drawn; lapseam, lockseam, and disc cathodes.	—	For oxide-coated and cold cathodes; also suitable for anodes and structural parts.
Nickel 270	New product	99.95	0.04	0.003	0.005	0.003	0.003 max.	0.003	0.003 max.	0.003 max.	—	0.003	0.003	Rods, bars, HR, and CD; strip and sheet, CR; tubing, seamless, and wire, CD.	Passive	Very high purity material.

[1] Huntington Alloy Products Division, International Nickel Company, 67 Wall Street, New York 5, New York. Data published by permission. Copyright by INCO, 1961.
[2] CR: cold-rolled; CD: cold-drawn; HR: hot-rolled.

relaxation and load losses at temperatures up to 350°C at relatively high stresses and prolonged exposure. Higher temperatures can be withstood by Inconel for lower stresses and shorter times.

The composition of Inconel is nominally

Ni (+ Co)	72% min.	Cu	0.50 max.
Cr	14–17	Si	0.50 max.
Fe	6–10	C	0.15 max.
Mn	1.0 max.	S	0.015 max.

Some physical properties of Inconel are

Density .... 8.43 gm/cm³ or 0.304 lb/in³
Melting point .... 1395°C
Magnetic transformation temperature ... −40°C (nonmagnetic at room temperature)
Mean specific heat:
(25°–100°C) (gm-cal/gm/°C) 0.109
Coefficient of linear thermal expansion (in/in):
38°–93°C ...... 11.5×10^{-6} 38°–760°C ..... 16.1×10^{-6}
Electrical resistivity:
microhm-cm³ (20°C) ... 98.2 ohm-mil-ft (68°F) 590
Thermal conductivity, cgs:
27°–100°C ...... 0.036 600°C 0.050
200°C ...... 0.041 800°C 0.054
400°C 0.045
Modulus of elasticity (psi $\times 10^6$)
tension and compression ...... 31 torsion 11

Tensile and Magnetic Properties of Inconel Alloy 600

Condition	Tensile strength (psi)	Permeability at room temperature (H = 200 oersteds)	Curie temperature (°F) for permeability of: 1.01	1.02	1.05	1.1
Annealed	98,000	1.006	−18	−49	−126	−158
Cold-drawn 20%	129,000	1.008	—	−76	−148	−170
Cold-drawn 50%	150,500	1.007	—	−49	−140	−178
Cold-drawn 50%, stress-equalized 12 hr at 525°F	154,000	1.007	−14	−94	−164	−170
Cold-drawn 50%, annealed for carbide precipitation*	100,000	1.008	−30	−76	−154	−188

* One hour at 1700°F, furnace-cooled at 1400°F, and held for 16 hours, followed by air-cooling.

Tensile Properties and Modulus of Elasticity of Hot-rolled Inconel Alloy 600 at Elevated Temperatures

TEMPERATURE (°C)	TENSILE PROPERTIES			MODULUS OF ELASTICITY IN TENSION (PSI × 10^6)
	TENSILE STRENGTH (PSI × 10^5)	YIELD STRENGTH 0.2% OFFSET (PSI × 10^5)	ELONGATION (% IN 2 IN.)	
Room temperature	90.5	36.5	47	31
315	90.5	31.0	46	29.5
425	88.5	29.5	49	28
540	84.0	28.5	47	25
650	65.0	26.5	39	20
760	27.5	17.0	46	17
870	15.0	9.0	80	14
980	7.5	4.0	118	11.5

Inconel alloy 600 has great strength and resistance to oxidation at high temperatures. It also has the important property of being free from intergranular deterioration when subjected to high temperatures. It can be used up to 1150°C in a hydrogen atmosphere, and up to 1090°C in an oxidizing atmosphere (air).

Corrosion Resistance of Inconel Alloy 600

Indoor atmosphere	good	Oxidizing acids, concentrated	good
Outdoor atmosphere (with some sulfur)	fair	Oxidizing acids, dilute	poor
Fresh and distilled water	good	Organic acids and compounds (foods, etc.)	good
Salt water:		Acetic and formic acids hot, concentrated	fair
(sea, motion)	good	Alkalies	good
(stagnant)	poor	Dry gases	good
Refrigeration brines	good	Wet gases (Cl, Br, SO_2)	poor
Acid salts	good	Steam	good
Oxidizing acid salts	fair	Molten metals:	
Oxidizing alkaline salts	fair	Pb	good
Mineral acids:		Other low-melting metals	poor
cold	fair		
hot	poor		

Annealing Inconel alloy 600. Internal stresses on cold-worked Inconel alloy 600 begin to be relieved by heating to 540°C. Practically complete stress-relief occurs by heating to 760°C for $1\frac{1}{2}$ hours with only slight softening. Softening by annealing begins at about 870°C and is reasonably complete in 10–15 minutes at 980°C. Above this temperature there may be objectionable grain growth, although very brief heating at 1035°C will cause complete softening without undue grain growth. The rate of cooling has no effect on the softening so that the alloy may be either quenched or furnace-cooled. For bright-annealing, an atmosphere of dry hydrogen is required (dewpoint −40°C or lower).

Inconel alloy X-750 (formerly called Inconel X). An age-hardenable nickel-chromium alloy in wrought form, having high rupture strength and low creep rates under high stress at temperatures up to 815°C in the fully heat-treated condition. Its short-time tensile strength at 650°C in the equalized and aged condition is about 80% that of its room temperature properties. Inconel X is virtually non-magnetic, its curie point being −175°C and its permeability about 1.003 at room temperature.

COMPOSITION

Nickel (and cobalt)	70 minimum	Iron	5–9
Chromium	14–17	Manganese	1.0 max.
Titanium	2.0–2.75[1]	Silicon	0.5 max.
Columbium (and tantalum)	0.7–1.2	Copper	0.5 max.
Aluminum	0.4–1.0	Carbon	0.08 max.
Sulfur	0.01 max.		

PROPERTIES

Electrical resistivity (microhm-cm^3 at 0°C)	123
Melting range (°C)	1395–1425
Specific gravity (gm/cc)	8.3
Density (lb/in^3)	0.3
Thermal conductivity (cgs 0°–100°C)	0.036
Coefficient of linear thermal expansion (in/°C) 25°–100°C	13.7
Specific heat	0.105
Rockwell hardness, soft	B90–100
as drawn	C20–32
soft, age-hardened	C30–37
as drawn, age-hardened	C34–44
Modulus of elasticity, in tension (psi)	31×10^6
in torsion (psi)	11×10^6

	Wire 0.002–0.010 inch	Wire 0.010–0.032 inch
Tensile strength (psi $\times 10^3$)		
annealed	130–160	130–160
full hard (spring)	245–275	220–250
annealed – age hardened	180–210	180–210
spring temper, age hardened	280–310	270–300
Yield strength (psi $\times 10^3$)		
annealed	70–125	65–110
full hard (spring)	225–265	190–230
annealed – age hardened	150–180	150–180
spring temper, age hardened	250–280	240–280
Elongation %, annealed	35–10	35–15
full hard (spring)	5–2	5–2
spring temper, age hardened	—	8–3

[1] For wire the titanium content is 2.0–2.5%; for other forms the titanium content can be 2.25–2.75%.

For spring parts subjected to elevated temperatures, the soft or mildly cold-worked (No. 1 temper wire) and aged material should be used for maximum resistance to relaxation or load loss for prolonged times at temperatures up to 540°C. For minimum relaxation at temperatures up to 540°C, appreciable cold work, such as spring temper prior to age hardening, should be avoided. In the heavily cold-worked (spring-temper) and aged condition, the alloy has a tensile strength of about 280,000 psi. In this condition Inconel alloy X-750 has low relaxation up to about 400°C and offers useful characteristics at higher temperatures for short time exposure. For temperatures over 540°–650°C, the spring temper and fully heat-treated (triple heat treatment) offers relatively low relaxation and rate of relaxation. It is recommended that parts be blanked or formed and subsequently age hardened. Only liberal radii should be used for heavily cold-worked material. After aging, its surface should be cleaned chemically or mechanically before welding or soldering.

The triple heat treatment consists of the following steps:

1. Solution-treat at 1150°C for two hours; air-cool.
2. Age at 843°C for 24 hours; air-cool.
3. Normal-age at 704°C for 20 hours; air-cool.

This treatment, to be done after forming operations, results in a Rockwell hardness of C-40. Some machining can be done with carbide tools. The service temperatures for the age-hardened material are 650°–815°C. The alloy in this condition resists relaxation and has a fairly fine and uniform grain size.

Inconel alloy 604. The addition of 2% columbium to the alloy 600 base composition improves creep and rupture properties at intermediate temperatures in the range 650°–815°C, and increases resistance to high-temperature corrosion.

Inconel alloy 610. This is the casting alloy corresponding to the wrought alloy 600. Slight changes in the base composition have been made to increase fluidity; corrosion resistance is equivalent.

Inconel alloy 611. This is similar to the alloy 610, except that the composition is modified to improve welding characteristics.

Inconel alloy 700. This alloy is a modified form of the base alloy, suitable for highly stressed parts in the temperature range 675°–955°C.

Incuro brazing alloy (see items 76 and 101 in the Table of Brazing Filler Metals, pp. 180, 182).

Incusil brazing alloy (see items 129 and 137 in the Table of Brazing Filler Metals, pp. 184, 185).

Indium.[1] A silvery-white, soft, low melting-point metal having a low vapor pressure and useful in vacuum applications either alone or alloyed with other metals (see pp. 259 *et seq.*). It is a highly plastic metal and, under pressure, can be deformed almost indefinitely, since it does not work-harden. This property makes it useful as gaskets in some types of vacuum or sealing devices which are to be operated below its melting point.[2, 3]

---

[1] Much of the material on indium is taken from "The Metal Indium," Consolidated Mining & Smelting Co. of Canada, Ltd., Montreal, Canada (1952). Reproduced by permission.

[2] R. C. Block and R. H. Ward, *Rev. Sci. Instr.*, **31**, 60, 1960.

[3] A. W. Knudsen, *ibid.*, **23**, 566, 1952. See also Paper #13, "Indium," J. R. Mills, R. A. King, and C. E. T. White, *Rare Metals Handbook*, second edition, p. 220, Reinhold Publishing Corp., New York, New York, 1961.

The physical and mechanical properties of indium are as follows:

Atomic number	49
Atomic weight	114.76
Density at 20°C (gm/cc)	7.31
Specific heat at 20°C, (gm-cal/gm/°C)	0.057
Melting point (°C)	156.4
Boiling point (°C)	2000 ± 10
Coefficient of linear expansion at 20°C (per $°C \times 10^{-6}$)	33
Thermal conductivity (cgs)	0.057
Electrical resistivity, at 20°C (ohm-cm)	9×10^{-6}
at 156.4°C (melting point) (ohm-cm)	29×10^{-6}
at 3.38°K	superconducting
Temperature coefficient of resistivity	0.00498/°C
Standard electrode potential	0.34 v
Magnetism: diamagnetic; susceptibility	-0.11×10^{-6}
Brinell hardness	0.9
Tensile strength (psi)	380
Elongation (% in 1 inch)	22
Reduction in area (%)	87
Compressive strength (psi)	310
Modulus of elasticity (psi)	1.57×10^6

The surface of indium resists oxidation in air up to a point a little beyond its melting point; above this a film of indium trioxide is formed. At high temperatures in hydrogen or vacuum, the metal sublimes. It is attacked slowly in cold, dilute mineral acids and more readily in hot dilute acids. The reaction with concentrated mineral acids is more vigorous. It is not attacked by solutions of strong alkalies. Acetic acid does not dissolve it, but oxalic and some other organic acids do.

Indium forms amalgams with mercury, and it alloys with silver, gold, platinum, lead, copper, tin, cadmium, bismuth, and certain other metals.

It is nontoxic and not irritating to the skin, but since it is likely to be attacked by food or skin acids, its use should be restricted when these are present.

Addition of indium to Wood's metal (see p. 570) lowers the melting point by approximately 1.45°C for each 1% of indium, with the lowest melting point at 47°C for 19.1% indium. The 24% indium, 76% gallium eutectic (see GALLIUM, p. 259) melts at 16°C and is therefore liquid at room temperature.

A useful application of indium is in the form of an alloy containing equal amounts of tin and indium. This alloy is capable of wetting glass and of thus making glass-to-glass and glass-to-metal seals. The alloy is first applied to the preheated glass by swabbing or rubbing. Joints and seals may then be made in conventional ways. Where high temperatures cannot be used to make joints with glass, this tin-indium alloy should find use.[1]

An alloy containing 37.5% lead, 37.5% tin, and 25% indium has been developed which is found to be an improvement over standard 50–50 (Pb-Sn) solder in terms of alkali corrosion resistance. There is only a minor decrease in soldering strength.

The oxides, sulfides, selenides, and tellurides of indium are all semiconductors.

---

[1] See R. B. Belser, *Rev. Sci. Instr.*, **25**, 180, 1954.

Indium metal makes good low-resistance contacts to such transducer materials as titanium oxide, barium titanate, and cadmium sulfide.[1]

Indium sulfide (In_2S_3) has a large negative temperature coefficient of resistivity and is chemically and electrically stable at fairly high temperatures. It may therefore find use as a thermistor.

Indium dissolves readily in sodium, and small additions lower the melting point.[2]

Because of its low melting point and low vapor pressure, and also because of its tendency to wet glass, indium and its alloys have been used to effect closure in a high-vacuum valve,[3] and to form seals.[4, 5]

Induction heating (see pp. 45, 51–53, 221, 222, 231).

Inert gases (see GASES, NOBLE, pp. 160, 263).

Inlet pressure (of a pump). The pressure at the low-pressure end of a pump. In a diffusion pump, this would be the end of the pump connected to the chamber being evacuated, or to a trap or baffle.

Since the pressure gradients are very high at the inlet of a pump, a reference plane or cross section must be decided upon, and this is normally the plane of the pump inlet.

Insalute cement (see pp. 194, 195).

Interface impedance (of oxide-coated cathodes). The nature of the bonding between the base metal and the cathode coating has been studied extensively.[6, 7, 8, 9] The bonding layer changes during the life of the cathode, with low interface impedance attained by a clean, well-activated coating, and the impedance increasing due to the presence of some contaminating materials in the base metal and the coating, and others arriving as gases, vapors, and/or deposited or evaporated substances from other parts of the tube.

The resistive component alone, unless extremely high (perhaps indicating a poor bond), is not harmful to tube operation, especially in amplifiers at all frequencies, but the increase in capacitive components of the impedance can cause serious reductions in transconductance and plate current. (See pp. 546–548.)

Invar. A very low coefficient of expansion alloy having this approximate composition: nickel 36%, manganese 0.5%, silicon 0.25%, carbon 0.1%, and the balance iron.

When the coefficient of linear expansion at room temperature of the nickel-iron alloys is plotted against the nickel content, the resulting curve, according to C. E.

---

[1] V. T. Sihvonen and D. R. Boyd, *ibid.*, **31**, 992, 1960.

[2] "Constitution of Indium Alloy Systems," E. A. Peretti, The Indium Corp. of America, Utica, New York.

[3] L. Pátý and P. Schürer, *Rev. Sci. Instr.*, **28**, 654, 1957.

[4] "Inflatable Gasket," L. P. Lucas and H. P. Hernandez, *ibid.*, **30**, 941, 1959.

[5] "Simple Demountable Indium O-Ring Seal," H. Seki, *ibid.*, **30**, 943, 1959.

[6] J. F. Waymouth, Jr., "Determination of Oxide-Coated Cathodes under Low-Duty-Factor Operation," *J. Appl. Phys.*, **22**, 80, 1951.

[7] E. G. Widell and R. A. Hellar, "Effect of Coating Composition of Oxide-Coated Cathodes on Electron Emission," *ibid.*, **21**, 1115, 1950.

[8] A.S.T.M. Committee B-4, Annual Report 1950, "Proposed Method of Test for Relative Thermionic Emissive Properties of Materials Used in Electron Tubes," *Proc. A.S.T.M.*, **50**, 142, 1950.

[9] H. B. Frost, "The Measurement of Cathode Interface Impedance," Report of the 12th Annual Conference on Physical Electronics, M.I.T., p. 23, 1952.

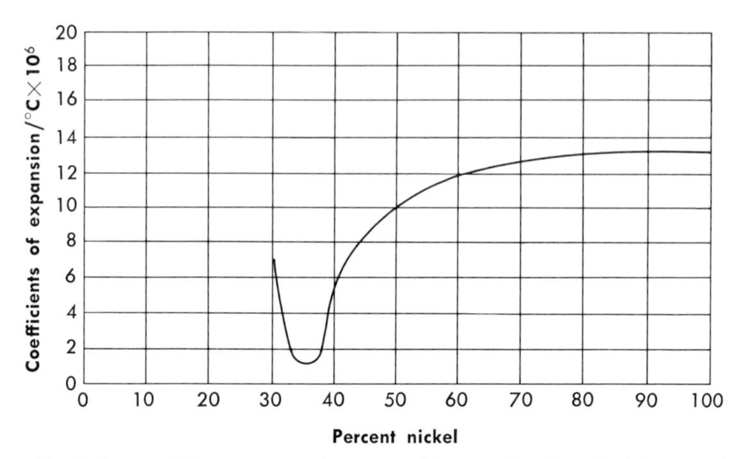

FIG. 79. Coefficients of linear expansion per °C at 20°C of typical iron-nickel alloys containing 0.4% manganese and 0.1% carbon. (From E. Guillaume.)

Guillaume,[1] has the form shown in Fig. 79. The composition corresponding to the minimum, in the vicinity of 36% nickel, maintains its dimensions so nearly constant when subjected to ordinary atmospheric temperature variations that it has received the appropriate name of "Invar" (invariant or invariable).

The values given in the figure apply *only* over a narrow range of temperatures.

Invar is magnetic at the temperatures at which it exhibits the low expansion characteristic, its curie temperature (p. 231), where it becomes nonmagnetic, being 277°C (530°F).

The physical and mechanical properties of invar (or 36% nickel-iron alloy) are given below. The values apply to the annealed metal.

Average coefficient of expansion (in/°C)	
between −130° and −18°C	1.98×10^{-6}
between −18° and +93°C	1.26×10^{-6}
between 93° and 204°C	2.70×10^{-6}
between 204° and 316°C	11.40×10^{-6}
between 316° and 427°C	15.5×10^{-6}
between 427° and 538°C	17.0×10^{-6}
Curie temperature (°C)	277
Tensile strength (psi)	70,000
Yield point (psi)	24,000
Elongation in 2 inches (%)	36
Reduction in area (%)	68
Brinell hardness	143
Modulus of elasticity (psi)	21×10^6
Temperature coefficient of modulus of elasticity per °C	486×10^{-6}
Modulus of rigidity (psi)	8.1×10^6

(Cont.)

[1] "The Anomaly of the Nickel-Steels," *Proc. Phys. Soc.* (London), **32,** 374, 1920.

Temperature coefficient of modulus of rigidity per °C	576×10^{-6}
Poisson's ratio	0.290
Electrical resistivity	
ohm-mil-ft	490
microhm/cm	81
Temperature coefficient of electrical resistivity per °C	1.21×10^{-3}
Specific heat (gm-cal/gm/°C) (25°–100°C)	0.123
Thermal conductivity (cgs)	0.025
Melting point °C	1425
Density (gm/cc)	8.13
(lb/in^3)	0.294

Invar cannot be hardened by heat treatment, although its strength can be increased somewhat by cold-working. The work-hardening rate is less than that of the stainless steels.

According to Guillaume, each 1% of manganese increases the minimum coefficient of expansion of the 36% nickel alloy about 14.4×10^{-6}/°C, while each 0.1% of carbon raises it by about 11.1×10^{-6}/°C. Thus the carbon content should be kept as low as is metallurgically possible. Some manganese is probably necessary to ensure forgeability. Silicon does not affect expansivity but tends to lower the inflection temperature (at which the alloy begins to lose its low expansion characteristic).

The effect of heat treatment upon the expansion of the iron-nickel alloys is dependent upon the method of cooling. Rapid cooling (quenching) decreases the rate of expansion, while the reverse is true when slow cooling is employed. Cold-working is even more effective than quenching in lowering the expansivity. Subsequent reheating (annealing) will remove the lowering of the coefficients induced by cold work in proportion to the temperature employed, the alloy assuming values corresponding to the annealed condition when a temperature of about 600°C is reached. The variations in expansion induced by these factors are not of very great moment except in cases where the lowest expansion is the objective, that is to say, in the case of the 36% nickel alloy.

Invar which has been subjected to cold working or machining may require a stress-relieving heat treatment for stabilization if the metal is to be used for high precision work. A successful cycle which has been widely used comprises the following steps:

1. Heat to 315°–370°C for about 1 hour.
2. Air-cool.
3. Heat to a temperature somewhat above the top operating temperature.
4. Cool slowly to somewhat below the lower operating temperature.
5. Again heat slowly to above the top operating temperature.
6. Cool slowly to room temperature.
7. Cooling very slowly through the curie range is also considered to improve stability.

Hot-working of invar can be done at any temperature below about 1260°C. Cold-working hardens the alloy to a maximum of about C32 Rockwell.

Invar machines best at a hardness of about C20 Rockwell. The alloy softens progressively in annealing, when heated in the range 540°–1260°C. Pronounced grain growth does not appear until 1040°C has been passed. The alloy can be air-cooled or water-quenched from the annealing temperature.

Pickling is done in a 25 percent solution of hydrochloric acid at 70°C.

Invar can be welded by any of the conventional methods, including acetylene torch, metallic arc, carbon arc, flash-butt and spot-welding, and atomic hydrogen. The welding rod should be invar, although 18–8 stainless steel can be used. Invar can be brazed very successfully in dry hydrogen by the method given for stainless steel on pp. 41–51).

Machining is somewhat difficult because of the toughness and ductility of invar. High-speed steel or sintered carbide tools should be used, and the cutting edges should be kept sharp. Cutting speeds should be relatively low, and ample cutting fluid should be used. A grade of invar is obtainable containing approximately 0.15% selenium, which one manufacturer[1] claims greatly improves the machinability.

Invar is fairly resistant to ordinary atmospheric or salt-spray corrosion, although less so than the 18–8 stainless steels.

Ion, positive. A gas atom or molecule which has lost one or more electrons owing to collision with a fast-moving electron, thus acquiring a positive charge (i.e., losing a negative charge), is called a positive ion. It is unstable and seeks to regain its lost charge by recombination with free electrons, and is thus influenced (deflected, attracted, repelled) by other charged bodies and by magnetic fields according to the laws of such phenomena.

Ion bombardment (see pp. 101, 167, 417).

Ion emission, positive. This is a type of emission in which a heated electrode is made positive with respect to other structures in the tube or device. Any electrons emitted are immediately drawn back, but materials adsorbed on the surfaces (gases, etc.) are ionized and given off as positive ions. The electrode is thus an emitting anode, the positive ions being attracted to a negatively charged (cold) cathode, which is nonemitting.

Various interesting aspects of positive ion emission are exhibited,[2] and a use has been found for the phenomenon in the detection of leaks. White and Hickey[3] describe such a device which is sensitive to halogen vapors as little as a few parts per million in dry air. Nontoxic, nonflammable Freon 12 can be used, and the circuit can be arranged to give a visual or an audible indication when a leak is present.

Ion pumping (see TITANIUM-ION PUMPING, pp. 106–109).

Ionization and ionization potential (see BREAKDOWN VOLTAGE, pp. 188–9). The ionization potential of a gas is that quantity, in electron volts (which is numerically equal to simple volts), of the energy required to ionize an atom or molecule, i.e., to split the atom or molecule into a positive ion and an electron. The process consists first of *excitation*, in which one or more electrons are moved from an inner orbit in the atom to one farther removed from the nucleus; and second, that in which an electron is completely removed from the atom, which is the condition of *ionization*. With the removal of one or more electrons, the atom will take on a positive charge (become a positive ion). When the electron(s) recombines with the ionized atom,

---

[1] Latrobe Steel Company, Latrobe, Pennsylvania.

[2] R. B. Jacobs and H. F. Zuhr, "New Developments in Vacuum Engineering," *J. Appl. Phys.*, **18,** 43, 1947.

[3] W. C. White and J. S. Hickey, *Electronics,* **21,** 100, 1948.

which it does eventually by virtue of mutual attraction, some form of electromagnetic radiation, such as light, is given off.

One way in which an atom can become excited or ionized is by the collision of an electron (from an external source, such as a cathode) with the atom. The function of the cathode (see pp. 191–193) is to provide a source of high-energy electrons. The condition for the passage of an electron beam is that there should be sufficient distance between gas atoms or molecules (mean free path) for the electrons emitted by the cathode to attain momentum. The condition necessary for this type of ionization is that both high-energy electrons and gas atoms or molecules be present. Obviously, then, the number of collisions will be very small if (1) there are too many gas atoms (high pressure, electrons not free to move about), *or* (2) there are too few gas atoms. In other words, ionization can take place only within a certain range of gas pressures and cannot occur, as a rule, either at atmospheric or at very low pressures under normal circumstances.

In a tube (see p. 213) which has been evacuated and then filled with a gas at a low pressure (say about 10 torr), excitation and ionization can occur at voltages given in the table below.

GAS OR VAPOR	EXCITATION VOLTAGE	IONIZATION VOLTAGE
Argon (A)	11.6	15.6
Helium (He)	19.7	24.5
Hydrogen (H_2)	—	15.4
Krypton (Kr)	9.9	13.3
Mercury (Hg)	4.7	10.4
Neon (Ne)	16.6	21.5
Nitrogen (N_2)	—	15.8
Xenon (Xe)	8.3	11.5

Ionization gauge, cold cathode (see PHILIPS GAUGE, p. 431).

Ionization gauge, hot cathode (see p. 162). The conventional type of ionization gauge is constructed like a triode (see Fig. 80). There is a central filament (emitter) of tungsten wire *F* surrounded by a bifilar-wound grid *G* which can be outgassed by the passage of current through it, since both ends are brought out through leads in the press. An outer metal cylinder *C* serves as the ion collector and is mounted from the top, with the lead brought out separately, as shown.

In operation the electrons emitted by the filament are accelerated by a positive voltage on the loose-structured grid; some of them pass through it and collide with gas atoms or molecules in the space between grid and collector. This produces positive ions which are attracted to the negatively charged collector; the value of the current thus made to flow is a measure of the quantity of gas atoms present within the range of the device. The high pressure limit is determined[1] by (a) the mean free path of the electrons (or mean distance between gas atoms) and (b) by the physical deterioration of the tungsten filament which becomes noticeable at 10^{-3}

[1] See Schulz-Phelps high-pressure gauge, p. 471.

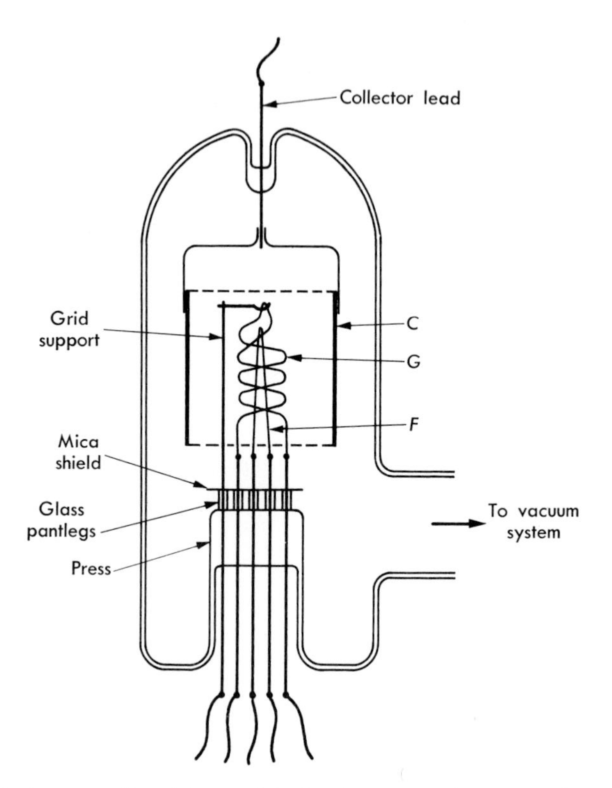

FIG. 80. A conventional type of ionization gauge for measuring pressures in the range 10^{-4} to 10^{-8} torr.

torr. (A type of ionization gauge is commercially available[1] which has a filament of thoriated iridium, which the maker claims will not burn out even at atmospheric pressure.) The low-pressure limit is determined by the presence of a small amount of soft X-rays arising from the collision of electrons with the structures within the tube, which causes emission of photoelectrons by the collector, and this effect will be manifested in the same way as positive ions, i.e., as an ion current.[2] Thus even though no gas atoms are present, a small background or minimum "ion" current is always indicated, which is independent of pressure and has been found to be a linear function of anode voltage.[3] The effect of these soft X-rays can be minimized by making the collector a fine wire, thus reducing the surface area presented to the electron stream. (See BAYARD-ALPERT GAUGE, p. 162).

It must be remembered that any vacuum gauge measures only the conditions in its immediate vicinity and thus in a vacuum system with long or small-bore passages,

[1] Vacuum-Electronic Engineering Co., New Hyde Park, New York.

[2] The Alphatron gauge (NRC Equipment Corp., Newton, Massachusetts) utilizes this principle. Instead of a hot filament or cathode, the gauge has a reservoir of radioactive material which furnishes the small amount of ionization required.

[3] *Materials Technology for Electron Tubes*, second edition, W. H. Kohl, Reinhold Publishing Company, New York, New York, 1959.

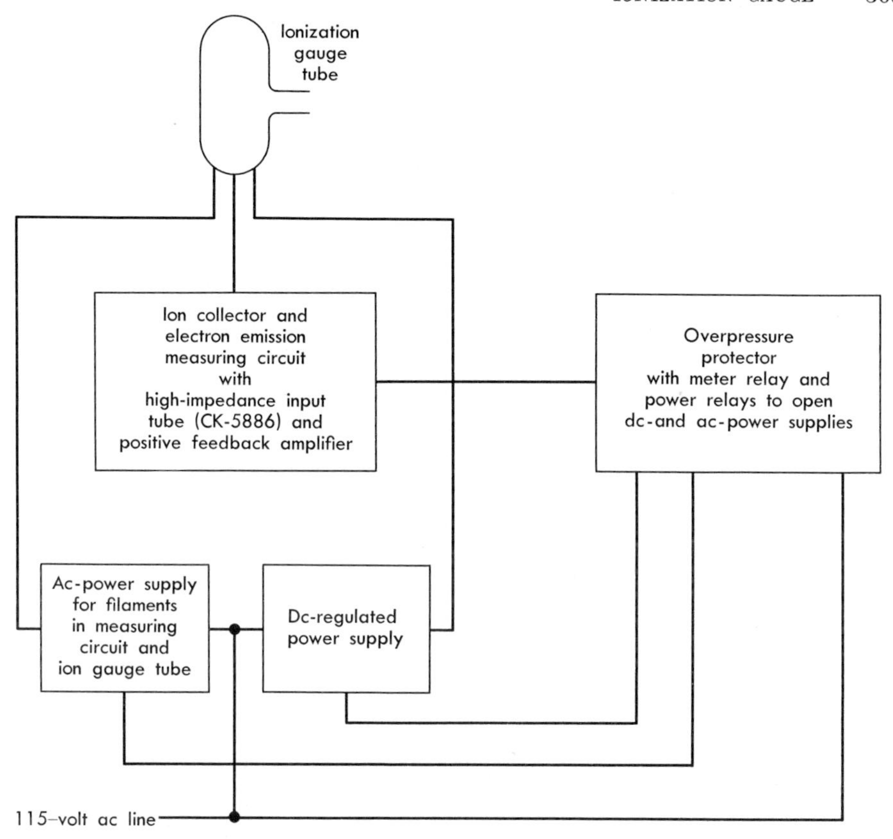

FIG. 81. Block diagram of measuring, amplifying, and protective circuits, with power supplies, for use with ionization gauges.

where a real or virtual leak exists (e.g., outgassing of components) at some point remote from the gauge, the pressure at that point will be higher than at the gauge itself. Also, ionization gauges generally effect some gas clean-up or gettering action so that the pressure indicated by (and actually in) the gauge might be considerably lower than in the rest of the vacuum system. See bibliography below.

In the ionization gauge shown in Fig. 80, if the filament is a 0.007-inch hairpin tungsten filament about 5 cm overall length, the grid is 0.015-inch tungsten, double helix, approximately 9 cm long overall, wound on a 1-cm diameter mandrel, the collector is a cylinder, open at both ends, 3 cm long and 3 cm in diameter, the following formula is applicable:

$$P = K\frac{i^+}{i^-},$$

where P is pressure in mm Hg, K is a constant (0.04 for this gauge), i^+ is grid current, i^- is collector current.

An amplifier and control circuit for use with this gauge are shown in block form in Fig. 81.

BIBLIOGRAPHY

Scientific Foundations of Vacuum Technique, S. Dushman, 2nd edition, p. 301, John Wiley & Sons, Inc., New York, 1962.

J. Blears, *Proc. Roy. Soc.,* (Br), **A188,** 62, 1947.

G. Reich, *Trans. Am. Vacuum Soc.,* 7th Ann. Symp. (1960), Pergamon Press, Inc., New York, 1961.

R. A. Haeffer and J. Hengevoss, *ibid.*

L. L. Levenson and N. Milleron, *ibid.,* 8th Ann. Symp. (1961), p. 96.

D. Lee, H. Tomaschke, and D. Alpert, *ibid.,* p. 151.

T. E. Hartman, *Rev. Sci. Instr.,* **34,** 281, 1961, and **35,** 1190, 1963.

D. R. Denison, *ibid.,* **33,** 1115, 1962.

F. L. Torney, Jr. and F. Feakes, *ibid.,* **34,** 1041, 1963.

G. Kantorowicz, *ibid.,* **35,** 126, 1964.

D. Alpert and R. S. Buritz, *J. Appl. Phys.,* **25,** 202, 1954.

W. B. Nottingham, *Trans. Am. Vacuum Soc.,* p. 76, Pergamon Press, London, 1954.

T. A. Vanderslice, *Science,* **142,** 178, 1963. (This is an educational paper dealing with the newer ionization gauges and instrumentation.)

R. W. Roberts and T. A. Vanderslice, *Ultrahigh Vacuum and its Applications,* p. 30, Prentice-Hall, Inc., Englewood Cliffs, N.J., 1963.

Iridium. This is a very hard, brittle metal of the platinum group, extremely resistant to wear and corrosion at ordinary temperatures, although an oxide is formed at high temperatures. It is unaffected by boiling lead and molten copper and iron.

The alloys of platinum with iridium have the hardness of iridium (long-wearing) with the ductility of platinum, and the iridium imparts a resistance to corrosion not possessed by platinum alone. Two alloys are in use as resistance windings for precision electrical potentiometers; these have the following properties:[1]

Alloy		Resistivity at 20°C		Temperature coefficient/°C of resistivity (0–100°C)	Ultimate tensile strength (psi × 10³)	
% Ir	% Pt	μΩ-cm	Ω/cmf		Annealed	Hard-drawn
10	90	24.5	147	0.0013	35	80
20	80	32.0	192	0.00085	45	105

Alloys containing more than 20% iridium are difficult to work.

Iron. A pure form of commercial iron is known as Armco Ingot Iron.[2] A typical analysis of sheet Armco iron is the following: carbon 0.015%, manganese 0.028%, phosphorus 0.005%, sulfur 0.025%, silicon 0.003%. The total of these five elements will not exceed 0.1%.

Armco ingot iron is a refined metal produced in open-hearth furnaces. It is supplied in the form of cold-rolled sheet and strip, cold-drawn and hot-drawn bar, flats and rounds, and plates and billets. It can also be supplied as forgings.

[1] K. J. Willis, *Platinum Metals Review,* **2,** 74, 1958, Johnson, Matthey & Company, Ltd., London.

[2] Data on Armco Ingot Iron from Armco Steel Corporation's brochure, "Magnetic Ingot Iron for D-C Applications." (1956).

The physical properties of annealed Armco iron (see below for annealing procedure) are as follows:[1]

Ultimate tensile strength (psi)	42,000
Yield strength (psi)	27,000
Percent elongation in 2 inches	38
Percent reduction in area	73
Rockwell hardness	B40–50
Modulus of elasticity, psi	30×10^6
Melting point (°C)	1532
Melting point (°F)	2790
Specific gravity	7.86
Pounds/in^3	0.284
Specific heat (gm-cal/gm/°C)	0.1075
Thermal conductivity (cgs)	0.175
(Btu/ft^2-sec)/(°F/in)	508
Coefficient of linear expansion per °C (20–400°C)	13.7×10^{-6}
Coefficient of linear expansion per °F (68–750°F)	7.6×10^{-6}

Volume resistivity (microhm-cm) at temperature (°C):

°C	microhm-cm	°C	microhm-cm
0	9.6	400	43.1
20	10.7	500	55.3
100	15.0	600	69.8
200	22.6	700	87.0
300	31.4	800	105.5

Volume resistivity, ohm-mil-ft	64.3
Magnetic saturation, gausses (ferric induction)	21,550

The magnetic properties of Armco iron are affected by cold-rolling, drawing, or forging. Permeability is lowered sharply by moderate working, and severe working causes a still further decrease in permeability. To restore the magnetic properties, the following annealing procedure is recommended.

When the material is to be used at high inductions (above 12 kilogausses), a low temperature anneal at 650° to 700°C is generally satisfactory. For optimum magnetic properties at all inductions, a temperature from 815° to 870°C is recommended (cycle *A*, Fig. 82). Where parts are large, or when only the permeability at very high inductions is of interest, even this low temperature anneal may be unnecessary.

To obtain better magnetic quality at low and medium inductions, use cycle B.

For anneals A and B and for the normal magnetic characteristics, a neutral or "burned-out" atmosphere is used to surround the parts during heating and cooling.

Some users of Armco iron have annealed in hydrogen at temperatures 150° to 540°C higher than those shown in the figure in order to obtain still better magnetic properties. (This treatment—annealing in dry hydrogen in a cycle similar to that in the figure, except that the plateau is raised to 1100°C—is the method practiced at M.I.T. with good results.)

[1] Data on Armco Ingot Iron from Armco Steel Corporation's brochure, "Magnetic Ingot Iron for D-C Applications." (1956).

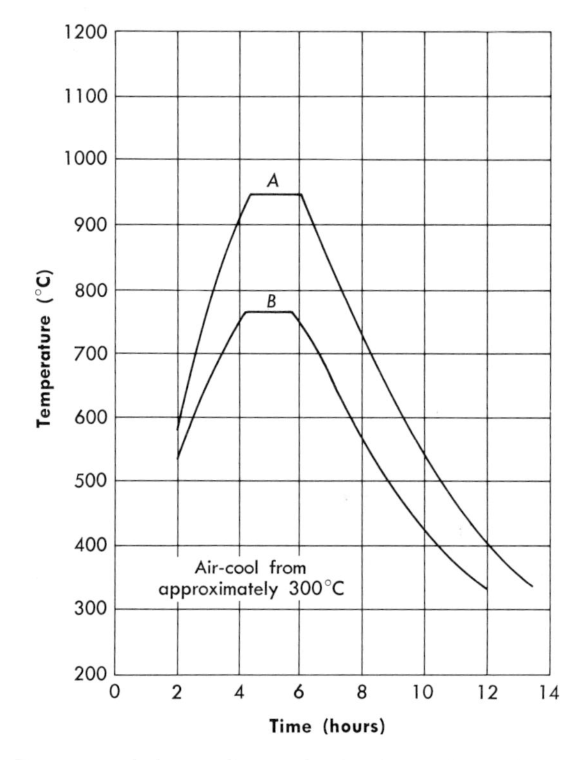

FIG. 82. Recommended annealing cycles for Armco Ingot Iron (Armco).

Svea metal (or Swedish iron) is a purified iron of European origin with properties similar to those of Armco iron.

The *machinability* rating of ingot iron is 50, as compared with 100 for B1112 steel.

Iron oxide, removal of (see pp. 8, 9).

Iron, vapor pressure of (see pp. 143, 146).

Isopropyl alcohol (see ALCOHOLS, p. 150).

Jigs for brazing (see p. 37).

Kanthal. This is the trade name of a number of electrical-resistance materials used for resistors and high-temperature furnace heaters. They are manufactured by Aktiebolaget Kanthal, Hallstahammar, Sweden, and marketed in the U.S. by the Kanthal Corporation, Amelia Place, Stamford, Connecticut.

The table on p. 310 gives the properties of some of the Kanthal alloys. It is to be noted that Nikrothal 8 is similar to Nichrome V and to Tophet A. Nikrothal 6 is likewise similar to Nichrome and to Tophet C. Cuprothal 294 is similar to Cupronickel 55–45. Kanthal DR is similar to Alchrome.

In addition to the alloys given in the table on p. 310, the manufacturer supplies a material known as **Kanthal-super** which consists chiefly of molybdenum disilicide and is useful up to temperatures of 1600°C in air. Kanthal-super is produced by a powder-metallurgy process in the form of rods of circular cross section which, when heated, can be formed into suitable heating elements. Surface loads as high as 10–20 w/cm^2 (64–128 w/in^2) can be sustained by such elements.

The material is essentially vitreous in nature and is relatively hard and brittle at room temperature, with low impact strength. It should not be subjected to substantial bending or impact stresses below 1100°C. Above this temperature the material is fairly ductile, and at still higher temperatures, it can be bent or wound into elements of the desired shape. Elements which have been in use, however, cannot be subjected to such treatment.

Kanthal-super has the following mechanical properties:

Hardness .... 1200 Vickers at 20°C
Density .... 5.6 gm/cc
Bending strength ...... 36 kg/mm^2 ± 30% at 20°C (or 51.2 ± 15.4 lb/in^2 at 68°F)
Tensile strength
  Breaking strength: 10 kg/cm^2 ± 25% (142 ± 35 lb/in^2) at 1550°C (2820°F)
  Elongation at rupture: 4–5%

Kanthal-super has a high temperature coefficient of resistivity so that for a constant voltage, the power consumption will decrease as the temperature rises. The resistance of the material does not change with use so that new and used elements can be connected in parallel or series without detrimental effects.

The longest useful life of the material as a furnace-heating element is obtained when operated in an oxidizing atmosphere such as air, oxygen, water vapor, or carbon dioxide. However, the material can be used in carbon monoxide, dissociated ammonia, and hydrocarbon gases provided that the elements have been previously oxidized by operation in air. Since the oxide layer tends to scale on cooling, it is necessary to reoxidize the elements before they are again used in a reducing atmosphere. *Pure and dry hydrogen* reacts with the surface layer, causing a gradual deterioration, but the elements can be operated satisfactorily in wet hydrogen. Sulfur and its compounds should not be allowed to come in contact with the material, nor should metals and materials tending to form easily fusible materials (e.g., silicates).[1]

Kel-F[2] plastic. This is a tough, moldable, fluorinated material with high chemical and thermal stability. It is resistant to many common solvents and reagents, including acetone, benzene, ethanol, methyl ethyl ketone, trichlorethylene, ammonium hydroxide (10%), Freon 113, hydrochloric acid (10%), sodium hydroxide (10%), fuming nitric acid (90%), and hydrofluoric acid (anhydrous). It is impervious to water (21 days at 77°F). The mechanical, physical, and electrical properties of two types of Kel-F plastic are given on pp. 312–320. Also note data in Figs. 83 through 87.

KIC-getters (see p. 105, footnote 3).

K-Monel (and KR Monel) (see MONEL ALLOY K-500 and MONEL ALLOY 501, pp. 382, 383).

Knife-edge seal (see also STEP-SEALS, pp. 117, 118). In this type of high-vacuum seal, illustrated in Fig. 88 (p. 320), one or more metal ridges (A, A) press uniformly into a ring or gasket (B, B) of softer metal, which can be copper, aluminum, gold, etc., previously annealed. The seal is misnamed, because the ridges (A, A) must be smooth and rounded in contour so as not to shear the gasket when the flanges are

---

[1] Kanthal-Super, The Kanthal Corporation, Stamford, Connecticut (1957).

[2] Data and tables reproduced by permission of the Minnesota Mining & Manufacturing Company.

PHYSICAL PROPERTIES OF KANTHAL ALLOYS[1]

ITEM	COMPOSITION	MAXIMUM CONTINUOUS OPERATING TEMPERATURE (°C)	FORMS[2]	RESISTIVITY AT 20°C		COEFFICIENT OF RESISTIVITY $\times 10^{-6}$	COEFFICIENT OF LINEAR EXPANSION PER °C $\times 10^{-6}$
				A[3]	B[3]		
Kanthal A-1	Fe-Cr-Al-Co	1350	W, S	145	872	32.4 (20–1350°C)	a–17.4[4] b–21.5 c–23.9 d–26.8
Kanthal A	Fe-Cr-Al-Co	1300	W, R	139	837	48.5 (20–1300°C)	a–16.8 b–20.1 c–23.0 d–24.2
Kanthal D	Fe-Cr-Al-Co	1150	W, R, S	135	812	65.0 (20–1150°C)	a–15.9 b–19.5
Kanthal DS	Fe-Cr-Al-Co	1150	W, R, S	135	812	65.0 (20–1150°C)	a–15.9 b–19.5
Kanthal DR	Fe-Cr-Al-Co Magnetic; low temperature coefficient (for resistors)	350	W	135	812	20.0 (−55°–150°C)	—
Kanthal DL	Fe-Cr-Al-Co High creep strength	1200	R	135	812	—	—
Alkrothal 14	Fe-Cr-Al	1050	W, R	125	750	—	—
Nikrothal 8	80Ni-20Cr	1150	W, S	108	650	—	—
Nikrothal 6	60Ni-16Cr Bal. Fe	980	W, S	112	675	—	—
Nikrothal L (low resistivity coefficient alloy)	75Ni-16Cr Si, Mn	250	W	133	800	20.0 (−50°–150°C)	—
Cuprothal 294	45Ni-55Cu	540	W	49	294	20–60	—
Cuprothal 180	22Ni-78Cu	540	W	30	180	180	—
Cuprothal 90	11Ni-89Cu	430	W	15	90	450	—
Cuprothal 60	6Ni-94Cu	315	W	10	60	800	—
Cuprothal 30	2Ni-98Cu	315	W	5	30	1400	—

[1] Courtesy of the Kanthal Corp., Stamford, Connecticut.
[2] Forms include: W–wire, R–ribbon, S–strip.
[3] A–microhm-cm^3; B–ohm-mil-ft.

ITEM	DENSITY (gm/cc)	THERMAL CONDUCTIVITY AT 20°C[5] (cgs)	MELTING POINT (°C)	TENSILE STRENGTH (PSI × 10^3)	YIELD POINT (PSI × 10^3)	BRINELL HARDNESS	ELONGATION IN 8-IN. LENGTH(%)	REDUCTION IN AREA
Kanthal A-1	7.1	0.045	1510	114–121	85–92	230–250	12–16	70
Kanthal A	7.15	0.045	1510	107–114	78–85	210–230	13–17	70
Kanthal D	7.25	0.045	1510	100–114	71–85	200–230	14–18	70
Kanthal DS	7.25	0.045	1510	114–121	80–92	230–250	12–16	70
Kanthal DR	—	—	1510	—	—	—	—	—
Kanthal DL	—	—	1510	—	—	—	—	—
Alkrothal 14	—	—	1510	—	—	—	—	—
Nikrothal 8	—	—	1400	—	—	—	—	—
Nikrothal 6	—	—	1343	—	—	—	—	—
Nikrothal L	—	—	1343	—	—	—	—	—
Cuprothal	—	—	1204	—	—	—	—	—
Cuprothal	—	—	1093	—	—	—	—	—
Cuprothal	—	—	1093	—	—	—	—	—
Cuprothal	—	—	1093	—	—	—	—	—
Cuprothal	—	—	1093	—	—	—	—	—

[4] Coefficient of linear expansion: a, 20° – 1000°C; b, 20° – 1100°C; c, 20° – 1200°C; d, 20° – 1300°C.

[5] See p. 520.

Typical Mechanical Properties—Grade II Kel-F Plastic

ASTM TEST METHOD	PROPERTY	TEMPERATURE (°F)	CRYSTALLINE	AMORPHOUS	UNIT	CALIPER (INCH)
D792-50	Specific gravity	77	2.1312	2.1047		0.064
D1430-58T	Zero strength time	482	250	248	seconds	0.062
	ZST clarity		translucent	transparent		
D638-56T	Tensile strength	77	4900	5070	psi	0.110
		77	5430	5650	psi	0.064
		158	3450	3020	psi	0.064
		258	530	525	psi	0.064
	Elongation	77	105	175	%	0.110
		77	125	190	%	0.064
		158	390	375	%	0.064
		258	>525	>450	%	0.064
	Yield point	77	5710	4650	psi	0.110
		77	5885	4920	psi	0.064
		158	2610	1400	psi	0.064
		258	530	290	psi	0.064
	Yield strength 0.2% offset	77	2660	1940	psi	0.110
		77	3620	2840	psi	0.064
		158	1320	770	psi	0.064
		258	270	110	psi	0.064
	Modulus of elasticity (tensile)	77	186×10^3	162×10^3	psi	0.110
		77	185×10^3	153×10^3	psi	0.064
		158	83×10^3	58×10^3	psi	0.064
		258	15×10^3	5.4×10^3	psi	0.064

D790-59T	Flexural strength	77	10,700	7810	psi	0.112
		158	4950	2355	psi	0.112
		258	1650	686	psi	0.112
	Modulus of elasticity	77	254×10^3	190×10^3	psi	0.112
	flexure	158	149×10^3	54×10^3	psi	0.112
		258	32×10^3	13×10^3	psi	0.112
	compressive	77	180×10^3		psi	0.495
D695-54	Compressive yield strength 0.2% offset	77	5440		psi	0.495
D732-46	Shear strength	77	5440	6010	psi	0.066
D621-59	Deformation under load 24 hrs/1000 psi	77	0.20	0.37	%	
		158	0.40	7.32	%	
		258	3.57	>25.00	%	
D648-56	Heat deflection					
	66 psi	265			°F	
	264 psi	167			°F	
D256-56	Impact strength, Izod	77	3.1	7.3	ft/lbs/in notch	
	Hardness	77				
D1474-57T	Knoop		10.7	8.2	KNP	0.062
D1706-59T	Durometer		78	74	Shore D	0.062
D785-51	Rockwell		85	80	S scale	0.110
Taber	Abrasion resistance kg load-loss/1000 cycle	77	0.013	0.011	grams	

(Continued)

TYPICAL MECHANICAL PROPERTIES—GRADE II KEL-F PLASTIC (*Continued*)

ASTM TEST METHOD	PROPERTY	TEMPERATURE (°F)	CRYSTALLINE	AMORPHOUS	UNIT	CALIPER (INCH)
Taber	Coefficient of friction					
	on aluminum—static		0.23	0.23		
	—kinetic		0.18	0.15		
	on Mylar —static		0.30	0.27		
	—kinetic		0.24	0.25		
	on Kel-F —static		0.33	0.36		
	(amorphous) —kinetic		0.27	0.34		
	Useful temperature range	−400 to +400°F				
	Thermal conductivity		6.32×10^{-4}	6.12×10^{-4}	cgs	
			1.83	1.78	(Btu/ft^2-sec)/(°F/in)	
D696-44	Coefficient of linear expansion					
	Below T_g*		4.8×10^{-5}		in/in/°F	
	Above T_g		15×10^{-5}			
D635-56T	Flammability		Nonflammable			
	Mold shrinkage		0.005–0.010		in/in	
D1182-54	Apparent density					
	powder		16.1		gm/in^3	
			61.5		lb/ft^3	
	Pellets		20.3		gm/in^3	
			77.3		lb/ft^3	

* T_g varies from 125°F to 140°F.

TYPICAL MECHANICAL PROPERTIES—GRADE III KEL-F PLASTIC

ASTM TEST METHOD	PROPERTY	TEMPERATURE (°F)	CRYSTALLINE	AMORPHOUS	UNIT	CALIPER (INCH)
D792-50	Specific gravity	77	2.124	2.107		0.064
D1430-58T	Zero strength time	482	370	375	Seconds	0.062
	ZST clarity		translucent	transparent		
D638-56T	Tensile strength	77	4630	4650	psi	0.110
		77	5200	5260	psi	0.064
		158	3550	2900	psi	0.064
		258	540	575	psi	0.064
	Elongation	77	120	160	%	0.110
		77	125	180	%	0.064
		158	330	330	%	0.064
		258	>400	>400	%	0.064
	Yield point	77	5200	4800	psi	0.110
		77	5300	4700	psi	0.064
		158	2700	1600	psi	0.064
		258	560	340	psi	0.064
	Yield strength	77	2450	2000	psi	0.110
	0.2% offset	77	3350	2600	psi	0.064
		158	1600	1100	psi	0.064
		258	350	180	psi	0.064
	Modulus of elasticity	77	190×10^3	157×10^3	psi	0.110
	tensile	77	190×10^3	160×10^3	psi	0.064
		158	97×10^3	55×10^3	psi	0.064
		258	20×10^3	6×10^3	psi	0.064

(Continued)

Typical Mechanical Properties—Grade III Kel–F Plastic (*Continued*)

ASTM TEST METHOD	PROPERTY	TEMPERATURE (°F)	CRYSTALLINE	AMORPHOUS	UNIT	CALIPER (INCH)
	flexural	77	238×10^3	185×10^3	psi	0.110
		158	133×10^3	79×10^3	psi	0.110
		258	37×10^3	15×10^3	psi	0.110
	compressive	77	170×10^3		psi	0.500
D790-59T	Flexural strength	77	9600	8600	psi	0.110
		158	5070	3150	psi	0.110
		258	1700	700	psi	0.110
D695-54	Compressive yield strength, 0.2% offset	77	5500		psi	0.500
D732-46	Shear strength	77	5400	5600	psi	0.064
D621-59	Deformation under load, 24 hr/1000 psi	77	0.20	0.40	%	
		158	0.40	7.12	%	
		258	4.00	>25.00	%	
D648-56	Heat deflection					
	66 psi		258		°F	
	264 psi		167		°F	
D256-56	Impact strength (Izod)				ft·lb per in. of notch	
	Hardness		3.01	5.10		
D1474-57T	Knoop		10.9	7.5	KNP	
D1706-59T	Durometer		79	76	Shore D	
D785-51	Rockwell S		84	79	S scale	
	Rockwell R		110	108	R scale	
	Specific heat		0.2		gm-cal/gm/°C	

ELECTRICAL PROPERTIES—GRADE III KEL-F PLASTICS

ASTM TEST METHOD	PROPERTY	TEMPERATURE (°F)	CRYSTALLINE	AMORPHOUS
D150-54T	Dielectric constant 10^2—10^5 cps, $\frac{1}{16}$ inch section	77–392	2.41–2.74	2.34–2.82
D150-54T	Dissipation factor 10^2—10^5 cps, $\frac{1}{16}$ inch section	77–392	0.0004–0.0617[1]	0.0007–0.0399[1]
D149-59	Dielectric strength, volt/mil $\frac{1}{16}$ inch section short time, oil bath, 2 inch electrodes	77	495	1010
	Step-by-step 1000 volt/mil $\frac{1}{16}$ inch second	77	431	510
D257-58	Electrical resistivity (vol/ohm-cm)			
	50% relative humidity	77	2.5×10^{16}	4×10^{16}
	0% relative humidity	70	—	7.5×10^{16}
	Surface resistivity	77	5×10^{15} ohms	$>10^{18}$ ohms
D495-58T	Arc resistance, seconds $\frac{1}{16}$ inch section	77	360	>360

[1] The higher values are generally at the higher temperatures and the lower frequencies

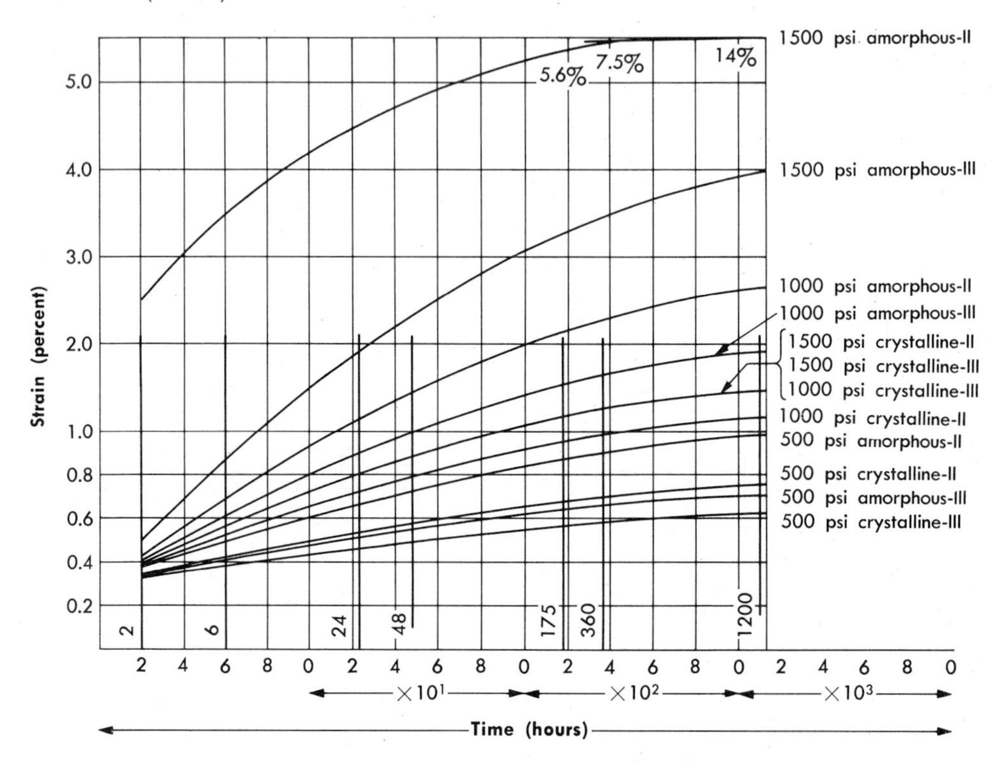

FIG. 83. Creep curves for Kel-F 81 plastic. Crystalline (air-cooled) and amorphous (water-quenched) resins at 82°F. Dumbbells 0.010 inch thick. Gauge marks 0.50 inch.

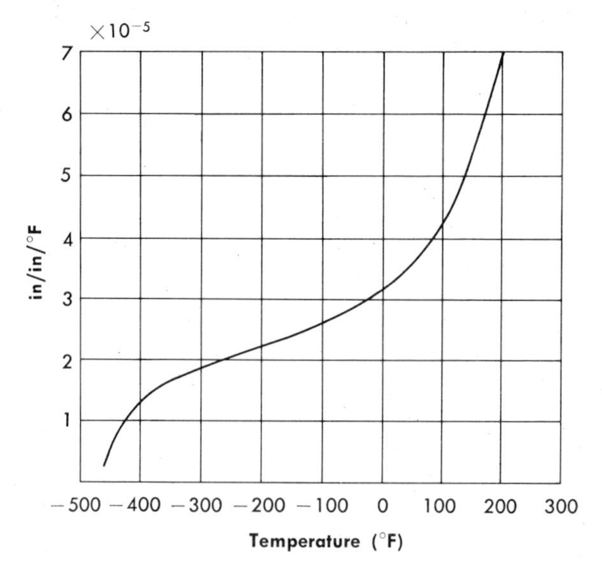

FIG. 84. Coefficient of linear thermal expansion versus temperature for Kel-F 81 brand plastic.

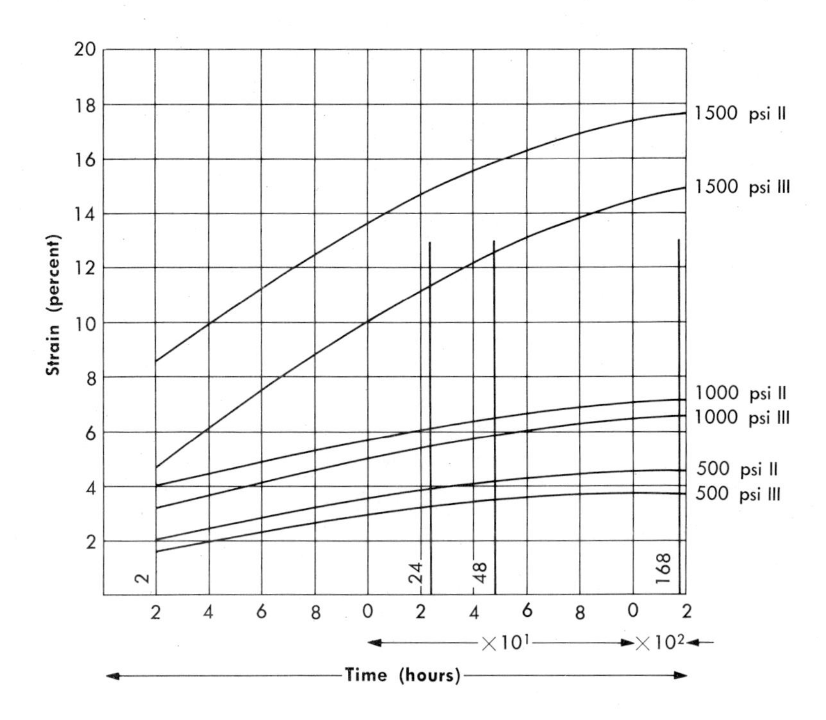

FIG. 85. Creep curves for crystalline (air-cooled) Kel-F 81 plastic at 158°F. Dumbbells 0.010 inch thick. Gauge marks 0.50 inch.

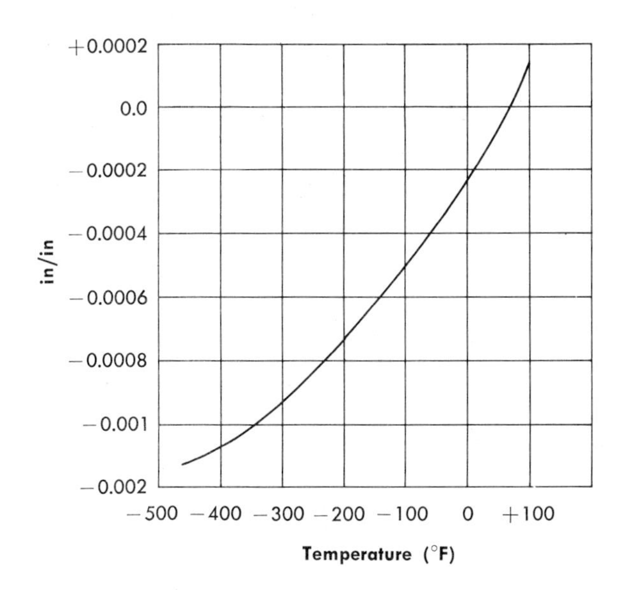

FIG. 86. Thermal linear expansion of Kel-F 81 brand plastic versus temperature.

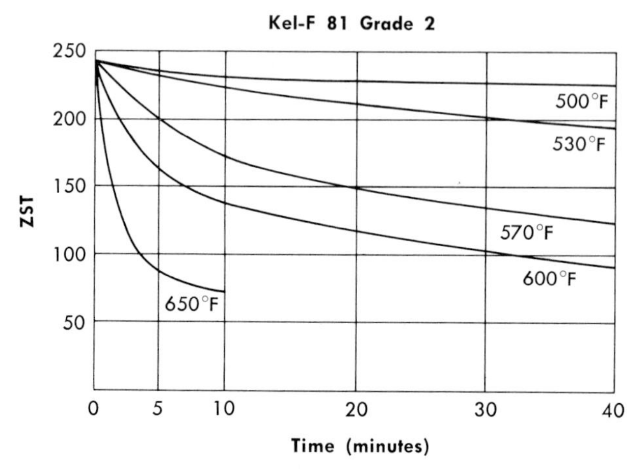

FIG. 87. Zero-strength time versus time and temperature for Kel-F 81 brand plastic.

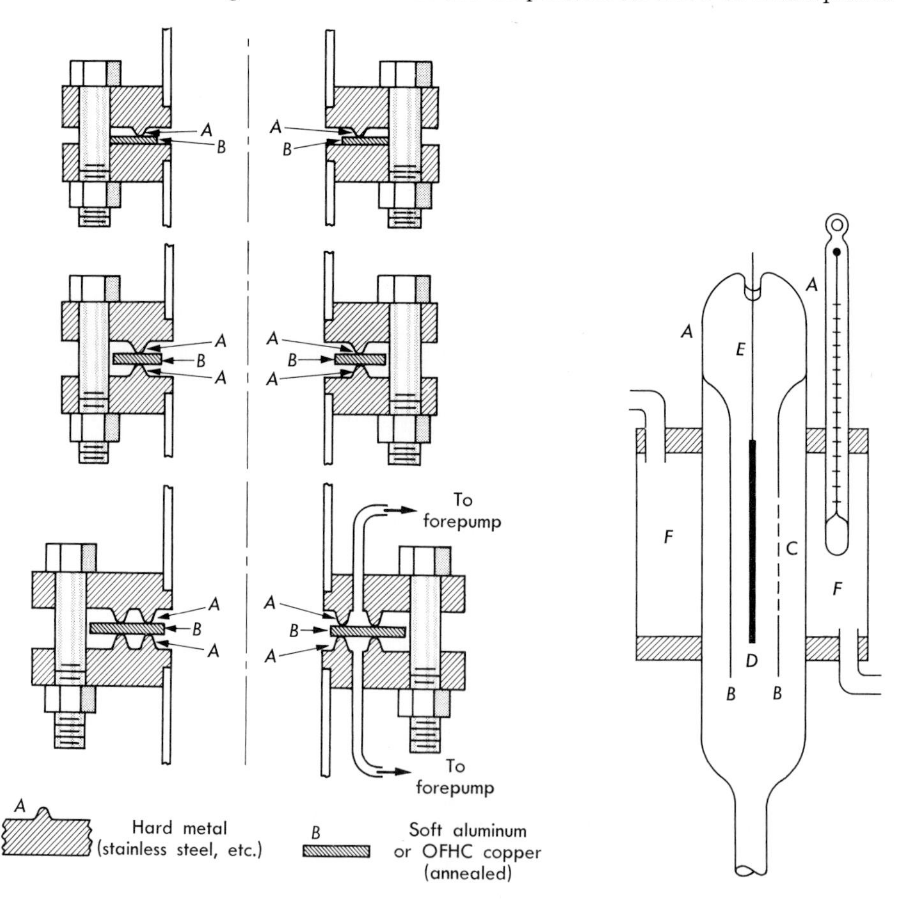

FIG. 88. Three types of knife-edge vacuum seal with metal gasket.

FIG. 89. Knudsen gauge.

bolted together. Various modifications of this type of seal have been suggested.[1, 2, 3] In both the step-seal and the knife-edge seal, the gaskets are expendable and can usually be used only once. But in general these seals have the advantage that they can be baked out and/or used at higher temperatures (e.g., for ultrahigh vacuum applications) than would be permissible with O-ring or plastic seals.

Knudsen gauge. This vacuum gauge is based on the principle that molecular motion exerts a mechanical force between two surfaces which are at different temperatures, provided that the separation between the two surfaces is less than the mean free path, i.e., that the pressure is low enough (below atmospheric) so that molecular motion can achieve sufficient kinetic energy. The molecules striking the hotter surface will rebound with a higher kinetic energy than those striking the cooler surface.

The familiar *radiometer* is an illustration of this principle, in which heat from the source of light is absorbed by the blackened surfaces (of the vanes) which are thus at a higher temperature than the unblackened surfaces and the walls of the bulb. Molecules of the residual gas in the bulb will thus exert a greater reactive push against the blackened side of the vanes, and the rotor will turn.

This phenomenon consequently depends on the number of molecules present; at very low pressures there are not enough molecules to exert sufficient force to move the vanes, and at high pressures the molecules are too crowded to move about freely.

A simple type of Knudsen gauge is shown in Fig. 89. *AA*—glass tube about 1.4 cm diameter, *BB*—narrower tube with rectangular piece cut out at *C,* 0.41 cm wide by 2.95 cm long, *D*—piece of mica suspended in front of opening *C, E*—fiber attached to mica piece, *FF*—a heating waterjacket. As the temperature of the water in *FF* is raised, the mica plate *D* is repelled by the "hot" molecules traveling through the opening *C,* and the amount of deflection can be observed by means of a microscope. (See references below.) Since all the parameters of such a gauge can be measured directly, the device is essentially an *absolute manometer,* without the necessity of calibration against another gauge. It can also be shown that the indications of this gauge are independent of the nature of the gas to be measured.

Bibliography

M. Knudsen, *Ann. Physik,* **32,** 809, 1910.
G. D. West, *Proc. Phys. Soc.* (London), **25,** 324, 1912–13.
G. D. West, *ibid.,* **28,** 259, 1915–16.
G. D. West, *ibid.,* **31,** 278, 1918–19.
G. D. West, *ibid.,* **32,** 122, 166, 1919–20.
M. Knudsen, *Ann. Physik,* **44,** 525, 1914.
E. von Angerer, *ibid.,* **41,** 1, 1913.
J. W. Woodrow, *Phys. Rev.,* **4,** 491, 1914.
J. E. Shrader and R. G. Sherwood, *ibid.,* **12,** 70, 1918.
L. F. Richardson, *Proc. Phys. Soc.* (London), **31,** 270, 1918–19.
H. Riegger, *Z. tech. Physik,* **1,** 16, 1920.
E. Fredlund, *Ann. Physik,* **13,** 802, 1932.

---

[1] M. J. Higatsberger and W. W. Erbe, *Rev. Sci. Instr.,* **27,** 110, 1956.
[2] G. W. Hees, W. Eaton, and J. Lech, *Vacuum* (Br), **IV,** 438, 1954.
[3] R. Carpenter, *J. Sci. Instr.* (Br.), **39,** 533, 1962.

E. Fredlund, *ibid.*, **14**, 617, 1932.
E. Fredlund, *ibid.*, **30**, 99, 1937.
J. W. M. DuMond and W. M. Pickels, Jr., *Rev. Sci. Instr.*, **6**, 362, 1935.
A. E. Lockenvitz, *ibid.*, **9**, 417, 1938.
A. L. Hughes, *ibid.*, **8**, 409, 1937.
H. Klumb and H. Schwarz, *Z. Physik*, **122**, 418, 1944.
W. Gaede, *Z. tech. Physik*, **15**, 664, 1934.
E. Brüche and W. Littwin, *Z. Physik*, **52**, 318, 1928.
G. Spiwak, *ibid.*, **77**, 123, 1932.
W. Steckelmacher, *Vacuum*, **1**, 266, 1951.
C. N. W. Litting and W. K. Taylow, *Proc. Inst. Elec. Engrs.* (London), Pt. IV, **99**, 241, 1952.
H. G. Jensen, *Vacuum*, **2**, 388, 1952.
H. Schwarz, *Bull. Am. Phys. Soc.*, Ser. II, **4**, 221, 1959.
H. Schwarz, *Rev. Sci. Instr.*, **31**, 433, 1960.

Kovar.[1] An iron-nickel-cobalt alloy widely used for making glass-to-metal vacuum-tight seals. Its thermal expansion curve closely matches that of several hard glasses (see p. 58), and it suitable for making seals for use at baking temperatures up to 450°C.

The properties, uses, and methods of application and fabrication of Kovar alloy are described below.

Kovar is available in the form of sheet, wire, bars, tubing, forged and drawn cups, and shapes of various kinds. Ready-made Kovar-glass seals and feedthroughs in a wide variety of types are also available.

Chemical composition:

Nickel	29% (nom.)
Cobalt	17% (nom.)
Iron	Remainder
Manganese	0.50% (max.)
Silicon	0.20% (max.)
Carbon	0.06% (max.)
Aluminum	0.10% (max.)
Magnesium	0.10% (max.)
Zirconium	0.10% (max.)
Titanium	0.10% (max.)

The total of aluminum, magnesium, zirconium, and titanium shall not exceed 0.20%.

Physical constants:

Density	0.302 lb/in^3
Annealed temper (Rockwell hardness)	B82 (max.)
Cold-worked temper (Rockwell hardness)	B100 (max.)

Thermal properties:

Melting point	1450°C

[1] All the data on Kovar alloy are reproduced with permission of the Carborundum Company.

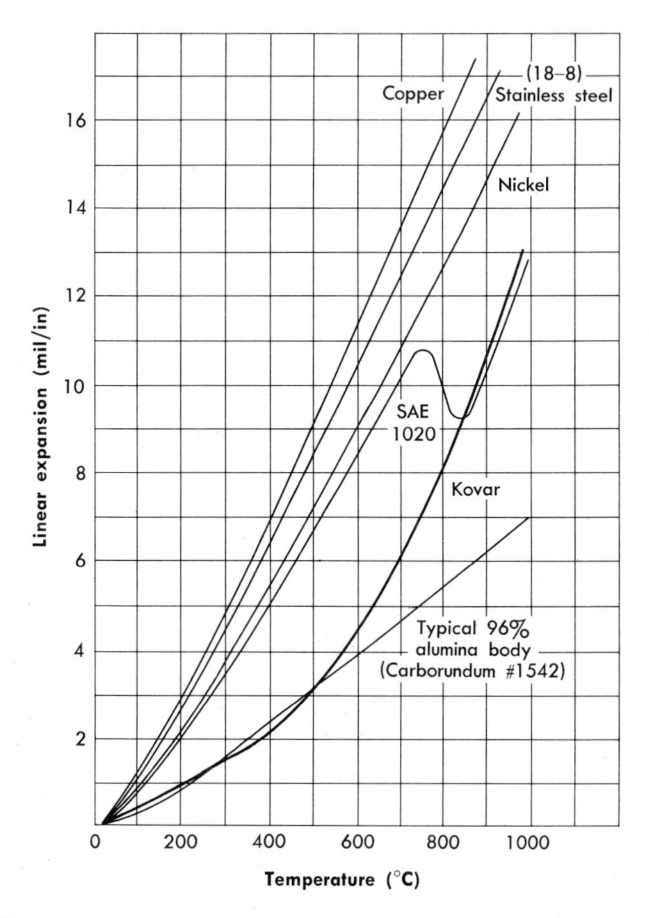

FIG. 90. Expansion of Kovar (after annealing in hydrogen for one hour at 900°C and for 15 minutes at 1100°C) compared with other materials.

Thermal expansion. See curves in Figs. 90, 91

Thermal conductivity (cgs)

30°C	0.0395 (determined)*
300°C	0.0485 (calculated)
400°C	0.053 (calculated)
500°C	0.0585 (calculated)

Curie point	435°C
Specific heat (gm-cal/gm/°C at 0°C)	0.105
(gm-cal/gm/°C at 430°C)	0.155
Heat of fusion (cal/gm)	64
Vapor pressure (microns at 1000°C)	10^{-2}
Transformation point (gamma to alpha phase)	below −80°C

* A plot of these values yields a curve which is almost parallel to the curve for stainless steel.

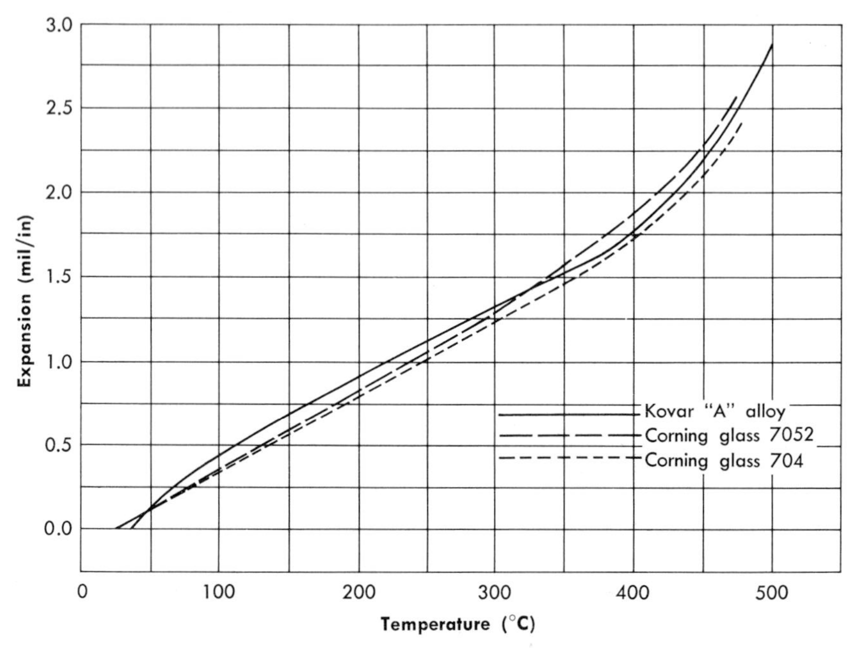

FIG. 91. Expansion of Kovar compared with two hard glasses.

Electrical properties:

Specific resistance at 25°C .... 49 microhms-cm (294 ohms-mil-ft)

Temperature (°C)	Relative resistivity
25	1.0
100	1.28
200	1.64
400	2.19
600	2.38

Magnetic properties:

Magnetic permeability	Flux density (gausses)
1000	500
2000	2000
3700	7000 (max. value)
2280	12000
213	17000

Magnetic losses (watts/lb)

Thickness	10 kilogausses 60 cycles/sec	10 kilogausses 840 cycles/sec	2 kilogausses 5000 cycles/sec	2 kilogausses 10,000 cycles/sec
0.010	1.05	23.4	16.6	41.0
0.030	1.51			
0.050	2.77			

Note: The values of the various properties are to be considered as nominal except where limits are shown.

KOVAR-GLASS SEALING PROCEDURE (FOR ELECTRON TUBES)

The recommendations given refer particularly to electron tube construction. For less critical applications the procedure may be altered to meet less exacting conditions.

I. *Preparation of metal surface*
   A. On edge-type seals, the edge should be rounded by metal removal with a radius equal to approximately one-half the metal thickness.
      Machine lubricants to be noncorrosive mineral-oil-base capable of being completely removed by trichlorethylene degreasing.
   B. Polish sealing surface with 100-grit aluminum oxide (Aloxite) abrasive cloth, followed by 180-grit to remove all scratches, tool marks, etc.
      1. Emery cloth and other abrasives containing carbides must be avoided.
      2. Centerless ground rod requires no additional polishing.
      3. For best oxide adherence, avoid highly polished sealing surfaces.
   C. On butt-type seals, instead of cloth polishing, it is preferable to have a matte finish, as resulting from sand blasting using pure alumina (silica sand is to be avoided).
      The metal surface which will be enveloped by glass should be clean and free from longitudinal die marks, scratches, and similar imperfections. Slight circular marks put in by grinding or polishing are not considered objectionable.

II. *Preparation of glass* (typical sealing glasses for Kovar are Corning 7052 or 7056)
   A. Remove dust by wiping with lint-free cloth.
   B. Rinse in 10 percent (by volume) hydrofluoric acid solution (with wetting agent).
   C. Rinse in running tap water.
   D. Rinse in distilled water.
   E. Dip in methanol and hot air dry.

III. *Processing Kovar alloy prior to glass sealing*
   A. Vapor-degrease in trichlorethylene.
   B. Immerse for one to three minutes in concentrated hydrochloric acid without inhibitor heated to about 80°C. (Optionally followed by rinse in alkali solution.)
   C. Rinse thoroughly in cold running water for five minutes, followed by immersion in distilled water.
   D. Dip in methanol and dry in hot air blast.
   E. Furnace heat-treat in wet hydrogen atmosphere one hour at 900°C or 30 minutes at 1000°C. Hydrogen to be saturated by passing through water-bubbling bottle at room temperature.
   F. Store in lint-free containers (bell-jar or wrap in polyethylene bags).
   G. Precautions.
      1. Sealing surface of cleaned parts not to be touched by bare hands.
      2. Processing of metal parts to be done as soon as practical before glass sealing.

IV. *Glass sealing*

A. Equipment.

1. Burner preferably using gas-oxygen flame (gas and air or hydrogen and air combinations may be used, either of which are harder to adjust to required hard-sharp oxidizing flame than the preferred gas-oxygen flame).
2. Glass lathe.

B. Heat metal and glass parts to approximately 850°C (dull red heat) in air to develop oxidized surface and bring parts together by pressure.
Before glassing, the oxide should be just thick enough to obscure all metallic reflection. (See note at bottom of p. 331.)

C. Glass to be worked so that the meeting of the edge with the Kovar approaches a 90° angle. (Feather-edging of the glass and glass having a re-entrant angle both result in mechanically weak seals.)

D. Flame-anneal seal.

E. Furnace-program anneal for large seals.

1. Advance to annealing temperature for 30 minutes.
2. Reduce temperature to 50°C below strain point at approximately 1°C per minute.
3. Strain point to room temperature at approximately 10°C per minute. (*Note:* Small seals may be flame-annealed by smoky flame instead of program-annealed.)

For high-quantity production, the glass sealing operation may be done by automatic stem machine, induction heating, or neutral atmosphere furnace. Preoxidized metal parts are generally used on the latter two methods. A typical cycle for preoxidation is heating for three minutes at 900°C in an electric furnace with air atmosphere. The cycle must be varied according to furnace-heating capacity and humidity conditions.

V. *Inspection*

A. Seal to have desired stress condition as determined by polariscope viewing or by other stress analysis method.

B. The color of the seal depends upon the grade of glass and thickness of the oxide. A general color description is:

1. Light gray for 7052 glass.
2. Mouse brown for 7040 glass.
3. Dark gray-black for 7056 glass.

C. A shiny appearance indicates insufficient oxide and an extremely black surface indicates excessive oxidation. The ideal condition is just sufficient oxide to obscure metallic appearance.

D. Examination under 10- to 15-power magnification will show freedom from a string or excessively large group of bubbles entrapped in the glass.

E. Transformation test: wrap seal in tissue paper and immerse in dry ice and acetone mixture (−80°C) for 30 minutes.

1. Adequate paper wrapping is required to allow for difference in thermal conductivities of metal and glass.
2. After the sample is allowed to cool to room temperature, no cracks in the glass should be visible under 7- to 10-power magnification.

VI. *Oxide removal*

A. Vapor-degrease in trichlorethylene (if parts are greasy).

B. Immerse parts for one minute (longer if heavily oxidized) in concentrated hydrochloric acid at 80° to 85°C.

C. Rinse.

1. Running hot water—30 seconds.
2. Cold concentrated HCl—5 to 10 seconds.
3. Running cold water—3 minutes.
4. Rinse in distilled water.
5. Dip in acetone and air-dry.

MACHINING OF KOVAR ALLOY

Kovar machines readily at slow speeds with high-speed or tungsten-carbide tools when properly lubricated.

Feed

Use same rules as normally applied to Monel Alloy R-405. With carbide tools, satisfactory results are obtained at 155–225 SFM, 0.005 inches per revolution feed, and depth of cut 0.010 inch.

Lubricant

Lard oil or commercial coolant, such as Socony Mobil Oil Company's Vacmul N-5 (4 to 7% sulfur) or Union Carbide Company's UCON-660 or Fiske Refining Company's S-277 (sulfur-free mineral oil). (*Cf.* CUTTING OILS, p. 222.)

Tools

High-speed material, such as Rex-95.

Tungsten carbide, such as Kennametal Grade K-6 or K-3H.

Tool clearance

Side clearance angle	10°–12°
Front clearance angle	8°
Back rake angle	2°–14°
Side rake angle	12°–14°

These angles are typical but vary considerably with conditions of each individual job.

DEEP-DRAWING OF KOVAR ALLOY

Special care must be used to ensure the highest quality drawn shapes. Some of the major factors to observe follow:

1. Tooling should be designed to prevent overstressing the metal.
   (a) Keep hold-down pressures to a minimum to ensure metal flow from the outside rather than stretching.
   (b) Open-end eyelets should be cupped with a closed end before final piercing.
   (c) On the initial draw, punch radius should be a minimum of four times material thickness. Reduce successively on redraws.
   (d) On the initial draw tools, the difference between die and punch diameter should be three times the thickness of the material.
   (e) Radius on the final draw should be not less than material thickness. Sharper radii should be made by a subsequent coining operation.
2. Scratches and tool marks.
   (a) On large parts, all defects must be removable by light polishing with 180-grit Aloxite aluminum oxide abrasive cloth.
   (b) Surface defects of small parts must be removable by a nominal amount of tumbling.

Design of formed parts

1. Inside radii at the corners should be not less than the thickness of the metal to avoid the expense of coining sharper radii.
2. To prolong tool life, allow as great a tolerance on all dimensions as will satisfy the requirements of the assembly and function of the part.
3. On diameters, apply tolerances to either OD or ID, whichever is the more important. Close tolerances on both OD and ID require an additional "ironing" operation which thins out the wall.
4. In the deep-drawing of a flanged cup or eyelet, the metal thickens at the flange under ideal conditions of free metal flow. Consequently, plus tolerance on flange thickness should be greater than initial metal tolerance. For example, a typical eyelet made from 0.010 inch ± 0.0005-inch strip could have a flange thickness of 0.011 inch ± 0.001 inch measured after burr removal.
5. On pierced holes, specify whether piercing is from outside or inside so that any objectionable burrs will not develop on a critical surface.

Drawability

Kovar is easily deep-drawn in conventional presses. In general, normal rules pertaining to mild steel apply.

Sheet and strip are furnished fully annealed as a final operation, with nominal values (at room temperature) listed below:

0.5% yield strength	59,500
Ultimate strength	77,500
Breaking strength	44,000
Uniform elongation	16.8%
Total elongation	35.4%
Reduction of area	69.0%
Temper (Rockwell)	B82 max.

The recommended rule for deep-drawing Kovar on a double action press is as follows:

	Maximum reduction
Initial draw	45%
First redraw	25%
Subsequent redraws	20%
Subsequent redraws on annealed cups	25%

Note: The percentages of reduction are to be calculated on mean cup diameter (average of OD and ID).

Example:

	Diameter
Blank	1.0 inch
Initial draw	0.55 inch
First redraw	0.30 inch
Second redraw	0.24 inch
Anneal third redraw	0.18 inch

The percentage of reduction also depends on the type of press. For example, Kovar parts have been made in one operation on a Hydroform press, whereas three operations were required on a toggle-type press.

Lubricants

In general, any sulfur-free drawing compound or lubricant applicable to the particular part may be used provided that all traces of the lubricant are completely removable by conventional trichlorethylene degreasers.

For electron tube parts, extreme care must be taken in selection of lubricants, for any contaminants that remain after degreasing might lead to gas formation on subsequent reheatings. Many electron tube manufacturers establish their own approved list of lubricants.

Some of the generally approved lubricants (*cf.* CUTTING OILS, p. 222) are

Sulfur-free mineral oil (Fiske S-277)
Lard oil
Chlorinated paraffin-base mineral oil (Internation Chemical Co. No. 1211)
Castor oil
International Chemical #484 (heavy work)
International Chemical #1093 (light work)
Water-soluble paste (W. L. Spencer Draw-Soluble 501)
Water-soluble compound (Brooks Oil Co., Grade OW)
Houghton Steel Draw #40

Cleaning and tumbling

Cleaning procedures naturally vary with type of lubricant used. It is essential that cleaning and drying be thorough. Any remaining oils and rust preventives should be of compositions that can be removed by degreasing equipment.

Tumbling and polishing abrasives should preferably be aluminum oxide. Avoid the use of emery and other abrasives containing carbonaceous or other materials that might lead to gas. For example, silica sand is objectionable for electron tubes.

Annealing for redraws

As the result of drawing operations, Kovar work hardens to about the same extent as mild steel. Most commonly used Kovar shapes can be drawn without intermitten anneals. The need for annealing is indicated by the following guides:

1. Cylindrical cups in which the length is less than twice the diameter can be made without anneal.
2. Small parts produced on high-speed presses, such as eyelet machines, can be made with a greater ratio than above, due to heat generated during forming. (For example, a Kovar eyelet 0.250 inch body diameter with a length of 0.538 inch and flange diameter of 0.438 inch is produced regularly without anneal.)
3. Large cups with close diameter tolerances are sometimes annealed before the final sizing operation to minimize stresses that might cause distortion when subjected to final anneal.
4. Cups having a coined projection on the flange often require an anneal before the flattening operation when the body diameter size approaches the length dimension. Deep drawing obviously introduces greatest stress at the open or flanged end.

Annealing

1. Wash and degrease parts.
2. Anneal in an atmosphere-controlled furnace (atmosphere may be wet or dry, hydrogen, dissociated ammonia, cracked gas, or similar neutral atmosphere).
3. Annealing temperature is not critical. Complete stress relief is obtained in the range of 700°C (1292°F) to 1100°C (2012°F) held for a minimum of 15 minutes after the parts have attained the temperature of the hot zone, and then placed in the cooling zone before exposure to air. A typical schedule follows:
   (a) Hold at 870°C (1600°F) for 20 minutes.
   (b) Place in cooling zone for one-half hour, or until the parts are at less than 180°C (350°F) before removal to the air.

It will be understood that the foregoing intermediate annealing procedure is distinct from heat treatment for cleaning, strain relief, and degassing just prior to glass sealing. The latter should be done in a wet hydrogen atmosphere for a longer period, such as 1000°C for 30 minutes.

Spinning

Many of the rules and precautions outlined for deep-drawing apply to spinning, a fabrication method that requires greater care due to introduction of severe stresses that may lead to fracture. Spinning should be done with very gradual reductions and with frequent anneals to remove the work-hardening effects.

Spinning involves lower tooling costs than fabrication in presses and, therefore, is used extensively for development models or for large-size pieces with limited production quantities.

JOINING KOVAR ALLOY TO OTHER METALS—BRAZING, WELDING, SOLDERING

Kovar may be readily welded, brazed, or soldered to other metals, but certain precautions must be observed to meet the following conditions:

1. For high-vacuum applications it is essential that fluxes be avoided and that no brazing alloy be used that contains a high vapor-pressure constituent, such as cadmium, zinc, or lead.
2. Brazed and welded joints must be designed and processed to take into consideration the fact that Kovar alloy has a considerably lower thermal expansivity than most other metals to which it is joined.
3. Different processing methods must be employed on similar types of joints, depending on whether the joint is made before or after the glass-sealing operation.
4. Uniform heating methods are preferred to minimize thermal stresses which may lead to fracture, especially when joining dissimilar metals.
5. Kovar has low thermal conductivity (see p. 522) which permits making a welded or brazed joint closer to Kovar-glass or Kovar-ceramic seals than is possible on other types of seals.
6. Kovar, in common with other metals, must be chemically clean before joining to other metals. See p. 337.

The information that follows is intended to supplement standard practice and published data on the general techniques of joining metals, emphasizing some of the special points to be observed, due primarily to the lower thermal expansion of Kovar alloy and the fact that most end-use applications require vacuum-tightness.

Definitions

Intergranular penetration is a condition in which the grain boundary rather than the grain of metal is penetrated by some element, such as oxygen, carbon, sulfur, etc.

Stress corrosion is also penetration of the grain boundary, but usually by a liquid and only when applied or residual stresses are present in the metal.

Wetting is the ability of molten metal to adhere to the surface of a material in the solid state and to make a strong bond when cooled.

Flow is the property of the brazing alloy which determines the distance it will travel by capillary attraction from its original position.

Preferred joining materials and methods

A joint with Kovar must meet the following conditions:

1. The brazing material must not be injurious to the operation of the device.
2. The method of joining should not disturb the equilibrium of prior joints or induce appreciable tensional stress on either glass or ceramic insulation.
3. The joint must be capable of withstanding the temperature of subsequent thermal conditions.
4. The cost of brazing material and equipment availability must be compatible with end product and reliability requirements.

Listed below, *in order of preference,* are recommended filler materials and methods. Final selection is determined by considering the factors listed above and other particular existing conditions.

Kovar alloy to copper

	Temperature °C	
	Melting point	Flow point
1. 30% gold, 70% copper	1015	1035
2. 35% gold, 65% copper	1000	1020
3. 18% nickel, 82% gold	950	950
4. 3% nickel, 15.5% copper, 81.5% gold	900	910
5. 28% copper, 72% silver	780	780

Kovar alloy to Kovar, steel, or nickel

1. OFHC copper

2–6. See items 1 through 5 above

7. Resistance-welding (projection type)
8. Inert-gas shielded-arc welding

Note: A method for sealing *unoxidized* Kovar and other metals to Corning glasses (for alkali-vapor tubes) is described by F. E. Gifford and A. Dolenga in *Rev. Sci. Instr.*, **35**, 591, 1964.

Kovar alloy to metallized ceramics

1. OFHC copper
2. 30% gold, 70% copper
3. 28% copper, 72% silver (except for certain types of electron tubes because of high vapor pressure)

Soft soldering

For applications involving low operating temperatures and limited to devices not affected by high vapor pressure constituents of soft solders.

	Maximum operating temperatures °F
1. 63% tin, 37% lead	350
2. 16% tin, 32% lead, 52% bismuth	200
3. 97.5% lead, 2.5% silver	550

Reference notes

(a) See below for comments on specific joining methods.
(b) For more complete listing of brazing alloys, see the table on pp. 175 *et seq.*
(c) Other methods of joining Kovar are in the development stage at this writing. In this category of promising utility are gold welding, ultrasonic welding, and electron-beam welding.

Design of joints with Kovar

The details of good designs of brazed and welded joints are covered by a vast amount of literature, such as *Brazing Manual,* prepared by Committee on Brazing of American Welding Society and published by Reinhold Publishing Company, as well as by manufacturers of brazing alloys and manufacturers of welding equipment.

In addition to incorporating the general principles of good design, the following factors require special attention when Kovar is involved.

1. Tensional stresses on Kovar at brazing temperatures are to be avoided.
2. Compression joints are preferable (higher expansion member on the outside).
3. Adequate clearance between metal members, especially if higher expansion material is on the inside. (See *Clearance in Brazed Joints.*)
4. Brazing alloy selected to have good "wettability" on Kovar.
5. Brazing alloy on the primary joint to have sufficiently high melting point so that this original joint does not deform and introduce thermal stresses due to the heating operations of secondary brazes or other thermal cycles which may be introduced.
6. Joint must be designed to permit a method of uniform heat application such as furnace or RF coil.
7. When Kovar is on the outside of a higher expansion member, tapering of the Kovar cross section at the joint minimizes transmittal of expansion effects to the glass or ceramic seal.
8. When conditions permit, copper brazing is generally preferred to any other type of joining. (The uniform high temperature ensures stress relief, and the technique is less critical than welding.)

9. Butt-type joints are to be avoided whenever possible.
10. Ceramic jigs are preferred over carbon because of greater wear resistance, longer furnace life, and freedom from contamination on the brazing surface.

Clearance in brazed joints

1. When joining Kovar to Kovar or with Kovar on the inside of higher expansion metal, the maximum diameter clearance should be
   (a) 0.002 inch for copper brazing,
   (b) 0.003 inch for lower melting brazes.
2. When a *furnace*-brazed joint has Kovar on the outside of a higher expansion member, use the following formula for the minimum diameter clearance:

$$D(E_1 - E_2) + 0.003''.$$

D is Diameter of joint in inches.
E_1 is actual expansion in in/in of higher expansivity member from room temperature to brazing temperature.
E_2 is same for Kovar alloy (see expansion curve).

Example: To find minimum clearance for a 2-inch-diameter joint with Kovar on outside of copper, using 72% silver, 28% copper (eutectic) brazing alloy (780°C) *in a furnace:*
Clearance $= 2 \times (0.0152 - 0.0077) + 0.003$
$= 0.018$ inch (minimum clearance between diameters)

3. A high-frequency coil (eddy-current concentrator)[1] can be used to apply the heat to the joint area for a very short time, thereby permitting smaller clearance between the parts.
   The calculations of clearance for this type of heating are very complex, due to the variables of coil design, magnitude of current and time, thermal conductivities of the different metals, etc. Consequently, the optimum clearance should be determined experimentally, possibly starting with a clearance 10 percent less than the value calculated for furnace brazing.
4. Tolerances on the matching metal pieces must be held rather close to prevent either too much clearance, which would weaken the joint, or too little clearance, which introduces tensile stresses when the higher expansion member is on the inside of the assembly.
   When assigning tolerances to the metal parts, consideration should be given to the possibility that one part might have the maximum-plus tolerance and the other part the minimum-plus value. Generally, a plus or minus 0.001-inch tolerance on both metal parts will not introduce injurious effects.

Brazing of Kovar alloy

1. Selection of brazing filler materials
   Supplementing the information given in the section, *Preferred Joining Materials and methods,* the following should be considered:
   (a) Successful joints can be made with Kovar, using silver-brazing alloys, provided that certain precautions are taken.

---

[1] See page 222.

(b) Brazing with OFHC copper is preferred whenever conditions permit.

(c) Gold-brazing alloys are used in preference to silver alloys, when subsequent thermal exposure requires the higher melting point, or to secure more thorough relief of induced stress by the higher brazing temperature of the gold alloys.

2. Silver-brazing alloys

To understand the precautions that must be observed when silver-brazing to Kovar, it is well to consider the causes of fractures in the combination.

Experiments on the brazing of Kovar with various alloys have proved that intergranular cracking is produced only when the Kovar is under tensional stress at the time of fusion and when the brazing alloy is in the liquid phase. The cracking starts at the point of highest tensional-stress concentration and is progressive. The cracking occurs whether the stresses are externally applied or residual as long as they are tensional. Stress corrosion is also accentuated by subsequent heat treatment. Actual experience has shown cases where Kovar-brazed joints were under tensional stress but with insufficient penetration of the brazing alloy to cause cracking immediately upon cooling. However, on subsequent thermo-cycling, these joints would leak through cracks extending along the grain boundaries whose roots were in the areas where the brazing alloy had originally penetrated.

Among silver-brazing alloys, the predominantly favored type is the 72% silver and 28% copper eutectic, which has the following advantages:

(a) Being a eutectic, the brazing time can be kept low, thereby minimizing intergranular penetration.

(b) It will "wet" and "flow" well on Kovar.

(c) Elements have sufficiently low vapor pressure for most applications.

3. Precautions to be observed when silver-brazing Kovar

(a) Brazing surface to be free of longitudinal scratches (to avoid capillary effects).

(b) Anneal Kovar parts before brazing (when brazing time or temperature does not provide relief of stresses).

(c) Plate the brazing surface of Kovar with nickel or copper (to retard intergranular penetration). The plated surface may be subjected to a sintering operation.

(d) Allow sufficient clearance (at brazing temperature) when Kovar is on the outside of the higher expansion member.

(e) Preferably use a eutectic brazing alloy (such as 72% silver, 28% copper, melting and flow point 780°C).

(f) Brazing heat is to be applied uniformly to avoid thermal stressing, using such methods as inert or reducing atmosphere furnace, RF heating coil or resistance coil under a bell-jar.

(g) Keep brazing time at a minimum.

(h) Keep the reheating of brazed joints to a minimum.

4. Gold alloy and copper-brazing of Kovar

Stress corrosion can also occur when brazing with pure copper or with gold-brazing alloy, but the effect is minimized since their higher melting points stress-relieve the Kovar when being brought to brazing temperature. Consequently, the same precautions as given in (3) above should be followed, except that the plating of Kovar may be omitted, and the choice of brazing materials should be made with the following considerations:

(a) Use OFHC copper brazing whenever joining permits exposure of assembly to 1100°C.
(b) Gold alloys are preferred over silver when the value of the completed item warrants the additional cost as insurance against stress corrosion.
(c) Use OFHC copper or gold alloy on primary joints when the temperature of subsequent joints or other thermal treatment would cause the primary joint to be deformed and, therefore, introduce thermal stresses.
(d) For special cases when better flow characteristics of the brazing alloy are desired, nickel-bearing brazes are preferred, such as 35% gold, 62% silver, and 3% nickel.
(e) For a complete study of individual brazed joints, reference should be made to equilibrium or phase diagrams of the constituents.[1]

Soft soldering of Kovar alloy. (See p. 332.)

Among the applications for soft-soldering Kovar are:

1. Low temperature electron tubes, such as Geiger counter types.
2. Covering of welded pinch-off tubes after exhausting.
3. For attaching Kovar alloy-glass terminals to the cans of such devices as transformers, capacitors, relays, crystal holders, and similar hermetically sealed devices.

Surface preparation for the actual soldering operation is of primary importance. Generally, solder dipping or electro-tin plating is most easily accomplished, although other methods, such as copper plating, are sometimes used.

Typical procedure for solder-dipping Kovar-glass assemblies:

1. Remove oxide. See pp. 337 *et seq.*
2. Flux in 50% aqueous solution of zinc chloride with 5 to 10% ammonium chloride. Agitate for complete coverage.
3. Solder-dip in bath of 63–37 solder at approximately 250°C.
4. Remove excess solder, preferably by centrifugal means.
5. Remove flux by dipping in hot water containing a wetting agent, followed by a running water rinse. If necessary immerse in 5% hydrochloric acid followed by thorough rinses in running hot and cold water.
6. Dry in hot-air blast.
7. Oil-flow by immersion in cottonseed oil at approximately 250°F until surface is molten. Allow parts to cool in the oil.
8. Vapor degrease in trichlorethylene. Ultrasonic attachment facilitates oil removal, especially from small tubes.

Typical procedure for electro-tin plating:

1. Remove oxide. (See p. 337.)
2. Bright dip. (See p. 337.)
3. Electroplate in alkaline sodium-stannate bath to a thickness of about 0.0002 inch, followed by thorough rinsing and drying.

---

[1] *ASM Metals Handbook,* 1948, and subsequent supplements; *Metals Reference Book,* C. J. Smithells, Butterworth's, London, 1955.

4. Oil-flow as soon as possible after the plating, rinsing, and drying operation, using the procedure outlined in the preceding section.
5. Degrease as in step 8 above.

The soldering of either of the above types of preferred surface treatments may be done by conventional heating methods, using the preferred solders listed. However, it should be borne in mind that although Kovar alloy and the glass have closely matching thermal expansivity, the thermal conductivities are considerably different. Consequently, the heating should be uniformly applied in such methods as furnace, hot plate, infrared heat, heating coil, etc. Torch-heating is to be avoided.

Welding of Kovar alloy

Since welding involves a change in crystalline structure, with different expansion characteristics in the welding area, great precautions must be taken to avoid stresses which will lead to fracture. Additional thermal stresses are introduced by those heating methods which are applied progressively. Therefore, resistance-welding is preferred for most high-vacuum applications with Kovar when conditions prevent the use of copper or other high-temperature braze.

Resistance welding, with a projection on one of the matching flanged surfaces, has been found satisfactory, especially for large production. For resistance-welding of Kovar alloy, the following facts are pertinent:

1. The projection should be machined or coined. (Embossed projections, with a space underneath, are generally not sufficiently rigid.)
2. Kovar-to-Kovar is ideal. When welding Kovar to other metals, however, the projection is preferably placed on the Kovar part for thermal considerations.
3. The matching surfaces of the welding area are to be kept as flat as practical.
4. Surfaces must be smooth, clean, and of as uniform thickness as practical. High or nonuniform electrical resistivity values will cause difficulties.
5. Welds should be made with minimum heat-input.

Inert-gas-shielded arc welding sets up severe thermal stresses due to the fact that, at the point of welding, Kovar temperatures are above the melting temperature, while other portions may be as low as room temperature. Stress-corrosion effects are accentuated when Kovar is arc-welded to other metals, as well as from the resulting mixture of heterogeneous grains of differing expansivity.

Some designs of vacuum devices do not permit using more preferable types of joints. In these cases, sound arc-welded joints with Kovar alloy are secured by employing extreme care and precaution, as indicated by the following:

1. Kovar-to-Kovar is preferred.
2. Sections in weld area should be as thin as practical, down to about 0.020 inch minimum.
3. Preferred design is one in which two flanged sections are butted and a bead welded on the outer circumference. Before arc welding, the butted surfaces should have continuous metal-to-metal contact.
4. When dissimilar thicknesses are joined, the thicker material should be beveled.
5. The joint should be designed to prevent undue stress concentration at the time of making the weld. This includes allowance of sufficient clearance. (See p. 333.)

6. Before they are welded, the parts are to be chemically cleaned and free of oxide film, as well as stress-relief-annealed.
7. Either helium or argon is satisfactory for shielding, but the gas supply should be ample (30 to 50 ft^3/hr). The work must be protected from drafts.
8. Electrodes of 1% or 2% thoriated tungsten, ground to an extremely sharp point, are recommended.
9. The electrode must be held very close to the work (preferably within 0.030 inch). To cut down turbulent flow, the electrode should be held at an angle of 10 to 15°, pointed towards the direction of weld.
10. Copper jigging rings are sometimes found helpful in keeping the assembly cool during the welding operation.
11. When welding Kovar to steel or other alloys, the interposition of a thin nickel strip (or nickel-plating the Kovar) is often helpful.

CLEANING OXIDIZED KOVAR ALLOY

1. *Vapor degrease*
   (a) Trichlorethylene or equivalent (if parts are greasy)
2. *Pickle*
   (a) Solution composition:
      Concentrated hydrochloric acid 100%
      preferably with inhibitor (such as Rodine #50, made by American Chemical Paint Co., Ambler, Pennsylvania) 1+%
   (b) Temperature .... 80–85° C
   (c) Time of immersion, minutes
      light scale ½–1
      heavy scale 1–5
3. *Rinse time,* seconds
   (a) Running hot water 30
   (b) Cold concentrated hydrochloric acid .... 5 to 10
   (c) Running cold water 30
4. *Bright dip* (omit steps 3b and 3c)
   (a) Solution composition
      Acetic acid .... 750 cc
      Nitric acid .... 250 cc
      Hydrochloric acid .... 15 cc
   (b) Temperature .... room
   (c) Time of immersion, seconds 3–10
5. *Rinse*
   (a) Running cold water
      Note: If brightness is not achieved in the first immersion, repeat step 4.
      Caution: The action of the bright dip on Kovar alloy is very rapid. To shorten the immersion time, only cleaned pieces are to be bright-dipped.
   (b) alcohol
   (c) Air-dry

Considerable work has been done at Bell Telephone Laboratories, Murray Hill, New Jersey, on a novel method for cleaning all parts for electron-tube applications.

This hydrogen peroxide process is especially applicable for final cleaning of Kovar alloy just prior to sealing to glass, as follows:[1]

1. *Materials*
   (a) C. P. 30 percent hydrogen peroxide (Superoxol)
   (b) Deionized water is preferred although distilled water may be used.
2. *Procedure*
   (a) Immerse parts in deionized water, bring to boil, adding enough peroxide to make a 5% solution.
   (b) Boil 20–30 minutes.
   (c) Overflow rinse with tap water.
   (d) Rinse in deionized water.
   (e) Dry in air furnace.
   (f) Store in glass containers which have been previously cleaned by the hydrogen peroxide method described above.

The hydrogen peroxide procedure has been found to be effective in removing all traces of surface contamination, including pick-up of organic materials from the atmosphere. The efficacy of this cleaning may be determined by a wettability test.

A further refinement in eliminating organic surface contaminants in the preliminary cleaning of Kovar alloy is to heat the Kovar alloy parts to 400°C in an air atmosphere just prior to hydrogen-firing.

KR-Monel (see MONEL ALLOY 501, p. 383).

Lampblack. A somewhat impure form of amorphous carbon resulting from the smoky flames of incompletely burned hydrocarbons, such as kerosene, benzene, paraffin, gasoline, etc. It is sometimes used as an anode coating for the indication of electron beams because a focused beam produces an incandescent spot on the carbon which has been deposited on a metal substrate. Lampblack may be deposited by cataphoresis[2] or by exposing the base or substrate to a kerosene or pure paraffin candle flame, or to the flame of fuel gas without air.

Langmuir formula. This is the same as the THREE-HALVES POWER LAW for electron emission given on p. 238. The Langmuir formula, as given by Penning,[3] is

$$j = \frac{2.3 \times 10^{-6} V_a^{3/2}}{d^2}$$

where j is current in amp/cm^2, d is anode-cathode distance or spacing in cm, V_a is potential difference between anode and cathode. This formula is for a plane cathode raised to a sufficiently high temperature T and mounted opposite a plane anode at a distance d.

The current j, as given by this equation, is *"space-charge-limited current,"* which may be increased by raising V_a but not by raising T, the temperature of the cathode. In contrast, the *saturation current* can be increased by raising T, but it is increased not at all, or insignificantly, when V_a is increased. The equation is valid for small values of V_a and high values of T; the Richardson equation (p. 236), on the other hand, is valid for large values of V_a and low values of T.

---

[1] ASTM Special Technical Publication No. 246, American Society for Testing Materials, Philadelphia, Pa., 1959.

[2] J. I. Wagner, M.I.T. chemical engineering thesis, "Cataphoresis of Lampblack," 1938.

[3] *Electrical Discharges in Gases,* F. M. Penning, Macmillan Co., New York, New York, 1957.

— Langmuir (unit)

Lasers and Masers. (Acronyms for "Light Amplification by Stimulated Emission of Radiation" and "Molecular Amplification by Stimulated Emission of Radiation.") Light and electromagnetic waves, as generated by various sources, are identical in quality, differing only in wavelength. The wavelength and frequency of an electromagnetic radiation are related by the expression:

$$\lambda = \frac{c}{f}$$

where λ is the wavelength in meters, c (a constant) is the speed of light (approximately 3×10^8 m/sec), and f is the frequency in cycles/sec. The term *coherent* light is the same as monochromatic light or single-wavelength (or frequency) light. Ordinary light sources generate *incoherent* light, i.e., polychromatic light or light of many wavelengths.

Electron tube oscillators generate a single wavelength and are therefore analogous to a monochromatic or coherent radiation. But electron tube oscillators are limited to the far infrared (high) and radiowave (lower) frequencies at best. Lasers and masers provide a source of coherent or monochromatic radiation by virtue of the fixed atomic, ionic, or molecular resonance of a particular substance. A particular atom of a substance in its normal or "ground" state can absorb energy from an electromagnetic wave or radiation of the proper frequency and thereby undergo a change to an excited (sometimes called *metastable*) state. (*Cf.* p. 160.) In this state the atom could emit a wave quantum of the same frequency and in doing so, lose energy, and thus revert to the ground state. The atom could also emit such radiation by the impingement of a similar quantum from another source which is in phase with it.

It is not difficult to maintain an excess of metastable atoms by "pumping" incoherent (polychromatic) light or radiation into certain atoms or molecules in their ground state. The fluorescent and neon lamps are examples of this. In this way an incoming radiation of the proper frequency can gain energy by stimulating emission from the particular atoms or molecules.

Oscillation of the laser or maser is accomplished by feeding back some of the amplified output. This is brought about by forming the active material or container with optically flat reflecting end walls arranged so that the waves which travel along the axis of the material can bounce to and fro, returning to their starting place and beginning again. If the reflection losses are less than the amplification, sustained oscillation is achieved. In order to get the signal or beam out of the device, one of the reflecting end walls is made semitransparent so that some of the amplified coherent light can pass through it.

Maser and laser materials can be solids or gases (solid-state or gas-phase). Examples of laser solids are synthetic ruby doped with chromium, in which the chromium is the active atom, and calcium tungstate crystals doped with neodymium, in which the neodymium atom is active. Neon and ammonia are examples of gas-phase maser and laser materials.

Bibliography

"Infrared and Optical Masers," A. L. Schawlow, *Bell Telephone Record,* November, 1960.

"Operating Characteristics of an Ammonia Beam Maser," F. S. Barnes, *Proc. I. R. E.,* **47,** 2085, 1959, with bibliography.

"Optical Masers," A. L. Schawlow, *Sci. Am.*, **204,** 52, June, 1961.
"The Maser," J. P. Gordon, *ibid.*, **199,** 42, December, 1958.
"Masers" (a review), J. Weber, *Revs. Mod. Phys.*, **31,** 681, 1959.
"Quantum Mechanical Amplifiers," W. W. Lamb, Jr., *Lectures in Theoretical Physics,* edited by W. Brittin and B. Downs, Interscience, New York, **II,** 1960.
Elements of Maser Theory, A. A. Vuylsteke, D. VanNostrand Co., Inc., New York, New York, 1960.
"Systems Applications of Solid-State Masers," J. W. Meyer, *Electronics,* November 4, 1960, with bibliography.
"Principles and Applications of Lasers," D. E. Garr, C. Lehr, and S. Kass, presented at a meeting of the New York Society of Security Analysts, New York, May 8, 1962. (Reprints of this paper are available from the Raytheon Company, Lexington 73, Massachusetts.)
"The Maser," A. M. Hilton, *Electronic Design,* p. 81, September 27, 1962.
"The Laser," A. M. Hilton, *ibid.*, p. 63, October 25, 1962.
(The last two papers have bibliographies.)

Lava (ceramic). This is the trade name of two natural stone products, both varieties of talc. Both Lavas are furnished in an unfired or "green" state which can be easily machined like wood or brass. Lava can be cut with steel saws or abrasive discs. Turning, drilling, tapping, milling, etc., may be done with high-speed tools on standard machines. The material is abrasive and the machines should be protected from the dust created by machining. Coolants must not be used. The material is somewhat brittle so that only light cuts should be taken on thin sections.

Firing converts the Lava into a very hard material. For the highest precision, parts may be ground after firing, since the shrinkage factor is only approximate, and a small amount of distortion may take place on firing.

Grade A Lava is a hydrous aluminum silicate, obtainable in prisms up to a cubic foot or larger. Pieces made from this material should not have wall thicknesses or sections over ½ inch because, since the firing removes water of crystallization, rupture cracks may develop in thicker sections. The fired material is a good electrical insulator, although the dielectric loss factor is considerably higher than for steatite, so that its use at high frequencies is limited.

PROPERTIES OF UNFIRED OR GREEN LAVA[1]

PROPERTY	UNIT	GRADE A HYDROUS ALUMINUM SILICATE	GRADE 1136 HYDROUS MAGNESIUM SILICATE
Density	lb/in^3	0.098	0.100
Volume	in^3/lb	10.2	10.0
Color		Gray	Light gray
Hardness	Mohs' scale	1–2	1
Shrinkage factor		Material grows; 0.980 in. unfired will be 1.000 in. fired	Material shrinks; 1.020 in. unfired will be 1.000 in. fired.

[1] See Footnote 1 on next page.

Grade 1136 Lava is an imported natural talc material low in iron. It is available in sizes approximately up to 2 inches × 2 inches × 3 inches. Pieces made from it should not have a wall thickness over ¼ inch for the same reason as that stated for Grade A Lava.

During the firing operation chemically bound water is driven off and the Lava undergoes crystalline changes. Because these changes are connected with small changes in volume, heating and cooling must be done carefully to avoid cracking. The pieces are placed in the furnace at room temperature, and should be protected against a direct flame by refractory boxes or muffles. The rate of heating should not be more than 260°C per hour. For sections thicker than ½ inch, the rate of heating should be reduced considerably, to approximately 150°C per hour.

PROPERTIES OF FIRED LAVA[1]

PROPERTY	UNIT	GRADE A	GRADE 1136
Density	lb/in^3	0.085	0.102
Volume	in^3/lb	11.75	9.76
Water absorption	percent	2.5	2.5
Color		Pink	White, gray; white or speckled[2]
Softening temperature	°C	1600	1475
	°F	2912	2687
Resistance to heat (safe limit	°C	1100	1250
for constant temperature)	°F	2012	2282
Hardness	Mohs' scale	6	6
Linear coefficient of thermal expansion:			
25–100°C	in/in/°C	2.9×10^{-6}	11.3×10^{-6}
25–600°C	in/in/°C	3.4×10^{-6}	11.9×10^{-6}
Flexural strength	lb/in^2(psi)	9000	9000
Dielectric strength (step 60 cycle)			
Test discs ¼ in. thick	v/mil	80	100
Volume resistivity at various temperatures:			
25°C	$ohm\text{-}cm^3$	$>10^{14}$	$>10^{14}$
100°C	$ohm\text{-}cm^3$	6×10^{11}	9×10^{12}
300°C	$ohm\text{-}cm^3$	2×10^{9}	1.2×10^{10}
500°C	$ohm\text{-}cm^3$	5×10^{6}	1.1×10^{8}
700°C	$ohm\text{-}cm^3$	3.5×10^{5}	3.3×10^{6}
900°C	$ohm\text{-}cm^3$	5×10^{4}	4.2×10^{5}
Dielectric constant, 1000 kc 25°C		5.3	5.8
Power factor, 1000 kc 25°C	%	0.01	0.0003
Loss factor, 1000 kc 25°C	%	0.0530	0.002

[1] All data on Lava are from Bulletin No. 576 of the American Lava Corporation, subsidiary of Minnesota Mining & Manufacturing Co., Chattanooga 5, Tennessee. By permission.

[2] Hydrogen-treated. Light brown when fired in air.

The maximum curing temperature is 1010°–1093°C, and this maximum should be held 30 minutes for ¼ inch or thinner sections, and 45 minutes for ¾ inch sections, with intermediate thicknesses held in proportion. This firing is done in an air muffle. After the heating period, the heat is shut off and the furnace is allowed to cool without opening the doors. Fired pieces can be taken from the oven when the temperature has dropped to below 90°C. In most normal firing schedules, the pieces are placed in the cold muffle in the morning, the temperature is brought up to the maximum, which takes several hours, and the muffle is not opened until the following morning.

Hairline cracks sometimes occur in fired pieces. Some of these are unavoidable, being caused by cracks in the original unfired stone. Large cracks, however, are caused by too rapid heating or cooling.

Grade 1136 Lava does not change in size until a temperature of approximately 870°C is reached. At this temperature the material begins to shrink rapidly (see the table on p. 340).

Grade A Lava, on the other hand, expands on heating, growing larger in size after a temperature of 650°C is reached. The expansion attains 1.9% (approximately) at 982°C, and 2% (approximately) at 1038°C. Only a negligible change in dimensions takes place above this temperature. In the firing of Grade A Lava, a temperature of 1093°C should not be exceeded.

While the heat treatment, as described above, is the same for the two materials, Grade 1136 should be fired in a hydrogen atmosphere if the parts are to be used in evacuated devices. Lava thus fired in hydrogen comes out white in color.

The tables above give some of the properties of both Grade A and Grade 1136 Lavas. These tables show the more important properties of unfired and fired Lava. Special attention to the shrinkage factor is recommended in order to obtain correct dimensions after firing. More detailed information is available from the manufacturer. (See also p. 196.)

Lead and lead alloys. Lead is a constituent of common *soft solders,* useful in joining parts of vacuum devices which are not to be operated at elevated temperatures. The vapor pressure of lead at various temperatures, as given by Honig,[1] is shown in the curve in Fig. 92.

The vapor pressure of tin, the other major element in common soft solders, is quite low as compared with lead, so that the latter is the offending constituent in these alloys from the standpoint of vacuum work. However, pure tin, as a solder, does not have the ductility of the lead-tin alloys.

It will be seen from the curve that solders containing lead can be used in vacuum systems if the temperature is kept below 300°C. In devices which are to be heated, soft-soldered joints are permissible if water-cooling is provided at or near the site of the joint.

Lead-silver solders. The alloying of a small amount of silver with lead raises the melting point. One alloy, 97.5% lead and 2.5% silver, has been used with titanium hydride to effect low-temperature bonds between quartz and Invar by the process described on p. 67 *et seq.* The bonding is done in vacuum; the melting point of this alloy is about 305°C.

---

[1] "Vapor Pressure Data for the More Common Elements," R. E. Honig, *RCA Review,* **23,** 574, 1962.

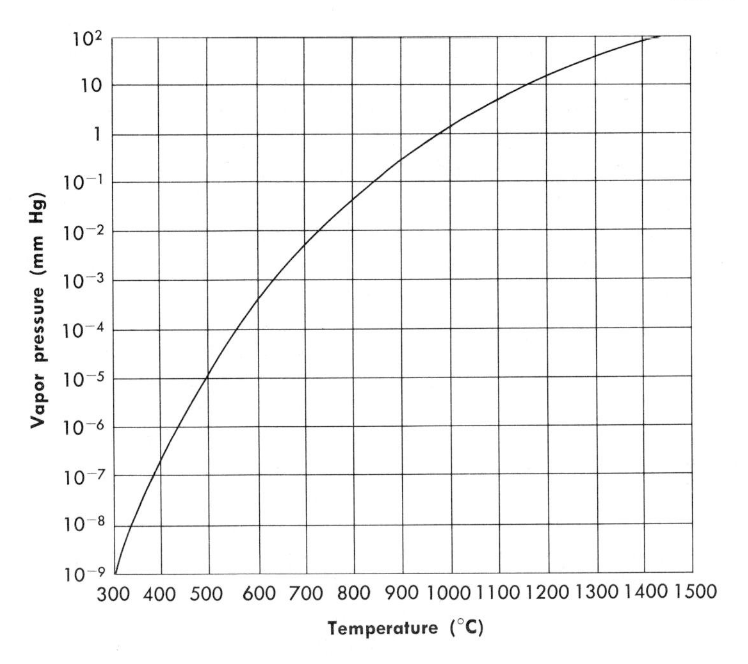

FIG. 92. Vapor pressure of lead versus temperature.

Lead in stainless steel. Ingredients are added to the melt in stainless steel manufacture for the purpose of increasing the ease of machinability. Type 303 (18–8) has, for example, selenium, phosphorus, or sulfur added to the extent of 0.07% (minimum). There is a possibility that some manufacturers add small amounts of lead. Any of the constituents named could be harmful in tube elements which are near an oxide-coated cathode.

Leaks, adjustable and fixed. It is sometimes necessary to allow very small amounts of air or stated gases to leak into a vacuum system for purposes of checking, calibrating, sampling, or gas-filling. There are many references in the literature to various methods of accomplishing this, only a few of which are given below.

J. Morrison (*Rev. Sci. Instr.*, **24**, 230, 1953) describes a leak system employing porous porcelain rods similar in material to those described by H. D. Hagstrom and H. W. Weinhart (*ibid.*, **21**, 394, 1950). The rate of flow of gas through the ceramic rod is determined by the pressure of gas. Area is controlled by the displacement of surrounding mercury with a magnetically operated plunger. A steady pressure in the range from 5×10^{-7} to 5×10^{-3} mm can be maintained by this means in a vacuum system which is being exhausted continuously at a rate of approximately 2–3 liters sec.

R. J. Forman (*ibid.*, **24**, 326, 1953) describes a vacuum valve in which the sealing action is dependent upon the degree of contact of optically polished glass surfaces. The control of the valve is dependent on the differential expansion of valve parts brought about by heating. The use of a valve of this type may be advantageous for either or both of two reasons: (a) it is not necessary to use grease on the sealing surfaces, (b) the rate of flow of gas through the valve can be quite accurately controlled over an extensive range of leak rates.

J. Morrison (*ibid.*, **24,** 546, 1953) discusses a method of changing the conductance of a pumping impedance—for example, an impedance may be located between the tube containing a getter and the manifold of the pumping system. For maximum sensitivity in the determination of gettering rates, the conductance of the pumping impedance should be approximately twice the gettering rate. A leak control tube has therefore been designed which consists of two stainless steel plates ground flat to ensure a close contact. Four holes of different diameters are drilled in one plate, and the other plate slides across it, driven by a screw which is magnet-actuated so that the entire mechanism is inside the vacuum.

E. F. Babelay and L. A. Smith (*ibid.*, **24,** 508, 1953) describe a high-vacuum needle valve used as an adjustable leak for regulating the flow rate of gas samples to a mass spectrometer. The valve is equipped with a wedge and lever system providing very sensitive control of the needle position. Flow through the leak is molecular at spectrometer pressures, but mass flow may be obtained by inserting a capillary tube between the sample and the leak. The leak may be closed completely, thereby simplifying the design of the sample inlet system.

A solenoid-operated needle valve is described by A. J. Stinnett (*ibid.*, **24,** 883, 1953) in which the solenoid is actuated by alternating current, opening and closing the valve at double the frequency of the current supplied. The length of the stroke of the needle is limited with an adjustable screw so that the gas flow can be regulated from zero to nearly full opening. Change in pressure in the vacuum system can be controlled in the 10^{-5} torr region as closely as the ionization gauge can be read. The regulation is smooth and stepless, and the setting can be duplicated. Gas admission through the valve was air at atmospheric pressure.

A somewhat related device is described by G. Urry and W. H. Urry (*ibid.*, **27,** 819, 1956).

An improvement in the porcelain-rod gas leak (see J. Morrison, *op. cit.*, p. 343) is described by C. D'Amico and H. D. Hagstrom (*ibid.*, **28,** 60, 1957).

A variation of the palladium-diffusion leak for hydrogen, as discussed on pp. 121–123, is given by E. R. Harrison and L. C. W. Hobbis (*ibid.*, **26,** 305, 1955). An extensive bibliography on the diffusion leak principle is given in this paper.

R. K. Smither (*ibid.*, **27,** 964, 1956) describes a relatively simple adjustable capillary leak in which the gas flow is controlled by regulating the temperature of the gas in the capillary. This capillary contains no moving parts and can be controlled from a distance. The actual controlled flow is compared with the theoretical predictions, and a calibration curve is shown. Two small leaks, as constructed by the author, had approximate ranges for air of (a) 40–180 microliters/sec and (b) 4–20 microliters/sec.

Glass capillary leaks with extremely small flow rates are discussed by S. A. Gordon (*ibid.*, **29,** 501, 1958). The predictability of these leak rates is determined by the resolution of an optical system used in measuring the bore diameter. Data are given for the construction of such leaks. A manifold of leaks is described which will introduce gas into a high-vacuum system at several different leak rates. It contains no moving parts or high-vapor-pressure materials on the high-vacuum side, yet leak rates can be manipulated over a wide range. The characteristic features of these leaks are shown to be reasonable in the light of well-established theory.

Fixed and variable leaks are obtainable commercially.

Leak detectors and Leak detection (see pp. 134, 360).

Lehr. An annealing oven for glass, etc., which consists of a chamber maintained in the annealing range of temperatures, with a long passage or tunnel in which slow cooling takes place.

Life expectancy of tungsten filaments (see the table on p. 90).

Liquid helium. Cryogenic investigations make wide use of liquid helium as a refrigerant since its boiling point is −269°C. It is also used as a refrigerant in ultrahigh vacuum systems.[1] Liquid helium can be stored in special containers[2] having an outer chamber filled with liquid nitrogen (see below).

Liquid nitrogen. This refrigerant is widely used in cold traps on vacuum systems.[3] Its liquid range is from 63.1°K (−210°C = melting point) to 77.2°K (−196°C = boiling point), thus making it capable of wholly or partly condensing many of the common gases such as water vapor, air, carbon dioxide, carbon monoxide, and many hydrocarbon gases, as well as oil vapors and mercury. It is relatively inexpensive and storable for periods of several days in Dewar flasks, or in commercially available containers.[2] (See Low TEMPERATURE INSULATION, p. 346.)

Liquid nitrogen is used in preference to *liquid air,* which has a slightly higher temperature range. Since liquid air is a mixture, the more volatile nitrogen boils off first, leaving increasing concentrations of liquid oxygen, which constitute an explosion or fire hazard.

Nitrogen is nonflammable and nonpoisonous.

Some devices have been described for detecting and controlling the level of a liquid refrigerant in a vacuum cold trap.[4, 5, 6, 7] Commercial devices for accomplishing this purpose are available from Consolidated Vacuum Corporation, Rochester, New York; Cryogenics, Inc., Stafford, Virginia; NRC Equipment Corporation, Newton Highlands, Massachusetts; and others. Special tubes for transferring liquid refrigerants in a system from the storage chamber to other containers have been suggested.[8, 9, 10, 11, 12]

---

[1] G. W. Sears and J. W. Cahn, *J. Chem. Phys.*, **33,** 494, 1960; J. P. Hobson, *Trans. Am. Vacuum Soc.*, 8th Ann. Symp. (1961), p. 146, Pergamon Press, Inc., New York, 1962; J. Hengevoss and E. A. Trendelenburg, *ibid.*, 10th Ann. Symp., p. 101, Macmillan Company, New York, 1963; W. W. Stickney and B. B. Dayton, *ibid.*, p. 105; I. Ames, R. L. Christensen, and J. Teale, *Rev. Sci. Instr.*, **29,** 736, 1958.

[2] Hoffman Laboratories, Inc., Newark 5, New Jersey; Linde Company, Division of Union Carbide Corp., Long Island City 1, New York; Superior Air Products Company, Newark 5, New Jersey.

[3] F. W. Schmidlin, L. O. Heflinger, and E. L. Garwin, *Trans. Am. Vacuum Soc.*, 9th Ann. Symp., p. 197, Macmillan Company, New York, 1962; B. A. Buffham, P. B. Henault, and R. A. Flinn, *ibid.*, p. 205; B. C. Moore, *ibid.*, p. 212; L. O. Mullen and R. B. Jacobs, *ibid.*, p. 220; S. M. Kindall and E. S. J. Wang, *ibid.*, p. 243.

[4] A. Maimoni, *Rev. Sci. Instr.*, **27,** 1024, 1956.

[5] W. T. Kitts and F. L. Harler, *ibid.*, **25,** 926, 1954.

[6] R. L. Gamblin, E. Goldberg, and D. T. Scag, *ibid.*, **30,** 371, 1959.

[7] B. Richelman, *ibid.*, **30,** 598, 1959.

[8] R. C. Mathewson, *ibid.*, **26,** 616, 1955.

[9] R. B. Jacobs and R. J. Richards, *ibid.*, **28,** 291, 1957.

[10] M. D. Fiske, *ibid.*, **26,** 90, 1955.

[11] J. W. Stout, *ibid.*, **25,** 929, 1954.

[12] A. Wexler, *ibid.*, **25,** 442, 1954.

Litharge and glycerin cement. This is a heat-resistant material useful as a basing cement for electron tubes. Its composition is

Litharge (lead monoxide, PbO) . . . 260 gm
Glycerin (USP) solution—glycerin 2 parts, water 1 part . . . 100 ml.

Thoroughly heat the dry litharge powder at 400°C. When cool, place in a mortar and add the diluted glycerin slowly while grinding. Heat will be evolved and the mixture will begin to set. While it is still soft, pour into place, and with a spatula, work it into position like putty. The cement is thoroughly hard in 24 hours. Since the reaction is irreversible, only the amount required should be made up.

This cement is strong and hard but is not vacuum-tight. It can be used up to 260°C and is inert to water and most acids and alkalies.

Low-temperature insulation. The National Bureau of Standards (U.S. Department of Commerce, Washington 25, D.C.) gives the following report on low-temperature insulating materials.[1]

The best Dewar flask has a heat leakage by radiation across its vacuum jacket of the order of one microwatt/cm^2 between walls at 300°K and 76°K, and two microwatts/cm^2 between walls at 76°K and 4°K, although the leakage is considerably higher (20–30 microwatts/cm^2) for most flasks with the latter temperature difference. Investigations at the National Bureau of Standards Cryogenic Laboratories in Boulder, Colorado, have indicated that for a large-scale apparatus, evacuated powders such as perlite, diatomaceous earths, and silica aerogel provide a decided improvement over the standard vacuum-walled Dewar vessel. In addition the evacuated-powder insulated vessel can have high emissivity walls and a thousand times greater gas pressure, and remain an efficient low-temperature vessel. Reduction of heat transfer through powders can be achieved in a number of ways. Total heat transport is lowered by pumping out gases, by increasing the degree of subdivision, by increasing or decreasing the powder density, by adding metallic powders to make the material "opaque" to thermal radiation, and by disrupting or minimizing the amount of crystal structure. The thermal resistance of a vessel with a 2- to 3-cm thickness of some evacuated powders is as good as or better than a vacuum-jacketed vessel in the temperature interval 300° to 76°K. At present, single-component evacuated powders find their principal commercial application in large-scale storage and transportation of liquid oxygen. A further step has been the construction of a powder-insulated vessel for transportation and short-time storage of liquid hydrogen without an auxiliary refrigerant such as liquid nitrogen. The superior performance of metal powder mixtures permits extension of these applications and should encourage the use of this insulating principle in other applications requiring efficient heat insulation.

Lubricants for use in vacuum. Ordinary oils and greases obviously cannot be used in vacuum vessels for lubricating moving parts because of their high vapor pressures. For room-temperature use, the special oils used in diffusion pumps (see pp. 400, 401), such as Octoil, Octoil S, Apiezon oils (see pp. 157, 158), Silicone diffusion pump oils, etc., can be used in small quantities. For moderate temperatures, up to 250°C, colloidal graphite[2] is sometimes used, although it tends to be gassy. For higher temperatures the surfaces are rubbed with dry molybdenum disulfide MoS_2,[3] which is useful up to 400°C.

---

[1] *Rev. Sci. Instr.*, **28**, 747, 1957.
[2] See Aquadag, p. 157.
[3] Molykote (Type Z, or microsize powder).

A chlorofluorocarbon grease containing no silica, soap, or thickeners can be used up to 135°C as a grease, and up to 285°C as an oil. The manufacturer[1] claims a low vapor pressure for this material.

For some conditions, Teflon (see pp. 513–517) can be used as a bearing material without lubrication.[2]

In some cases, jeweled bearings (synthetic sapphire, etc.) may be used instead of hardened steel or tungsten.

Lucite. An acrylic thermoplastic product that has properties similar to those of Plexiglas (see p. 446).

Magnesium in getters (see GETTERS, pp. 105, 107).

Magnesium, vapor pressure of (see pp. 143, 147).

Magnetic shielding. A useful modern treatment of the design of cylindrical magnetic shields, such as those used for photomultipliers, particle accelerators, and the like, is given by W. G. Wadey in *Rev. Sci. Instr.*, **27**, 910, 1956.

Manganese, vapor pressure of (see pp. 144, 147).

Manganin. This is an electrical resistance alloy used, as wire or ribbon, in making precision resistors for Wheatstone bridges, potentiometers, decade boxes, meter shunts, and other electrical measuring devices. It has a very low thermal coefficient of resistivity, being slightly positive (resistance increases) from 15°C to approximately 25°C, then slightly negative until the resistance at 35°C is about the same as at 15°C. The maximum change in resistance is not more than 15 parts per million, and often less than one-third this figure.

Manganin must be aged after coils or resistors are formed to their finished shape and dimensions to avoid a slow decrease of resistance with time. This is done by holding at a temperature of 120°C to 140°C for 24 to 48 hours.

Manganin has a low thermal emf with copper (not more than 0.0025 mv/°C between 0°C and 100°C).

Manganin is available from the Driver-Harris Company, Harrison, New Jersey, and from the W. B. Driver Company, Newark, New Jersey. It can be obtained in wire form, insulated with enamel, silk, nylon, cotton, or glass.

Manifold is that portion of a vacuum system to which the vessels or tubes to be evacuated are attached. It is customary in industry or semiproduction to seal a number of tubes to the system (hence manifold) to be vacuum-processed simultaneously. Figure 22, p. 99, and Fig. 99, p. 362 shows examples.

Manometer is strictly speaking, any gauge for measuring the pressure of gases or vapors. Manometers can be roughly classified into the following types:

1. Those using mercury or some low vapor-pressure oil, as for example, the mercury barometer (see below).

2. Those in which the pressure causes a deformation of a thin wall or membrane. The Bourdon gauge (essentially a coiled-up length of flattened metal tubing which tends to become tighter or looser as the pressure inside the tubing is lowered or increased); and the aneroid barometer (in which a diaphragm or membrane closing the end of a partially evacuated metal cylinder is moved in and out by the changing external atmospheric pressure.

3. Those which operate on the principle of the viscosity of gases, a property which changes with pressure.

4. Those operating by virtue of the rate of transfer of momentum from a hot to a cold surface. The radiometer and Knudsen gauge (p. 321) are examples of this principle.

---

[1] Halocarbon Products Corp., Hackensack, New Jersey.

[2] R. H. Willens, *Rev. Sci. Instr.*, **31**, 574, 1960.

5. Those depending on the thermal conductivity of gases in which the heat transfer is a function of gas pressure. A hot filament will thus lose heat more rapidly in a gas than in a vacuum.[1] The Pirani gauge (p. 438) and the thermocouple gauge (p. 440) are examples.

6. Ionization gauges. If a high-velocity electron collides with a gas molecule, a positive ion is formed. The population of positive ions, and therefore the current flowing to a negative collector of these ions, will be partly dependent on the density of gas present within certain limits. (See IONIZATION, p. 302, and IONIZATION GAUGE, p. 303.)

A simple mercury manometer, as in example 1 above, is shown in Fig. 30, p. 120. The U-tube, which is less than 76 cm (folded length), is partially filled with mercury so that when sealed to a system at atmospheric pressure in the position shown, the mercury level will be at the point indicated on the right side of the tube and completely fill the left side. When the system is evacuated, the mercury level will fall in the closed end of the tube until the levels in the two arms are equal, since there is now a vacuum on both sides. If gas is then admitted to the system, the level in the right side will be depressed, and the pressure in millimeters of mercury will be read directly by the difference in levels of the two sides of the U-tube. This type of manometer is used for metering gases in the millimeter range of pressures. The type of mercury barometer commonly used by meteorologists is a manometer in which a glass tube a little over 76 cm (30 inches) long, closed at one end, is filled with mercury and then inverted over an open mercury reservoir (Torricelli, 1643). The column of mercury will fall to a height corresponding to the atmospheric pressure at the moment, leaving a vacuum at the top. The barometric pressure in millimeters of mercury, or in inches, is the distance from the top of the column to the surface of the mercury in the reservoir. (This reading must be corrected for altitude above sea level and for temperature.)

The standard manometer for measuring vacuum conditions, and the one by which many other gauges are calibrated, is the *McLeod gauge*[2] in which a given volume of gas at a certain pressure is compressed into a much smaller volume, the pressure in the smaller volume being observed and measured. In accordance with Boyle's Law (p. 265):

$$p = \frac{PV}{v}, \qquad \text{Equation (1)}$$

where p is pressure in the smaller volume, P is pressure in larger volume, V is the larger volume, v is the smaller volume.

A typical McLeod gauge is illustrated in Fig. 93, p. 349.[3] The bulb B to which is attached a capillary tube a-a is connected to the low-pressure system as shown and

---

[1] Thermistors are useful as elements in thermal pressure gauges. In this connection, see "Thermistor Pressure Gauge Design," A. P. Flanick and J. E. Ainsworth, *Rev. Sci. Instr.*, **32**, 356, 1961; also, "Vacuum Gauge Calibration System," same authors, *ibid.*, **32**, 408, 1961.

[2] H. McLeod, *Phil. Mag.*, **48**, 110, 1874.

[3] All data on McLeod gauge from S. Dushman, *Scientific Foundations of Vacuum Technique*, second edition, 1962. John Wiley & Sons, Inc., New York, New York. By permission.

also to the barometric column below. In order to avoid errors due to the effect of capillarity, a tube *b-b* of the same diameter as *a-a* is sealed on as a bypass to the larger tube *E*. To operate the gauge, the reservoir *R* is raised, thus forcing the mercury up in the barometric column *T* until the gas in the bulb *B* and the capillary *a-a* is shut off from the rest of the system at *C*. As the mercury reservoir *R* is raised higher, the gas in *B* is compressed until finally the mercury in the capillary *b-b* is level with the top of the inside of the capillary *a-a* (corresponding to the point 0 on the scale). The pressure on the gas in the capillary is then equal to the sum of the pressure in the system and that of the mercury column of length *h*, which is also the length of the capillary *a-a* that contains the compressed gas.

The symbols in the formulas below have the following meanings:

V is the given volume of the capillary *a-a* plus the bulb *B* down to the shut-off point *C* (cm^3).

P is the pressure in the vacuum system (mm Hg or torr). This is the pressure to be measured.

b is the volume of the capillary *a-a* (cm^3/mm length).

h is the length of the mercury column in *a-a* (Fig. 93).

v is volume of gas trapped in *a-a*, plus $B = bh$ (cm^3).

d is inside diameter of the capillary (mm).

p is the pressure in the capillary $= P_{mm} + h$.

$$(P_{mm} + h)bh = P_{mm}V$$

or

$$P_{mm} = \frac{bh^2}{V - bh}, \qquad \text{Equation (2)}$$

$$b = 7.854 \times 10^{-4}d^2 \text{ (cm}^3\text{/mm length)}$$

and

$$P_{mm} = \frac{7.854 \times 10^{-4}d^2h^2}{V - 7.854 \times 10^{-4}d^2h^2}.$$

For a capillary 150 mm in length (an upper limit for length):

$$P_{mm} = \frac{17.67d^2}{V - 0.1179d^2};$$

for $d = 3$ mm, and $V = 100$ cm^3,

$$P_{mm} = \frac{159.1}{100 - 1.06} = 1.607.$$

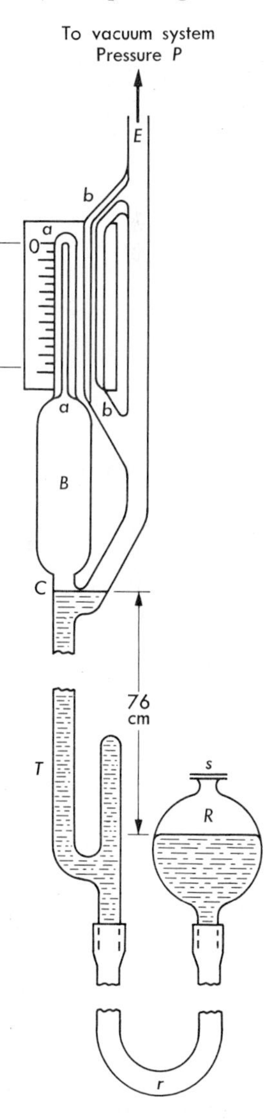

FIG. 93. McLeod's gauge.

For a capillary of 3 mm or less in internal diameter and a bulb volume of 100 cm^3, the error resulting from the omission of the term bh in the denominator of Equation (2) is less than 1%.

Many McLeod gauges are designed for measuring maximum pressures of 1 mm (i.e., to 1000 microns). For such gauges a more simple formula is valid:

$$P_{mm} = \left(\frac{b}{V}\right)h^2 = Kh^2, \qquad \text{Equation (3)}$$

where K, the *gauge constant,* is expressed in mm Hg/mm length,
h is length of mercury column in a-a (mm),
b is volume of capillary a-a (cm^3/mm length).

If h (length of column a-a) and d (ID of capillary) are in mm, and V (volume of capillary a-a) is in cm^3, the values of K for typical McLeod gauges in common use are given in the following table.

d	V	10^5K
1	100	0.785
1	60	1.309
1.5	100	1.767
1.5	60	2.945
2.5	100	4.909

The values in the 10^5K column correspond to the *pressure in microns* for $h =$ 10 mm.

To avoid errors which arise when the value of h is small, it is preferable to compress the gas in the capillary a-a to a definite volume v, and then observe the height h_1 (in mm) of the mercury above this level in the side capillary b-b. In this case, since

$$P_{mm} = \frac{vh_1}{V},$$

it is evident that h_1 is directly proportional to P_{mm}, and the magnitude of this quantity can be determined by means of a cathetometer or telescope.[1,2] This method is not, however, as sensitive at low pressures as that described above.

The sensitivity of the McLeod gauge can be made extremely high by increasing the ratio V/v, i.e., V/b. However, in the case of gauges such as in Fig. 93, practical considerations limit the size of V because of the weight of mercury to be lifted. Also, with capillaries of very small inside diameter (0.5 to 0.7 mm), the mercury has a tendency to stick rather badly as the level is raised, and the column tends to break as the level is lowered, thus leaving a portion hanging in the capillary.

Only vacuum-distilled mercury is to be used in McLeod gauges and other mercury manometers, and the glass tubing must be entirely clean and dry.

In vacuum systems which cannot tolerate mercury vapor, a refrigerant trap (e.g., liquid nitrogen) must be inserted between the gauge and the rest of the system. The disadvantage, however, is that condensible gases are trapped and do not reach the gauge for measurement.

---

[1] *Cf.* G. A. Bottomley, *J. Sci. Instr.* (Br) **35,** 254, 1958.
[2] R. Eichhorn and T. F. Irvine, Jr., *Rev. Sci. Instr.,* **29,** 23, 1958.

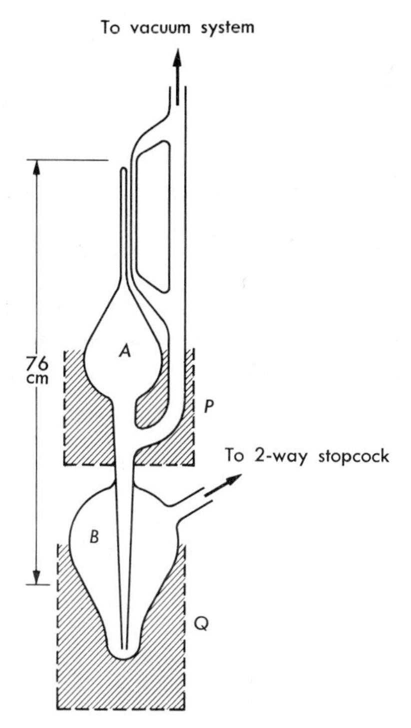

FIG. 94. Rosenberg's gauge.

Some modifications of the McLeod gauge have been proposed, and are briefly referred to below.

Haase[1] has constructed an accurate gauge having the dimensions: $V = 1400\ \text{cm}^3$ and $d = 0.7$ mm, for which

$$P_{\text{mm}} = 3 \times 10^{-7} h^2,$$

where h is in mm. For $h = 180$, $P_{\text{mm}} = 10^{-2}$. In the construction of such a gauge, the mercury reservoir is connected by stopcocks to the rough vacuum and the atmosphere. The mercury is raised by opening the stopcock to the atmosphere, and lowered by opening the other stopcock to the vacuum. Both the reservoir and the upper bulb B should be supported solidly in plaster of paris, and provision made for a box around the bottom of the reservoir to contain the mercury in case of spillage or breakage.

In the gauge of Rosenberg[2] the volume of bulb A (Fig. 94) is $1300\ \text{cm}^3$ and that of bulb B about $2500\ \text{cm}^3$. Bulb B contains about 60 lb of mercury. Both bulbs are thick-walled and are supported by plaster of paris blocks P and Q. With capillaries of 0.63 mm inside diameter, the value of b/V (which Rosenberg designates the *compression ratio*) is 2.4×10^{-7}. In the construction of the capillaries, a method of roughening them was used. This consisted of repeatedly passing a wire loaded with fine abrasive such as alumina carefully through the capillary. The object of

[1] *Z. tech. Physik*, **24**, 27, 53, 1943.
[2] P. Rosenberg, *Rev. Sci. Instr.*, **10**, 131, 1939.

the roughening is to prevent sticking and breaking of mercury threads while the mercury is in motion.

A McLeod gauge sensitive to hydrogen is described by Cochran,[1] and a compact *oil* McLeod gauge is the subject of a paper by Florescu.[2] A method of using a McLeod gauge for pressures higher than the usual ranges is given by Kreisman.[3] A gauge with several prescribed volumes as standards is proposed by Jansen and Venema.[4]

Manometric pressure measurements are discussed in a paper by Cartier,[5] an abstract of which follows:

> One of the most common devices for measuring pressure is the manometer in which the pressure is balanced against a column of liquid. In this case the pressure is given by the relation
>
> $$P = hdg,$$
>
> where h is the height of the column (cm),
> d is the density of the liquid (gm/cm^3),
> P is the pressure (dynes/cm^2),[6]
> g is the acceleration due to gravity (981 cm/sec^2).
>
> The following sources of error are discussed. These may become important in very precise work. (a) Temperature may cause an error in the values of d and the scale readings of h. (b) The value of g depends upon the location, i.e., latitude and elevation, according to the following formula:
>
> $$g_c = 980.616 - 2.5928 \cos 2\phi + 0.0069 \cos^2 2\phi - 3.086 \times 10^{-6}H$$
>
> where g_c is the corrected value of g,
> ϕ is the latitude in degrees,
> H is the elevation in cm.
>
> (c) Errors may result from capillarity (sticking of the fluid, and nonuniformity of bore) and from compressibility of the fluid.
>
> Methods for correcting each of these errors are given. For the well-type manometer (barometer), it is possible to provide compensation for the errors by careful choice of well and tube areas together with a tapered plug in the well,

---

[1] C. N. Cochran, *ibid.*, **29**, 69, 1958.

[2] N. A. Florescu, *ibid.*, **29**, 528, 1958.

[3] W. S. Kreisman, *ibid.*, **31**, 782, 1960.

[4] C. G. J. Jansen and A. Venema, *Vacuum* (Br), **9**, 219, 1959. See also: "Improvement in Operation with McLeod Gauge," N. A. Florescu, *Vacuum*, **10**, 329, 1960; "A Precision McLeod Gauge for Volumetric Gas Measurements," H. H. Podgurski and F. N. Davis, *Vacuum*, **10**, 377, 1960; "Use of McLeod Gauge at Room Temperature for Gases with High Critical Temperatures," H. J. Bixler, A. S. Michaels, and R. B. Parker, *Rev. Sci. Instr.*, **31**, 1155, 1960; "Use of McLeod Gauge with Gas-Vapor Mixtures," A. T. J. Hayward, *J. Sci. Instr.* (Br), **39**, 367, 1962; "Mechanical McLeod Gauge for Accurate Measurement of Pressures in the 5–500 μ Range," J. T. Park, *Rev. Sci. Instr.*, **35**, 242, 1964.

[5] R. J. Cartier, *Instruments and Automation*, **31**, 1980, 1958. Reprinted by permission of Instruments Publishing Co., Pittsburgh, Pennsylvania.

[6] 1 dyne/cm^2 = 7.5006 mm Hg at 0°C. (See the table on p. 218.)

which provides the final correction for area ratio and also provides for volume displacement to compensate for capillarity. Its taper is chosen to compensate for compressibility, which is a nonlinear function of the column height.
The correction can easily amount to 0.1 inch in a 30-inch manometer. No data are given indicating the gain in accuracy which has been realized by the taper plug technique.

A convection-type manometer (not included in the classification given on pp. 347–348, but which is a subspecies of class 5) is described by Johnson[1] which depends on heat convection rather than on molecular heat conductivity. Its range may be from a few torr to atmospheric pressure or higher. See below.

A manometer for measuring vapor pressures is given by Ernsberger and Pitman.[2] This is an absolute manometer with a range of 0.5 to 20 microns Hg, and a precision and accuracy of better than 1 percent. The design embodies a freely suspended piston in a cylinder, with the pressure to be measured on one side and a reference vacuum on the other.

A device for measuring low gas pressures has been constructed by Nester.[3] In this manometer a magnet-operated plunger compresses a volume of gas in a capillary, as in the McLeod gauge. A silicone oil of low vapor pressure is used, and the gauge has a pressure range of 0.1 to 20 torr. The same author has previously described an absolute manometer[4] that utilizes a leak-proof needle valve of Teflon in place of the closed end of the manometer.

A pressure gauge for the centimeter range is given by Johnson and Williams.[5] This manometer uses a metal bellows without any fluid and can thus be baked out for outgassing.

A wide-range manometer operating on the principle of thermal convection is described by McMillan and Buch.[6] In this gauge the lower pressure range is measured by the principle of thermal conductivity (class 5) and at higher pressures by that of the convection of a gas stream. The range of this gauge is given as 0.5 to 5 torr.

A study of the principle of *convection gauges* is given by Langmuir[7] and by Brody and Körözy.[8]

Gauges for the measurement of pressures up to 15 and 10 torr, respectively, are given by Ritter[9] and by Leck and Martin.[10]

The Dubrovin gauge[11] is a float-type manometer which has a range of 0.1 to 20 torr. The construction of this manometer is shown in Fig. 95. It consists of a stainless steel cylinder of small diameter, closed at one end, floating vertically in mercury

---

[1] J. B. Johnson, *Rev. Sci. Instr.*, **27**, 303, 1956.
[2] F. M. Ernsberger and H. W. Pitman, *ibid.*, **26**, 584, 1955.
[3] R. G. Nester, *ibid.*, **28**, 577, 1957.
[4] R. G. Nester, *ibid.*, **25**, 1136, 1954.
[5] J. B. Johnson and N. T. Williams, *ibid.*, **25**, 393, 1954.
[6] J. A. McMillan and T. Buch, *Rev. Sci. Instr.*, **28**, 881, 1957.
[7] I. Langmuir, *J. Am. Chem. Soc.*, **37**, 417, 1915.
[8] I. Brody and F. Körözy, *J. Appl. Phys.*, **10**, 584, 1939.
[9] R. Ritter, *Rev. Sci. Instr.*, **17**, 113, 1946.
[10] J. H. Leck and C. S. Martin, *J. Sci. Instr.* (Br), **33**, 181, 1956.
[11] A gauge of this description is commercially available from the W. M. Welch Scientific Company, Chicago 10, Illinois.

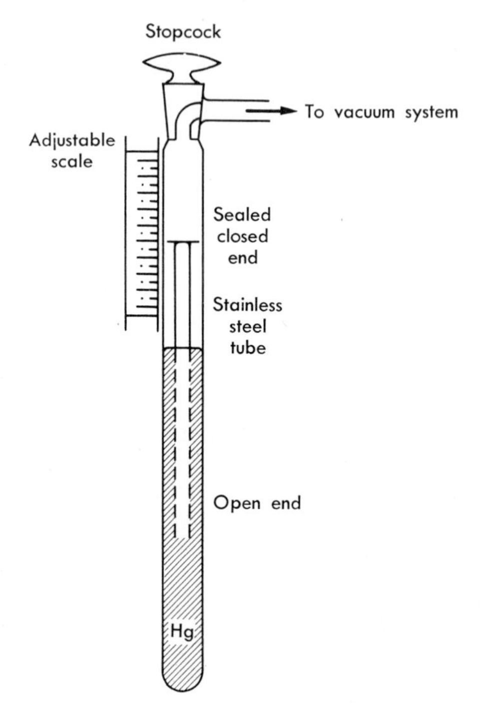

FIG. 95. Dubrovin's gauge.

with its open end submerged. The air is evacuated from the chamber thus formed by the floating cylinder. The outer glass tube is connected to the vacuum system through a stopcock, as shown. An adjustable scale is provided and is read at the indicator at the top of the floating stainless steel tube.

When both the float chamber and the gauge chamber have been evacuated, the buoyant force acting on the float (the weight of mercury displaced by its submerged walls) is in equilibrium with the weight of the float. Under these conditions the float is in its highest position. When the pressure in the outer chamber increases, it exerts a downward force on the float, causing it to sink until the additional mercury displaced is sufficient to compensate for the downward force and again produce equilibrium. The magnification factor is a function of the dimensions of the float.

OIL MANOMETERS

For use in oil manometers, an oil should be chosen like those used in oil diffusion pumps. Obviously, the pressure in the system cannot be below the vapor pressure of the oil used in such a manometer without suffering a loss of oil due to evaporation.

It should be borne in mind that all liquids, even mercury to a small extent, absorb gases from the atmosphere. Most oils absorb considerable quantities of atmospheric gases, and will therefore bubble copiously, even vigorously, while being evacuated for the first time. For this reason the pumping of fluid manometers should take place at a slow rate until the fluid is degassed, to prevent it from boiling up into unwanted parts of the manometer. Degassing is accelerated by warming, but heat should also be applied with caution.

Consistent with the foregoing remarks is the fact that a small amount of the gas *being measured* in a fluid-type manometer may slowly diffuse through the fluid from the high pressure side to the low, and thus give rise to an error in reading if there is a long interval between admission of gas and observation. For short time intervals, however, this effect is negligible.

Many other manometers and devices for measuring pressure are to be found in the literature, a partial list of which is given below:

"A Precise Differential Manometer," G. J. Maslach, *Rev. Sci. Instr.*, **23**, 367, 1952.

"A Manometer for Pressures above 770 mm (Precise Gas Manometer)" L. Akobjanoff, *ibid.*, **23**, 447, 1952.

"Improvements in Null-Reading Absolute Manometer," D. H. Pringle and R. M. Kidd, *ibid.*, **24**, 877, 1953.

"Oil Manometer for Ultrahigh-Vacuum System," M. A. Biondi, *ibid.*, **24**, 989, 1953.

"Measurement of High Vacuum at Low Temperatures," M. P. Garfunkel and A. Wexler, *ibid.*, **25**, 170, 1954.

"Recording Vacuum Gauge," D. T. Hurd and M. L. Corrin, *ibid.*, **25**, 1126, 1954.

"Construction of Small Pirani Gauges," D. G. H. Marsden, ibid., **26**, 1205, 1955.

"Micrometer Mechanism for Reading Bourdon Gauge," M. T. Rogers, J. G. Malik, H. B. Thompson, *ibid.*, **26**, 730, 1955.

"Permanent Record from Manometer," S. M. Ross and E. E. Suckling, *ibid.*, **27**, 409, 1956.

"Micromanometer of High Sensitivity," S. Lynn, W. H. Corcoran, and B. H. Sage, *ibid.*, **27**, 368, 1956.

"Automatic Device for Reading Bourdon Gauge," W. S. Tandler, M. Grossman, and R. H. Tourin, *ibid.*, **27**, 108, 1956.

"Thermoelectric Vacuum Gauge," A. König and J. Antal, *ibid.*, **27**, 417, 1956.

"Vacuum Gauge for Helium Pressures at Low Temperatures," G. A. Slack, *ibid.*, **27**, 241, 1956.

"Simple Sensitive Pressure Gauge," K. M. Sancier and W. Richeson, *ibid.*, **27**, 134, 1956.

"Precision Automatic Manometer Reader," J. Farquharson and H. A. Kermicle, *ibid.*, **28**, 324, 1957.

"Extended-Range Thermal Conductivity Vacuum Gauge," A. R. Hamilton, *ibid.*, **28**, 693, 1957.

"Null-Reading Manometer Using Brass Bellows," M. DeCrescente and G. J. Janz, *ibid.*, **28**, 468, 1957.

"Feedback-Controlled, Heat-Conductivity Vacuum Gauge," J. H. Leck and C. S. Martin, *ibid.*, **28**, 119, 1957.

"Ionization Gauges for High Pressures (up to mm range)," G. J. Schulz and A. V. Phelps, *ibid.*, **28**, 1051, 1957. (See p. 471.)

"The Pirani Gauge 'Vactroller,' " C. J. Penther, *ibid.*, **28**, 460, 1957.

"Wide-Range Thermistor Vacuum Gauge," P. E. Seiden, *ibid.*, **28**, 657, 1957.

"Self-Degassing Oil Manometer," R. L. Phipps and J. H. Bloom, *Vacuum* (Br), **11**, 35, 1961.

"Electrical Micromanometer," H. R. Hart, *J. Sci. Instr.* (Br), **38**, 300, 1961.

Some additional references to vacuum measurement and instruments follow:

R. G. Nester, *Rev. Sci. Instr.*, **28**, 577, 1957.

J. R. Anderson, *ibid.*, **29**, 1073, 1958.

A. G. Kramer and P. M. Platzman, *ibid.*, **29**, 897, 1958.
P. Zigman, *ibid.*, **30**, 1060, 1959.
M. Varićak and B. Saftić, *ibid.*, **30**, 891, 1959.
C. A. Reynolds, G. Pearson, F. Burchbuckler, and J. Burham, *ibid.*, **30**, 1050, 1959.
P. A. Redhead, H. Schwarz, G. Reich, W. B. Nottingham, and I. Fish, American Vacuum Society Symposium Panel Discussion, *Proc. A. V. S.*, 1960.
G. Barnes, *Rev. Sci. Instr.*, **31**, 608, 1960.
H. J. Bixler, A. S. Michaels, and R. B. Parker, *ibid.*, **31**, 1155, 1960.
N. A. Florescu, *Vacuum* (Br.), **10**, 329, 1960.
A. M. Thomas, D. P. Johnson, and J. W. Little, *Trans. Am. Vacuum Soc.*, 9th Ann. Symp., p. 468, Macmillan Company, New York, 1962.
A. T. J. Hayward, *J. Sci. Instr.* (Br), **40**, 173, 1963.

Marinite.[1] This is an insulating sheet and board material. It is composed of asbestos fiber, diatomaceous silica, and an inorganic binder. While not suitable for use inside vacuum tubes, it finds application in the construction of ovens, for heat insulation in a rigid form, and as plugs and jigs in glass-blowing operations. It can be sawed, drilled, and machined, and has sufficient structural strength by itself for use as oven walls. It can be bolted or screwed together. Ordinary handsaws or power saws can be used for cutting, but the abrasive nature of Marinite tends to dull the cutting edges unless carbide-tipped or abrasive-edged wheels are used. The material is cut dry. Ordinary high-speed steel drills can be used for drilling.

Marinite has the following physical and thermal properties:

PHYSICAL AND THERMAL PROPERTIES OF MARINITE

		MARINITE-23	MARINITE-36	MARINITE-65
Density, dry (lb/ft^3)		23	36	65
Moisture content, normal (% of dry weight)		5	5	5
Transverse strength, dry, (psi) (modulus of rupture)		550	900	1500
Transverse strength after 24-hr soaking heat at indicated temperature (psi)		450 (900°F)	900 (900°F)	1500 (800°F)
Modulus of elasticity (dry) psi (from transverse test)		0.20×10^6	0.36×10^6	0.65×10^6
Consolidation, normal (in/in)				
Load (psi)	500	0.02	0.02	0.01
	2000	0.45	0.15	0.07
	4000	0.62	0.38	0.18
	6000	0.65	0.51	0.26
	8000	0.68	—	0.31
	10,000	0.71	—	0.35
	12,000	0.74	—	0.39

[1] All the data on Marinite are reproduced with permission of Johns-Manville Company.

Physical and Thermal Properties of Marinite (*Cont.*)

	MARINITE-23	MARINITE-36	MARINITE-65
Compressive strength, normal (psi)	14,000	7,000*	16,000
Charpy impact resistance normal (in-lb) (ASTM D256-54T, Method B-4″ span, 5″ × ½″ × ½″, unnotched samples)	1.4	1.6	3.4
Screw-holding strength, normal (lb/screw) (withdrawal load for Type A, No. 6-12 sheet-metal screws) ½ inch penetration	35	80	180
⅞ inch penetration	130	240	460
Brinell hardness no. (dry)		—	—
10-kg load, 10-mm ball, 10 sec	0.5		
50-kg load, 10-mm ball, 10 sec	—	1.8	4.6
Dimensional change due to moisture (in/in)			
Shrinkage, normal to dry	0.0008	0.0011	0.0007
Expansion, normal to 90% RH	0.0001	0.0001	0.0001
Expansion, dry to saturated	0.0010	0.0013	0.0009
Thermal expansion, in/°F (average over temperature range indicated)	2.3×10^{-6} up to 200°F shrinkage thereafter	1.3×10^{-6} up to 250°F shrinkage thereafter	2.9×10^{-6} up to 250°F shrinkage thereafter
Maximum service temperature (°F) for continuous service	900	900	800
Fire hazard classification: (listed under Underwriters' Labs. Inc., Label Service Guide No. 40 U8.13	Flame spread 0; smoke developed 0; and fuel contributed negligible		
Thermal conductivity (Btu/ft²-hr)/(°F/in)†			
Mean temperature (°F) 100	0.55	0.76	1.50
200	0.57	0.77	1.56
300	0.58	0.78	1.62
400	0.60	0.79	1.68
500	0.61	0.80	1.74
600	0.63	0.81	1.80

* For three layers of 1-inch-thick material. One-inch thickness alone shows no clearly defined failure up to 13,500 psi.

† See p. 520 for conversion factors to cgs units.

When using screws in Marinite, always drill preliminary holes. Sheet-metal screws are recommended in preference to wood screws. Where type A sheet-metal screws are used, the recommended drill sizes are as follows:

Type A sheet-metal screw size	Drill size
No. 6 (0.138 inch)	No. 36 (0.106 inch)
8 (0.165 inch)	29 (0.136 inch)
10 (0.191 inch)	20 (0.161 inch)

To prevent stripping of the thread in the material, screws should not be turned after they have been screwed home. A round-head, No. 10 × 7/8-inch type A sheet-metal screw correctly turned in a properly drilled hole will withstand a pull-out load of approximately 130 lb in Marinite-23, 240 lb in Marinite-36, and 460 lb in Marinite-65.

The surfaces and edges of Marinite can be painted with a solution of sodium silicate (water-glass) to obtain a harder surface.

Maser (see LASERS and MASERS, p. 339).

Masking for brazing. The same aluminum oxide used as a spray for tungsten heaters (p. 81) has been used successfully to prevent molten brazing alloys from wetting metal surfaces in atmosphere-brazing procedures. This is especially necessary in pure, dry-hydrogen brazing, where the oxide on stainless steel is reduced and therefore ineffective to protect jigs and fixtures of that material close to brazing operations. (It can do this in ordinary or wet hydrogen; see p. 37.)

The aluminum oxide (Alundum) is applied in the same way as for tungsten heaters—by spraying on the degreased surfaces. It can also be applied with a brush. The spray can be masked off with clean bond or druggist's paper held on with masking tape. The masking tape should not come in contact with the clean metal. Firing of the Alundum material is not required. The solvent dries very quickly, and the binder is evaporated in the furnace at a temperature far below the brazing temperature, leaving a coat of practically pure, inert powder, which can be removed easily after brazing and cooling by wiping with a clean brush. No solvent is required for removal.

A ready-mixed preparation, "Nicrobraz Green Stop-off," is available from Wall Colmonoy Corporation, Detroit 3, Michigan.

Masking lacquer (see STOP-OFF LACQUER for use in electroplating, p. 25).

Mass spectrometer. This is basically a device in which the atoms or molecules of a gas at low pressure are ionized by a stream of electrons. A magnetic field, which has no effect on the neutral or unionized gas particles, imparts a curved trajectory or path to the ions, the radius of which is a function of the mass of the ion and of the strength of the magnetic field.

The radius of curvature R of the path of any given type of *singly* charged ion (e.g., He) is determined by the relation[1]

$$R = 143.9 \frac{\sqrt{MV}}{H},$$

[1] S. Dushman, *Scientific Foundations of Vacuum Technique,* second edition, John Wiley & Sons, Inc., New York, New York, 1962, p. 361.

where R is in centimeters, V is in volts, H is in oersteds, M is the molar mass of the ion in grams.

Example: for He, $M = 4$; let $H = 1500$ oersteds and $V = 434$; then

$$R = 143.9 \frac{\sqrt{4 \cdot 434}}{1500} = 4 \text{ cm (approx.)}.$$

Nitrogen ($M = 14$) would assume a radius of 4 cm with a voltage of 124 and a field of 1500 oersteds.

Other conditions being the same, ions with greater mass have larger path radii. For example, the mass of hydrogen is 2, that of helium is 4, and nitrogen and oxygen are 14 and 16, respectively.

With a constant magnetic field, the radius of the ion path can also be affected (as noted in the relationship above) by varying the intensity of the voltage between the two slits (Fig. 96) through which the ions must pass before entering the magnetic field.

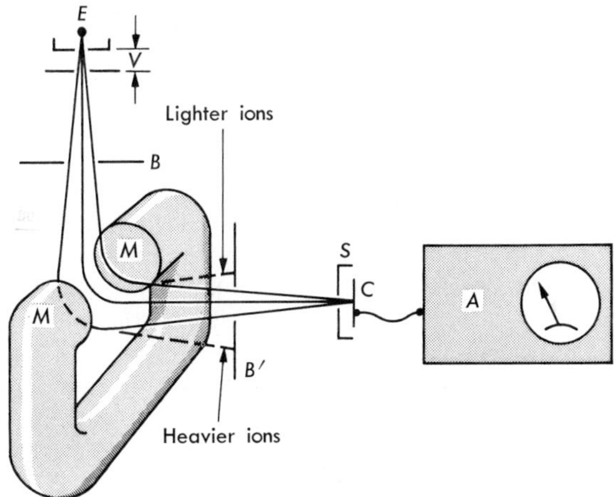

FIG. 96. Mass spectrometer principle.

If a narrow slit is so arranged that ions of a certain radius can impinge upon and pass through it, and if a negatively charged collector plate C is placed behind the slit, a current will be produced which can be detected and amplified by external circuits. The magnitude of this current will be determined by the quantity of the particular kind of ions present. As in optical spectrographs, the resolution will depend partly upon the narrowness of the slit and partly on the quality of refocusing. With a continuous change or sweep of V (or of the magnetic field, which is usually not convenient), a *spectrum* of ions of the various gases present in the chamber will pass across the slit and be detected in turn.

The device is calibrated by first securing as high a vacuum as possible (by baking, outgassing of parts, gettering, cryopumping, etc.) and then admitting a small quantity of a known pure gas at low pressure. The ion collector will pick up a *peak* of this gas at some setting of the controls. With high-resolution mass-spectrometers, it is a routine matter to separate isotopes of elements with only slightly differing masses.

Figure 96 is a simplified outline of one type of mass-spectrometer. The ions are produced at E by collisions of the gas molecules with electrons from a source which is usually a tungsten filament, although other kinds of sources have been used. The ions emerge from the slits in straight lines and pass through the baffle B. Upon reaching the space between the magnet pole-faces M, the ions are deflected or curved in their paths; some pass through the second baffle B' and impinge upon the collector slit S to strike the collector C. The heavier ions, being deflected less, do not reach the baffle B' and are therefore lost to the chamber walls, and the lighter ions suffer the same fate by being deflected more. The collector is connected externally to an amplifier A for presentation of the signal.

The mass-spectrometer principle is utilized in vacuum *leak detection* (see pp. 134–138). In this application all the conditions are held constant by suitable circuitry at values which make the instrument sensitive only to one element. Helium is commonly used for the following reasons:

1. It is rare in the atmosphere[1] and therefore produces little or no background "noise."[2]
2. Its atom is small enough to penetrate very tiny leaks.
3. It is inert, nonflammable, and nontoxic.

A suggested procedure for leak-testing vacuum devices is shown in block diagram form in Fig. 97. The throttle valve $V3$ is kept closed until the actual leak-testing operation, although the pumping system $P2$, $P3$ is kept running for everyday use, and the valve $V4$ is open. The cold trap is filled with liquid nitrogen, and the device to be tested, T, is then attached to the prepumping system (left of dashed line). The bleeder valve $V2$ is closed, valve $V1$ is opened, and the forepump $P1$ is started. If no gross leaks are present (p. 134), this system will pump down until the gauge $G1$ (a thermocouple-type gauge is suitable) indicates a pressure low enough so that the throttle valve $V3$ can be opened without danger of contaminating the electron source filament. (The connection between the prepumping system and the mass-spectrometer is made through Tygon vacuum tubing or a metal bellows-type hose.) Valve $V3$ is opened slowly in case of trapped air bubbles. The gauge $G2$[3] on the mass-spectrometer system will usually indicate a lower pressure than the gauge $G1$ because of its proximity to the cold trap and the diffusion pump $P3$.

If the location of suspected small leaks is not known, the device to be tested is covered with a loose-fitting plastic bag which is then filled with tank helium at a pressure only slightly above atmospheric. The presence of a leak will be indicated on the mass-spectrometer because of its sensitivity to helium alone. If the leak is very small, a few minutes may elapse before the instrument responds. The mass-spectrometer indicator is equipped with a multipoint shunt so that the relative size of a leak, if any, can be judged, and so that relatively large leaks need not drive the indicator off scale.

If a leak is indicated, the plastic bag is removed and the helium is applied with a small probe (a hypodermic needle) to all the places such as welds, brazes, and other joints which might be suspect. The probe is moved over the surface slowly. Always

---

[1] Approximately 1:200,000 parts of air.

[2] "Helium Diffusion Through Glass," V. O. Altemose, *J. Appl. Phys.*, **32**, 309, 1961.

[3] A Philips or Penning-type cold-cathode ionization gauge (p. 431).

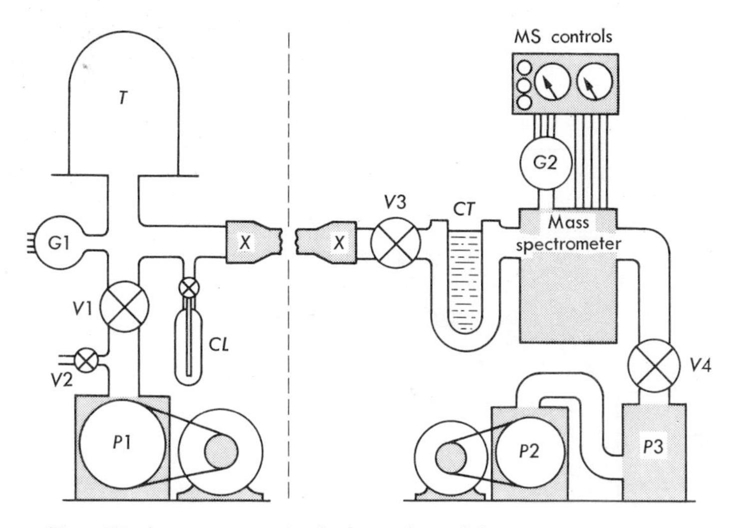

FIG. 97. Arrangement for leak-testing with mass spectrometer.

keep in mind that helium will rise in the air, so the searching should begin at the *top* of the device.

A good mass-spectrometer leak detector should have a sensitivity of 10^{-12} liter/sec, and should be equipped with a circuit to produce an audible signal whose pitch increases with the quantity of helium entering the system through a leak. With this accessory, the operator can apply the probe without having to watch a meter. A calibrated leak, *CL*,[1] is placed in the system as shown so that the calibration of the mass-spectrometer can be checked from time to time. A simple helium/glass leak is illustrated in Fig. 98. The tube is pumped and filled with helium at atmospheric pressure. The small tube has a thin wall such that the helium atoms can slowly diffuse through it.

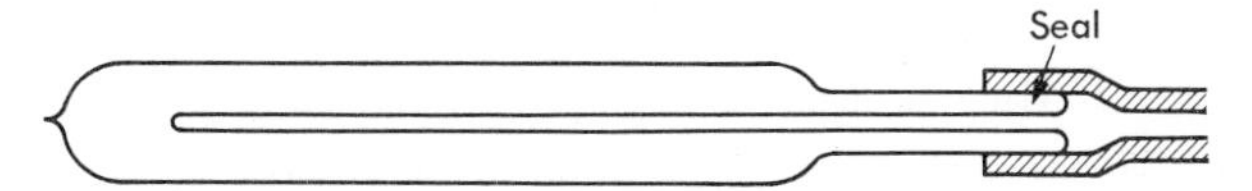

FIG. 98. Helium-calibrated leak for adjusting mass spectrometer.

Before removing the vessel under test, the electron source and amplifier are turned off, the valve *V*3 closed, and the forepump *P*1 shut down. Opening the bleeder valve *V*2 admits air to the prepump section to allow removal of the vessel *T*.

A manifold setup for leak-testing in production is suggested in Fig. 99. The valves are arranged on the manifold so that individual test pieces can be removed or added without disturbing the vacuum.

A partial bibliography on the subject of mass-spectrometers and helium leak-test apparatus is given on the next page.

[1] "Purity of Helium Permeating through Quartz into a Vacuum System," J. R. Young and N. R. Whetten, *Rev. Sci. Instr.*, **32,** 453, 1961.

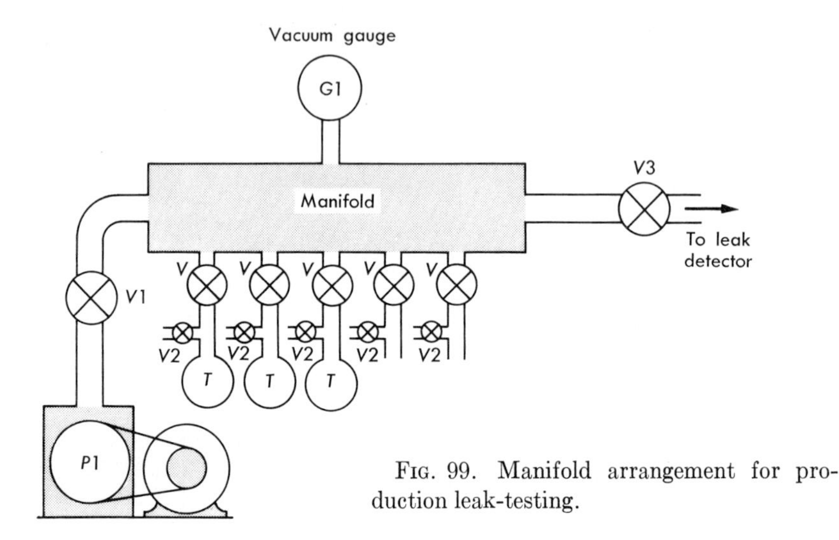

Fig. 99. Manifold arrangement for production leak-testing.

General—Bibliography

F. W. Aston, *Phil. Mag.*, **38**, 707, 1919; **39**, 611, 1920.

F. W. Aston and R. H. Fowler, *ibid.*, **43**, 514, 1922.

A. J. Dempster, *Phys. Rev.*, **11**, 316, 1918; **18**, 415, 1921; *Proc. Am. Phil. Soc.*, **7**, 45, 1921; *Phys. Rev.*, **20**, 631, 1922.

Mass Spectroscopy in Physics Research, National Bureau of Standards Circular No. 522 (Government Printing Office, Washington 25, D.C.), January 23, 1953. Authors: J. Mattauch, O. C. Nier, H. Ewald, N. Svartholm, R. F. K. Herzog, W. Paul, M. G. Inghram, H. D. Hagstrom, and others.

Mass Spectrometry, Conference of Institute of Petroleum, London, 1952. Authors: J. W. Warren, J. D. Craggs, G. P. Barnard, D. L. Nicholson, and others.

Methoden und Anwendungen der Massenspektroskopie, H. Ewald and H. Hintenberger, *Verlag Chemie,* GMBH, Weinheim Bergstrasse, 1953.

A. O. C. Nier, *Rev. Sci. Instr.*, **11**, 212, 1940.

Helium leak detection—Bibliography

A. O. Nier, C. M. Stevens, A. Hustrulid, and T. A. Abbott, *J. Appl. Phys.*, **18**, 30, 1947.

W. G. Worcester and E. G. Doughty, *Trans. Am. Inst. Electr. Engrs.*, **65**, 946, 1946.

H. A. Thomas, T. W. Williams, and J. A. Hipple, *Rev. Sci. Instr.*, **17**, 368, 1946; *Westinghouse Engr.*, **6**, 108, 1946.

See also:

Characteristics of Electrical Discharges in Magnetic Fields, J. Backus, National Nuclear Energy Series, Div. I, **5**, Chapter 11; McGraw-Hill Book Co., Inc., New York, New York, 1949.

R. Loevinger, University of California Radiation Laboratory Reports RL 20.6.23, May 6, 1944; RL 20.6.34, September 26, 1944.

J. Backus, University of California Radiation Laboratory Reports 20.6.36, March 19, 1945.

Vacuum Equipment and Techniques, A. Guthrie and R. K. Wakerling, McGraw-Hill Book Co., New York, New York, 1949.

Mass Spectrometer Researches, G. P. Barnard; Her Majesty's Stationery Office, London, 1956.

Mass Spectroscopy, H. Duckworth, Cambridge University Press, London, 1958.

Electron Impact Phenomena, F. H. Field and J. L. Franklin, Academic Press, Inc., New York, New York, 1957.

Scientific Foundations of Vacuum Technique, Second edition, S. Dushman, John Wiley & Sons, Inc., New York, pp. 361, 344, 1962.

J. L. Peters, *Rev. Sci. Instr.,* **30,** 1093, 1959.

N. R. Daly, *ibid.,* **31,** 720, 1960.

S. Jnanananda, *High Vacua,* D. Van Nostrand & Co., New York, New York, 1949.

Materials for tube construction (see pp. 35–53, 112–117, 138–148; also note specific materials in glossary or index.

McLeod gauge (see pp. 348 *et seq.*).

Mean free path (mfp or free path). In a gas at atmospheric pressure, the distance between molecules is very small, but as the pressure is reduced (i.e., as evacuation proceeds), this distance is progressively increased. However, the distribution of molecules is not uniform, and therefore we speak of an average, or mean, distance. The concept assumes that the molecules are stationary, which, of course, is not strictly true because they all have random motion. Nevertheless, compared to the speed of an electron, or other charged particle, the motion of the neutral gas molecules can be considered as small enough to allow the calculation of mean free path to be approximately correct.

Mean free path can therefore be defined, for all practical purposes, as the average distance between collisions of a charged moving particle with neutral molecules.

$$L = \frac{u}{nu\pi d^2} = \frac{1}{n\pi d^2},$$

where L is the mean free path, πd^2 is the area for collision, u is the velocity of the moving particle, $u\pi d^2$ is the volume of collision.

In the case of a high-speed electron in a gas at reduced pressure (the relative sizes of the electron and the molecule being taken into account), $L_e = 5.64L_g$, where L_e is the mfp of the electron and L_g that of the molecule.

In the above formulas, L is proportional to the *temperature* at constant pressure, and inversely proportional to the *pressure* at constant temperature.[1]

A rough approximation of the magnitudes involved in the mean-free-path concept is given below.

PRESSURE (TORR)	MFP (METERS)
(1 atm) 760	10^{-7}
6	10^{-5}
0.2	4×10^{-3}
4×10^{-3}	10^{-1}
2×10^{-4}	6
6×10^{-6}	100
8×10^{-8}	5000
9×10^{-9}	50,000

[1] See *Gaseous Conductors,* J. D. Cobine, second edition, 1958, p. 20, Dover Publications, Inc., New York, New York.

Mercury (Hg) is a metal, liquid at room temperature (melting point −38.77°C, boiling point 356.9°C), with a specific gravity of 13.546 gm/cm³ at 20°C. It is a fair conductor of electricity, having a resistivity of 575 ohm-mil-ft (95.78 microhm-cm) or about the same as certain stainless steels and nickel-chrome-iron resistance alloys. It is used in thermometers because of its regular expansion coefficient. Up to about 300°C, the space above the mercury in a thermometer is evacuated; up to about 540°C, nitrogen or carbon dioxide under pressure is used. If fused quartz is used for the capillary tube, temperatures up to 800°C can be measured. The lower limit for all mercury themometers is −39°C.

Because of its electrical conductivity, mercury is used in thermometer-type thermostatic switches, in which two contact wires are sealed into the glass, or one wire and an adjustable probe at the top.

In vacuum work, mercury is used in manometers and McLeod gauges (see pp. 348 *et seq.*), and in mercury-vapor or diffusion pumps. It is also introduced into various types of discharge tubes (see MERCURY-ARC VERSUS MERCURY-VAPOR TUBES below).

Mercury oxidizes slightly in air at room temperature, hence for most purposes, it should be used in sealed or atmosphere-protected enclosures. As an example, mercury switches consist of glass ampoules containing a small quantity of liquid mercury and having electrodes sealed in so that tilting of the ampoule, manually or by an electromagnet, makes and breaks the contact.

For use in most devices, such as those mentioned, the mercury should be carefully filtered and distilled.

The vapor of mercury is utilized in many electron discharge devices, and is admitted to the tube or device by distillation, as described on pp. 123, 124.

Mercury evaporates in the air and its vapor is poisonous. Any spilled metal must be removed promptly and the room thoroughly ventilated.

Mercury forms alloys or amalgams with a number of other metals, notably copper, tin, zinc, gold, silver, platinum, and alloys of these. With aluminum, mercury forms a chemical compound at a rapid rate. Therefore, none of these metals can be used as containers for liquid mercury, and caution should be observed even in the use of these metals in mercury-vapor discharge devices. However, since mercury's rate of attack on steel and stainless steel is extremely low, these alloys can be used for practical containers of mercury.

Mercury-arc versus mercury-vapor tubes. In the mercury-arc tube, an actual arc is struck on a pool of mercury by mechanical or other means and is "kept alive" by a relatively small standby current which flows continuously. The mercury-arc tube is capable of handling very large currents for short periods without injury. These currents are limited only by the efficiency of the cooling system (water cooling in the case of large, steel-tank units) in keeping the vapor pressure inside the tube from reaching an excessive value.

In the mercury-vapor tube, on the other hand, the presence of a hot cathode obviates the necessity for a "keep-alive" current, so that as long as the cathode is heated, current may be drawn or shut off at any time. The maximum current handled by such a hot-cathode, mercury-vapor tube is determined by the available emission from the cathode and the ambient temperature. If this current is exceeded, the tube would suffer serious damage.

Small glass mercury-arc tubes are used as rectifiers for battery-charging and spot-welding control service. Larger tubes, of steel-tank construction with water-cooling, are used to supply dc loads for power applications such as electric transportation systems.

Mercury-vapor tubes are widely used as rectifiers in low- or high-voltage circuits where relatively large currents are handled, for example as rectifiers in induction heating and radio communication equipment. Mercury vapor lamps, such as the Cooper-Hewitt lamp, have been in use for many years for illumination purposes. The modern fluorescent lamp is a modification of this, incorporating hot cathodes and a mixed phosphor with which the inside of the tube is coated.[1] This phosphor glows brilliantly as a result of the much less luminous mercury discharge.[2] Fluorescent lamps operate at not much above room temperature and are more efficient sources of light than incandescent lamps. These lamps can also be made to glow by the action of a high-frequency field and can be used as indicators of such fields.

Mercury-diffusion (or vapor) pump. This is similar to the oil-diffusion or vapor pump (pp. 227, 228, 231, 232) in that the mercury is vaporized in a boiler and passes through a jet or jets, the mercury atom stream carrying with it or propelling particles of other gases. The mercury is then condensed on a cooled surface and the pumped gases are drawn into a conventional mechanical or forepump (pp. 253–256).

Mercury-vapor pumps must be designed so that the heater power is adequate to evaporate the mercury at the forepump pressure. Efficient cooling must be provided to condense the mercury vapor. Tap water at about 10°C or lower, used in a jacket disposed around the high-pressure section of the pump, is usually suitable. Mercury pumps do not operate with air cooling, as in the case of some oil-diffusion pumps.

Mercury-vapor pumps are used in vacuum systems (a) where oil vapors cannot be tolerated, (b) where tubes are to be filled with mercury or mercury vapor, and (c) where "clean" vacuum conditions are imperative. In the cases of (a) and (c) efficient cold-trapping must be inserted between the pump and the vacuum line. This can be solid carbon dioxide ("dry ice") with acetone; liquid nitrogen, or liquid helium, each contained in a Dewar flask or other suitable container. (The vapor pressure of mercury at the sublimation temperature of carbon dioxide, −78.6°C, is about 3×10^{-9} mm, and at liquid nitrogen or liquid helium temperatures considerably lower). (See COLD TRAP, pp. 211–212.)

Metal-to-ceramic seals (see CERAMIC-TO-METAL SEALS, p. 67).

Metal-to-glass seals (see GLASS-TO-METAL SEALS, pp. 54, 281, 282, 326).

Metal-to-mica seals (see MICA-TO-METAL SEALS, p. 374).

Metallizing (see DEPOSITION, p. 224; also EVAPORATION, VACUUM, pp. 247, 564).

Metal gaskets (see GASKETS, METAL, pp. 117, 118, 223, 309, 320, 408, 571).

Metal powders for use in brazing. It is sometimes desirable to use metal powders instead of wire or foil for furnace (atmosphere) brazing. This is especially true in joining parts with odd contours or that have relatively inaccessible corners or pockets. As with wires or foils, the alloy powder should not contain volatile constituents which might contaminate the furnace atmosphere.

---

[1] See pp. 250 *et seq.*

[2] See *Gaseous Conductors,* J. D. Cobine, Dover Publications, Inc., New York, New York, p. 542, 1958.

Brazing alloy powders are obtainable in most compositions from 20 to 300 mesh (or finer). The mesh size should be as fine as possible, especially for small work. The powder can be mixed with a small quantity of a binder, such as that given on p. 81, or with a simple ethyl or amyl acetate or pyroxylin lacquer, and applied with a fine brush. The binder is evaporated during heating and leaves no residue. A stop-off or masking procedure, such as that outlined on p. 358, can be applied to powder brazing for special effects.

Metals, refractory. The following table shows 10 metals[1] with melting points above 2000°C. These can therefore be considered *refractory.*

METAL	MELTING POINT (°C)	CORROSION RESISTANCE*	STRENGTH*	FABRICABILITY*
Tungsten	3410	3	1	4
Rhenium	3180	—	—	(See p. 462)
Tantalum	2996	1	4	1
Osmium	2700	—	—	—
Molybdenum	2610	4	2	3
Iridium	2454	—	—	—
Columbium	2415	2	3	2
Ruthenium	2400	—	—	—
Hafnium	2130	—	—	—
Boron	2100	—	—	—

* These values are given only for tungsten, tantalum, molybdenum, and columbium; 1 is the highest degree.

Metals, vacuum-melted. Certain obvious advantages are gained by smelting or refining metals in a vacuum furnace. The metal is freed from gross contamination with gases and volatile alloying elements and, as a consequence, often has superior crystalline structure, mechanical properties, and corrosion resistance. At the present time, fairly large melts of some common metals in tonnage quantities can be produced, and considerable work is being done on a laboratory or even semiproduction basis to produce ultrarefined metals by zone-refining (p. 578) and by the growing of single crystals (p. 485).

The properties of some commercially available vacuum-melted metals and alloys are given below.

Ferrovac E[2] is a gas-free, high-purity iron produced by melting and purifying electrolytic iron under high vacuum. This treatment removes gases and minimizes inclusions, which results in improved magnetic properties. Ferrovac E has high magnetic saturation, relatively good permeability, and low coercive force. Saturation induction values as high as 21,600 gausses have been obtained. The only material with a higher saturation flux density is the 35% cobalt-iron alloy, which has a saturation value of approximately 24,200 gausses.

[1] "The Refractory Metals and Their Alloys," J. Chelius, presented at Petroleum Mechanical Engineering Conference, Kansas City, Missouri, September 25–27, 1961. Reprints are available from Fansteel Metallurgical Corporation, North Chicago, Illinois.

[2] All data on Ferrovac E are reproduced by the courtesy of the Crucible Steel Company of America, 1961.

Because high-purity iron has a relatively low electrical resistivity (high conductivity), it is most suitable for magnetic apparatus operating on direct current.

The typical composition of Ferrovac E is given below:

C	0.007%	P	0.003%	V	0.004% max.
O_2	100 ppm	S	0.006%	Al	0.010%
H_2	0.60 ppm	Ni	0.010%	Mo	0.010% max.
N_2	3.0 ppm	Pb	0.001% max.	Co	0.007% max.
Mn	0.001%	Sn	0.005% max.	Cu	0.010% max.
Si	0.005%	Cr	0.010% max.	W	0.010% max.
		Fe	balance		

The annealing temperature for optimum magnetic quality (high permeability and low hysteresis) may vary from 1200–1600°F (650°–870°C). For optimum ductility and grain size, heat to 690°–720°C in a controlled atmosphere of dry hydrogen or cracked ammonia or in a vacuum. Hold for 1 to 4 hours; furnace-cool to 540°C. The steel may then be air-cooled, if desired. Best results are obtained by applying 60 to 80% cold reduction prior to the final anneal.

For optimum magnetic properties at all inductions, the annealing temperature range normally employed is 815° to 870°C. The metal should be annealed in the controlled atmosphere, and all heating and cooling at temperatures above 540°C should be at a rate not over 50°C per hour. Parts should be protected from oxidation or carburization at all times; any atmospheric contamination is harmful to the magnetic performance. Some low flux-density improvement can be obtained by annealing the iron in very dry hydrogen (−50°C dew point or less) at temperatures from 1093° to 1316°C. A critical transformation occurs at about 910°C. Holding the metal just below this transformation (e.g., 900°C), followed by slow cooling, results in desirable grain growth, with an increase in permeability at low or moderate induction levels. Holding at 843°C for several hours after a high-temperature anneal may also aid in improving permeability. Thermal treatments above 870°C are not necessary when the material is to be used in high-flux-density applications (e.g., not over 15,000 gausses).

Ferrovac E in the annealed condition is soft and ductile and can be fabricated at room temperature by any of the commercial methods. It is especially well suited for rolling, spinning, bending, and stamping operations. These cold-working processes induce stresses which are harmful to the magnetic properties. However, optimum magnetic properties can be restored by subsequent annealing or stress relieving. The stress-relieving temperature range is 760° to 870°C (in dry hydrogen), and the metal should be furnace-cooled.

Ferrovac E is not difficult to machine, although it produces a continuous-type chip with a builtup edge that is always associated with ductile metals. The chips are long and stringy, and chip breakers can be used to advantage. Fine feeds and deep cuts, using tools ground to sharper cutting angles than for carbon steels, are recommended. High-speed cutting tools are generally used for most machining operations. The machinability index rating of Ferrovac E is about 60% of that of AISI B-1112 Bessemer screw stock.

The steel may be readily welded by any of the commercially established methods. It is suitable for oxyacetylene-, resistance-, and metallic-arc welding. Oxygen or carbon pickup should be avoided. Stress-relief annealing (in dry hydrogen) will eliminate stresses (and reduce pickup) set up during the welding operation. Brazing and soldering can be easily carried out.

(*Note:* This material is amenable to the processes described for stainless steel, pp. 41 *et seq.*)

The crystal structure of Ferrovac E is: alpha iron (to A_3), bcc, 2.8664A at 25°C.
Transformation temperatures (°C):

A_2 (curie temperature)	755–791
Ac_3 (alpha to gamma)	910
Ac_4 (gamma to delta)	1390
Melting point (approximate)	1539°C
Thermal conductivity at 20°C (cgs)	0.20
Latent heat of fusion (cal/gm)	65.5
Specific heat (gm-cal/gm/°C)	0.105
Mean linear coefficient of thermal expansion:	
20°–260°C	12.55×10^{-6} in/in
260°–816°C	15.75×10^{-6} in/in

Electrical resistivity:

Temperature (°C)	Microhm-cm
24	10.13
93	13.89
204	21.74
316	31.75
427	49.94

Modulus of elasticity (psi)	30×10^6
Specific gravity at 20°C (gm/cc)	7.88
Density at 20°C (lb/in^3)	0.285

Magnetic properties (ac), annealed at 854°C:

Gauge (in.)	Core loss (watts/lb)	
	$B = 10$ kg	$B = 15$ kg
0.025	1.74	4.80

The dc magnetic properties of Ferrovac E compared with those of ingot iron are listed on p. 369. All tests were made on 1 inch × 5/8 inch × 12 inch bars.

The properties given are typical. Normal variation in chemical analysis, size, and thermal treatment may cause deviation from the values indicated. Temperatures shown are metal temperatures.

Nivac P[1] is a high-purity nickel which is produced by melting and refining electrolytic nickel in high vacuum. Gases and high-vapor-pressure elements are removed,

[1] All data on Nivac P from data sheet of the Crucible Steel Company of America, 1961, by whose courtesy the material is reproduced.

MAGNETIC PROPERTIES OF FERROVAC E AND INGOT IRON

	A		B		C	
	FERROVAC E	INGOT IRON	FERROVAC E	INGOT IRON	FERROVAC E	INGOT IRON
1	9900	920	32200	2200	37200	6200
2	9100	690	14600	950	22300	2600
3	0.37	2.60	0.18	2.60	0.14	0.90
4	7600	6200	11200	11100	8900	13600
5	1100	—	750	11750	550	4690

EXPLANATION

1 — Maximum permeability (μ_{max}).
2 — Permeability at B= 10kg (μ).
3 — Coercive force from B = 10kg, H_c (oersteds).
4 — Residual induction from B = 10kg, B_r (gausses).
5 — Hysteresis loss from B = 10kg (ergs/cm^3).
A — As forged and machined; B — Stress-relieved 5 hours at 760°C in dry nitrogen;
C — Annealed for 35 hours at 854°C in wet hydrogen.

Effect of cold work on tensile properties and hardness:

COLD WORK BY ROLLING (%)	TENSILE STRENGTH (PSI)	YIELD STRENGTH 0.2% OFFSET (PSI)	ELONGATION IN 2 IN. (%)	HARDNESS ROCKWELL B (R_b)
Annealed	35,000	20,000	60.0	20
20	44,000	40,000	35.0	50
40	54,000	50,000	20.0	65
60	66,000	64,000	10.0	72
80	80,000	78,000	5.0	78

and the purified metal is virtually free of nonmetallic inclusion. Nivac P is used in vacuum tubes and in some types of gas-filled tubes in which it is necessary for the components which operate at elevated temperatures to be very pure so that the vacuum or the gas pressure will be maintained. Because of its low work-hardening rate, its fabricating properties are superior; i.e., spinning, drawing, rolling, cold coining, and forming. Nivac P, with controlled small additions of silicon, magnesium, etc., is used in strip form and in tubing in the manufacture of cathodes for electron tubes. The quality of these cathode nickel alloys is consistently uniform, and the close chemical control which can be achieved by vacuum-melting assures reliability of tube performance.

Typical composition of Nivac P is given below (in percent):

C	0.007	Co	0.130	Ca	>0.001
O_2	0.002	Cu	0.008	Cr	>0.003
N_2	0.0001	Mn	>0.004	Al	>0.005
S	0.004	Si	>0.007	Mg	>0.003
P	0.001	Pb	>0.010	Mo	>0.001
Fe	0.009	Sn	>0.005	Ni	balance

For soft-temper, fine-grain stock, anneal 1 hour at 500°C (in hydrogen) after 70% cold reduction. For continuous anneal, use 550°C, adjusting speed to get 5 to 15 Rockwell B or 60 to 65 Rockwell F. For deep-drawing stock, anneal 1 hour at 450°C (in hydrogen) after 40% reduction. For continuous anneal, use 500°C with speed adjustment for hardness, as in fine-grain anneal.

Nivac P can be easily spot-welded and heated by induction. Soldering, welding, and brazing present no problems.

Nivac P has high corrosion resistance. Oxidation at high temperatures is low, and any oxide formed is tightly adherent.

Nivac P is ferromagnetic, with a saturation induction of 6100 gausses (pure iron = 21,600 gauss). The curie temperature is 360°C.

Other physical properties:

Crystal form and lattice constant at 24.8°C	fcc, 3.5168 A
Density at 20°C (gm/cc)	8.885
Melting point (°C)	1453
Specific heat, (gm-cal/gm/°C) (0–100°C)	0.13
Latent heat of fusion (cal/gm)	73.0
Thermal expansion coefficient per °C, 25–100°C	13.3×10^{-6}
Thermal conductivity (cgs)	0.145
Electrical resistivity at 20°C (microhm-cm)	9.5
Temperature coefficient of resistivity (microhm-cm/°C) 20–100°C	0.00474
Modulus of elasticity at 20°C (psi)	30×10^{6}
Hardness (sheet) annealed (fine-grained)	60 Rockwell F
cold-worked 10%	68 Rockwell F
cold-worked 20%	79 Rockwell F
cold-worked 40%	87 Rockwell F
cold-worked 80%	92 Rockwell F

Properties shown for Nivac P are typical values. Normal variations in chemistry, size, and condition of heat treatment may cause deviations from values shown.

Other vacuum-metallurgy products of the Crucible Steel Company are as follows:

Ferrovac-52100: a 1% carbon steel with excellent machinability, high tensile strength, and oil-hardening properties. It has a Rockwell hardness of C-65-66 in the hardened condition.

Waspalloy (M-252 Alloy): a high-nickel alloy containing chromium (19%), cobalt (10%), molybdenum (10%), and other constituents. It is essentially non-magnetic and can be used in high-temperature applications, its tensile strength at 930°C being 40,000 psi.

1020 Alloy: a low-carbon steel (mild steel), useful for making vacuum tubes and vessels. It has excellent machinability.

Alloy 304: an austenitic 18–8 type stainless steel with a low carbon content (less than 0.01%) for vacuum-tube components. It is essentially nonmagnetic. This alloy is not hardenable.

Alloy 440C: a hardenable, magnetic stainless steel.

Metastable atoms (see ATOM, METASTABLE, p. 109; see also p. 160).

Methanol (Methyl or wood alcohol) (see ALCOHOLS, p. 150).

Mica.[1] Many groups of natural mica exist, but for electrical insulation two types are used: *Muscovite* $(H_2KAl_3(SiO_4))_3$, often referred to as India, white, or ruby mica; and *Phlogopite* $(H_2KMg_3Al(SiO_4))_3$, usually called high-heat amber mica.

Phlogopite mica varies in color from light silver to very dark brown, and is nearly opaque. It can withstand higher temperatures, generally in the range of 760° to 980°C, than any other kind of mica. However, it does not have the desirable properties found in the higher qualities of Muscovite mica. Therefore, except where temperatures beyond the limits of Muscovite mica (540°C) are involved, Phlogopite is used to a minor degree in electronic applications.

Optically flat mica is obtainable only in small sizes up to 20 in.^{2} Its cost is approximately 20 times the cost of an equivalent size in radio quality. It is good engineering to utilize the smallest piece of mica of the lowest quality that will serve the purpose in order to obtain economy.

Blocks (or "books" or plates) of mica are specified by ASTM-D351-57T as 0.007 inches-0.030 inches thick. However, only a very small percentage of the plates are over 0.015 inches.

The better qualities of mica will withstand 1000 v/mil. On applications requiring heavier thicknesses, a number of thinner pieces can be assembled or loosely stacked.

Mica is one of the most difficult of all insulating materials to work with tools because it is an abrasive and also can be a lubricant. Die-stamping of radio tube micas requires such specialized compound blank-and-pierce dies that only a few die shops in the country can make them.

Snubber points are usually specified on the perimeters of radio tube micas, and these are designed to correct the necessary variations of the inside diameters of glass tube envelopes. The points or serrated edges are usually specified to two diameters, with every other point being longer. The longer points will "give" inside the tube at the upper limit of the tolerance so as to keep the working components of the tube centrally located and free from vibration. Also, with the inside diameters of the glass envelope at the lower limit of the tolerance, the longer points will bend without flaking, to allow the slightly shorter points to center the mounted components.

Natural mica of a quality selected for flatness, machinability, and low electrical losses at ultrahigh frequencies can be used for microwave windows. A mica window can readily be assembled to another material by low-temperature methods to provide a vacuum-tight seal (see p. 374). Sections about 0.005 inch thick by one-half square inch can withstand up to 50-psi pressure. Windows for this purpose must be fabricated by the finest machining methods rather than by die-stamping, since the

[1] From "Natural Mica for Industry," J. A. Bufalino, Mica Industry Association, Inc., 420 Lexington Ave., New York 17, New York. Reproduced by permission.

latter method causes delamination along the edges. The pieces must be free of scratches, partial layers, inclusions, and fingerprints.

For production vacuum-tube applications, precision tolerances on hole spacing, etc., must be held to close limits. Holes having diameters as small as 0.012 can be punched. Since mica is a hard material, the maximum thickness of the piece should not exceed 50% of the diameter of the smallest hole to minimize breakage of steel punches. Dies made from tungsten carbide have been successful for punching mica blanks.

Micas for windows, targets, mosaics, and other applications where the highest quality is demanded are selected from the best V-1 grade. It must be optically flat and of uniform color, free of fingerprints, scratches, imperfections, and contamination. The pieces are usually inspected by polariscope or by holding the mica facing a window. If the mica can be "seen," it is rejected.

The dielectric constant (i.e., the ratio between the electrical capacity of a condenser using solid material and the same capacity with air as a dielectric) of Muscovite mica is about 7 and of Phlogopite or amber mica about 6, both tested at 1000 kc. For most insulating materials, the dielectric constant changes with frequency; ruby Muscovite mica, however, remains unchanged from 60 cycles up to 3×10^9 cycles. Temperature has little or no effect on the dielectric constant of mica.

Muscovite mica contains about 5% water of crystallization; amber or phlogopite mica has about 3%. At elevated temperatures this water is driven off, and the mica calcines or crumbles (flakes) and loses its mechanical strength. In Muscovite, dehydration can start at 540°C; high-heat grades of Phlogopite begin to dehydrate at 760°C to 980°C. These temperatures may thus be considered as the limits for continuous service.

The dielectric strength of natural mica varies greatly with quality and thickness. Good-quality ruby mica should withstand 1500 to 3000 volts per mil in thicknesses of 0.001 inch or 0.002 inch. Heavily stained qualities will average 600 v/mil. The dielectric strength of mica may be considerably less at radio frequencies than at 60 cycles.

Natural mica has excellent chemical stability, with the following exceptions: Muscovite will not resist hydrofluoric acid; amber mica will not resist sulfuric acid. Oil is damaging to mica because it tends to creep into and separate the laminations; however, it is not injurious from a chemical standpoint.

The approximate chemical composition of the two micas is as follows:

Muscovite mica		Phlogopite mica	
Silica	45.5%	Silica	40.0%
Alumina	37.5	Alumina	17.0
Potash	12.0	Potash	10.0
Water	5.0	Magnesia	26.5
		Ferric oxide	3.5
		Water	3.0

Natural mica is optically negative and doubly refractive. The optic axial angle of Muscovite is 50° to 75°, and of amber mica 5° to 25°.

The coefficient of thermal expansion of Muscovite is 9 to 12×10^6 in/°C (20–600°C); for phlogopite it is 12 to 15×10^6 in/°C (20–600°C).

Other properties of mica are tabulated below:

PROPERTIES	MUSCOVITE (RUBY MICA)	PHLOGOPITE (AMBER MICA)
Specific gravity (gm/cc)	2.8 average	2.8 average
Weight factor (in^3/lb)	10	10
Specific heat (gm-cal/gm/°C)	0.207	0.207
Hardness, Mohs' scale	2.8 to 3.2	2.5 to 3.0
Hardness, Shore scale	80 to 150	70 to 100
Volume resistivity (ohm-cm)[3]	2×10^{13} to 1×10^{17}	Somewhat less
Modulus of elasticity (psi)	25×10^6 approximate	25×10^6 approximate
Compressive strength (psi)	32,000	32,000
Thermal conductivity (cgs)	0.0018	—
Dc volume resistivity at 25°C (ohm-cm)	5×10^{13}	—

Below are descriptions of visual quality classification of some grades of Muscovite mica (ASTM(D351–57T)):

V-1. Clear, hard, of uniform color, nearly flat; free from all stains, foreign inclusions, cracks, and other defects.
V-2. Clear and slightly stained, hard, of uniform color, nearly flat; may contain slight crystallographic discoloration; very slight air inclusions in not more than one-fourth of usable area.
V-3. Fair-stained, hard, of uniform color; may contain slight waves, slight crystallographic discolorations, and slight air inclusions in not more than one-half of usable area.
V-4. Good-stained, hard, of uniform color; may contain medium waves, slight crystallographic discoloration, and medium air inclusions in not more than two-thirds of usable area.
V-5. Stained A quality, hard; may contain medium air inclusions uniformly distributed in the usable area, slight green vegetable stains, and medium waves.

Small particles of mica used in electron tubes can become conductive from sputtered cathode material or from material evaporated by other tube elements; hence, mica insulators should be shaped to avoid points or sharp angles or edges which might easily be frayed.[1]

Splitting of mica is accomplished by scraping the edge gently with a very sharp blade (double-edge razor blade), which is then inserted between the laminae.

An inexpensive type of mica is available as "builtup" sheets in which thin mica splittings or flakes of relatively small size are cemented together with various kinds of binders. While this material is, in general, not suitable for use in vacuum devices because of the binder, it finds wide use in the construction of heating elements for ovens, and is therefore useful in the laboratory. Both the Muscovite and amber mica splittings are used for making builtup sheets, the latter being

[1] "The Life and Reliability of Valves," K. Rodenhuis, H. Santing, and H. J. M. van Tol, *Philips Technical Review,* **18,** (7), 181–192, 1956–7.

preferable for higher-temperature service. This material is available from Insulation Manufacturers Corporation, 565 West Washington Boulevard, Chicago 6, Illinois.

A flexible Fiberglas tape coated with Silicone resin and mica will withstand temperatures up to 250°C. It is known as "MGS Class H+" and is available from the Mica-Coated Products Company, 426 Essex Street, Salem, Massachusetts. It comes in sheets 36 inches wide and in thicknesses from 0.003 inch to 0.010 inch.

Mica-to-metal seals. The following material is excerpted from an article by N. Anton.[1] Muscovite mica (see p. 371) is used in thin plates, with type 446 stainless steel (Allegheny-Ludlum Glass-Sealing Alloy HC-1: 28% Cr, which has a coefficient of thermal expansion of $10.5 \times 10^{-6}/°C$ between $-40°$ and 500°C). Sylvania Alloy No. 4 can be used.

The mica must be clear and free from defects and inclusions, and must be sharply cut without frayed edges.

The seal is an "outside" seal (metal outside) so that the mica and glass are in compression.

Corning glass No. 7570 (p. 270) is used in the form of a powder which will pass a 100-mesh but not a 200-mesh screen. If the powder is too fine, it will form a suspension with water which hardens too rapidly and does not allow time for application to the work. Corning 7570 "solder" glass wets mica when fused, and flows easily in an oxidizing atmosphere at 600°C. Its softening point is 440°C. (See SOLDER GLASS, p. 486.)

The mica is washed in two or more changes of clean alcohol, or degreased (pp. 7, 10). The 7570 glass is made up as a paste with a little distilled or deionized water and applied with a fine camel hair or sable brush, first to the seat in the metal tube (see Fig. 100), and then to the edges of the mica plate, which is then put in place and more glass painted around the entire seal.

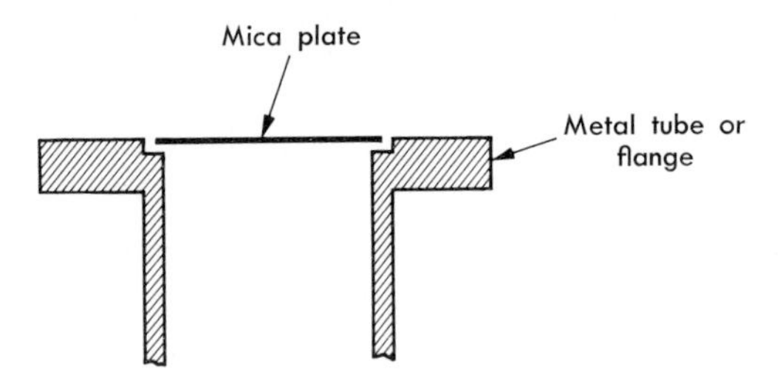

Fig. 100. Mica-to-metal seal

The assembly is fired in an air oven using a Marinite (p. 356) tray. The temperature is raised slowly, over approximately one-half hour or so, to between 550° and 600°C (the actual temperature of the work). After fusion of the glass, the work is

[1] "Fused Vacuum-Tight Metal-to-Ceramic, Ceramic-to-Glass, and Metal-to-Mica Sealing by Powdered Glass Techniques," N. Anton, *Ceramic Age,* **63,** pp. 15–19, June, 1954. See also J. S. Donal, Jr., *Rev. Sci. Instr.,* **13,** 266, 1942; L. Malter, R. L. Jepsen, and L. R. Bloom, *RCA Rev.,* **7,** 622, 1946; and *Microwave Magnetrons,* G. B. Collins, pp. 684, 685, McGraw-Hill Book Co., Inc., New York, New York, 1948.

left in the oven and allowed to cool, with the power shut off. The oxide formed on the metal is removed by careful polishing.

Seals made in this manner are vacuum-tight and can be baked at 400°C for long periods, or up to 450°C for short periods, during the exhaust.

Other types of seals are feasible using the same technique, such as Kovar with Corning No. 7052 glass powder, in which case the firing temperature is higher. Finished tubes can be baked to a maximum temperature of 550°C. A seal using Canadian amber mica (Phlogopite, p. 371) versus titanium, made with Corning No. 7572 Pyroceram, which can be baked at temperatures in excess of 500°C, is described by Anderson.[1]

Mica windows. In addition to the method for making mica windows by the "solder" glass-sealing technique described above, soft copper gaskets can be used (*cf.* pp. 117–118) in a manner described by Sterzer[2] and by Strnad[3] (gold washer). Both types can be baked at elevated temperatures.

Micron is a unit of length equal to one-thousandth of a millimeter (10^{-3} mm). In vacuum parlance, this is used directly as 1×10^{-3} mm Hg (= 1/760,000 of atmospheric pressure, standard, at 0°C). The symbol is the Greek letter mu (μ).

Mild steel (low-alloy, or mild-alloy, steels). This is a general designation for steels having a low carbon content (not over 0.4%) and small proportions of other alloying elements. Mild steels are characterized by good yield-strength and ductility, and better resistance to atmospheric corrosion than ordinary open-hearth steel has. The so-called cold-rolled steels (p. 209) are usually mild steels.

Millimeter (*cf.* MICRON, above) is one-thousandth of a meter. The term is used in vacuum terminology as 1 mm Hg, which equals 1/760 of atmospheric pressure at 0°C.

Mischmetal. An alloy containing 50 to 55% cerium, 22 to 25% lanthanum, 15 to 17% neodymium, 8 to 10% of a mixture of praeseodymium, terbium, yttrium, illinium, and samarium, and 0.5 to 3.0% iron. It is sometimes used as a getter in electron tubes for the cleanup of oxygen, hydrogen, nitrogen, carbon dioxide, and other gases (see p. 105).

Molecular beams, atomic beams. Various substances are used in atomic or molecular beam clocks, masers, and the like, and can be produced as a stream or "beam" more or less by physical means as contrasted to beams of electrons or ions which are produced by electrical (or magnetic) forces. For example, cesium metal, used in some atomic clocks, is heated *in vacuo* in special ovens to above the vaporization temperature and ejected with considerable energy through thin straight channels which are very long compared with the atomic dimensions. In this way, only those particles which are traveling through and parallel to the axis of the channel emerge from the oven, and these continue in a straight line for some distance. The intensity of such a stream can be measured in various ways, one of which is for the particles to be met by an electron beam moving in the opposite direction and thus producing,

---

[1] "Thin Vacuum-Tight Mica Window Suitable for Baking at 500°C," J. M. Anderson, *Rev. Sci. Instr.*, **31**, 898, 1960.

[2] "Simple High-Temperature Vacuum-Tight Mica Window," F. Sterzer, *Rev. Sci. Instr.*, **28**, 208, 1957.

[3] "Mica Window Assembly for Use at Elevated Bake-out Temperatures," A. R. Strnad, *Rev. Sci. Instr.*, **29**, 533, 1958.

by collision, ionization of some of the atoms or molecules, which can then be deflected magnetically and made to impinge upon a negatively charged collector.[1] (*Cf.* MASS SPECTROMETER, p. 358.)

Molecular or atomic beams can be successfully produced and utilized only in a good vacuum (10^{-7} mm Hg or better) to avoid collision of the particles with each other. For this reason low oven pressures must be used.

The mean free path of the molecules or atoms should be small compared with the width of the exit channel of the oven. Beam density can be increased by using multiple parallel channels.

Molecular and viscous flow of gases.[2] In the consideration of the flow of gases through pipes and orifices, there are three more or less defined kinds of flow:

(1) VISCOUS FLOW takes place at atmospheric pressures or slight vacuums, in which the mean free path (average distance between molecules) is small compared with the dimensions of the channel through which the gas is flowing. As a consequence the molecules collide with each other much more often than they do with the walls of the tube. In this case the usual viscous fluid properties can be ascribed to the gas. Viscous flow is sometimes called Slip Flow.

(2) When the pressure is low enough so that the mean free path is large compared with the vessel dimensions, collisions of molecules with the walls occur much more often than with each other. This condition is known as MOLECULAR FLOW, in which the molecules are acting more or less independently of each other.

(3) From the above reasoning, it follows that a condition can exist in which, at intermediate pressures (moderate vacuum), both types of collision can occur and thus the flow conditions are influenced both by molecular and viscous properties. This, for want of a better name, is called the TRANSITION RANGE.

If L_a equals mean free path and a equals a characteristic dimension of the channel (e.g., the radius, in the case of a pipe or tube), then:

Viscous flow exists when $\frac{L_a}{a} < 0.01$;

Molecular flow exists when $\frac{L_a}{a} > 1.00$;

Transition range exists when $\frac{L_a}{a}$ lies between 0.01 and 1.00.

Or if we let P_μ equal pressure of gas in microns of mercury (see above), then the same statements can be expressed as follows:

Viscous flow exists when $aP_\mu > 500$;
Molecular flow exists when $aP_\mu < 5$;
Transition range exists when aP_μ lies between 5 and 500.

---

[1] "Some New Applications and Techniques of Molecular Beams," J. G. King and J. R. Zacharias, *Advances in Electronics and Electron Physics*, **VIII**, Academic Press, Inc., New York, 1956.

[2] See *Scientific Foundations of Vacuum Technique*, Saul Dushman, second edition revised, Chapter 2, John Wiley & Sons, Inc., New York (1962).

Molecular sieves. (Artificial zeolites).[1] The Linde Air Products Company (Division of Union Carbide) makes a series of adsorbents for water and other vapors which are composed of crystalline sodium and calcium alumino-silicates that have been heated to remove their water of hydration. The resulting crystals exhibit a high porosity, with pores of molecular dimensions 1.5 to 2.0×10^{-8} inch in diameter and of uniform size.

The Linde Type 4A molecular sieve, when loaded with 15 gm water/100 gm of adsorbent has a water-vapor pressure of only 0.2 mm, as compared with 6.9 mm for silica gel and 14.4 mm for activated alumina. It has an adsorptive capacity of 18 gm H_2O/100 gm of desiccant at a relative humidity of 5%. Since the material does not deliquesce or become damaged when adsorbing water vapor, free passage of air or gas through the desiccant is obtained.

Molecular sieves can be regenerated by heating and purging. Before heat is applied, the container is drained of any liquid water that may have accumulated at the bottom. The recommended temperature range for regeneration is 150° to 315°C, although the material will withstand higher temperatures without serious damage.[2]

An arrangement for drying hydrogen is described on pp. 42–44. For regenerating, a purge gas such as dry (oil-pumped) nitrogen or dry air can be used. The purge gas should, if possible, be circulated in a direction opposite to the normal flow during adsorption.

The length of time heat is applied for regeneration will be determined by experiment, but, in general, it is very much shorter than the adsorption time. Regeneration is more complete at the higher temperature.

Molecular sieves can also be used for the selective adsorption of materials other than water vapor.[3]

Molybdenum. A refractory metal commonly used in making electron tube components. Its properties are given in the following table.[4]

Atomic number	42
Atomic weight	95.95
Atomic volume	9.41
Lattice type	bcc
Lattice constant at 20°C (A)	3.1468
Isotopes (natural)	92, 94, 95, 96, 97, 98, 100
Density at 20°C (gm/cc)	10.2
Density at 20°C (lb/in^3)	0.368
Melting point (°C)	2610
Boiling point (°C)	4830
Linear coefficient of thermal expansion per °C	4.9×10^{-6}
Thermal conductivity at 20°C (cgs)	0.35
Specific heat at 20°C (gm-cal/gm/°C)	0.061

[1] See also "The Vacuum Use of Molecular Sieves and other Desiccants," E. M. Robson, *Vacuum* (Br), **11**, 10, (1961).

[2] Temperatures as high as 500°C for 4 hours can be tolerated.

[3] "Linde Molecular Sieves," Linde Air Products Company, Division of Union Carbide Corp., 30 East 42nd Street, New York 17, New York (1956).

[4] Fansteel Metallurgical Corporation, North Chicago, Illinois, 1960.

Properties of Molybdenum (*cont.*)

Electrical conductivity, %IACS (copper)	30
Temperature coefficient of electrical resistivity/°C (0–100°C)	0.0046
Tensile strength at 20°C (psi × 10^3)	120–200
Tensile strength at 500°C (psi × 10^3)	35–65
Tensile strength at 1000°C (psi × 10^3)	20–30
Young's modulus of elasticity (psi × 10^6)	
20°C	46
500°C	41
1000°C	39
Poisson's ratio	0.321
Thermionic work function, ev	55
Magnetic susceptibility (10^{-6} cgs)	0.04
Spectral emissivity, wavelength approximately 0.65 mμ	0.37 (1000°C)
Total emissivity	
at 1500°C	0.19
at 2000°C	0.24
Working temperature	1600°C down
Recrystallization temperature	900–1200°C
Stress-relieving temperature	800°C
Nuclear cross section	
Thermal neutrons (barns/atom)	2.4

Metallography: polishing—emery to 000 levigated alumina to finish.
etchant—alkaline $K_2Fe(CN)_6$ solution; etch and polish repeatedly until grain boundaries appear.

Vapor pressure (mm Hg)	
at 1600°C	2.5×10^{-8}
at 2200°C	5×10^{-4}
at 2500°C	1×10^{-2}

Electrical resistivity (microhm-cm)

Temp.	Resistivity	Temp.	Resistivity
0°C	5.2	1727	53.5
27	5.78	1927	59.5
727	23.9	2127	66.0
927	29.2	2227	69.2
1127	35.2	2327	71.8
1327	41.2	2527	78.2
1527	47.2	2622	81.4

Electron work function, ev	4.37
Ionization potential, v	7.18
Positive ion emission, ev	8.6

Chemical: Molybdenum does not noticeably tarnish or corrode at room temperature in air, but some oxidation begins at about 250°C, and the oxidation becomes quite rapid at 600°C, with evolution of MoO_3. Rapid oxidation also takes place in saturated water vapor at 700°C.

Molybdenum is practically unaffected by dilute or concentrated hydrochloric acid or sulfuric acid at room temperature, but is rapidly dissolved in hot dilute HCl and in H_2SO_4 at 200°C. At 110°C dilute H_2SO_4 has no effect on it. Concentrated nitric acid slowly reacts with molybdenum at room temperature, forming a layer of MoO_3. Dilute HNO_3 reacts fairly rapidly with the metal at room temperature, and can be used as a pickling solution. Aqua regia at room temperature does not react with molybdenum in any concentration, but attacks it rapidly when warm, forming H_2MoO_4.

Hydrofluoric acid does not attack molybdenum in any concentration, cold or warm, but in an equal-parts mixture of HF and HNO_3, the metal is rapidly dissolved.

There is no reaction with cold solutions of sodium or potassium hydroxide, and only a weak reaction when these solutions are warmed. Ammonium hydroxide produces a moderate reaction. NaOH and KOH solutions can be used electrolytically to clean molybdenum (see p. 17). Sodium hypochlorite, NaOCl, Clorox, or an equivalent can be used in dilute solution for the cleaning of this metal (see p. 11).

Molybdenum reacts violently with molten oxidizing salts such as KNO_3, KNO_2, NaO_2, K_2CO_3, $Na_2CO_3 + KNO_3$, $KClO_3$, and PbO_2.

Oxidation of molybdenum at red heat (about 600°C) takes place in nitrous oxide (N_2O), nitric oxide (NO), or sulfur dioxide (SO_2), with formation of molybdenum trioxide (MoO_3). There is no reaction with ammonia gas (NH_3).

At 1200°C hydrogen sulfide (H_2S) reacts with the metal to form molybdenum sulfide. There is no reaction with sulfur up to 440°C, but sulfides are formed at higher temperatures. Phosphorus does not react with Mo even at elevated temperatures, but the metal forms a silicide with silicon at high temperatures.

The solubility (amalgamation) of Mo with mercury is very slight (less than $2 \times 10^{-5}\%$).

Molybdenum reacts with fluorine at room temperature, with chlorine at about 300°C, and with bromine at about 700°C. There is no reaction with iodine up to 500°C.

In contact with carbon or hydrocarbons at 1100°C, there is a partial carbide formation, and complete carbonization occurs at 1300° to 1400°C.

Hydrogen does not react with Mo even up to the melting point; it does, however, have a strong reducing effect on the oxides, even in the presence of water vapor, so that the metal can be cleaned and annealed by hydrogen-firing at 800°C.

There is no reaction of Mo with nitrogen up to 1500°C, although nitrides are formed above this temperature.

Carbon dioxide oxidizes Mo above 1200°C, but there is no reaction of the metal with carbon monoxide up to 1400°C.

The *mechanical properties* of molybdenum are given on the following page.

Molybdenum sheet or wire in the lighter gauges (up to 0.030 inch) can be formed easily at room temperature. Heavier material should be warmed or heated in proportion to the thickness or diameter. Sheet of 0.050 inch or thicker should not be sheared to finish dimensions. To assure clean, square edges, the sheet should be sheared to within $\frac{1}{16}$ inch or so of desired dimensions and then machined or ground to size.

Molybdenum sheet less than 0.020 inch can be drawn or spun at room temperature, although the work is facilitated if both the work and tools or dies are heated moderately.

MECHANICAL PROPERTIES OF MOLYBDENUM AT ROOM TEMPERATURE*

FORM (IN.)	CONDITION	TENSILE STRENGTH (PSI $\times 10^{-3}$)	ELONGATION IN 2 IN. (%)	ROCKWELL HARDNESS
Rod				
0.250	Unannealed	75	5	90B
0.100	Unannealed	100	5	97B
0.050	Unannealed	120	5	100B
0.050	Annealed	90	15	95B
Wire				
0.025	Unannealed	130	5	100B
0.025	Annealed	100	15	95B
0.010	Unannealed	170	1	24C†
0.010	Annealed	125	15	100B
0.005	Unannealed	190	1	—
0.005	Annealed	140	15	—
Sheet D				
0.040	Unannealed	120	1	22C†
0.040	Annealed	85	4	95B
0.020	Unannealed	165	1	26C†
0.020	Annealed	125	7	95B
0.010	Unannealed	175	1	27C†
0.010	Annealed	130	7	95B

* From "Fansteel Tungsten and Molybdenum," Fansteel Metallurgical Corp., North Chicago, Illinois, 1954.
† Converted: 22C = 99.5B, 24C = 101B, 26C = 102.5B, 27C = 103.5B.

MECHANICAL PROPERTIES OF G.E. "HD" MOLYBDENUM SHEET*

SHEET THICKNESS (IN.)	TENSILE STRENGTH (PSI $\times 10^{3}$)	ROCKWELL B HARDNESS	ALEXANDER DUCTILITY (USING "A" TOOL) DEPRESSION (MM)
0.100	105–120	69–71	10.51
0.080	105–120	69–71	10.09
0.060	105–120	69–71	9.54
0.040	105–120	69–71	8.77
0.020	105–120	69–71	6.83

* Courtesy of General Electric Company, Lamp Metals and Components Dept., Cleveland 17, Ohio, 1959.

Stress-relieving of molybdenum after partial working is done at 1000°C in hydrogen for not more than three minutes. Excessive exposure to heat will cause embrittlement.

The metal can be turned, milled, drilled, threaded, and tapped, but it has a tendency to chip. The piece should be firmly and rigidly held, and tools should be sharp and well supported. Molybdenum is best ground with relatively soft-bonded wheels of not too fine a grit. Alumina wheels are suitable for most purposes, and plenty of coolant should be used. For cutting rod, tubing, and wire, a rubber-bonded abrasive cutoff wheel is recommended.

Molybdenum can be brazed in regular-grade hydrogen with the usual furnace-brazing metals, but for best results alloys containing nickel (gold-nickel, copper-nickel) should be used, or the molybdenum piece should be nickel-plated (see below) before brazing, whereupon silver-copper eutectic can be used.

Molybdenum can be spot-welded to itself if the surfaces are first etched to provide projections for localized heating. Fluxes (p. 116), such as thin tantalum, nickel, or platinum foil, can be used for making sandwich spot-welds. In using tantalum, immerse the work in water to prevent oxidation.

Methods of cleaning molybdenum are given on pp. 10, 11, 17.

Nickel plating of molybdenum can be carried out by the following procedure:

1. Etch lightly in the following solution:

HNO_3	40%
H_2SO_4	25%
Water	35%
Temperature	room

2. Rinse in running water.

3. Electropolish in dilute chromic-sulfuric cleaning fluid (p. 5), with the Mo piece connected as anode:

Time	1 minute
Current density	200 ma/cm^2

4. Rinse quickly and immerse in a nickel strike bath (pp. 30, 31).

This etching and electrolytic treatment removes about 0.0002 inch–0.00025 inch of the metal, and the dimensions are built up to their original values by plating (see below). All solutions must be kept in good condition or made up fresh for occasional work.

5. Plate in one of the orthodox baths, as given on p. 29.

6. Rinse thoroughly after plating and immerse in methyl alcohol, reagent-grade, for rapid drying. Dry in a warm oven or air-blast.

A method for identifying molybdenum versus tungsten and tantalum is given by H. Bleecher[1] and summarized as follows:

After a short immersion in a hot solution of two parts nitric acid to one part water, molybdenum shows a dark brown stain, but tungsten is unaffected.

If specimens of the three metals are subjected to treatment in an electrolytic potassium hydroxide bath (see p. 17), tungsten and molybdenum show a clean-etched appearance, while tantalum exhibits a royal blue stain.

[1] "Identification of Tungsten, Tantalum, and Molybdenum," *Rev. Sci. Instr.*, **27**, 241, 1956.

This identification method is summarized in the following table:

METAL	HOT DILUTE HNO_3 SOLUTION	KOH ELECTROLYTIC BATH
Tungsten	clean	clean-etched
Molybdenum	brown	clean-etched
Tantalum	clean	royal blue

Molybdenum-tungsten thermocouple (see THERMOCOUPLES, p. 531).

Monel alloy 400 (formerly called Regular Monel). In wrought form monel nickel-copper alloy 400 offers high strength, ductility, weldability, and excellent corrosion resistance. It is useful in many electronic applications. It is highly resistant to corrosion by chlorinated solvents, glass-etching agents, sulfuric and many other acids, and practically all alkalies. It is somewhat magnetic at room temperatures. (The Alloy K-500 is nonmagnetic; see below.) The composition of Monel alloy 400 is given below.

COMPOSITION

Nickel (+ cobalt)	63–67%	Carbon	0.30 max.
Copper	balance	Silicon	0.50 max.
Iron	2.50 max.	Aluminum	0.50 max.
Manganese	2.00 max.		

Monel alloy 400 can be welded, brazed, soft-soldered, deep-drawn, spun, and blanked. It can be bright-annealed in dry hydrogen (dew point about −30°C). Its electrical resistivity is 290 ohm-mil-ft at 0°C. Its melting point is 1300°–1350°C. The alloy is stress-relieved by holding it at a temperature of 300°C for ½ to 1 hour in dry hydrogen.

Monel alloy 404 is similar in mechanical properties to Monel alloy 400 but has a slightly lower nickel content, which has the effect of making it essentially non-magnetic at and above room temperature. Its magnetic properties are not appreciably affected by hot or cold work. It can be fired and brazed in wet hydrogen (dew point about 25°C). The approximate permeability of alloy 404 at −3°C with a field strength of 0.5 oersted is 1.1. Its electrical resistivity is about 300 ohm-mil-ft at 25°C (50 microhm-cm). The melting point of alloy 404 is 1300°–1350°C. Its composition is given below.

COMPOSITION

Nickel (+ cobalt)	52–57%	Carbon	0.15 max.
Copper	balance	Silicon	0.10 max.
Iron	0.50 max.	Aluminum	0.05 max.
Manganese	0.10 max.	Sulfur	0.024 max.

Monel alloy R-405[1] is a variation of the 400 alloy to which a small amount of sulfur has been added for improved machinability.

---

[1] Formerly called R-Monel.

COMPOSITION

Nickel (+ cobalt)	63–70%	Manganese	2.00 max.
Copper	balance	Carbon	0.30 max.
Iron	2.50 max.	Silicon	0.50 max.
Sulfur	0.25–0.60		

Other properties of R-405 are similar to those of the alloy 400.

Monel alloy K-500[1] is an age-hardenable, wrought, high-nickel alloy having high strength and hardness comparable to those of heat-treated steels. It is nonmagnetic (permeability 1.0015 at 20°C, 1.1 at −118°C) down to −101°C, and it retains its strength up to about 600°C. Heat-treating of K-Monel is to be done in dry hydrogen (dew point −40°C) if oxidation is to be avoided.

The electrical resistivity of K-500 is 350 ohm-mil-ft at 0°C. Its melting point is 1315°–1350°C. The composition of Monel alloy K-500 is given below.

COMPOSITION

Nickel (+ cobalt)	63–67%	Manganese	1.00 max.
Copper	balance	Silicon	1.00 max.
Iron	2.00 max.	Carbon	0.25 max.
Aluminum	2–4		

Cold-worked K-500 is stress-relieved by holding at 300°C for ½ to 1 hour in dry hydrogen. The rate of cooling is not critical. Full annealing is accomplished by heating to 980°C in dry hydrogen for a short period. Age-hardening is done by holding at 540°C for 4 hours, followed by slow cooling at the rate of 15°C per hour down to 480°C.

K-500 can be used as a spring or tension member in electron tubes and also as fixtures for brazing in wet hydrogen since a preformed oxide film protects it from being wet by braze alloys.

Monel alloy 501.[2] This is similar to K-500 except for a slightly higher carbon content, which makes it more easily machinable. Parts made from alloy 501 can be age-hardened after machining. Its other physical and heat-treating properties are similar to those of K-500.

Motion into vacuum. A number of devices have been used to transmit movement, through seals of various kinds, to elements inside evacuated devices.

Simple, short-thrust, reciprocating motion can be imparted to plungers, probes, and the like inside the vacuum chamber by means of a metal diaphragm (Fig. 101). The diaphragm D can be of stainless steel, Monel, beryllium copper, or any other suitable metal. This can be formed from annealed sheet by means of a single steel or brass die turned to the desired shape and pressing the metal against a rubber mate in a hydraulic ram. The diaphragm is brazed vacuum-tight to the body of the vessel at its periphery and to the moving members at the center. A suitable positioning jig is used in the brazing operations. In this design, provision is made for holding the diaphragm against atmospheric pressure by the use of the yoke Y and the retaining ring R. Some means should also be provided for preventing over-extension of the diaphragm in either direction.

[1] Formerly called K-Monel.

[2] Formerly called KR-Monel.

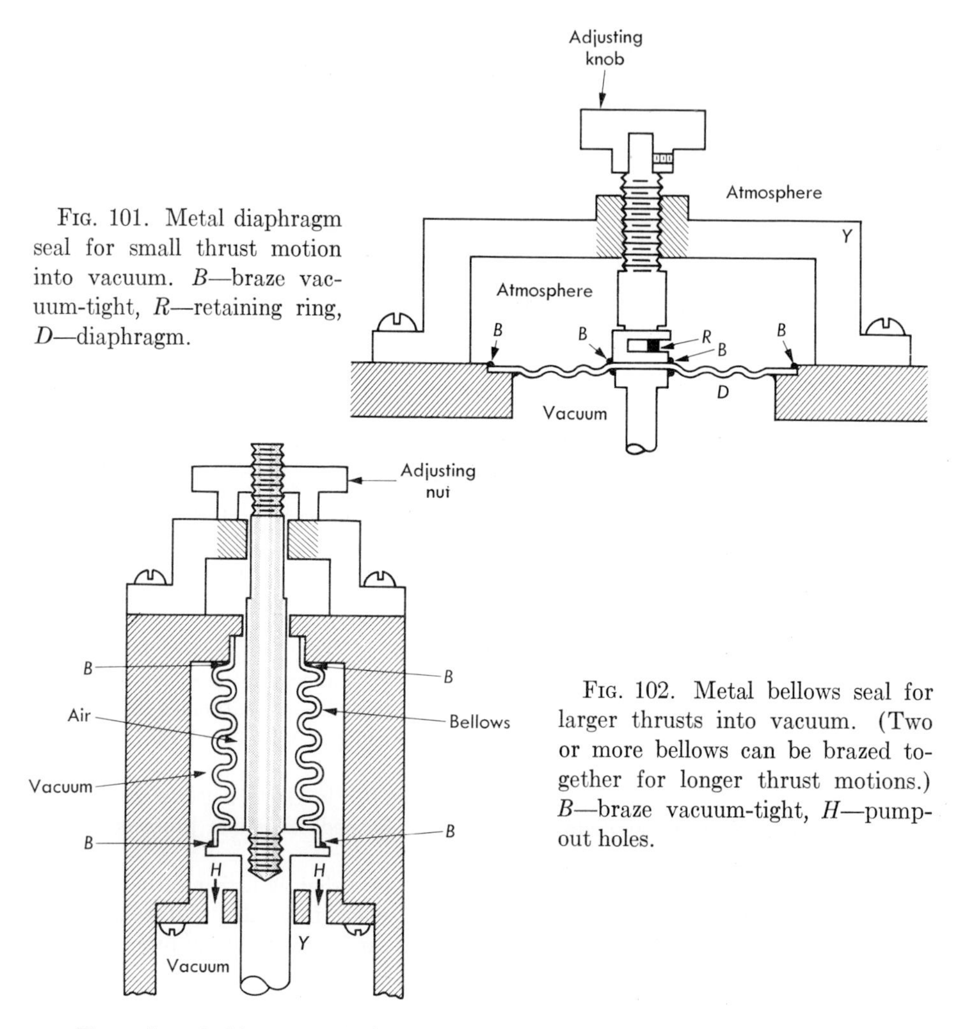

Fig. 101. Metal diaphragm seal for small thrust motion into vacuum. *B*—braze vacuum-tight, *R*—retaining ring, *D*—diaphragm.

Fig. 102. Metal bellows seal for larger thrusts into vacuum. (Two or more bellows can be brazed together for longer thrust motions.) *B*—braze vacuum-tight, *H*—pump-out holes.

Examples of this type of mechanism: bakable, high-vacuum valves with metal diaphragms, have been described by various workers.[1, 2, 3, 4]

For longer thrusts one or more metal bellows can be used. A suggested method of mounting is shown in Fig. 102. For micrometer movements the adjusting nut could be replaced with a differential screw. In this design the adjusting nut also serves the purpose of holding the bellows against atmospheric pressure, and the stop *S* prevents the bellows from being overextended.

---

[1] D. Alpert, *Rev. Sci. Instr.*, **22**, 536, 1951; *J. Appl. Phys.*, **24**, 860, 1953.

[2] S. C. Brown and J. E. Coyle, *Rev. Sci. Instr.*, **23**, 570, 1952.

[3] H. H. Pattee, Jr., *Phys. Rev.*, **98**, 283A, 1955.

[4] D. G. Bills and F. G. Allen, *Rev. Sci. Instr.*, **26**, 654, 1955.

See also: "Method for Obtaining Screw Adjustment in Vacuum," H. R. King, *Welch Duo-Seal Digest*, **4**, 3, 1961; also "A Greaseless Vacuum Seal for Rotating Shafts," E. A. Billett and J. Bishop, *J. Sci. Instr.* (Br), **35**, 70, 1958.

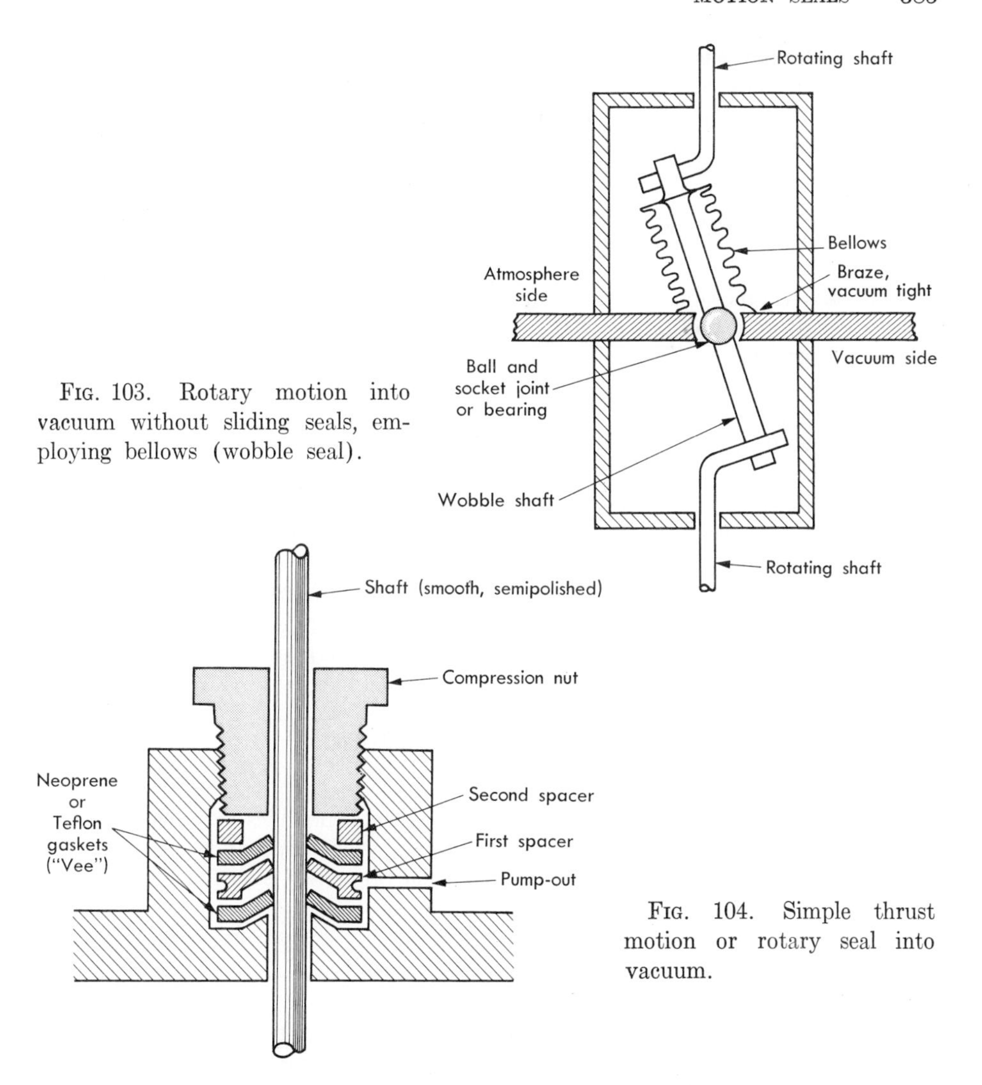

Fig. 103. Rotary motion into vacuum without sliding seals, employing bellows (wobble seal).

Fig. 104. Simple thrust motion or rotary seal into vacuum.

Because any given metal bellows has a limit to its useful extension or compression (see the table on p. 126, col. 8), the amount of total excursion can be increased by brazing two or more bellows units together longitudinally, in which case the extension limits are additive.

A device for obtaining rotary motion in a vacuum employing a metal bellows (wobble seal) without the use of a sliding seal is described by Guthrie and Wakerling.[1] This device is illustrated in Fig. 103. Here, again, the limits of bellows-convolution motion must not be exceeded.

Thrust or rotary seals in which Neoprene- (p. 387) or Teflon-formed (p. 513) "Vee" seals are used are shown in Fig. 104.

[1] *Vacuum Equipment and Techniques,* A. Guthrie and R. K. Wakerling, McGraw-Hill Book Company, Inc., New York, New York, 1949.

Multipliers, electron, photo (see p. 239).

Mumetal.[1] An alloy of nickel, 77.2%; iron, 14.9%; copper, 4.8%; and chromium, 1.5% (nominal composition). It is often used in electron tube work for magnetic shielding (see below). Some of its properties are given in the table below.

TYPICAL PHYSICAL, MECHANICAL, AND MAGNETIC PROPERTIES OF MUMETAL
Cold-rolled sheets and strip

Specific gravity (gm/cc)	8.5
Curie temperature (°C)	400
Electrical resistivity (microhm-cm)	56
Coercive force (Hc) (oersteds for B_{max} from 5000 gausses)	0.015
Hysteresis loss (ergs/cm³/cycle for B_{max} of 5000 gausses)	20
Saturation induction (B_s), (gausses)	7500
Modulus of elasticity (psi × 10⁶)	
cold rolled	30
hydrogen annealed	25

Ultimate tensile strength (psi × 10³)	
mill anneal	90
hydrogen anneal	64
Yield strength (psi × 10⁻³)	
mill anneal	38
hydrogen anneal	18.5
Elongation in 2 inches (%)	
mill anneal	35
hydrogen anneal	27

Coefficient of Linear thermal expansion (mean)

Temperature range (°C)	Coefficient (°C × 10⁻⁶)
20– 100	12.5
20– 500	14.4
20–1000	16.2

When properly annealed in dry hydrogen, Mu metal provides very high magnetic shielding efficiency at low inductions and over a wide range of frequencies. The annealing procedure for developing its maximum properties is as follows:

1. Heat to 1180°C at any convenient rate in dry hydrogen (dew point reduced to at least −50°C).
2. Hold temperature for approximately 4 hours for heavy sections, less for lighter sections, to ensure uniform heating throughout the batch.
3. Furnace-cool to 600°C at a rate not to exceed 80°C per hour.
4. Furnace-cool to 315°C at a rate not to exceed 120°C per hour.
5. Charge can be withdrawn from the furnace at any time after the temperature has dropped below 300°C.

(See the section on heat-treating stainless steel, pp. 41 *et seq.* Purging the retort with dry nitrogen before and after the annealing cycle is a necessary safety precaution).

Muscovite (see MICA, p. 371).

Mutual conductance (see pp. 546–547).

Neoprene.[1] A synthetic, rubber-like material which has many of the physical properties of natural rubber, such as toughness and resilience. It does not deteriorate

[1] Data are courtesy of Allegheny-Ludlum Steel Corp., Pittsburgh 22, Pennsylvania, from "Allegheny-Ludlum Mumetal—Em-12, Edition 8," 1961 (Allegheny-Ludlum Blue Sheet).

like natural rubber when exposed to oils, greases, sunlight, and weather, nor is it affected by ozone and relatively high temperatures. The hardness, elastic modulus, tensile strength, and elasticity can be controlled in the process of manufacture so that many Neoprene formulations are available.

Neoprene is useful in vacuum work in the form of O-rings (see pp. 407–409) and gaskets. Some of its properties are tabulated below:

Physical and mechanical properties of Neoprene:

Dc resistivity (ohm-cm)	10^{12}
Dielectric strength (volt/mil)	400–600
Dielectric constant	6.7
Power factor (%)	2.5
Tensile strength (psi)	over 3000
Hardness range, Durometer A	40–95
Thermal conductivity (Btu/hr/ft^2/in/°F)	1.45
(cgs)	0.0005
Specific gravity, base material	1.23
Specific gravity of compounds with pigments	1.4 to 3.0
Vulcanizing properties	excellent
Adhesion to metals	excellent
Tear resistance	good
Abrasion resistance	excellent
Compression set	fair to good
Rebound	very good

Neoprene is considerably less permeable to gases than natural rubber, as shown in the following table.[1]

Relative Permeability of Three Elastomers to Common Gases at 25°C (Natural Rubber is Arbitrarily Set at 100)

MATERIAL	HYDROGEN	OXYGEN	NITROGEN	CO_2	METHANE
Natural Rubber	100	100	100	100	100
Neoprene	26	17	13	19	11
GR-S (Buna-S)	78	72	73	93	73

The electrical properties of Neoprene are somewhat inferior to those of *fresh* natural rubber, but since Neoprene withstands weathering, aging, and chemical attack better than rubber, its electrical properties can be considered to be good.

Neoprene compounds will withstand temperatures up to 150°C for continuous exposure, and even higher for short periods. Above 150°C Neoprene gradually hardens and will ultimately become brittle, the effect appearing first on the surface.

[1] All the data (with exceptions as noted) are reprinted by permission of E. I. du Pont de Nemours & Company, Wilmington, Delaware.

Neoprene resists hot 30% sulfuric acid or hydrochloric acid. Hydrofluoric acid causes slow deterioration. The material is practically unaffected by solutions of alkalies, including ammonium hydroxide. Neoprene should *not* be used in contact with nitric or chromic acids. It is fairly stable in contact with Freon, methyl chloride, and sulfur dioxide in the liquid phase (for refrigeration applications), and also with chlorine, bromine, and iodine.

Carbon tetrachloride and trichlorethylene (see below) cause some swelling of Neoprene, but it is less affected by the alcohols. Acetone and esters such as amyl acetate have a very deteriorating effect on Neoprene.

Some small percentage of water is absorbed by the material when immersed for a period of time. For vacuum purposes this can be removed by drying in an oven at 80–100°C for several hours or overnight.

J. R. Young[1] has found that the vacuum limitation of Neoprene in vacuum systems is due to the liberation of butane. This effect appeared to be caused by the practice of cleaning the O-rings in solvents,[2] and largely disappeared when new, fresh O-rings were used which were not subjected to any cleaning procedure.

A summary of the properties of various common elastomers, including Neoprene, is given in the table on p. 390.

Nichrome and Nichrome alloys (see also OVENS AND HEATERS, p. 417).

Nichrome is a corrosion-resistant alloy of 60% nickel, 16% chrominum, and 24% iron and is used as a heating element in appliances, ovens, and furnaces operating in air and other atmospheres up to 930°C. It is also used for resistors, acid and pickling baskets and containers, and wire mesh components of high-temperature conveyor belts. Nichrome is somewhat magnetic at room temperatures.

Nichrome V is a corrosion-resistant alloy of 80% nickel and 20% chromium and is used for heating elements in devices operating in air and other atmospheres up to 1093°C. It is also used for resistors where its lower coefficient of resistivity makes it superior in performance to regular Nichrome. Nichrome V is nonmagnetic at room temperatures and can be used in electron devices where this quality is required. Nichrome V has a very low thermal conductivity (0.112 w/cm/°C at 100°C, as compared with a value of 0.133 for type 304 stainless steel, 0.582 for pure nickel, and 3.88 for copper), so that it can be used, for example, to thermally isolate a nickel cathode button or sleeve from its supports.

Some caution must be exercised in spot-welding Nichrome V because its high resistivity causes it to heat more than other metals. A lower setting than for nickel-to-nickel would be called for.

Nickel. This is an extremely useful metal in the construction of electron tubes and devices. Not only does it provide an excellent base for barium-strontium oxide cathode material, but it is useful for making grids and anodes, lead wires, getter-shields, heat shields, and the supporting and mechanical structures in the tube. Nickel is easily formed, cleaned, outgassed, and spot-welded.

Nickel 200[3] is a commercially pure wrought nickel having the nominal composition:

Nickel	99.5 %	Iron	0.15 %
Carbon	0.06%	Sulfur	0.005%
Manganese	0.25%	Copper	0.05 %

[1] J. R. Young, "Vacuum Limitation of O-Ring Joints," *Rev. Sci. Instr.*, **29**, 795, 1958.
[2] J. R. Young, "Cleaning Techniques for O-Rings," *Rev. Sci. Instr.*, **30**, 291, 1959.
[3] Formerly called Grade A nickel.

Nickel 200 is very ductile when annealed at or above 600°C in hydrogen, and can be easily formed, stamped, and spun. It can be welded by conventional methods, spot- and butt-resistance welded, and readily brazed with silver, copper, and alloy filler metals. Nickel is resistant to corrosion, and oxidizes but slowly at elevated temperatures. The oxide film is tightly adherent but can easily be reduced in an atmosphere furnace using tank hydrogen.

Nickel 200 has magnetic and magnetostrictive properties and a high temperature coefficient of resistivity which makes it useful for resistance thermometry at moderate temperatures.

Some of the properties of Nickel 200 are as follows:

Density (lb/in^3)	0.321
Modulus of elasticity in tension (psi $\times 10^6$)	30
Modulus of elasticity in torsion (psi $\times 10^6$)	11
Melting range (°C)	1435–1446
Specific heat (gm-cal/gm/°C)	0.109 (21°C)
Coefficient of thermal expansion ($10^{-6} \times$ in/in/°C)	
20–93°C	13.3
20–260°C	14.2
20–540°C	15.3
20–816°C	16.4
20–1093°C	17.3
Thermal conductivity (cgs)	
at 20°C	0.134
at 260°C	0.128
at 540°C	0.127
Electrical resistivity	
(ohm-mil-ft)	57 (32°F)
(microhm-cm)	9.48 (0°C)
Curie temperature, annealed (°C)	360
Poisson's ratio	0.31
Tensile strength (psi) at 20°C (hot-rolled)	67,000
at 540°C	31,500
at 1093°C	3,500
Yield strength, annealed at 20°C	21,500
at 540°C	13,500
at 1093°C	1,400
Elongation (%) annealed at 20°C	47
at 540°C	69
at 1093°C	205
Hardness, Brinell—hot-finished (3000 kg)	90–150
cold-drawn (3000 kg)	140–230
annealed (3000 kg)	90–120

Nickel 200 is available in all commercial forms including wire, sheet, strip, rods and bars, angles, seamless and welded tubing, plate, forgings, and wire mesh.

Nickel work hardens fairly rapidly during cold-forming (hammering, forging, bending, spinning, etc.) but cannot be hardened by heat treatment. For very deep draws, a stress-relief treatment consisting of holding for 3 hours at 275°C or 1 hour

GENERAL PROPERTIES OF VARIOUS ELASTOMERS*

CHEMICAL AND PHYSICAL PROPERTIES	BUTYL	GR-S OR BUNA S	HYCAR PA	NATURAL RUBBER	NITRILE RUBBER OR BUNA N
Composition	Isobutylene-isoprene	Butadiene styrene	Copolymer of acrylic acid ester and a halogen-containing derivative		Butadiene acrylonitrile
Tensile (lb/sq. in)					
Pure gum	Over 1500	Below 1000	Over 1000	Over 3000	Below 1000
Black	Over 2000	Over 2000	Over 2000	Over 3000	Over 2000
Practical hardness range Shore Duro A	40–75	40–90	40–90	30–90	40–95
Rebound					
Cold	Bad	Good		Excellent	Good
Hot	Very good	Good		Excellent	Good
Tear resistance	Good	Fair	Fair	Good	Fair
Abrasion resistance	Good	Good to excellent		Excellent	Good
Ozone resistance	Very good	Fair	Very good	Fair	Fair
Sunlight aging	Very good	Poor	Excellent	Poor	Poor
Oxidation resistance	Excellent	Good	Excellent	Good	Good
Heat resistance	Excellent	Very good	Excellent	Good	Excellent
Solvent resistance					
Aliphatic hydrocarbons	Poor	Poor	Poor to good	Poor	Excellent
Aromatic hydrocarbons	Poor	Poor	Poor	Poor	Good
Oxygenated solvents, alcohols (ketones, etc.)	Good	Good	Poor	Good	Poor
Oil and gasoline	Poor	Poor	Excellent	Poor	Excellent
Animal and vegetable oils	Excellent	Poor to good	Excellent	Poor to good	Excellent
Acid resistance					
Dilute	Excellent	Fair to good	Poor	Fair to good	Good
Concentrated	Excellent	Fair to good	Poor	Fair to good	Good
Flame resistance	Poor	Poor	Poor	Poor	Poor
Permeability to gases	Very low	Fair		Fair	Fair
Electrical insulation	Good	Good	Fair	Good	Poor
Water swell resistance	Excellent	Excellent	Poor	Fair	Excellent

The above table presents comparative properties of rubber compounds that the industry has found through experience. There may be exceptions to these properties where special compounding techniques are used.

* Courtesy of Acushnet Process Company (1958). Reprinted by permission.

NEOPRENE	SILICONE	VITON A	ELASTACAST	POLYURETHANE ELASTOMERS
Chloroprene	Polysiloxane polymer	Copolymer of vinylidene fluoride and hexafluoro-propylene	Polyurethane elastomer cast from liquid	Molded from millable gum
Over 3000 Over 3000	Below 1500	Over 2000 Over 2000	From 4000 to 7000 From 4000 to 7000	From 3000 to 5500 From 3000 to 5500
40–95	40–85	60–90	60–95	55–80
Very good Very good	Excellent Excellent	Good Excellent	Poor at low temperature Good at room temperature	Poor at low temperature Good at room temperature
Fair to good	Poor	Fair	Outstanding	Outstanding
Excellent	Poor		Outstanding	Outstanding
Very good	Very good	Very good	Outstanding	Outstanding
Very good	Excellent	Excellent	Excellent	Excellent
Excellent	Excellent	Excellent	Excellent	Excellent
Excellent	Outstanding	Outstanding	Excellent to 250°F	Excellent to 250°F
Good Fair	Poor Poor	Excellent Excellent	Excellent Good	Excellent Good
Poor	Fair	Poor	Poor	Poor
Good	Fair	Excellent	Excellent	Excellent
Good	Excellent	Excellent	Excellent	Excellent
Excellent Good	Excellent Fair	Excellent Good	Poor Poor	Poor Poor
Good	Fair	Good	Poor	Poor
Low	Fair			Test incomplete
Fair	Excellent	Excellent	Fair	Fair
Fair	Excellent	Excellent	Good at room temperature Poor at 212°F	Good at room temperature Poor at 212°F

Comparison of Resistances of Nickel and Copper Wires

B & S GAUGE	DIAMETER (INCHES)	NICKEL (OHM-FT)	COPPER (OHM-FT)	FEET LB*	B & S GAUGE	DIAMETER (INCHES)	NICKEL (OHM-FT)	COPPER (OHM-FT)	FEET LB*
1	0.289	0.0007	0.00012	3.95	25	0.0179	0.1809	0.0324	1,018
2	0.258	0.0009	0.00016	4.95	26	0.0159	0.2293	0.0408	1,305
3	0.229	0.0011	0.0002	6.29	27	0.0142	0.2876	0.0515	1,636
4	0.204	0.00139	0.00025	7.92	28	0.0126	0.365	0.0649	2,085
5	0.182	0.00175	0.00031	9.96	29	0.0113	0.454	0.0818	2,548
6	0.162	0.00221	0.0004	12.5	30	0.010	0.579	0.1032	3,300
7	0.144	0.00281	0.0005	15.9	31	0.0089	0.732	0.1301	4,166
8	0.128	0.00354	0.0006	20.1	32	0.008	0.905	0.1641	5,156
9	0.114	0.00445	0.0008	25.3	33	0.0071	1.15	0.2069	6,546
10	0.102	0.0056	0.001	31.7	34	0.0063	1.45	0.2609	8,314
11	0.091	0.0070	0.0013	39.8	35	0.0056	1.84	0.329	10,522
12	0.081	0.0088	0.0016	50.2	36	0.005	2.31	0.4148	13,200
13	0.072	0.0112	0.002	63.6	37	0.0045	2.87	0.5231	16,296
14	0.064	0.0142	0.0025	80.5	38	0.004	3.62	0.6596	20,625
15	0.057	0.0179	0.0032	101.	39	0.0035	4.75	0.8318	26,938
16	0.051	0.0223	0.004	126.	40	0.0031	6.03	1.05	33,410
17	0.045	0.0286	0.005	162.	41	0.00275	7.66	1.37	43,636
18	0.040	0.0362	0.0064	206.	42	0.0025	9.27	1.66	52,800
19	0.036	0.0447	0.008	254.	43	0.00225	11.45	2.05	65,185
20	0.032	0.0556	0.0102	322.	44	0.002	14.49	2.60	82,500
21	0.0285	0.0714	0.0128	406.	45	0.00175	18.94	3.39	107,755
22	0.0253	0.0905	0.0161	515.	46	0.0015	25.80	4.13	146,666
23	0.0226	0.1135	0.0204	646.	—	0.0012	—	7.07	229,400
24	0.0201	0.1450	0.0257	825.	—	0.001	—	10.19	303,000

* Since the densities of copper and nickel are very close, the number of feet per pound is approximately the same for both metals.

at 315°C should be done when the metal shows signs of resisting the forming operation.

A table of special nickels for oxide-coated cathode bases is given on pp. 292, 293. See also pp. 93–95.

Nickel is widely used as an electroplate, commonly over copper and under chromium for protecting steel against corrosion. Data on nickel-plating baths will be found on pp. 29–31.

Nickel is resistant to corrosion by ordinary and industrial atmospheres, and by fresh and salt water.[1] Hypochlorites (Clorox, etc.) attack nickel rapidly when the chlorine concentration is 3 gm/liter or more.[2] The metal is slowly attacked by hydrochloric acid at room temperature, the reaction becoming rapid above 50°C even in dilute solutions. Nitric acid attacks nickel vigorously. Corrosion by sulfuric acid is slow in a 5% solution at room temperature but becomes severe in hot 15% solutions.[2,3] Nickel resists corrosion by alkalies even at high temperatures, except for NH_4OH in concentrations over 1%.[2] It is not attacked by most organic acids.

Nickel is not resistant to wet gases such as chlorine (above 580°C), bromine, and sulfur dioxide. A mixture of nitrogen, hydrogen, and ammonia is destructive. Common dry gases do not affect the metal.[2]

Nickel can be used in contact with mercury below 371°C without appreciable amalgamation, but molten Al, Sn, Pb, Bi, Sb, Zn and soft solders and brass attack nickel rapidly.[4]

Nickel strongly adsorbs hydrogen, which forms a solid solution. It also adsorbs carbon monoxide, dioxide, and ethylene.[5,6] In the case of CO, dissociation occurs and free carbon is deposited.[7]

Under favorable conditions hydrogen, oxygen, and carbon monoxide and dioxide will diffuse through solid nickel.[8] (See pp. 121, 122.) The metal is impervious to the noble gases, He, Ne, A, Kr, and Xe. Gases begin to evolve from nickel at 200°C, and most of the hydrogen is expelled between 400° and 500°C.[9] Appreciable amounts of carbon monoxide are evolved at 600°C, and this increases with rising temperature. The metal retains its toughness while hydrogen is being evolved, but becomes brittle after evolution of CO. Nitrogen is only slightly soluble in nickel.[10] The electrical resistances of nickel and copper wires are shown in the table on p. 392. Note that the diameter is approximately halved for each increase in six gauge numbers. The resistance in ohm-ft for both copper and nickel is approximately doubled for each increase in three gauge numbers, and the carrying capacity in amperes is approximately halved. The number of feet lb is approximately doubled for each increase in three gauge numbers.

[1] J. N. Friend, *Metal Ind.* (London), **32**, 449, 1928.

[2] W. Z. Friend, *ASM Metals Handbook*, p. 1041, 1948.

[3] S. L. Hoyt, *Metals and Alloys Data Book*, Reinhold Publishing Corp., New York, New York, 1943.

[4] C. A. Crawford and R. Worthington, ASTM and ASME Symposium on Effect of Temperature on Properties of Metals, p. 403, 1931.

[5] A. Sievers, *Z. Phys. Chem.*, **77**, 591, 1911.

[6] C. J. Smithells and C. E. Ransley, *Proc. Roy. Soc.* (London), **157**, 292, 1936.

[7] C. J. Smithells, *Metal Treatment*, **1**, 165, 1935.

[8] W. Baukloh and H. Kayser, *Z. Metallkunde*, **27**, 281, 1935.

[9] W. Z. Köster, *ibid.*, **31**, 168, 1938.

[10] R. Juza and W. Sachze, *J. Inst. Metals* (Met. Abs.), **12**, 246, 1945.

The electrical resistivity and conductivity of pure nickel[1] is tabulated below:

TEMPERATURE (°C)	RESISTIVITY (MICROHM-CM[3])	(OHM-MIL-FT)	CONDUCTIVITY (IACS) % Cu
0	6.141	36.8	28.1
20	6.844	41	25.2
100	10.327	62	16.7

Temperature coefficient of resistivity, 0.00636/°C, 0°–100°C.

Additional information will be found in "Nickel and Its Alloys," National Bureau of Standards, U.S. Department of Commerce, NBS Circular 485 (1950).

Nickel 201.[2] This is a low-carbon version of Nickel 200. It is particularly suited to spinning and coining operations due to its low base hardness and low rate of work-hardening. Nickel 201 is preferred to Nickel 200 for service at temperatures in the range of 315° to 650°C. Its uses in tube construction include getter tabs, heating element sheathing, spun anodes, and structural components.

Nickel 201 is available in the form of rods and bars, hot-rolled or cold-drawn; strip, cold-rolled; sheet, cold-rolled; wire, cold-drawn; tubing, seamless, welded, and drawn; and plate.

The limiting composition of Nickel 201 is:

Nickel (plus Co)	99.00% min.	Manganese	0.35% max.
Copper	0.25 max.	Carbon	0.02 max.
Iron	0.40 max.	Silicon	0.35 max.
Sulfur	0.01 max.		

Nickel 211.[3] The strength and base hardness of Nickel 211, when fully annealed, are slightly greater than those of Nickel 205.[4] The annealing temperature is also higher, so that structural parts made of the alloy retain much of their strength when subjected to degassing temperatures in electron tubes. The manganese content imparts some resistance to attack by sulfur compounds at elevated temperatures. For this reason the alloy has been used for supports sealed into glass, when embrittlement from sulfur in the heating flame is a factor. Electron emission, even when contaminated with barium, is lower than that of Nickel 205,[2] making it useful for grid wires which may become contaminated by barium from the cathode. The electrical resistivity is about 110 ohm-mil-ft at 0°C (18.3 microhm-cm[2]). Nickel 211 is available as rods and bars, hot-rolled and cold-drawn; strip and ribbon, cold-rolled; tubing, seamless, cold-drawn; and wire, cold-drawn.

---

[1] G. F. Geiger, *ASM Metals Handbook,* p. 1644, 1939.
[2] Formerly designated as Low Carbon Nickel.
[3] Formerly designated as "D" Nickel.
[4] Formerly designated as "A" Nickel or Grade A Nickel, Electronic Grade.

The limiting composition of Nickel 211 is:

Nickel (plus Co)	93.70% min.	Manganese	4.25–5.25%
Copper	0.25 max.	Carbon	0.20 max.
Iron	0.75 max.	Silicon	0.15 max.
Sulfur	0.015 max.		

Nickel 212.[1] This alloy has properties intermediate between Nickel 200 and Nickel 211. Its limiting composition is:

Nickel (plus Co)	97.00% min.	Iron	0.75% max.
Manganese	1.75 min.	Carbon	0.20 max.
Copper	0.20 max.	Silicon	0.15 max.
Sulfur	0.015 max.		

Duranickel Alloy 301.[2] This is an age-hardenable alloy employing aluminum and titanium as the age-hardening elements. This amount of alloy in nickel reduces its thermal conductivity and its curie temperature. It increases its electrical resistivity but does not alter its corrosion resistance. The important features of Alloy 301 are high strength and hardness, good corrosion resistance, and spring properties up to 316°C.

This alloy is slightly magnetic at room temperature in the soft condition, but magnetic after age-hardening. The manufacturer recommends caution in frequent anneals on sections of 0.010 inch or less because the alloy may become decarburized and then not respond fully to subsequent age-hardening.

The limiting composition of Duranickel Alloy 301 is:

Nickel (plus Co)	93.00% min.	Copper	0.25% max.
Aluminum	4.00 min.	Iron	0.60 max.
	4.75 max.	Manganese	0.50 max.
Titanium	0.25 min.	Carbon	0.30 max.
	1.00 max.	Silicon	1.00 max.
Sulfur	0.01 max.		

Permanickel Alloy 300.[3] This alloy has somewhat greater resistance to corrosion than Alloy 301. It should be used in place of alloy 301 only when its lower electrical resistivity (16.6 microhm-cm^3 or 100 ohm-mil-ft at 0°C) and its more pronounced magnetic properties are required. Alloy 300 is magnetic both in the soft and the age-hardened condition. The nominal composition of Permanickel alloy 300 is:

Nickel (plus Co)	98.6 %	Sulfur	0.005%
Carbon	0.25	Silicon	0.06
Manganese	0.10	Copper	0.02
Iron	0.10	Titanium	0.50
Magnesium	0.35		

[1] Formerly designated as "E" Nickel.
[2] Formerly designated as Duranickel or "Z" Nickel.
[3] Formerly designated as Permanickel Alloy (or "Z" Nickel, Type B).

Nickel cathode bases[1] (International Nickel Company). For a summary of the composition and characteristics of the following Inco nickel cathode bases, see the table on p. 293.

New Designation	Old Designation
Nickel 200	A Nickel
Nickel 202	202 Nickel
Nickel 204	204 Nickel
Nickel 205	A Nickel (electronic grade)
Nickel 220	220 Nickel
Nickel 225	225 Nickel
Nickel 230	230 Nickel
Nickel 233	330 Nickel
Nickel 270 (new product)	

Nickel, carbonized. In electron tubes which are designed to have appreciable dissipation of power from the anode (i.e., in all but small, low-power tubes), it is desirable to use an anode material having high thermal emissivity. Molybdenum, tantalum, and graphite are often used for anodes in radiation-cooled tubes, but nickel can be used if it is coated with an adherent layer of carbon.

Such coatings can be formed in the following way: the surface of the nickel is chemically oxidized and etched slightly, or it is lightly sandblasted. Carbon is then deposited from a hot sulfur-free hydrocarbon gas, such as high propane mixtures (sulfur-free natural gases are suitable). The nickel oxide is reduced by the gas, which results in a catalytically active surface which aids in the deposition of carbon. Carbon coatings may range from rather hard, dark gray to softer, extremely black, depending on the adjustment of the carbonizing conditions.

The total emissivity of carbonized nickel is about 80% at 600°C, as compared to 15% for polished nickel, and even lower values for nickel which has been fired at 1100°C.[2] The carbonized surface has an additional useful effect in that the carbon has a tendency to combine with any sublimed barium from the cathode, thus rendering it inactive as a back-emitter of electrons.

Nickel, cathode etch (see N-1A, p. 12).

Nickel, chemical and electrolytic cleaning of (see pp. 9, 12, 13, 21).

Nickel, hydrogen-diffusion through; purification of hydrogen by diffusion through (see p. 121).

Nickel plating (see pp. 29, 30, 31).

Nickel plating on molybdenum (see p. 31).

Nicoro braze alloy (see item 72, p. 180). Note that this alloy has a melting range of 35°C and is therefore suitable for brazing parts with poor fits, or where a fillet is required. Nicoro 80 (item 99, p. 182) is a lower melting alloy, with a shorter range, which can also be used to produce fillets.

Nilvar. This is a very low-expansion 36% nickel, 64% iron alloy with properties similar to those of invar (p. 299).

---

[1] See also p. 93.

[2] B. T. Barnes, *Phys. Rev.*, **34**, 1026, 1929; also E. M. Wise, "Nickel in the Radio Industry," *Proc. I.R.E.*, **25**, 714, 1937.

Niobium (see COLUMBIUM, p. 215).

Nioro. This gold-nickel eutectic alloy (82% Au, 18% Ni or 82.5% Au, 17.5% Ni) has a liquidus and solidus temperature of 950°C (1742°F) and is suitable for brazing many metals as listed below.

Atmosphere	Metals
Dry H_2	Inconel, stainless steels, K and KR Monels, steels
Tank H_2	Kovar, molybdenum, copper, nickel, tungsten, rhenium
Vacuum	Tantalum, columbium, or any of the above metals.

This alloy is also sold as 19.8 karat white gold and as Alloy #255,[1] Ascobraze 82AE,[2] and Premabraze 130 VTG.[3]

Niromet 42 Alloy. A 42% nickel (the balance iron) alloy with expansion properties between those of Niromet 46 (see below) and Rodar (p. 465). It is used for some glass-sealing applications, closely matching Corning #1075 glass. It has a coefficient of linear thermal expansion of 47.5×10^{-7} in/°C in the temperature range 25° to 350°C. It is strongly magnetic and has a curie temperature of 360°C.

Niromet 46 Alloy. A 46% nickel (the balance iron) alloy with expansion properties between those of Niron (see below) and Rodar (p. 465). It is sometimes used for glass sealing. It has a coefficient of linear thermal expansion of 77×10^{-7} in/°C in the temperature range 25° to 425°C. It is strongly magnetic, with a curie point of 410°C.

Niron 52 Alloy. A 51% nickel (balance iron) alloy used extensively for making seals to soft glass (Corning #0120 potash-soda-lead glass). It has a coefficient of linear thermal expansion of 97×10^{-7} in/°C (25° to 300°C) and 98×10^{-7} in/°C (25° to 500°C). Niron 52 is strongly magnetic, with a curie temperature of 510°C.

Nitrocellulose binder is a lacquer-vehicle used in the compounding and application of oxide-cathode coatings and aluminum oxide heater coatings. The application is usually done by spraying but can be done by other means (see pp. 97, 166, 496).

During processing the constituents of this binder are harmlessly broken down and carried off as gases, largely at temperatures at or below 500°C. Because both cathodes and heaters are brought to much higher temperatures, no trace of the binder breakdown products remains.

Nitrogen. As an atmospheric gas, nitrogen constitutes 78% of the air by volume. Some of its properties are as follows:

Atomic weight	14.008	Density	1.2506 gm/liter
Atomic number	7	Specific gravity	
Melting point (°C)	−209.86	liquid at −195.8°C	0.808
Boiling point (°C)	−195.8	solid at −252°C	1.026

Vapor pressure at the melting point (−209.86°C) ... 96.4 mm Hg

Color	none
Odor	none
Toxicity	none

[1] American Platinum and Silver Division of Engelhard Industries, Inc., Newark 5, New Jersey.

[2] American Silver Company, Inc., Flushing 54, New York.

[3] Handy & Harman, New York, New York.

Activity: generally inert, but combines with some metals at elevated temperatures to form nitrides, which are usually quite stable at room temperatures.

Dry nitrogen (oil-pumped) is commercially available in steel cylinders and generally has a dew point lower than −40°C. It is useful in the laboratory for storing and handling oxygen- and/or water-vapor-sensitive materials in dry boxes, desiccators, or other closed chambers, and as a substitute for dry compressed air in the high-cleanliness spraying of cathode and Alundum coatings.

Dry nitrogen is also used in glassblowing and torch-brazing operations on electron tubes when it is necessary to protect the interior and the structure inside the tube against oxides, etc., caused by the torch. It can also be used as a purge gas to free a hydrogen retort from air (i.e., oxygen).

Liquid nitrogen is used as a refrigerant (see p. 345).

Nivac-P (see METALS, VACUUM-MELTED, p. 368).

Noise. Small voltages of a random nature arising in electronic devices from thermal, magnetic, chemical, electron motion, or external causes. In a simple temperature-limited diode, for example, where all the electrons emitted by the cathode are captured by the anode, a condition known as *shot noise* is observed; this is caused by the random fluctuations in the number of electrons emitted during any given period of time.

In tubes having a multiplicity of elements, perhaps of dissimilar metals, there exist also small voltages due to thermoelectric effects. Other effects may also be present. The combination of all these noises is sometimes called *receiver noise,* contributed mainly by the first amplifier stage and cascaded through successive stages in a receiver.

Noise in which all the components have a uniform energy spectrum is called *white noise.*[1]

Nude ion gauge. This term describes elements of an ionization gauge, mounted on a brazed or welded flange, or some type of demountable seal, and unencumbered by any envelope. With some justification, the argument is put forth that the pressure inside an ionization gauge is not the same as the pressure in a vessel to which it is connected by tubing, no matter how short. The ionization gauge, within itself, has some gettering or gas-cleanup effect either by electronic or chemical pumping,[1] which might never reach the same degree in the adjacent vessel being evacuated, and there is always a time lag in the pressure drop, as between ionization gauge and vessel, under these conditions.

Partially to overcome this problem, some workers have installed the *elements* of the ionization gauge, without an envelope of any kind, inside the vessel or chamber being pumped. If the procedure is feasible, this nude ion gauge is placed as close to the operating elements of the device as possible. If the device is large, several such

---

[1] "Noise," A. M. Hilton, *Electronic Design,* p. 85, September 13, 1962. See also: "Noise in Electron Devices," edited by L. D. Smullin and H. A. Haus. The M.I.T. Press, Cambridge, Massachusetts, 1959.

[1] See *Proceedings of the Seventh National Vacuum Symposium* of the American Vacuum Society, Inc., (Boston, Massachusetts) held at Cleveland, Ohio, 1960: "Panel Discussion on Pressure Measurements—Their Apparatus and Techniques," P. A. Redhead, H. Schwarz, G. Reich, W. B. Nottingham, and I. Fish.

ionization gauges could be used at strategic points, that is, those at which it is desired to know the pressure.

Nylon. Zytel[1] nylon is a thermoplastic resin, but unlike most thermoplastic materials, it does not soften gradually as the temperature is raised. Instead, it has a relatively sharp melting point, below which it remains rigid and above which it has a fluidity like that of lubricating oil. Zytel 101 does not exhibit unmolding until a temperature of about 230°C is approached, but it does lose rigidity and stiffness. For this reason general applications should be limited to service at temperatures below 150°C. When subjected to load, the service temperature should not exceed 135°C. For prolonged exposure to elevated temperature, the thermally stabilized grades should be used.

The resistance of Nylon to chemicals and solvents varies with the type. Zytel 101 and 31 are the most solvent-resistant, being insoluble in common solvents, alkalies, dilute mineral acids, and most organic acids. These compositions are unaffected by petroleum oils and greases at temperatures as high as 150°C, and the lubricants are, in turn, unaffected by the Nylon. Acids such as those used in photographic solutions, etc., have little or no effect on Nylon. *All Zytel compositions may be dissolved in phenols and in formic acid.*

Zytel 63 and 69 are soluble in isopropyl and ethyl alcohols, but have good resistance to lubricating oils and gasoline.

The high strength and toughness of the Nylon resins make them useful for many applications in the laboratory. Nylon has low vapor pressure at room temperatures (see p. 140) and can be used in some vacuum applications at temperatures not over 100°C.

Nylon is readily machinable, with coolants such as a soap solution to remove generated heat. Tools should be kept sharp, with plenty of clearance. High speeds and relatively low feeds produce the best results. Provision must be made to prevent flexing, vibration, and chatter. Holes drilled in the Nylon resins tend to be very slightly undersize because of local heating and expansion. Allowance for moisture absorption must be made on parts with close tolerances. For example, a part with a 1.000-inch dimension would normally increase to approximately 1.006 inches as a result of moisture absorption. This occurs in either an average environment or one air-controlled to 50% relative humidity.

Nylon parts should be stress-relieved or annealed after rough-machining (to within 0.010 inch of final dimensions). This can be done by heating at 150°C for 15 minutes for each $\frac{1}{8}$ inch of thickness.

Mylar (du Pont) is a type of Nylon in transparent film form. It is characterized by very high strength and durability.

Occlusion. Absorption (or sometimes adsorption) of a gas by a substance; the entering of a gas into the interior of a substance, as the occlusion of hydrogen by nickel or platinum.

OFHC copper (Oxygen-free, high-conductivity copper) (see p. 219).

Oils, cutting, for use in the machining of vacuum components (see p. 401).

Oils, forepump (mechanical). The fluids used in rotary mechanical forepumps (see pp. 253 *et seq.*) are usually petroleum lubricating-type oils specially refined and

[1] The data on Zytel nylons are by courtesy of the duPont Company (Plastics Department).

SOME WELL-KNOWN PUMP FLUIDS

	OCTOIL-S (1)	OCTOIL-[1] (1)	CONVACLOR[1]		CONVOIL[1]		BUTYL PHTHALATE	SILICONES[2]			AMOILS[1]	BUTYL SEBACATE	AROCHLOR 1254	NARCOIL 10[2]
			8	12	20	10		DC-702	DC-703	DC-704				
Ultimate pressure at 25°C (mm Hg) in a GA pump[1]	5×10^{-6}	6.5×10^{-6}	—	—	8×10^{-6}	2×10^{-3}	2.5×10^{-4}	1×10^{-5}	5×10^{-6}	10^{-8}	2×10^{-5}	5×10^{-5}	2×10^{-5}	1×10^{-8}
in a GF26 pump[1]	5×10^{-8}	2×10^{-7}	—	—	—	—	4×10^{-5}	—	—	—	2×10^{-6}	1×10^{-5}		
Resistance to oxidation	Poor	Poor			Fair	Fair	Fair	Good	Good	Good	Fair	Fair	Fair	Fair
Boiling point (°C)[3] at 0.5 mm Hg	199	183	138	152	190	135	135	175	220	—	172	150		
at 0.01 mm Hg	141	126	71	86	126	75	81	115	160	185	115	94		
Molecular weight	426.7	390.5	290	326	(400)[7]	(250)	278.3	530	570	—	342.5	314.5	326	326
Specific gravity at 25°C	0.9122	0.9827	1.447	1.538	0.86	0.91	1.0435	1.071	1.089	1.07	0.9277	0.9334	1.54	1.538
Viscosity (centistokes) at 27°C	18.2	51.5	169.2	4520	80.3	93.2	14.4	28.5	30.0	—	10.6	8.1		4500
at 38°C	12.6	29.6	45.6	462	45.8	48.6	9.6	19.0	20.0	39	7.9	6.1		
at 54°C	7.9	14.7	14.2	65.5	22.8	22.0	5.8	11.7	13.0	—	5.3	4.2		
Pour point (°C)	−56	−52	7.0	10	8.8	−23.5	−71	−40	−36	—	−4.5	−16.5		
Flash point (°C) (open)	209.5	195.5	193	None	218	191	160	194	227	210	189	174		None
Fire point (°C)	248	229	None	None	259	224	191	200	300	—	222	205		None
Heater input ratio[4]	1.15	1.0	0.80	0.85	1.0	0.6	0.75	0.95	1.3	—	0.93	0.85		
Refractive index (n_D at 25°C)	1.4487	1.4848	—	—	1.4770	1.4966	1.4905	1.4828	1.4999	—	1.4432	1.4395		

[1] Consolidated Vacuum Corporation, Rochester 3, New York.
[2] Dow-Corning Corporation, Midland, Michigan.
[3] Normal boiler temperature in diffusion pumps at moderate heater input is approximately equal to the boiling point at 0.5 mm Hg.
[4] The number by which to multiply the heater input specified for a pump with Octoil pump fluid to obtain the same limiting forepressure with the given pump fluid.
[5] Monsanto Chemical Company, St. Louis 4, Missouri.
[6] NRC Equipment Corporation, Newton 61, Massachusetts.
[7] Values in parentheses are estimated.

purified for this service. The manufacturer's recommendation for each make of pump should be followed for best performance, because these oils are selected to have the lowest vapor pressure, optimum viscosity, and lubricating qualities.

Oils, diffusion and vapor pump (see DIFFUSION PUMP, p. 227). The table on p. 400, with its explanatory notes, gives the characteristics of some of the well-known pump fluids. (See also POLYPHENYL ETHERS, p. 449).

Octoil and Octoil-S: These two fluids are used in high-vacuum diffusion pumps. Octoil is a general-purpose pump fluid used with metal and/or glass fractionating pumps and with nonfractionating and single compartment pumps. Octoil-S is used with fractionating glass diffusion pumps for the lowest ultimate pressure. Both fluids condense readily and are stable under normal operating conditions. When these fluids are used, the pump heaters should be turned off if the pressure rises above 800 microns Hg for more than a few minutes. This can be effected by some type of automatic shut-off actuated by a pressure gauge, e.g., of the Bourdon or mercury manometer type. An electrical gauge can also be used (thermocouple, Pirani, or Penning gauges).

In use, both pump fluids should be cooled to below 100°C before exposure to the atmosphere.

Octoil-S is sometimes used as a lubricant because of its low pour point and rate of evaporation. It can also be used in oil manometers where a fluid of extremely low vapor pressure is required.

Convoil-20 is a hydrocarbon oil for very large fractionating pumps. It does not respond as well as the organic oils to the self-purifying action in the pump; consequently, it needs more frequent replacement because of thermal cracking, polymerization, and loss of volatile fractions. On the other hand, it does not deposit solid products. This fluid can be used in booster pumps (see below) for backing high-vacuum diffusion pumps as an aid in avoiding contamination of the fluid in the diffusion pump by backstreaming of the more volatile fluids in the forepump.

Convoil-10 is a hydrocarbon oil for use in high-boiler-pressure pumps such as ejector pumps (p. 231) operating against forepressures as high as 3.5 mm Hg.

Butyl phthalate and butyl sebacate are esters used in small booster pumps which reach their peak efficiencies and speeds at higher pressures than do the high-vacuum diffusion pumps. Booster pumps are often inserted between the forepump and the high-vacuum diffusion pump (see p. 168). Butyl phthalate and butyl sebacate can be used in booster pumps against forepressures up to 400 microns Hg, as compared with 200 microns for Octoil. They should be cooled to 100°C or below before exposure to the atmosphere.

Silicones DC-702 and *DC-703* are used where there is danger of exposure at operating temperature to bursts of gas at pressures above 1 mm Hg. They sometimes tend to form an insulating layer or deposit on the collector of the ionization gauge tube, which results in erroneous readings. A Knudsen gauge (p. 321) is preferable. Although more stable than other pump fluids, the Silicone oils, when exposed to the atmosphere at full heat in a metal pump, are likely to cause deposits that are difficult to remove.

Amoil-S has higher thermal stability and longer operating life than the Octoil fluids. Its safe temperature for exposure to the atmosphere is about 120°C.

Myvane-20 and *Myvane-10* (Consolidated) are obsolete names for Convoil-20 and Convoil-10, respectively (see above).

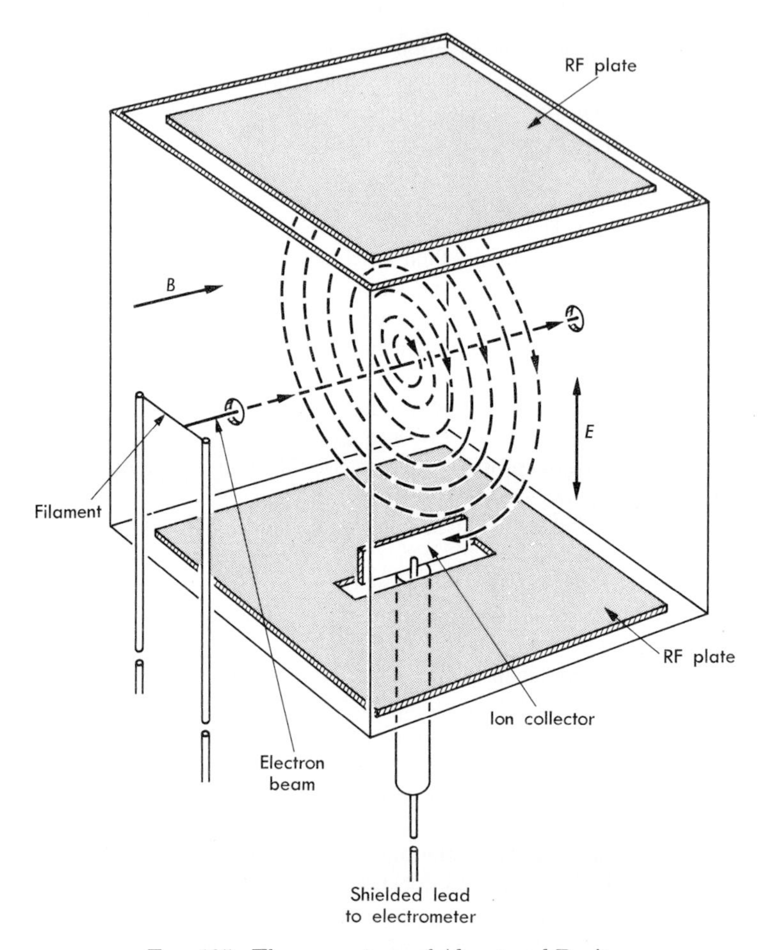

FIG. 105. The omegatron of Alpert and Buritz.

Cencoil-B (Central Scientific Company, Chicago 13, Illinois, and Boston, Massachusetts) is a low-vapor-pressure fluid for use in diffusion pumps. It has an ultimate vacuum of 5×10^{-7} at 25°C.

The *Apiezon* diffusion pump oils are described in the table on p. 158.

Polyphenyl ethers, (see p. 449).

Silicone XF-4660 (Dow-Corning Corporation, Midland, Michigan): This is a fluid which is capable of an ultimate pressure of 3×10^{-10} mm Hg with a baffle, and in the 10^{-9} range unbaffled. It can be operated at the same boiler temperature as other pump fluids, although there are some preliminary indications[1] that higher speeds and lower ultimate pressures can be attained with increased power to the heater.

Omegatron. A simplified and relatively inexpensive kind of mass-spectrometer which can be used to serve the dual purpose of identifying gases in a vacuum system and measuring their abundance or pressure.

---

[1] NRC Equipment Corporation, Newton 61, Massachusetts, markets this fluid.

Alpert and Buritz[1] have described one type of omegatron, illustrated in Fig. 105, p. 402). A narrow, cylindrical beam of ionizing electrons is formed parallel to the direction of a magnetic field B. Ions formed along the beam, upon collision with gas molecules, are accelerated by the RF alternating potential between the two flat plates, as in a cyclotron. When the value of the impressed RF frequency is equal to the cyclotron frequency,

$$\omega = \frac{eH}{M},$$

the ions of mass M and charge e are accelerated in orbits of increasing size and eventually strike the ion collector plate. The ion-collector current is a measure of the abundance of the gas of this charge-to-mass ratio. For a magnetic field of 2100 gauss, as used in some of the experiments, the calculated cyclotron frequency is 3.2 megacycles for mass 1, and 32 kilocycles for mass 100.

The RF plates and the surrounding shield box are made in the form of a cube from 0.015 inch Advance (copper-nickel alloy) sheet. Stainless steel, platinum-iridium, molybdenum, tantalum, and other metals can be used. The electrons are accelerated through holes $\frac{1}{16}$ inch in diameter in opposite walls. An electron collector (not shown) is provided behind the right-hand wall and also a filament heat shield and a collimating iris (not shown) to the left of the filament and between the filament and the left wall, respectively. The ion collector plate, also of 0.015 inch Advance, projects into the box (but is insulated from it) through a slit $\frac{1}{16}$ inch wide, a distance of about $\frac{1}{16}$ inch into the accelerator chamber. The conducting lead from the ion collector is brought out through an Inconel or stainless steel shielding cylinder, and an external shield must be provided for the lead to the electrometer to eliminate strays and noise.

The structure is mounted in a Pyrex glass envelope with Kovar and tungsten seals, and is thus capable of being baked out at 450°C during evacuation.

Alpert and Buritz made the shielding box in two sizes—2 cm and 1 cm cubes.

The impressed voltage (about 1 v in amplitude) was supplied by a Hewlett-Packard Model 650A Test Oscillator. The ion current in this device was measured with a vibrating reed electrometer, but other types of electrometers could be used.

It was sometimes desirable to apply a small negative "trapping" voltage of 1 v or less between the RF plates and the shielding box.

The essentially similar omegatron of Woodford and Gardner (see the reference on p. 404), together with the associated circuitry, is shown in Fig. 106.

A somewhat modified form of this device is available commercially as a "Residual Gas Analyzer," made by Consolidated Electrodynamics Corporation, Pasadena, California.

A modification of the omegatron, known as the Farvitron,[2, 3] is actually an electrostatic mass spectroscope requiring no magnet. While this device has less resolving power and lower sensitivity than the omegatron (suitable for measuring single

[1] "Ultra-High Vacuum II—Limiting Factors in the Attainment of Very Low Pressures," D. Alpert and R. S. Buritz, *J. Appl. Phys.*, **25,** 202, 1954.

[2] "An Electrostatic Mass Spectroscope," W. Tretner, *Vacuum* (Br), **10,** 1/2, p. 31, 1960.

[3] "Analysis of Partial Pressures by Means of Omegatron and Farvitron," G. Reich and F. Flecken, *ibid.*, (Br), **10,** 1/2, p. 35, 1960.

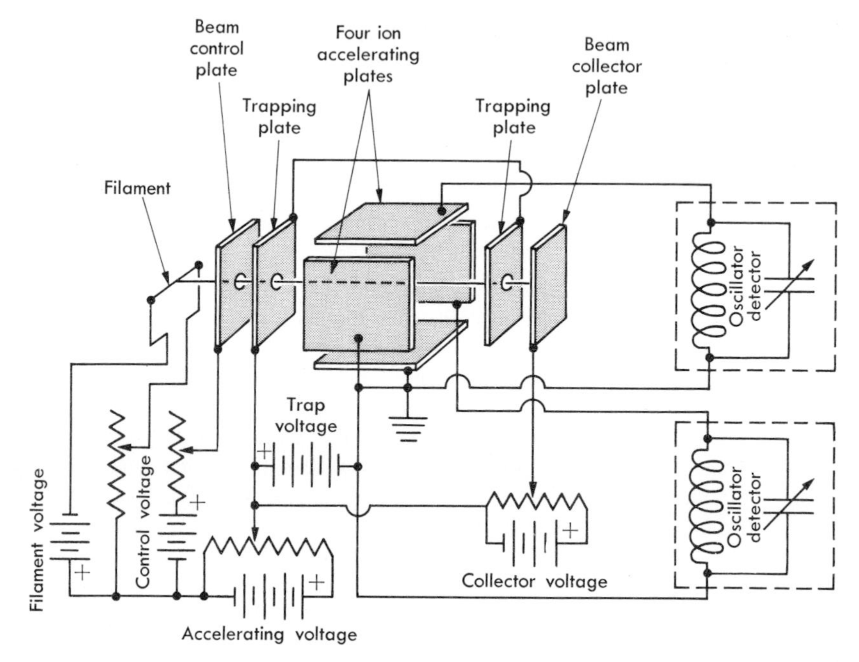

FIG. 106. Arrangement of the omegatron electrodes and the electrical connections to them.

partial pressures), it is capable of presenting, on an oscilloscope, a complete survey of the composition of gases in a vacuum system.

OMEGATRON—BIBLIOGRAPHY

J. A. Hipple, H. Sommer, and H. A. Thomas, *Phys. Rev.*, **76,** 1877, 1949.

H. Sommer and H. A. Thomas, *ibid.*, **78,** 806, 1950.

H. Sommer, H. A. Thomas, and J. A. Hipple, *ibid.*, **82,** 697, 1951.

J. E. Taylor and E. G. Brock, GE Research Laboratory Report No. 55-RL-1310, June, 1955.

A. G. Edwards, *J. Appl. Phys.* (Br), **6,** 44, 1955.

R. H. Bell, *J. Sci. Instr.*, **33,** 269, 1956.

H. J. Woodford and J. H. Gardner, *Rev. Sci. Instr.*, **27,** 378, 1956.

E. Zdanuk. R. Bierig, L. G. Rubin, and S. P. Wolsky, Proceedings 19th Annual Conference at M.I.T. on Physical Electronics, p. 162, March, 1959.

L. A. Cambey and C. J. Milner, *Rev. Sci. Instr.*, **31,** 776, 1960.

S. Dushman, *Scientific Foundations of Vacuum Technique,* second edition, p. 342, John Wiley & Sons, Inc., New York, New York (1962).

W. J. Grubbs and G. H. Snider, "A Quantitative Study of the Evolution of Gases from Electron Tubes and Materials," AF 19(628)–326, First Scientific Report prepared for Electronics Research Directorate, AFCRL, Bedford, Massachusetts, April 18, 1962.

P. F. Varadi, "Partial Pressure Gauge Tubes," *Cathode Press* (Machlett Laboratories, Inc., Springdale, Connecticut) **19,** 17, 22, 1962.

Opening glass tubes or ampoules in vacuum. It is sometimes necessary to open a small vacuum tube or a glass ampoule containing metal or other material to be analyzed or used to provide an atmosphere in a vacuum vessel. For example, when the residual or produced gases in a small sealed radio tube are to be analyzed (in a mass-spectrometer or omegatron), or when cesium, sodium[1] or the like is to be liberated into an evacuated tube, one of the following methods can be used:

1. For high-vacuum work, a thin-walled, annealed OFHC copper tube[2] is hydrogen-brazed to a short length of Kovar tubing, which in turn is sealed to a piece of Corning #7052 glass tubing. The end of the copper tubing is welded vacuum-tight, or cold-welded by the pinch-off procedure described on p. 119.

The ampoule or tube to be opened is placed in the closed copper tube, and the glass end is sealed to the vacuum system in question—through a graded seal if required. After evacuation and baking, the copper tube is wrapped with a few layers of suitable fabric or tape and squeezed with a pair of pliers or in a small hand vise, thus breaking the tube within.

2. A method similar to that described on p. 120 can be used. The containing glass tube can be made longer and the small iron slug can be replaced with a heavy ball of #416 (magnetic) stainless steel or a clean high-carbon steel ball bearing, raised with a magnet and allowed to fall on the ampoule or tube.

Optical baffle (see CHEVRON BAFFLE, p. 199).

Optical pyrometer. The temperature of incandescent objects can be conveniently measured with an optical device in which the color of a heated filament in the instrument is matched (or made to "disappear") against the background of the hot object being observed. The device is essentially an electrical potentiometer using a balance or null-method, in which a measurable current from a small battery (contained in the instrument) is proportional to the brightness of the filament. The adjustment control for this current reads directly in degrees of temperature. The battery is calibrated through a rheostat coupled to the measuring circuit, with a contained standard-cell, so that the voltage supplied to the lamp filament is accurate to a high degree.

A wide range of temperatures, from about 750° to 2800°C, can be measured, and this is sometimes accomplished in several overlapping ranges by the use of a corresponding number of colored filters held in a turret in front of the focusing lens. Measurements may be made at any convenient distance from the hot object.

Some errors are encountered in the use of an optical pyrometer. These are (a) emissivity errors, (b) transmission errors, and (c) subjective or personal errors.

Under (a): an optical pyrometer reads correct temperature only if the hot object is in a "black-body" condition, that is, when it is completely surrounded by other objects, all of which are at the same temperature. For example, consider an object in the center of a spherical oven or furnace which is provided with a small peep hole. If the object and the inner walls of the furnace are at the same temperature, black-body conditions exist for that object, sighted through the hole.

When viewed in the open, some nonreflecting materials, such as carbon and oxidized metal, approximate black bodies when incandescent, but polished or molten

---

[1] For mercury, a mild steel or stainless steel tube should be used, because copper readily amalgamates or dissolves in mercury.

[2] The wall should be thick enough to withstand atmospheric pressure but light enough to allow the subsequent operations.

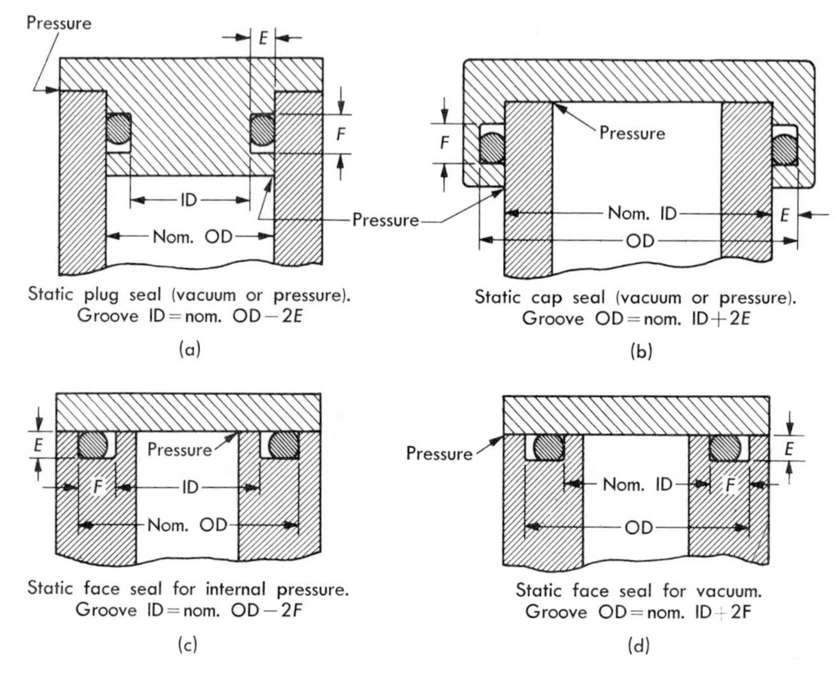

FIG. 107. O-rings and groove dimensions.

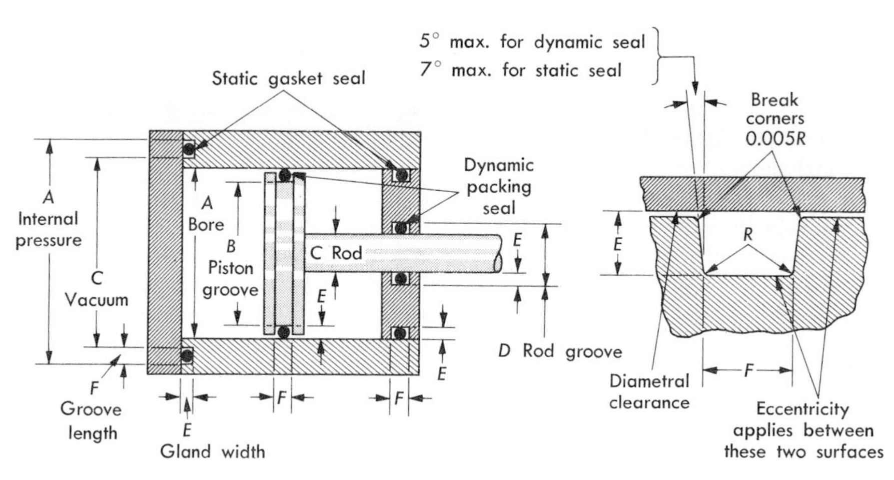

FIG. 108. Groove detail.

metals (without slag) will actually be at a *higher* temperature than that read on the instrument. Such metals are said to have a low emissivity. Materials with nonreflecting surfaces are said to have *high* emissivity. The emissivity of a black body is arbitrarily set at 1.0. Since most materials used in vacuum and electron tube work will have *low* emissivities, allowances will have to be made in measuring their temperatures by this method (see p. 240).

Errors under (b): Hot objects in black-body conditions, when viewed in the air, will not be subject to these errors to any appreciable extent, but when viewed through glass, allowance will be required for (1) the thickness and kind of glass, (2) the angle of view through the glass, and (3) the presence of even a small amount of evaporated material on the glass which further increases transmission loss. There are also reflection losses. As a rough rule-of-thumb, a hot object viewed at a normal angle (perpendicular to the surface) through $\frac{1}{8}$-inch-thick clean Pyrex glass will appear 50° to 100°C lower in temperature than it actually is. At high temperatures, where evaporation may occur, the error will progressively increase. This should be carefully guarded against to avoid overreaching the melting point.

Errors under (c): Even with considerable experience, some operators will consistently read higher or lower temperatures than others, and some will be able to see the incandescence of hot objects at actual lower temperatures than others (if their eye sensitivity to the deep reds is more acute). Individuals may suffer from eye-fatigue and thus make unknowing random errors.

The errors described in (a) and (b) are additive.

A related device, optical but not visual, and therefore free from subjective errors, is the *radiation pyrometer*, in which an element sensitive to the heat radiation is placed at the focus of a lens system, and measures the temperature continuously. This element can be a radiation thermocouple or thermopile (p. 525), a photoelectric or photoconductive cell (p. 432), a resistance-bolometer, or the like. In any event its output is coupled through an amplifier of some kind to an automatic indicator and/or controller. The sensitive element can be mounted in a fixed position relative to the hot body and some distance from it. Some types feature rapid response so that the temperature of moving bodies can be measured.

OPTICAL PYROMETER—BIBLIOGRAPHY

"Pyrometric Practice," Technical Paper of the National Bureau of Standards, Washington 25, D.C.; NBS Publication T-170 (1921).

"Techniques of Cathode Temperature Measurements as Applied to Commercial Cathode-Ray Tubes," P. P. Coppola, *Rev. Sci. Instr.*, **31**, 137, 1960.

O-Ring.[1] A toroidal-shaped ring of round cross section, commonly made from synthetic rubber (e.g., Neoprene, other elastomers such as Silicone rubber, Fluorel, Viton), and harder materials such as Kel-F, Teflon, and metals (see below).

O-rings are obtainable in the various materials, generally in sizes which are tabulated on pp. 410 *et seq.* The grooves for retaining them should be carefully made and be of such dimensions [see Figs. 107 (a), (b), (c), (d) and Figs. 108 and 109] that metal-to-metal contact between the flanges takes place when the bolts are tightened, yet leaves some space in the groove so that the O-ring is not compressed smaller than its volume, which would distort and cut it, thus destroying the seal. Neoprene[2] cannot be baked at temperatures over 100°C; Silicone rubber can be used up to 150°C; Viton can be baked up to 250°C, and Teflon can be used up to 250°C without damage.

---

[1] Descriptions of materials will be found in this glossary under their names.

[2] "Vacuum Limitations of Rubber O-Ring Joints," J. R. Young, *Rev. Sci. Instr.*, **29**, 795, 1958; also "Cleaning Techniques for Rubber O-Rings Used in Vacuum Systems," J. R. Young, *ibid.*, **30**, 291, 1959. See also the table on p. 140.

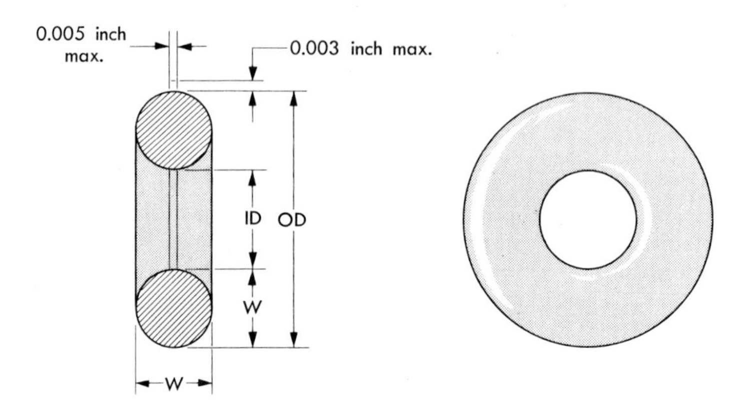

FIG. 109. O-ring dimensions.

If a demountable joint must stand higher bake-out temperatures, it will be necessary to use metal gaskets of annealed copper (see p. 117), gold, or aluminum. O-rings made of soft aluminum wire have been used successfully for making vacuum seals.[1]

GLAND DIMENSIONS

AN 6227 DASH NO.	NOMINAL CROSS SECTION	ACTUAL W	GROOVE DEPTH E ±0.001	GROOVE WIDTH F	INSIDE RADIUS R	DIAMETRAL CLEARANCE MAXIMUM	ECCENTRICITY TOTAL INDICATOR READING	CROSS-SECTIONAL SQUEEZE MINIMUM	CROSS-SECTIONAL SQUEEZE NOMINAL	ROTARY SEAL (0.005 −0.000)
1 to 7	$\frac{1}{16}$	0.070	0.057	0.094	$\frac{1}{64}$	0.005	0.002	0.010	0.013	0.094
8 to 14	$\frac{3}{32}$	0.103	0.090	0.141	$\frac{1}{64}$	0.005	0.002	0.010	0.013	0.125
15 to 27	$\frac{1}{8}$	0.139	0.123	0.188	$\frac{1}{32}$	0.006	0.003	0.012	0.016	0.170
28 to 52	$\frac{3}{16}$	0.210	0.188	0.281	$\frac{3}{64}$	0.007	0.004	0.017	0.022	0.240
53 to 88	$\frac{1}{4}$	0.275	0.240	0.375	$\frac{1}{16}$	0.008	0.005	0.029	0.035	0.315

O-rings are widely used as static seals in demountable vacuum systems, or equipment such as metal diffusion pumps, traps, baffles, and valves, and for sealing ports, doors, and electrical and mechanical feed-throughs. Generally, their use in motion seals is limited to systems requiring only moderate vacua. For the lower pressure regions, motion seals such as those described on p. 383 are recommended.

O-Rings, metallic.[2] These are sometimes used in static seals for elevated temperature applications. They are made from thin-walled metal tubing, formed into a ring, with the ends resistance-butt-welded. Type 321 stainless steel is commonly used, but rings are available in 304, 316, and 347 stainless steel, Monel, aluminum, copper, Inconel, Inconel-X, and carbon steel. These rings can be silver- or copper-plated, and also coated with Teflon.

---

[1] "Further Experiences with Aluminum Wire Seals for Bakeable Vacuum Systems," L. Elsworth, L. Holland, and L. Laurenson, *J. Sci. Instr.*, (Br) **37,** 449, 1960. See also "Standards for Vacuum Fittings," W. G. Wadey, *Vacuum* (Br), **IV,** 1, 53, 1954.

[2] Metal O-rings are available from United Metallic O-Ring Corp., Dayton, Ohio; and from Advanced Products Co., North Haven, Connecticut.

A variation of the metal O-ring is the Bar-X Seal (see p. 571) manufactured by E. B. Wiggins Oil Tool Company, Inc., Los Angeles, California. This seal is normally made of machined, hardened, and lapped Type 17-4PH stainless steel, although other materials can be used. The Bar-X is a seamless ring having an X cross section, with the top and bottom surfaces ground to a 16-microinch finish, and either chrome- or silver-plated. These can be used continuously at temperatures up to 650°C and are therefore bakeable.

Vee-rings and U-cup rings. Vee-rings, as the name indicates, are made of synthetic rubbers, Teflon, and other plastics, with a V cross section. They are sometimes used, with appropriate metal adapters and back-up rings, for sliding (piston-motion) or rotating seals. Teflon Vee-rings have been used with polished shafts (5 to 15 microinch finish) with some success in demountable vacuum systems. One disadvantage of this type of motion seal is that the shaft tends to drag moisture and gases adsorbed on its surface into the vacuum chamber, thus giving rise to a virtual leak.

Vee-rings of various materials are available from Acadia Synthetic Products, Division of Western Felt Works, Chicago, Illinois. See also p. 566, Fig. 152.

Concerning O-rings in general, it is very important in designing grooves or spaces for any type of seal for vacuum service, whether of rubber, plastic, or metal, that the two mating metal parts of the vacuum system make contact without distorting the O-ring or seal beyond its normal limit. In the case of rubber and plastic rings, enough room in the groove is to be provided so that the ring does not completely fill the space when the metal members touch. In the case of metal rings, the dimensions should be such that the ring will seal without going beyond the elastic limit. Properly designed mating members will thus be provided with a natural "stop." The safest procedure in designing such seals is to follow the manufacturer's recommendations.

Osmium. A heavy metal of the platinum group, formerly used for making lamp filaments, but now largely replaced by tungsten, which is cheaper and has a higher melting point. Osmium is the heaviest of all the metals. It is also very hard and brittle. Osmium alloys are used for phonograph needles, electrical contacts, and instrument pivots.

Some of the properties of osmium are:

Atomic weight	190.2	Specific heat	0.031
Atomic number	76	Melting point, °C	2700
Specific gravity	22.7 or 0.82 lb/in^3 at 20°C	Boiling point, °C	>5300
Color	bluish-white	Hardness, Brinell	350

Modulus of elasticity in tension, psi .... 80×10^6

Coefficient of thermal expansion at 25°C, in/in ... 6.5×10^{-6} (same as tantalum)

Resistivity, microhm-cm 9.5

Outgassing. The evolution of gas, especially as applied to metals, glass, ceramics, and other materials used in evacuated devices. All materials, even those with very low vapor pressure, adsorb or absorb atmospheric gases (including water vapor) which must be largely removed either before assembly or during vacuum processing. (See pp. 75, 98, 262. Refer also to D. J. Santeler, *Vacuum,* (Br) **11,** 1, 1961; and I. P. S. Fish, *Rev. Sci. Instr.,* **30,** 889, 1959.

SERIES AN-6227 O-RINGS

AN 6227 DASH NO.	NOMINAL SIZE ID × OD × W	ACTUAL MOLDED DIMENSIONS		*A* BORE DIAM. OR STATIC GROOVE OD ± 0.001	*B* GROOVE DIAM. +0.002 −0.000	*C* ROD DIAM. OR VACUUM GROOVE ID ± 0.001	*D* ROD GROOVE DIAM. +0.000 −0.002	STATIC FACE GROOVE OD + 0.000 −0.005 USE WITH COL. *C* AS ID	STATIC FACE GROOVE ID + 0.005 − 0.000 USE WITH COL. *A* AS OD
		ID	W						
1	$\frac{1}{8} \times \frac{1}{4} \times \frac{1}{16}$	0.114 ± 0.005	0.070 ± 0.003	0.250	0.137	0.123	0.236	0.313	0.063
2	$\frac{5}{32} \times \frac{9}{32} \times \frac{1}{16}$	0.145 ± 0.005	0.070 ± 0.003	0.281	0.168	0.154	0.267	0.344	0.093
3	$\frac{3}{16} \times \frac{5}{16} \times \frac{1}{16}$	0.176 ± 0.005	0.070 ± 0.003	0.312	0.199	0.185	0.298	0.375	0.125
4	$\frac{7}{32} \times \frac{11}{32} \times \frac{1}{16}$	0.208 ± 0.005	0.070 ± 0.003	0.344	0.231	0.217	0.330	0.407	0.156
5	$\frac{1}{4} \times \frac{3}{8} \times \frac{1}{16}$	0.239 ± 0.005	0.070 ± 0.003	0.375	0.262	0.248	0.361	0.438	0.188
6	$\frac{5}{16} \times \frac{7}{16} \times \frac{1}{16}$	0.301 ± 0.005	0.070 ± 0.003	0.4375	0.3245	0.310	0.423	0.500	0.250
7	$\frac{3}{8} \times \frac{1}{2} \times \frac{1}{16}$	0.364 ± 0.005	0.070 ± 0.003	0.500	0.387	0.373	0.486	0.563	0.313
8	$\frac{3}{8} \times \frac{9}{16} \times \frac{3}{32}$	0.362 ± 0.005	0.103 ± 0.003	0.5625	0.3835	0.373	0.552	0.657	0.242
9	$\frac{7}{16} \times \frac{5}{8} \times \frac{3}{32}$	0.424 ± 0.005	0.103 ± 0.003	0.625	0.446	0.435	0.614	0.719	0.344
10	$\frac{1}{2} \times \frac{11}{16} \times \frac{3}{32}$	0.487 ± 0.005	0.103 ± 0.003	0.6875	0.5085	0.498	0.677	0.782	0.407
11	$\frac{9}{16} \times \frac{3}{4} \times \frac{3}{32}$	0.549 ± 0.005	0.103 ± 0.003	0.750	0.571	0.560	0.739	0.844	0.469
12	$\frac{5}{8} \times \frac{13}{16} \times \frac{3}{32}$	0.612 ± 0.005	0.103 ± 0.003	0.8125	0.6335	0.623	0.802	0.907	0.532
13	$\frac{11}{16} \times \frac{7}{8} \times \frac{3}{32}$	0.674 ± 0.005	0.103 ± 0.003	0.875	0.696	0.685	0.864	0.969	0.594
14	$\frac{3}{4} \times \frac{15}{16} \times \frac{3}{32}$	0.737 ± 0.005	0.103 ± 0.003	0.9375	0.7585	0.748	0.927	1.032	0.632
15	$\frac{3}{4} \times 1 \times \frac{1}{8}$	0.734 ± 0.006	0.139 ± 0.004	1.001	0.756	0.747	0.992	1.125	0.625
16	$\frac{13}{16} \times 1\frac{1}{16} \times \frac{1}{8}$	0.796 ± 0.006	0.139 ± 0.004	1.063	0.818	0.809	1.054	1.188	0.688
17	$\frac{7}{8} \times 1\frac{1}{8} \times \frac{1}{8}$	0.859 ± 0.006	0.139 ± 0.004	1.126	0.881	0.872	1.117	1.250	0.750
18	$\frac{15}{16} \times 1\frac{3}{16} \times \frac{1}{8}$	0.921 ± 0.006	0.139 ± 0.004	1.188	0.943	0.934	1.179	1.313	0.813
19	$1 \times 1\frac{1}{4} \times \frac{1}{8}$	0.984 ± 0.006	0.139 ± 0.004	1.251	1.006	0.997	1.242	1.375	0.875
20	$1\frac{1}{16} \times 1\frac{5}{16} \times \frac{1}{8}$	1.046 ± 0.006	0.139 ± 0.004	1.313	1.068	1.059	1.304	1.438	0.938

21	$1\frac{1}{8} \times 1\frac{3}{8} \times \frac{1}{8}$	1.109 ± 0.006	0.139 ± 0.004	1.376	1.131	1.122	1.367	1.500	1.000
22	$1\frac{3}{16} \times 1\frac{7}{16} \times \frac{1}{8}$	1.171 ± 0.006	0.139 ± 0.004	1.438	1.193	1.184	1.429	1.563	1.063
23	$1\frac{1}{4} \times 1\frac{1}{2} \times \frac{1}{8}$	1.234 ± 0.006	0.139 ± 0.004	1.501	1.256	1.247	1.492	1.625	1.125
24	$1\frac{5}{16} \times 1\frac{9}{16} \times \frac{1}{8}$	1.296 ± 0.006	0.139 ± 0.004	1.563	1.318	1.309	1.554	1.688	1.188
25	$1\frac{3}{8} \times 1\frac{5}{8} \times \frac{1}{8}$	1.359 ± 0.006	0.139 ± 0.004	1.626	1.381	1.372	1.617	1.750	1.250
26	$1\frac{7}{16} \times 1\frac{11}{16} \times \frac{1}{8}$	1.421 ± 0.006	0.139 ± 0.004	1.688	1.443	1.434	1.679	1.813	1.313
27	$1\frac{1}{2} \times 1\frac{3}{4} \times \frac{1}{8}$	1.484 ± 0.006	0.139 ± 0.004	1.751	1.506	1.497	1.742	1.875	1.375
28	$1\frac{1}{2} \times 1\frac{7}{8} \times \frac{3}{16}$	1.475 ± 0.010	0.210 ± 0.005	1.876	1.502	1.497	1.871	2.063	1.313
29	$1\frac{5}{8} \times 2 \times \frac{3}{16}$	1.600 ± 0.010	0.210 ± 0.005	2.001	1.627	1.622	1.996	2.188	1.438
30	$1\frac{3}{4} \times 2\frac{1}{8} \times \frac{3}{16}$	1.725 ± 0.010	0.210 ± 0.005	2.126	1.752	1.747	2.121	2.313	1.563
31	$1\frac{7}{8} \times 2\frac{1}{4} \times \frac{3}{16}$	1.850 ± 0.010	0.210 ± 0.005	2.251	1.877	1.872	2.246	2.438	1.688
32	$2 \times 2\frac{3}{8} \times \frac{3}{16}$	1.975 ± 0.010	0.210 ± 0.005	2.376	2.002	1.997	2.371	2.563	1.813
33	$2\frac{1}{8} \times 2\frac{1}{2} \times \frac{3}{16}$	2.100 ± 0.010	0.210 ± 0.005	2.501	2.127	2.122	2.496	2.688	1.938
34	$2\frac{1}{4} \times 2\frac{5}{8} \times \frac{3}{16}$	2.225 ± 0.010	0.210 ± 0.005	2.626	2.252	2.247	2.621	2.813	2.063
35	$2\frac{3}{8} \times 2\frac{3}{4} \times \frac{3}{16}$	2.350 ± 0.010	0.210 ± 0.005	2.751	2.377	2.372	2.746	2.938	2.188
36	$2\frac{1}{2} \times 2\frac{7}{8} \times \frac{3}{16}$	2.475 ± 0.010	0.210 ± 0.005	2.876	2.502	2.497	2.871	3.063	2.313
37	$2\frac{5}{8} \times 3 \times \frac{3}{16}$	2.600 ± 0.010	0.210 ± 0.005	3.001	2.627	2.622	2.996	3.188	2.438
38	$2\frac{3}{4} \times 3\frac{1}{8} \times \frac{3}{16}$	2.725 ± 0.015	0.210 ± 0.005	3.126	2.752	2.747	3.121	3.313	2.563
39	$2\frac{7}{8} \times 3\frac{1}{4} \times \frac{3}{16}$	2.850 ± 0.015	0.210 ± 0.005	3.251	2.877	2.872	3.246	3.438	2.688
40	$3 \times 3\frac{3}{8} \times \frac{3}{16}$	2.975 ± 0.015	0.210 ± 0.005	3.377	3.003	2.996	3.370	3.563	2.813
41	$3\frac{1}{8} \times 3\frac{1}{2} \times \frac{3}{16}$	3.100 ± 0.015	0.210 ± 0.005	3.502	3.128	3.121	3.495	3.688	2.938
42	$3\frac{1}{4} \times 3\frac{5}{8} \times \frac{3}{16}$	3.225 ± 0.015	0.210 ± 0.005	3.627	3.253	3.246	3.620	3.813	3.063
43	$3\frac{3}{8} \times 3\frac{3}{4} \times \frac{3}{16}$	3.350 ± 0.015	0.210 ± 0.005	3.752	3.378	3.371	3.745	3.938	3.188
44	$3\frac{1}{2} \times 3\frac{7}{8} \times \frac{3}{16}$	3.475 ± 0.015	0.210 ± 0.005	3.877	3.503	3.496	3.870	4.063	3.313

(Cont.)

SERIES AN-6227 O-RINGS (*Continued*)

AN 6227 DASH NO.	NOMINAL SIZE ID × OD × W	ACTUAL MOLDED DIMENSIONS ID	ACTUAL MOLDED DIMENSIONS W	*A* BORE DIAM. OR STATIC GROOVE OD ± 0.001	*B* GROOVE DIAM. +0.002 −0.000	*C* ROD DIAM. OR VACUUM GROOVE ID ± 0.001	*D* ROD GROOVE DIAM. +0.000 −0.002	STATIC FACE GROOVE OD + 0.000 −0.005 USE WITH COL. *C* AS ID	STATIC FACE GROOVE ID + 0.005 − 0.000 USE WITH COL. *A* AS OD
45	$3\frac{5}{8} \times 4 \times \frac{3}{16}$	3.600 ± 0.015	0.210 ± 0.005	4.002	3.628	3.621	3.995	4.188	3.437
46	$3\frac{3}{4} \times 4\frac{1}{8} \times \frac{3}{16}$	3.725 ± 0.015	0.210 ± 0.005	4.127	3.753	3.746	4.120	4.313	3.563
47	$3\frac{7}{8} \times 4\frac{1}{4} \times \frac{3}{16}$	3.850 × 0.015	0.210 ± 0.005	4.252	3.878	3.871	4.245	4.438	3.688
48	$4 \times 4\frac{3}{8} \times \frac{3}{16}$	3.975 ± 0.015	0.210 ± 0.005	4.377	4.003	3.996	4.370	4.563	3.813
49	$4\frac{1}{8} \times 4\frac{1}{2} \times \frac{3}{16}$	4.100 ± 0.015	0.210 ± 0.005	4.502	4.128	4.121	4.495	4.688	3.938
50	$4\frac{1}{4} \times 4\frac{5}{8} \times \frac{3}{16}$	4.225 ± 0.015	0.210 ± 0.005	4.627	4.253	4.246	4.620	4.813	4.063
51	$4\frac{3}{8} \times 4\frac{3}{4} \times \frac{3}{16}$	4.350 ± 0.015	0.210 ± 0.005	4.752	4.378	4.371	4.745	4.938	4.188
52	$4\frac{1}{2} \times 4\frac{7}{8} \times \frac{3}{16}$	4.475 ± 0.015	0.210 ± 0.005	4.877	4.503	4.496	4.870	5.063	4.313
53	$4\frac{5}{8} \times 5\frac{1}{8} \times \frac{1}{4}$	4.600 ± 0.015	0.275 ± 0.006	5.128	4.649	4.621	5.100	5.375	4.375
54	$4\frac{3}{4} \times 5\frac{1}{4} \times \frac{1}{4}$	4.725 ± 0.015	0.275 ± 0.006	5.253	4.774	4.746	5.225	5.500	4.500
55	$4\frac{7}{8} \times 5\frac{3}{8} \times \frac{1}{4}$	4.850 ± 0.015	0.275 ± 0.006	5.378	4.899	4.871	5.350	5.625	4.625
56	$5 \times 5\frac{1}{2} \times \frac{1}{4}$	4.975 ± 0.015	0.275 ± 0.006	5.503	5.024	4.996	5.475	5.750	4.750
57	$5\frac{1}{8} \times 5\frac{5}{8} \times \frac{1}{4}$	5.100 ± 0.023	0.275 ± 0.006	5.628	5.149	5.121	5.600	5.875	4.875
58	$5\frac{1}{4} \times 5\frac{3}{4} \times \frac{1}{4}$	5.225 ± 0.023	0.275 ± 0.006	5.753	5.274	5.246	5.725	6.000	5.000
59	$5\frac{3}{8} \times 5\frac{7}{8} \times \frac{1}{4}$	5.350 ± 0.023	0.275 ± 0.006	5.878	5.399	5.371	5.850	6.125	5.125
60	$5\frac{1}{2} \times 6 \times \frac{1}{4}$	5.475 ± 0.023	0.275 ± 0.006	6.003	5.524	5.496	5.975	6.250	5.250
61	$5\frac{5}{8} \times 6\frac{1}{8} \times \frac{1}{4}$	5.600 ± 0.023	0.275 ± 0.006	6.128	5.649	5.621	6.100	6.325	5.375
62	$5\frac{3}{4} \times 6\frac{1}{4} \times \frac{1}{4}$	5.725 ± 0.023	0.275 ± 0.006	6.253	5.774	5.746	6.225	6.500	5.500
63	$5\frac{7}{8} \times 6\frac{3}{8} \times \frac{1}{4}$	5.850 ± 0.023	0.275 ± 0.006	6.378	5.899	5.871	6.350	6.625	5.625

64	$6 \times 6\frac{1}{2} \times \frac{1}{4}$	5.975 ± 0.023	0.275 ± 0.006	6.503	6.024	5.996	6.475	6.750	5.750
65	$6\frac{1}{4} \times 6\frac{3}{4} \times \frac{1}{4}$	6.225 ± 0.023	0.275 ± 0.006	6.753	6.274	6.246	6.725	7.000	6.000
66	$6\frac{1}{2} \times 7 \times \frac{1}{4}$	6.475 ± 0.023	0.275 ± 0.006	7.003	6.524	6.496	6.975	7.250	6.250
67	$6\frac{3}{4} \times 7\frac{1}{4} \times \frac{1}{4}$	6.725 ± 0.023	0.275 ± 0.006	7.253	6.774	6.746	7.225	7.500	6.500
68	$7 \times 7\frac{1}{2} \times \frac{1}{4}$	6.975 ± 0.023	0.275 ± 0.006	7.503	7.024	6.996	7.475	7.750	6.750
69	$7\frac{1}{4} \times 7\frac{3}{4} \times \frac{1}{4}$	7.225 ± 0.030	0.275 ± 0.006	7.753	7.274	7.246	7.725	8.000	7.000
70	$7\frac{1}{2} \times 8 \times \frac{1}{4}$	7.475 ± 0.030	0.275 ± 0.006	8.003	7.524	7.496	7.975	8.250	7.250
71	$7\frac{3}{4} \times 8\frac{1}{4} \times \frac{1}{4}$	7.725 ± 0.030	0.275 ± 0.006	8.253	7.774	7.746	8.225	8.500	7.500
72	$8 \times 8\frac{1}{2} \times \frac{1}{4}$	7.975 ± 0.030	0.275 ± 0.006	8.503	8.024	7.996	8.475	8.750	7.750
73	$8\frac{1}{2} \times 9 \times \frac{1}{4}$	8.475 ± 0.030	0.275 ± 0.006	9.003	8.524	8.496	8.975	9.250	8.250
74	$9 \times 9\frac{1}{2} \times \frac{1}{4}$	8.975 ± 0.030	0.275 ± 0.006	9.503	9.024	8.996	9.475	9.750	8.750
75	$9\frac{1}{2} \times 10 \times \frac{1}{4}$	9.475 ± 0.030	0.275 ± 0.006	10.003	9.524	9.496	9.975	10.250	9.250
76	$10 \times 10\frac{1}{2} \times \frac{1}{4}$	9.975 ± 0.030	0.275 ± 0.006	10.503	10.024	9.996	10.475	10.750	9.750
77	$10\frac{1}{2} \times 11 \times \frac{1}{4}$	10.475 ± 0.030	0.275 ± 0.006	11.003	10.524	10.496	10.975	11.250	10.250
78	$11 \times 11\frac{1}{2} \times \frac{1}{4}$	10.975 ± 0.030	0.275 ± 0.006	11.503	11.024	10.996	11.475	11.750	10.750
79	$11\frac{1}{2} \times 12 \times \frac{1}{4}$	11.475 ± 0.030	0.275 ± 0.006	12.003	11.524	11.496	11.975	12.250	11.250
80	$12 \times 12\frac{1}{2} \times \frac{1}{4}$	11.975 ± 0.030	0.275 ± 0.006	12.503	12.024	11.996	12.475	12.750	11.750
81	$12\frac{1}{2} \times 13 \times \frac{1}{4}$	12.475 ± 0.030	0.275 ± 0.006	13.003	12.524	12.496	12.975	13.250	12.250
82	$13 \times 13\frac{1}{2} \times \frac{1}{4}$	12.975 ± 0.030	0.275 ± 0.006	13.503	13.024	12.996	13.475	13.750	12.750
83	$13\frac{1}{2} \times 14 \times \frac{1}{4}$	13.475 ± 0.030	0.275 ± 0.006	14.003	13.524	13.496	13.975	14.250	13.250
84	$14 \times 14\frac{1}{2} \times \frac{1}{4}$	13.975 ± 0.030	0.275 ± 0.006	14.503	14.024	13.996	14.475	14.750	13.750
85	$14\frac{1}{2} \times 15 \times \frac{1}{4}$	14.475 ± 0.030	0.275 ± 0.006	15.003	14.524	14.496	14.975	15.250	14.250
86	$15 \times 15\frac{1}{2} \times \frac{1}{4}$	14.975 ± 0.030	0.275 ± 0.006	15.503	15.024	14.996	15.475	15.750	14.750
87	$15\frac{1}{2} \times 16 \times \frac{1}{4}$	15.475 ± 0.030	0.275 ± 0.006	16.003	15.524	15.496	15.975	16.250	15.250
88	$4\frac{1}{2} \times 5 \times \frac{1}{4}$	4.475 ± 0.015	0.275 ± 0.006	5.003	4.524	4.496	4.975	5.250	4.250

Series AN-6230 O-Rings

AN 6230 DASH NO.	NOMINAL SIZE ID × OD × W	ACTUAL MOLDED DIMENSIONS		FIG. 107(a) STATIC PLUG SEAL GROOVE ID +0.002 −0.000	FIG. 107(b) STATIC CAP SEAL GROOVE OD +0.000 −0.002	FIG. 107(c) STATIC FACE SEAL GROOVE ID +0.002 −0.000	FIG. 107(d) STATIC FACE SEAL GROOVE OD +0.000 −0.002
		ID	W				
1	$1\frac{5}{8} \times 1\frac{7}{8} \times \frac{1}{8}$	1.609 ± 0.010	0.139 ± 0.004	1.631	1.869	1.535	1.965
2	$1\frac{3}{4} \times 2 \times \frac{1}{8}$	1.734 ± 0.010	0.139 ± 0.004	1.756	1.994	1.660	2.090
3	$1\frac{7}{8} \times 2\frac{1}{8} \times \frac{1}{8}$	1.859 ± 0.010	0.139 ± 0.004	1.881	2.119	1.785	2.215
4	$2 \times 2\frac{1}{4} \times \frac{1}{8}$	1.984 ± 0.010	0.139 ± 0.004	2.006	2.244	1.910	2.340
5	$2\frac{1}{8} \times 2\frac{3}{8} \times \frac{1}{8}$	2.109 ± 0.010	0.139 ± 0.004	2.131	2.369	2.035	2.465
6	$2\frac{1}{4} \times 2\frac{1}{2} \times \frac{1}{8}$	2.234 ± 0.010	0.139 ± 0.004	2.256	2.494	2.160	2.590
7	$2\frac{3}{8} \times 2\frac{5}{8} \times \frac{1}{8}$	2.359 ± 0.010	0.139 ± 0.004	2.381	2.619	2.285	2.715
8	$2\frac{1}{2} \times 2\frac{3}{4} \times \frac{1}{8}$	2.484 ± 0.010	0.139 ± 0.004	2.506	2.744	2.410	2.840
9	$2\frac{5}{8} \times 2\frac{7}{8} \times \frac{1}{8}$	2.609 ± 0.010	0.139 ± 0.004	2.631	2.869	2.535	2.965
10	$2\frac{3}{4} \times 3 \times \frac{1}{8}$	2.734 ± 0.015	0.139 ± 0.004	2.756	2.994	2.660	3.090
11	$2\frac{7}{8} \times 3\frac{1}{8} \times \frac{1}{8}$	2.859 ± 0.015	0.139 ± 0.004	2.881	3.119	2.785	3.215
12	$3 \times 3\frac{1}{4} \times \frac{1}{8}$	2.984 ± 0.015	0.139 ± 0.004	3.006	3.244	2.910	3.340
13	$3\frac{1}{8} \times 3\frac{3}{8} \times \frac{1}{8}$	3.109 ± 0.015	0.139 ± 0.004	3.131	3.369	3.035	3.465
14	$3\frac{1}{4} \times 3\frac{1}{2} \times \frac{1}{8}$	3.234 ± 0.015	0.139 ± 0.004	3.256	3.494	3.160	3.590
15	$3\frac{3}{8} \times 3\frac{5}{8} \times \frac{1}{8}$	3.359 ± 0.015	0.139 ± 0.004	3.381	3.619	3.285	3.715
16	$3\frac{1}{2} \times 3\frac{3}{4} \times \frac{1}{8}$	3.484 ± 0.015	0.139 ± 0.004	3.506	3.744	3.410	3.840
17	$3\frac{5}{8} \times 3\frac{7}{8} \times \frac{1}{8}$	3.609 ± 0.015	0.139 ± 0.004	3.631	3.869	3.535	3.965
18	$3\frac{3}{4} \times 4 \times \frac{1}{8}$	3.734 ± 0.015	0.139 ± 0.004	3.756	3.994	3.660	4.090
19	$3\frac{7}{8} \times 4\frac{1}{8} \times \frac{1}{8}$	3.859 ± 0.015	0.139 ± 0.004	3.881	4.119	3.785	4.215
20	$4 \times 4\frac{1}{4} \times \frac{1}{8}$	3.984 ± 0.015	0.139 ± 0.004	4.006	4.244	3.910	4.340
21	$4\frac{1}{8} \times 4\frac{3}{8} \times \frac{1}{8}$	4.109 ± 0.015	0.139 ± 0.004	4.131	4.369	4.035	4.465
22	$4\frac{1}{4} \times 4\frac{1}{2} \times \frac{1}{8}$	4.234 ± 0.015	0.139 ± 0.004	4.256	4.494	4.160	4.590
23	$4\frac{3}{8} \times 4\frac{5}{8} \times \frac{1}{8}$	4.359 ± 0.015	0.139 ± 0.004	4.381	4.619	4.285	4.715
24	$4\frac{1}{2} \times 4\frac{3}{4} \times \frac{1}{8}$	4.484 ± 0.015	0.139 ± 0.004	4.506	4.744	4.410	4.840

25	$4\frac{5}{8} \times 4\frac{7}{8} \times \frac{1}{8}$	4.609 ± 0.015	0.139 ± 0.004	4.631	4.869	4.535	4.965
26	$4\frac{3}{4} \times 5 \times \frac{1}{8}$	4.734 ± 0.015	0.139 ± 0.004	4.756	4.994	4.660	5.090
27	$4\frac{7}{8} \times 5\frac{1}{8} \times \frac{1}{8}$	4.859 ± 0.015	0.139 ± 0.004	4.881	5.119	4.785	5.215
28	$5 \times 5\frac{1}{4} \times \frac{1}{8}$	4.984 ± 0.015	0.139 ± 0.004	5.006	5.244	4.910	5.340
29	$5\frac{1}{8} \times 5\frac{3}{8} \times \frac{1}{8}$	5.109 ± 0.023	0.139 ± 0.004	5.131	5.369	5.035	5.465
30	$5\frac{1}{4} \times 5\frac{1}{2} \times \frac{1}{8}$	5.234 ± 0.023	0.139 ± 0.004	5.256	5.494	5.160	5.590
31	$5\frac{3}{8} \times 5\frac{5}{8} \times \frac{1}{8}$	5.359 ± 0.023	0.139 ± 0.004	5.381	5.619	5.285	5.715
32	$5\frac{1}{2} \times 5\frac{3}{4} \times \frac{1}{8}$	5.484 ± 0.023	0.139 ± 0.004	5.506	5.744	5.410	5.840
33	$5\frac{5}{8} \times 5\frac{7}{8} \times \frac{1}{8}$	5.609 ± 0.023	0.139 ± 0.004	5.631	5.869	5.535	5.965
34	$5\frac{3}{4} \times 6 \times \frac{1}{8}$	5.734 ± 0.023	0.139 ± 0.004	5.756	5.994	5.660	6.090
35	$5\frac{7}{8} \times 6\frac{1}{8} \times \frac{1}{8}$	5.859 ± 0.023	0.139 ± 0.004	5.881	6.119	5.785	6.215
36	$6 \times 6\frac{1}{4} \times \frac{1}{8}$	5.984 ± 0.023	0.139 ± 0.004	6.006	6.244	5.910	6.340
37	$6\frac{1}{4} \times 6\frac{1}{2} \times \frac{1}{8}$	6.234 ± 0.023	0.139 ± 0.004	6.256	6.494	6.160	6.590
38	$6\frac{1}{2} \times 6\frac{3}{4} \times \frac{1}{8}$	6.484 ± 0.023	0.139 ± 0.004	6.506	6.744	6.410	6.840
39	$6\frac{3}{4} \times 7 \times \frac{1}{8}$	6.734 ± 0.023	0.139 ± 0.004	6.756	6.994	6.660	7.090
40	$7 \times 7\frac{1}{4} \times \frac{1}{8}$	6.984 ± 0.023	0.139 ± 0.004	7.006	7.244	6.910	7.340
41	$7\frac{1}{4} \times 7\frac{1}{2} \times \frac{1}{8}$	7.234 ± 0.030	0.139 ± 0.004	7.256	7.494	7.160	7.590
42	$7\frac{1}{2} \times 7\frac{3}{4} \times \frac{1}{8}$	7.484 ± 0.030	0.139 ± 0.004	7.506	7.744	7.410	7.840
43	$7\frac{3}{4} \times 8 \times \frac{1}{8}$	7.734 ± 0.030	0.139 ± 0.004	7.756	7.994	7.660	8.090
44	$8 \times 8\frac{1}{4} \times \frac{1}{8}$	7.984 ± 0.030	0.139 ± 0.004	8.006	8.244	7.910	8.340
45	$8\frac{1}{4} \times 8\frac{1}{2} \times \frac{1}{8}$	8.234 ± 0.030	0.139 ± 0.004	8.256	8.494	8.160	8.590
46	$8\frac{1}{2} \times 8\frac{3}{4} \times \frac{1}{8}$	8.484 ± 0.030	0.139 ± 0.004	8.506	8.744	8.410	8.840
47	$8\frac{3}{4} \times 9 \times \frac{1}{8}$	8.734 ± 0.030	0.139 ± 0.004	8.756	8.994	8.660	9.090
48	$9 \times 9\frac{1}{4} \times \frac{1}{8}$	8.984 ± 0.030	0.139 ± 0.004	9.006	9.244	8.910	9.340
49	$9\frac{1}{4} \times 9\frac{1}{2} \times \frac{1}{8}$	9.234 ± 0.030	0.139 ± 0.004	9.256	9.494	9.160	9.590
50	$9\frac{1}{2} \times 9\frac{3}{4} \times \frac{1}{8}$	9.484 ± 0.030	0.139 ± 0.004	9.506	9.744	9.410	9.840
51	$9\frac{3}{4} \times 10 \times \frac{1}{8}$	9.734 ± 0.030	0.139 ± 0.004	9.756	9.994	9.660	10.090
52	$10 \times 10\frac{1}{4} \times \frac{1}{8}$	9.984 ± 0.030	0.139 ± 0.004	10.006	10.244	9.910	10.340

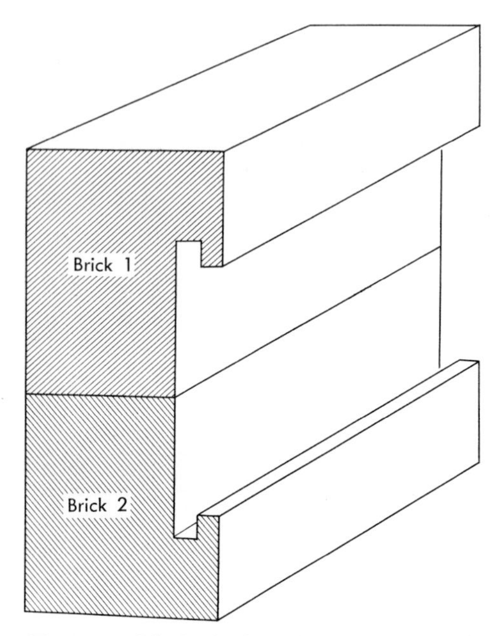

FIG. 110. Method of cutting grooves in firebrick for insertion of heating elements.

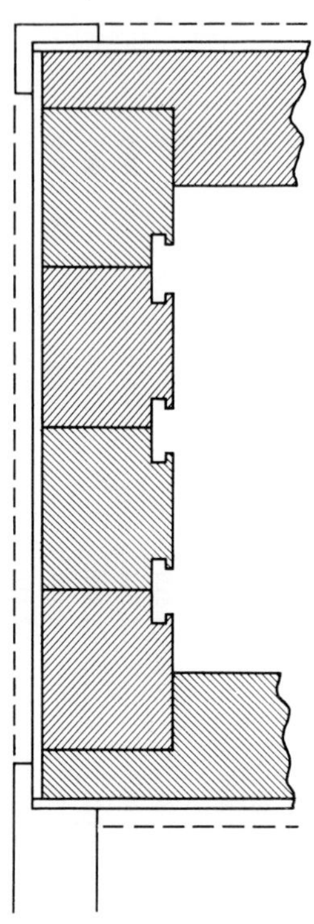

FIG. 111. Section of wall of annealing oven.

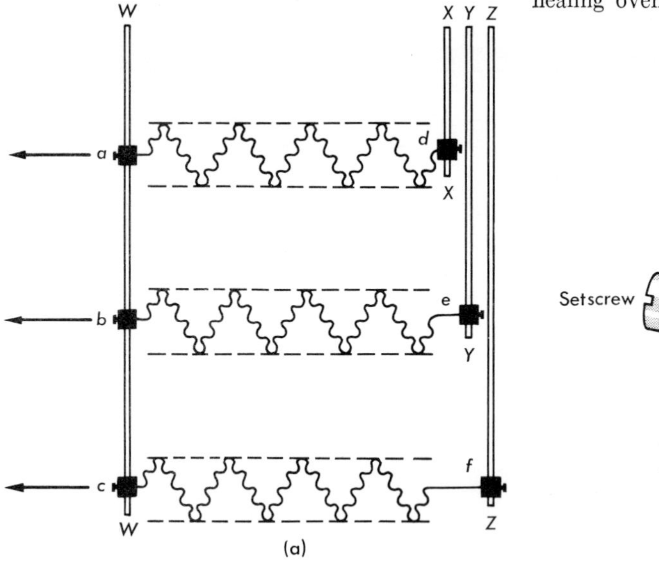

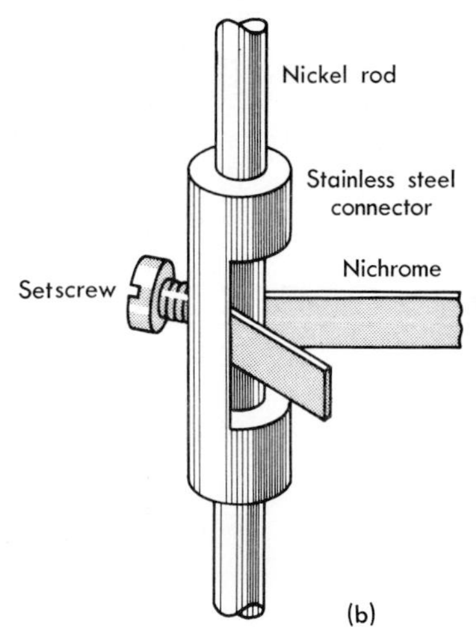

FIG. 112. (a) Arrangement of heating elements for three-phase star or delta connection. (The four rods are brought out near each other.) (b) Special connectors for attaching Nichrome ribbon to electrical leads.

Outgassing by bombardment, Electron bombardment (see pp. 101, 167).

Outgassing by ion bombardment. Where the pressure in a tube is allowed to rise, for example as a result of outgassing by induction heating or electron bombardment, the electromagnetic field which is present under these conditions will produce ionization of the gas particles. The acceleration and collision of these ions with the structures within the tube produce additional heating and consequent gas evolution, and this constitutes a kind of chain reaction which can build up to uncontrollable levels. The appearance of a glow discharge (gassy tube, p. 168) in what is supposedly a high-vacuum device is evidence of ion bombardment, which may be due to (a) overloading, i.e., drawing too much current, or application of too high an anode voltage; or (b) outgassing of materials in the tube;[1] or (c) an actual leak.

Ovens and heaters; Annealing and bake-out ovens. Details of the designs for a glass annealing oven (see p. 279) and for a bake-out oven (as part of a vacuum system or "trolley") are given in the following notes:[2]

The firebricks (B & W K-16 or K-20—see p. 250) on the three vertical walls of the annealing (or the four walls of the bake-out) oven have slots milled in them in the manner shown in Fig. 110 and Fig. 111. These cuts can be made in the soft brick with an ordinary woodworking circular saw. The arrangement of the three Nichrome V elements [shown in Fig. 112(a)] is for a three-phase oven connected either in star or delta.

The following example is given as a short method for calculating the design of heating elements for a typical vacuum bake-out oven of the type described. Temperature correction for heat losses through the firebrick walls, etc., is arbitrarily chosen as 300°C when the oven is operated at a maximum temperature of about 800°C.

Given the *inside* dimensions of the oven as 36 inches long, 24 inches deep, and 24 inches high, the inside horizontal perimeter is then:

$$2(36 + 24) = 120 \text{ inches.}$$

The heating elements are to be operated on a 3-phase, 230-volt line, delta-connected. (See Fig. 112.) Nichrome V No. 34 gauge (0.0063 inch), 1/4 inch wide, will be used. From the table[3] on pp. 420, 421), it will be seen that this ribbon has a room temperature resistance of 0.3237 ohms/ft, and the top of the table on pp. 422, 423 shows that the room temperature resistance is to be multiplied by the factor 1.078 to obtain the resistance at 1093°C. (Subtracting the heat loss of 300°C, we obtain the 800°C operating temperature. If the oven is to be used at a lower maximum temperature a smaller factor is used.) This gives us 0.35 (approximately) ohm/ft. From the table on p. 422 it will be evident that #34 gauge ribbon 1/4 inch wide has a resistance approximately equal to that of #17 gauge Nichrome V wire, and from the table on p. 424, the value of 28.1 amp is found to be required for a temperature of 1093°C. Applying Ohm's Law, we have

$$\frac{230 \text{ v}}{28.1 \text{ amp}} = 8.18 \text{ ohms.}$$

[1] Including glass; see B. Johnson, J. L. Lineweaver, J. T. Kerr, *J. Appl. Phys.*, **31**, 51, 1960.

[2] The ovens and systems described are fabricated to order by Intertech, Inc., 131 Bacon Street, Natick, Massachusetts.

[3] The tables are reproduced by courtesy of the Driver-Harris Company.

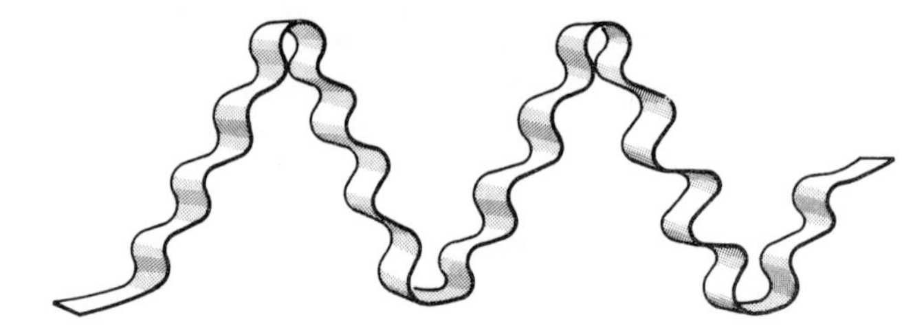

FIG. 113. Manner of folding Nichrome ribbon for heating elements.

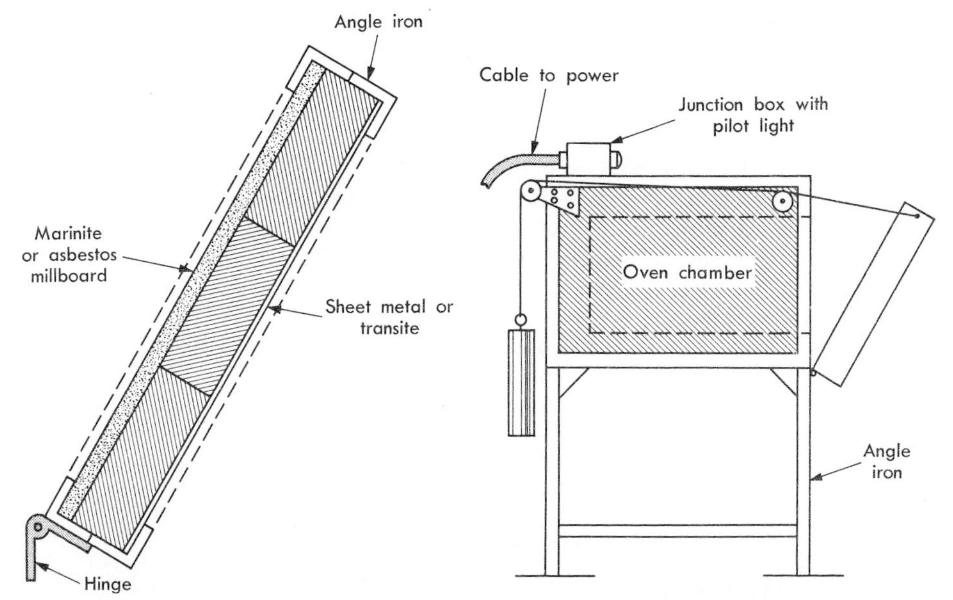

FIG. 114. Detail of door of annealing oven.

FIG. 115. Side view of annealing oven.

Since the hot resistance is 0.349 ohm/ft, we will require

$$\frac{8.18}{0.349} = 23.5 \text{ (approximate) feet, or 282 inches,}$$

of the #34 ribbon for each element. Thus it will be necessary to fold and corrugate the 282 inches of ribbon to fit into the 120-inch perimeter. The method of doing this is described immediately below.

This example is for an oven in which the elements will operate at the upper temperature limit for continuous service. Where lower temperatures are required, the heat loss in degrees that is to be taken into account will be proportional to the operating temperature of the oven (e.g., if an oven is to operate at 400°C continuously, the approximate heat loss will be 150°C, so that the ribbon elements will be at about 550°C, requiring a current, in the case of the #34 ribbon, of about 12.5 amperes).

The ribbon is corrugated by passing it between two meshing gear-toothed rollers (approximately 8 pitch) which have had their sharp edges or burrs buffed off with a wire brush. The corrugated ribbon is then folded as shown in Fig. 113. In this way a much longer length can be installed in a given space than if it were straight.

Each element is strung in almost a complete turn around the perimeter, and the ends of the ribbon are firmly attached to nickel rods W, X, Y, and Z [Fig. 112(a)], which are set in holes bored vertically through the firebrick fairly close together so that all four power leads can be terminated in a junction box with pilot light.

The special stainless steel connectors (a, b, c, d, e, f) in Fig. 112(a) are shown in detail in Fig. 112(b). The stainless steel sleeve is made with sufficient clearance so that the Nichrome ribbon can be fed through.

The door of the annealing oven is illustrated in Fig. 114. Construction materials are indicated. Since this door is heavy, it is arranged with steel cables running over pulleys to counterweights for ease in opening and closing (Fig. 115).

A suggested bake-out oven for a vacuum system is shown in Fig. 116. The construction is similar to that of the annealing oven described above, except that the bottom is open, and is raised and lowered by an arrangement of steel cables and counterweights. Additional inside vertical clearance can be obtained by setting up a "wall" of loose firebricks on the table to any height desired.

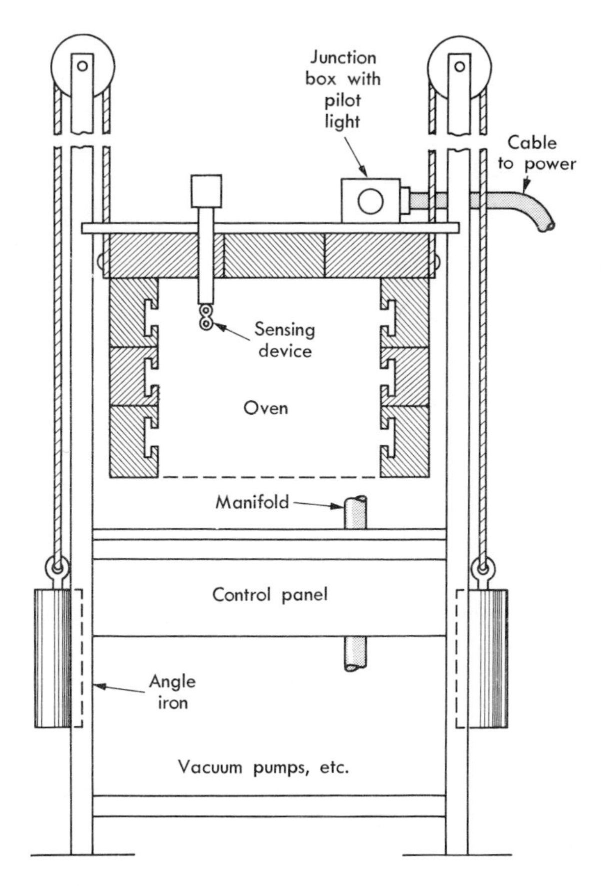

FIG. 116. Front view of bake-out oven and vacuum system.

RESISTANCE OF
NICHROME V RIBBON
(ohms/ft) at 68°F (20°C)

THICKNESS		WIDTH (INCHES)												
NO. B. & S.	INCHES	1/64	1/32	3/64	1/16	3/32	1/8	3/16	1/4	3/8	1/2	5/8	3/4	1
10	0.102								0.02128	0.01333	0.01000	0.008000	0.006667	0.005000
11	0.091								0.02385	0.01495	0.01121	0.008968	0.007473	0.005605
12	0.081								0.02680	0.01680	0.01260	0.01008	0.008398	0.006299
13	0.072								0.03014	0.01889	0.01417	0.01133	0.009445	0.007084
14	0.064							0.04523	0.03392	0.02126	0.01594	0.01275	0.01063	0.007971
15	0.057							0.05075	0.03807	0.02385	0.01789	0.01431	0.01193	0.008945
16	0.051							0.05674	0.04256	0.02667	0.02000	0.01600	0.01333	0.01000
17	0.045							0.06430	0.04822	0.03022	0.02266	0.01813	0.01511	0.01133
18	0.040						0.1085	0.07234	0.05426	0.03400	0.02550	0.02040	0.01700	0.01275
19	0.036						0.1205	0.08036	0.06027	0.03777	0.02833	0.02266	0.01888	0.01417
20	0.032						0.1356	0.09043	0.06782	0.04250	0.03188	0.2550	0.02125	0.01594
21	0.0285						0.1523	0.1015	0.07615	0.04772	0.03579	0.02863	0.02386	0.01790
22	0.0253						0.1716	0.1144	0.08579	0.05376	0.04032	0.03226	0.02688	0.02016
23	0.0226						0.1920	0.1204	0.09027	0.06018	0.04514	0.03611	0.03009	0.02257
24	0.0201			0.5758	0.4319	0.2879	0.2159	0.1353	0.1015	0.06766	0.05075	0.04060	0.03383	0.02537
25	0.0179			0.6466	0.4850	0.3233	0.2425	0.1520	0.1140	0.07598	0.05699	0.04559	0.03799	0.02849
26	0.0159		1.092	0.7279	0.5459	0.3640	0.2729	0.1711	0.1283	0.08553	0.06415	0.05132	0.04277	0.03207
27	0.0142		1.223	0.8150	0.6113	0.4075	0.3056	0.1915	0.1437	0.09577	0.07183	0.05746	0.04789	0.03591
28	0.0126		1.378	0.9186	0.6890	0.4593	0.3445	0.2159	0.1619	0.1079	0.08096	0.06477	0.05397	0.04048
29	0.0113		1.536	1.024	0.7683	0.5122	0.3841	0.2407	0.1805	0.1204	0.09027	0.07222	0.06018	0.04514

30	0.010	3.472	1.736	1.157	0.8681	0.5787	0.4340	0.2720	0.2040	0.1360	0.1020	0.08160	0.06800	0.05100
31	0.0089	3.903	1.951	1.301	0.9757	0.6505	0.4878	0.3057	0.2293	0.1529	0.1146	0.09169	0.07643	0.05732
32	0.008	4.340	2.170	1.447	1.085	0.7234	0.6145	0.3400	0.2550	0.1712	0.1275	0.1020	0.08500	0.06375
33	0.0071	4.892	2.446	1.631	1.223	0.8154	0.6926	0.3832	0.2874	0.1916	0.1437	0.1150	0.09581	0.07186
34	0.0063	5.511	2.755	1.837	1.378	0.9184	0.7801	0.4317	0.3237	0.2158	0.1619	0.1295	0.1079	0.08094
35	0.0056	6.202	3.101	2.067	1.550	1.171	0.8779	0.4858	0.3643	0.2429	0.1822	0.1457	0.1214	0.09109
36	0.005	6.945	3.472	2.315	1.736	1.311	0.9831	0.5440	0.4080	0.2720	0.2040	0.1632	0.1360	0.1020
37	0.0045	7.715	3.858	2.572	1.929	1.456	1.092	0.6044	0.4533	0.3022	0.2266	0.1813	0.1511	0.1133
38	0.004	8.681	4.341	2.894	2.458	1.639	1.229	0.6800	0.5100	0.3400	0.2550	0.2040	0.1700	0.1275
39	0.0035	9.921	4.960	3.307	2.809	1.873	1.404	0.7771	0.5828	0.3886	0.2914	0.2331	0.1943	0.1457
40	0.0031	11.20	5.601	4.229	3.172	2.114	1.586	0.8775	0.6581	0.4387	0.3291	0.2632	0.2194	0.1645
Do	0.00275	12.63	6.313	4.766	3.575	2.383	1.787	0.9890	0.7417	0.4945	0.3709	0.2967	0.2472	0.1854
not	0.0025	13.89	6.945	5.243	3.933	2.622	1.966	1.088	0.8160	0.5440	0.4080	0.3264	0.2720	0.2040
use	0.00225	15.43	7.716	5.825	4.369	2.913	2.184	1.209	0.9066	0.6044	0.4533	0.3626	0.3022	0.2266
B. & S.	0.002	17.36	9.831	6.554	4.916	3.277	2.458	1.360	1.020	0.6800	0.5100	0.4080	0.3400	0.2550
gauges	0.00175	19.84	11.240	7.490	5.618	3.745	2.809	1.554	1.166	0.7771	0.5829	0.4663	0.3886	0.2914
in	0.00150	23.15	13.11	8.739	6.554	4.369	3.277	1.813	1.360	0.9067	0.6800	0.5440	0.4533	0.3400
this	0.00125	27.78	15.73	10.49	7.865	5.243	3.932	2.176	1.632	1.088	0.8160	0.6528	0.5440	0.4080
range	0.00100	39.33	19.66	13.11	9.831	6.554	4.916	2.720	2.040	1.360	1.020	0.8160	0.6800	0.5100

Specific resistance 510 ohms-sq. mil-ft at 68° F. (20° C.)

Temperature resistance factors same as those on page 422.

After careful investigation by a Committee of the American Society for Testing Materials, working in conjunction with the U. S. Bureau of Standards, it has been found that the cross-sectional area of ribbon having rounded edges depends upon the ratio of width to thickness, and is always less than a true rectangle having the maximum width and thickness of the ribbon.

Ribbon sizes $\frac{1}{4}$ inch and $\frac{3}{16}$ inch by 0.0253 and thicker, and all ribbons narrower than $\frac{3}{16}$ inch are rolled with round edges. The data on ribbon with rounded edges and having a ratio of width to thickness less than 15 to 1 are calculated on a cross section of 6% less than a true rectangle, while those sizes which have a ratio of width to thickness greater than 15 to 1 are calculated on a cross section of 17% less than a true rectangle.

All sizes of material shown above to the right of the *heavy* line are based on slit edges with no correction; those to the left of *heavy* line are rolled with round edges. The data shown above the *light* line have a correction factor of 6% and those below *light* line 17%.

Material listed above is supplied soft temper.

Nichrome V Wire

Specific resistance 650 ohm-mil-ft at 68° F (20° C). Density 8.412: lb/cu/in 0.3039

Factor by which resistance at room temperature is to be multiplied to obtain resistance at indicated temperatures

(These figures are given as a basis for engineering calculations and represent average material as supplied.)

Temperature °F	68	200	400	600	800	1000	1200	1400	1600	1800	2000° F
Temperature °C	20	93	204	315	427	538	649	760	871	982	1093° C
Factor	1.000	1.016	1.037	1.054	1.066	1.070	1.064	1.062	1.066	1.072	1.078

NO. B. & S.	DIAMETER (INCHES)	OHMS/FT AT 68° F (20° C)	WEIGHT/1000 FT. BARE WIRE LB	FT/LB BARE WIRE	OHMS/LB BARE WIRE
000	0.410	0.003866	481.5	2.077	0.008030
00	0.365	0.004879	381.6	2.621	0.01279
0	0.325	0.006153	302.5	3.306	0.02034
1	0.289	0.007782	239.2	4.181	0.03254
2	0.258	0.009765	190.7	5.244	0.05121
3	0.229	0.01239	150.2	6.658	0.08249
4	0.204	0.01562	119.2	8.389	0.1310
5	0.182	0.01962	94.87	10.54	0.2068
6	0.162	0.02476	75.17	13.30	0.3293
7	0.144	0.03135	59.39	16.84	0.5279
8	0.128	0.03967	46.93	21.31	0.8454
9	0.114	0.05001	37.22	26.87	1.344
10	0.102	0.06248	29.80	33.56	2.097
11	0.091	0.07849	23.72	42.16	3.309
12	0.081	0.09907	18.79	53.22	5.273
13	0.072	0.1255	14.85	67.34	8.451
14	0.064	0.1588	11.73	85.25	13.54
15	0.057	0.2000	9.306	107.5	21.50
16	0.051	0.2499	7.450	134.2	33.54
17	0.045	0.3209	5.800	172.4	55.32
18	0.040	0.4062	4.583	218.2	88.63

19	0.036	0.5015	3.712	269.4	135.1
20	0.032	0.6374	2.933	340.9	216.4
21	0.0285	0.8002	2.326	429.9	344.0
22	0.0253	1.017	1.833	545.6	554.9
23	0.0226	1.272	1.463	683.5	869.4
24	0.0201	1.609	1.157	864.3	1,391.
25	0.0179	2.029	0.9177	1,090.	2,212.
26	0.0159	2.571	0.7241	1,381.	3,551.
27	0.0142	3.228	0.5775	1,732.	5,591.
28	0.0126	4.090	0.4547	2,199.	8,994.
29	0.0113	5.090	0.3657	2,734.	13,920.
30	0.0100	6.500	0.2864	3,492.	22,697.
31	0.0089	8.206	0.2269	4,407.	36,160.
32	0.0080	10.16	0.1833	5,456.	55,430.
33	0.0071	12.90	0.1444	6,926.	89,330.
34	0.0063	16.37	0.1137	8,795.	144,000.
35	0.0056	20.72	0.08982	11,130.	230,600.
36	0.0050	26.00	0.07160	13,970.	363,200.
37	0.0045	32.09	0.05800	17,240.	553,200.
38	0.0040	40.62	0.04583	21,820.	886,300.
39	0.0035	53.06	0.03509	28,500.	1,512,000.
40	0.0031	67.63	0.02752	36,340.	2,458,000.
	0.00275	85.98	0.02166	46,170.	3,970,000.
	0.00250	104.00	0.01790	55,870.	5,810,000.
Do	0.00225	128.5	0.01450	68,970.	8,863,000.
not	0.00200	162.5	0.01146	87,260.	14,180,000.
use	0.00175	212.4	0.008772	114,000.	24,210,000.
B. & S.	0.00150	288.9	0.006444	155,200.	44,840,000.
gauges	0.00140	331.6	0.005614	178,100.	59,060,000.
in	0.00130	384.6	0.004840	206,600.	79,230,000.
this	0.00120	451.4	0.004124	242,500.	109,500,000.
range	0.00110	537.2	0.003466	288,500.	155,000,000.
	0.00100	650.0	0.002864	349,200.	227,000,000.

Material listed above is supplied soft temper.

Current Temperature Characteristics of Nichrome V

Straight Wire

(Approximate amperes necessary to produce a given temperature. Applies only to straight wires stretched horizontally in free air.)

NO.	DIAMETER	TEMPERATURE								
B. & S.	(INCHES)	400° F 204° C	600 315	800 427	1000 538	1200 649	1400 760	1600 871	1800 982	2000° F 1093° C
1	0.289	78.20	109.0	140.0	177.0	219.0	268.0	322.0	378.0	434.0
2	0.258	65.41	91.59	117.5	148.7	184.1	225.1	270.4	317.3	364.5
3	0.229	54.71	76.94	98.57	124.9	154.7	189.1	227.1	266.4	306.2
4	0.204	45.76	64.64	82.71	104.9	130.0	158.9	190.7	223.6	257.3
5	0.182	38.28	54.30	69.40	88.09	109.3	133.4	160.1	187.6	216.0
6	0.162	32.02	45.62	58.23	73.99	91.86	112.1	133.5	157.5	181.4
7	0.144	26.78	38.33	48.85	62.15	77.21	94.16	112.9	132.2	152.4
8	0.128	22.40	32.20	41.00	52.20	64.89	79.10	94.80	111.0	128.0
9	0.114	18.80	27.00	34.60	43.90	54.60	66.90	80.00	94.00	108.0
10	0.102	16.11	22.95	29.35	37.17	46.22	56.66	67.79	79.62	91.41
11	0.091	13.82	19.52	24.90	31.47	39.12	47.99	57.44	67.44	77.36
12	0.081	11.84	16.59	21.12	26.65	33.12	40.65	48.67	57.12	65.48
13	0.072	10.15	14.10	17.92	22.57	28.03	34.64	41.24	48.38	55.42
14	0.064	8.70	11.98	15.20	19.11	23.73	29.16	34.95	40.98	46.91
15	0.057	7.465	10.19	12.89	16.18	20.08	24.70	29.62	34.71	39.70
16	0.051	6.390	8.66	10.94	13.70	17.00	20.90	25.10	29.40	33.60
17	0.045	5.53	7.48	9.51	11.80	14.50	17.60	21.10	24.60	28.10
18	0.040	4.964	6.53	8.23	10.17	12.48	15.11	18.06	21.00	24.03
19	0.036	4.26	5.70	7.12	8.77	10.74	12.97	15.46	17.92	20.55
20	0.032	3.73	4.97	6.17	7.56	9.24	11.13	13.23	15.30	17.57
21	0.0285	3.27	4.34	5.34	6.52	7.95	9.55	11.32	13.06	15.03
22	0.0253	2.87	3.78	4.62	5.62	6.85	8.20	9.69	11.15	12.85
23	0.0226	2.52	3.30	4.00	4.85	5.89	7.04	8.30	9.52	10.99
24	0.020	2.21	2.88	3.46	4.18	5.06	6.04	7.10	8.12	9.40
25	0.0179	1.92	2.52	3.02	3.58	4.32	5.18	6.10	7.25	8.04
26	0.0159	1.66	2.17	2.62	3.12	3.76	4.49	5.27	6.22	6.90
27	0.0142	1.43	1.87	2.28	2.73	3.26	3.89	4.55	5.33	5.92
28	0.0126	1.23	1.62	1.98	2.38	2.84	3.37	3.93	4.57	5.09
29	0.0113	1.06	1.40	1.72	2.08	2.47	2.92	3.39	3.92	4.37
30	0.010	0.915	1.21	1.50	1.81	2.14	2.53	2.93	3.36	3.75
31	0.0089	0.789	1.04	1.30	1.58	1.86	2.19	2.53	2.88	3.22
32	0.008	0.680	0.900	1.13	1.38	1.62	1.90	2.18	2.47	2.76
33	0.0071	0.580	0.780	0.980	1.18	1.40	1.62	1.87	2.12	2.35
34	0.0063	0.511	0.686	0.853	1.02	1.21	1.39	1.60	1.81	2.01
35	0.0056	0.451	0.603	0.742	0.884	1.04	1.20	1.38	1.55	1.72
36	0.005	0.397	0.530	0.646	0.766	0.902	1.04	1.18	1.33	1.47
37	0.0045	0.350	0.467	0.561	0.663	0.777	0.892	1.01	1.14	1.26
38	0.004	0.309	0.410	0.489	0.574	0.671	0.768	0.869	0.971	1.09
39	0.0035	0.272	0.361	0.425	0.497	0.579	0.662	0.746	0.830	0.923
40	0.0031	0.240	0.310	0.370	0.430	0.500	0.570	0.640	0.710	0.790

In the case of both ovens, the only bricks that require cementing are those at the top. Holes should be provided for (a) the electrical power leads, (b) a temperature-sensing device, and (c) a temperature-control-sensing device [if separate from (b)].

Oxide cathode (see pp. 93, 96).

Oxygen. A colorless, odorless gas which constitutes approximately one-fifth the atmosphere. The remainder is mostly nitrogen, with small amounts of other gases. (See ATMOSPHERE, p. 160.)

Oxygen is very active chemically, being the agent that supports life and combustion. Most metals are attacked by it—some at room temperature—to form oxides, which, in general, are stable.

Some of the properties of oxygen are as follows:

Atomic weight	16.000	Density at 0°C	1.429 gm/liter
Atomic number	8	Specific gravity (liquid) at −183°C	1.14
Melting point (°C)	−218.4	Valence	2
Boiling point (°C)	−183.0		

Liquid and solid oxygen are pale blue in color and somewhat magnetic. Liquid oxygen is a serious explosion hazard and should be kept away from other flammable materials, sparks, heated equipment, and easily oxidizable substances such as oils.

Oxygen is sometimes used at reduced pressures in electron tubes. It can be introduced by the method given on pp. 119–121, or by a method similar to that shown on p. 122, except that a silver tube is used instead of one of palladium.[1]

Oxygen gettering by ionization gauge. There is evidence that oxygen is gettered by an ionization gauge filament at temperatures as low as 25°C. This effect occurred after the filament had been outgassed by heating or electron bombardment. Nitrogen is also gettered, to some extent, by the filament, but in this case the filament must be heated.[2]

Palladium is a heavy white noble metal of the platinum group, having the following properties:

Atomic weight	106.7
Density at 20°C (gm/cc)	12.0
Melting point (°C)	1554
Boiling point (°C)	3980

Coefficient of thermal expansion (in/°C)	12.4×10^{-6}
Thermal conductivity at 20°C (cgs)	0.168
Electrical resistivity at 0°C (microhm-cm)	10.0
at 20°C (microhm-cm)	10.8
Temperature coefficient of electrical resistivity, 0–100°C	0.0038

Annealed hardness, Vickers	38
Annealed tensile strength (psi)	24,000
Modulus of elasticity (psi)	17×10^6
Reflectivity at 450 millimicrons	54
at 550 millimicrons	60–63
at 750 millimicrons	66

---

[1] N. R. Whetten and J. R. Young, *Rev. Sci. Instr.*, **30,** p. 472, 1959.
[2] B. J. Todd, *J. Appl. Phys.*, **29,** 232, 1958.

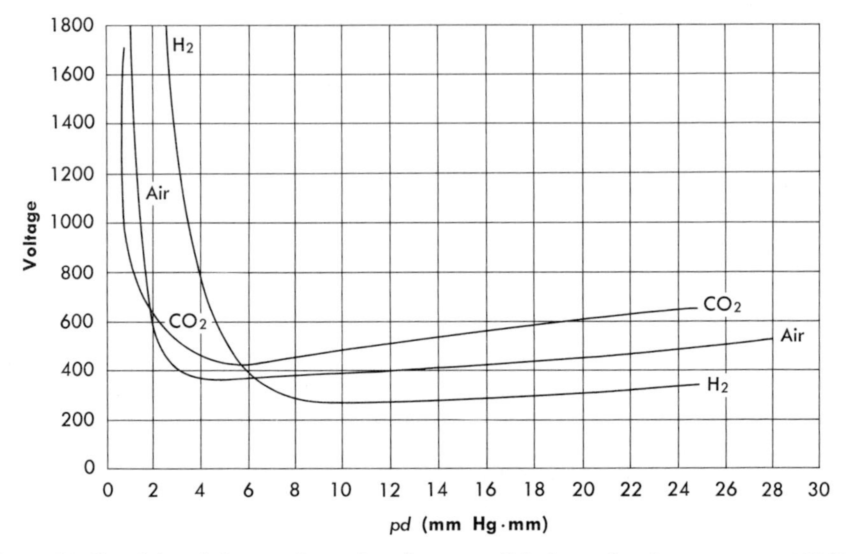

FIG. 117. Spark breakdown voltage for plane-parallel electrodes (temperature 20°C).

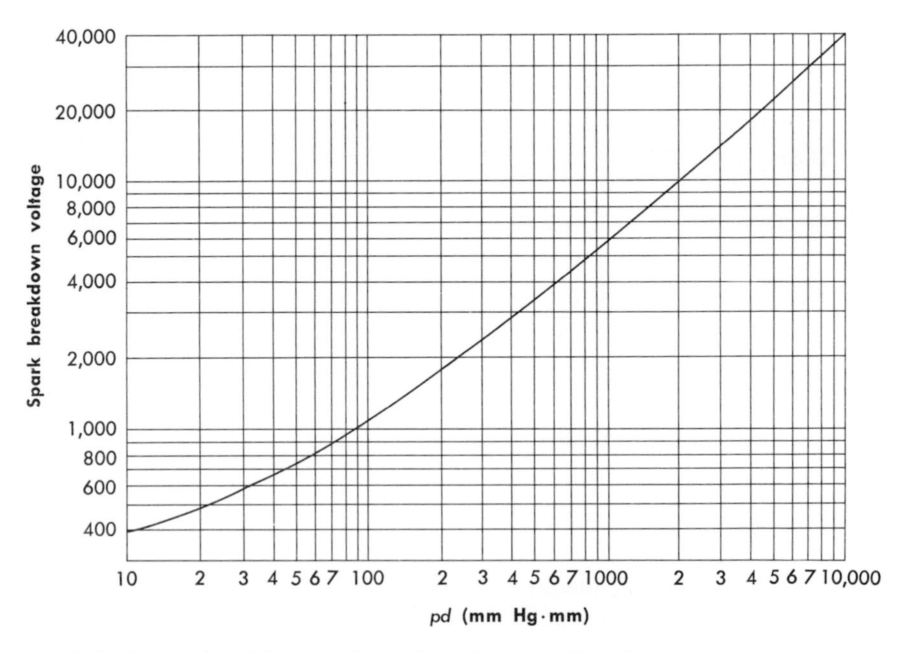

FIG. 118. Spark breakdown voltage for plane-parallel plates in air (temperature 20°C).

Unlike platinum, palladium becomes coated with an oxide film when heated in air, and this oxide dissociates at higher temperatures (870°C).[1]

Hydrogen can be made to diffuse through thin sheets of palladium at elevated temperatures, and this phenomenon is utilized in introducing pure hydrogen into electron tubes. Any gas mixture containing hydrogen can be used (e.g., illuminating gas), because the palladium has a selective action for hydrogen only. (See pp. 121, 122, 123.)

Palladium brazing alloys (see pp. 175–183).

Palladium, vapor pressure of (see p. 147).

Paper, filter, for making carbon films (see p. 190).

Partial pressure. *Hackh's Chemical Dictionary*[2] defines this term as follows: "The fraction of the total pressure exerted by each constituent of a gas mixture. The sum of the partial pressures is equal to the total pressure; hence, the partial pressures are proportional to the concentrations of the individual gases in a mixture."

Dalton's law is:

"The pressure of a gas mixture equals the sum of the partial pressures of the constituent gases."

(*Cf.* Charles' law, p. 265.)

Paschen's law.[3] Sparkling between electrodes at high voltage is defined as a breakdown in which the entire gap is bridged, as distinguished from *corona,* in which there is "dark" current over part of the space. Sparking is usually accompanied by an arc discharge, and the sparking potential is a function (not necessarily linear) of the product of the gas density and the gap length. This is known as Paschen's law. The sparking potential for air[4] at atmospheric pressure and uniform field is

$$V_s = 30d + 1.35 \text{ (kv)}$$

for a gap d of the order of 0.1 cm. (V_s is sparking potential). The gas density rather than the pressure is used in Paschen's law to account for the effect of temperature at constant pressure on the mean free path in the gas.[5, 6]

A consequence of this law to the scaling of a sparking discharge device is that the gas pressure must be reduced in proportion to the scale factor in order that all conditions may remain the same. When this is done, the breakdown voltage is the same for the model and the full-scale original.[5]

Experimental spark breakdown curves for plane-parallel electrodes, representing Paschen's law, are given in Figs. 117 and 118. The quantity pd in the figures is the product of the pressure in mm Hg and the gap length in mm.

---

[1] L. Wöhler and E. Witzman, *Z. Elektrochem.*, **14,** 97, 1908.

[2] Revised and edited by J. Grant, The Blakiston Company, Philadelphia, Pennsylvania, 1950.

[3] *Wied. Ann.*, F. Paschen, **37,** 69, 1889.

[4] *Electricity in Gases,* J. S. Townsend, Oxford University Press, New York, New York, 1914.

[5] *Gaseous Conductors,* Second edition, J. D. Cobine, pp. 163, 209, Dover Publications, Inc., New York, New York, 1958.

[6] *Electrical Discharges in Gases,* F. M. Penning, pp. 31, 32, Macmillan Co., New York, New York, 1957.

The table below gives some experimental values[1] of the minimum sparking voltage V_s, the corresponding value of pd, and the ratio of the mean free path L at atmospheric pressure to the minimum pd.

GAS	V_s MIN.	pd, MM HG × CM	L/pd ($\times 10^{-5}$)
Air	327	0.567	1.7
Argon	137	0.9	1.1
Hydrogen	273	1.15	1.6
Helium	156	4.0	0.74
Carbon dioxide	420	0.51	1.2
Nitrogen	251	0.67	1.4
Nitrous oxide	418	0.5	1.4
Oxygen	450	0.7	—
Sodium (vapor)	335	0.04	—
Sulfur dioxide	457	0.33	1.4
Hydrogen sulfide	414	0.6	1.0

The minimum sparking potential is very nearly equal to the normal cathode fall of potential of the glow discharge (see Fig. 78, p. 288).

The relative spark breakdown-strengths of various gases as compared to air are:[2]

Gas:	N_2	Air	NH_3	CO_2	H_2S	O_2	Cl	H_2	SO_2
V/V_{air}:	1.15	1	1	0.95	0.9	0.85	0.85	0.65	0.30

Figure 119 shows the relative breakdown strengths of various gases at three different pressures. From these curves and the above table, it will be seen that nitrogen has the highest breakdown strength and hydrogen the lowest.

Passivation of stainless steels. The corrosion resistance of stainless steels is largely due to the formation of an adherent layer of chromium oxide, too thin to be detectable by the unaided eye, on the surface of the metal. This film will form of its own accord in a short time on a newly machined or cut surface, but the process can be accelerated by a chemical passivation treatment, which also produces a thicker and more adherent film.

The working of stainless steel with, of necessity, steel tools (dies, cutters, rollers, drills, taps, etc.) gives rise to the probability that small particles or chips of "tramp-iron" can be picked up on the stainless surface, and if not soon removed, these particles oxidize (rust) and cause localized pitting and eventual destruction of the stainless steel. For this reason, stainless steel should *never* be cleaned with ordinary steel wool.

Passivation treatments are the final operations in the fabrication of stainless steel parts. For the austenitic (300 series) varieties, immersion in a 30% (by volume) nitric acid solution at 50–60°C for 15 to 30 minutes is suitable. This is to be followed by a thorough water rinse. For highly polished parts, use 20% nitric acid at 43–50°C. Surface clouding can be prevented by the addition of 1½ to 2½% sodium dichromate. Immerse for 15 to 30 minutes, then rinse thoroughly in water.

---

[1] J. J. Thomson and G. P. Thomson, *Conduction of Electricity through Gases*, Third edition, Vol. I (1928); Vol. II (1933); Cambridge University Press, London.

[2] J. D. Cobine, *op. cit.*

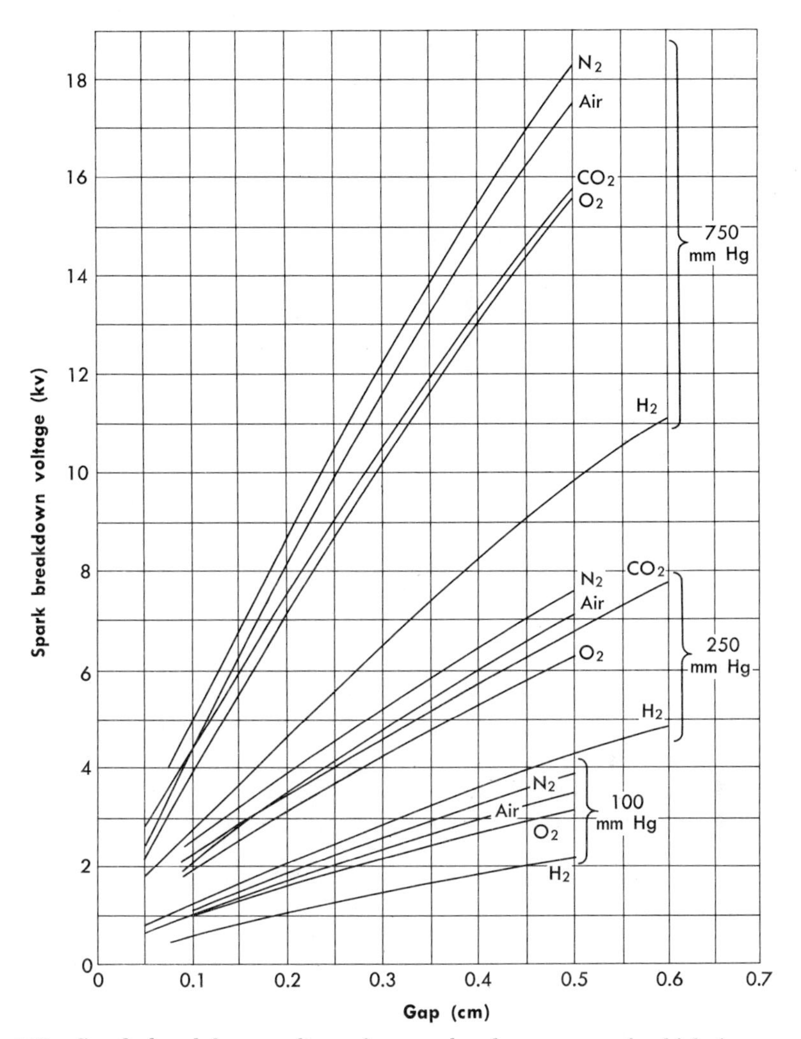

FIG. 119. Spark breakdown voltage for equal spheres, one of which is grounded (temperature 180°C, diameter 2.5 cm, direct current).

Stainless steel parts which are to be used as electron tube components are not to be passivated, or they should be depassivated before assembly. This is accomplished most effectively by hydrogen (pp. 41 *et seq.*) or vacuum-firing (pp. 75 *et seq.*) at 1050°C, which also anneals the metal.

There is some evidence that hydrogen-firing produces a micro-eggshell surface on polished stainless steel.[1] Where very highly polished surfaces are required (as for high–voltage components), the metal should be polished after hydrogen or vacuum-firing, using only levigated aluminum oxide (No. 1550AB Polishing Alumina #1, supplied by Buehler, Ltd., 2120 Greenwood Street, Evanston, Illinois, or any dealer

[1] J. H. Owen Harries, Devonshire, Bermuda (private communication).

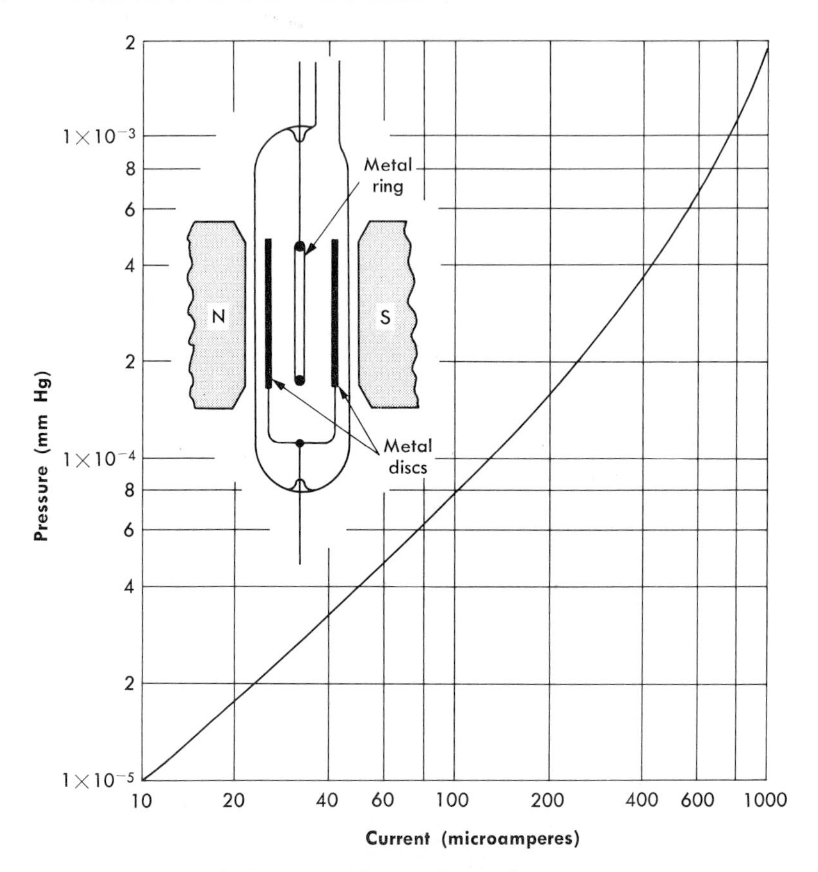

FIG. 120. Typical calibration curve for Penning gauge.

in metallographic supplies) diluted only with distilled or deionized water. This is to be used with a new cloth or cloth wheel which has been washed in a nonsoap detergent or mild alkaline solution and rinsed thoroughly.

Hydrogen-fired parts have the advantage that they do not absorb gases as easily as do vacuum-fired parts upon exposure to air. However, the hydrogen is given off easily when heated *in vacuo,* and this should be taken into account wherever there are elements within the tube which might be affected by hydrogen.

Metals which do not visibly oxidize easily in air (e.g., stainless steel, aluminum) at room temperature have relatively nonporous oxides; those that do oxidize easily (e.g., iron) have relatively porous oxides. In other words the porosity of an oxide roughly depends on how easily it can form at room temperature. This would be expected since iron begins to oxidize immediately upon exposure to air and continues until destruction, while aluminum and stainless steels form a tight skin which protects the metal from further oxidation.

After hydrogen- or vacuum-firing (and after polishing, if this is done), the pieces should be stored, if not to be assembled immediately, in an efficient vacuum desiccator until used. Polished parts should be rinsed in several changes of fresh, reagent-grade acetone before using or storing.

Penning gauge, Philips gauge.[1] This is the well-known "cold-cathode" (see pp. 192, 193) vacuum gauge in which electrons, provided by a high voltage between electrodes, collide with gas molecules to form ions, which in turn, under the influence of a strong external magnetic field, travel to a collector, and thus give rise to an ion current. The number of ions arriving at the collector is thus proportional to the gas pressure (see curve in Fig. 120). This current can be detected with a microammeter or amplified in a conventional circuit.

The electrons travel in a spiral path, which may be as much as several hundred times the direct distance between the two electrodes, and this greatly increases the probability of collision with gas molecules, and thus makes possible a greater sensitivity. The glow discharge (pp. 213, 214, 286, 288) is maintained at lower pressures where the mean free path (pp. 136, 363) of the electron greatly exceeds the distance between the electrodes.

The cold-cathode gauge is preferred in industrial vacuum systems in which the pressure is not lower than 10^{-7} torr because of its ruggedness and because there is no filament to burn out. Although it is believed in some quarters that the Penning or Philips type of gauge can be exposed to the atmosphere without damage, this is probably inaccurate since the presence of the high-voltage discharge causes breakdown of carbon products (e.g., diffusion pump oil particles) more easily than in hot-filament ionization gauges (pp. 162, 303–305). However, these gauges can be used to measure pressures up to about 25 microns (2.5×10^{-2} torr), and they will withstand higher pressures for short periods without damage. In modern cold-cathode gauges, the elements are demountable and easily cleaned.

R. Haefer[2] has designed a cold-cathode gauge with a symmetrical electrode system which extends the lower pressure limit of the original Penning gauge.

P. A. Redhead[3] has gone further in extending the lower pressure limit in a design which applies an auxiliary cathode for shielding the edges, to prevent field emission from these edges.

The work of Haefer and Redhead has been reported in "Panel Discussion, National Vacuum Symposium," American Vacuum Society, Cleveland, Ohio, October, 1960.

The Penning gauge is combined with the titanium-ion pump (p. 106) to attain the dual function of pump and pressure gauge.

Perveance. The relation, usually designated at G, between the space-charge-limited cathode current (p. 338) and the 3/2 power of the anode voltage (p. 238). The perveance in a tube is independent of the electrode voltages and currents, so long as the 3/2 law holds:

$$G = \frac{i_k}{e_b^{3/2}},$$

where i_k is the space-charge-limited cathode current, and e_b is the anode voltage.

---

[1] F. M. Penning, "Glow Discharge at Low Pressure between Coaxial Cylinders in an Axial Magnetic Field," *Physica*, **3**, 873, 1936; "New Manometer for Low Gas Pressures, Especially between 10^{-3} and 10^{-5} mm," *ibid.*, **4**, 71, 1937. See also: "A Philips-Type Ionization Gauge for Measuring of Vacuum from 10^{-7} to 10^{-1} mm of Mercury," E. C. Evans and K. E. Burmaster, *Proc. I. R. E.*, **38**, 651, 1950.

[2] R. Haefer, *Acta Physica Austriaca*, **9**, 200, 1955; Manufactured by Balzers Aktien-Gesellschaft für Hochvakuumtechnik und Dünne Schlichten, Balzers, Furstentum Liechtenstein.

[3] P. A. Redhead, *Can. J. Phys.*, **37**, 1260, 1959.

The perveance of the cathode-control-electrode area is approximately:

$$2.33 \times 10^{-6} \frac{\text{cathode area}}{(\text{cathode-to-first-electrode spacing})^2}$$

A detailed discussion of the meaning of perveance and the methods of measuring it will be found in *Radiotron Designers' Handbook,* fourth edition, edited by F. Langford-Smith, Radio Corporation of America, Harrison, New Jersey, pp. 14, 71, 117–118, 1952.

Phenolic. A generic name for a variety of thermosetting (i.e., irreversible with heat) plastics containing phenol and sometimes formaldehyde, together with fillers of paper, cloth, glass powder or fibers, mica, and other materials. These plastics are characterized by a high strength-to-weight ratio, good heat-resistance, and (except for those containing glass or mica, etc.) excellent machinability. The phenolics cannot be used inside vacuum devices because of the high vapor pressure of phenol, even at room temperature.

Phlogopite (see MICA, p. 371).

Phos-copper braze alloy (see items 103, 131, pp. 182, 184).

Phosphor (see pp. 251, 254).

Phosphorus. This element, in the white, yellow, or colorless form, has been used as a getter, chiefly for oxygen, for which it has a very strong affinity. It is very poisonous and flammable, burning spontaneously in the air to form phosphorus pentoxide (P_2O_5), a dense, white powder-vapor (see below).

Phosphorus pentoxide (phosphoric anhydride). A powerful desiccant, which, though having a large appetite for water, is not used as a drying agent as widely as other materials (see pp. 230, 377) because of its deliquescence to phosphoric acid, which is corrosive.

Phos-silver braze alloy (see items 123, 124, 128, 134, pp. 182, 184).

Photocells. An electron can be liberated from a metal surface if the energy of the radiation quanta is greater than the work function of the metal (p. 570). The table below gives the wavelength of the radiation corresponding to the energy of that radiation.[1]

ENERGY (EV)	TYPE OF RADIATION	WAVELENGTH (A)
10^8		10^{-4}
10^7	Cosmic rays	10^{-3}
10^6		10^{-2}
10^5	Gamma rays	10^{-1}
10^4	X-rays	1
10^3		10
10^2	Ultraviolet	10^2
10	Visible light	10^3
1		10^4
10^{-1}	Infrared	10^5
10^{-2}		10^6

[1] F. M. Penning, *Electrical Discharges in Gases,* Macmillan Co., New York, New York, 1957.

From this table it will be seen that only ultra violet light can liberate electrons from platinum (work function 6.27 ev), while visible and infrared radiation is sufficient to cause the emission of electrons from cesium (wf = 1.81) and cesium on cesium oxide (wf = 1.03–0.75), a combination which is much used in gas-filled photocells in which the light coming from an external source maintains a nonself-sustaining discharge in the cell.

Such gas-filled tubes, operating by virtue of ionization (see p. 302) caused by the collision of electrons with the gas molecules, are extremely sensitive but likely to be somewhat unstable, partly due to a small delay in deionization. This makes the gas-filled tube usable in rapidly fluctuating light applications only up to about 5000 cps. For operation at higher light frequencies, the high-vacuum phototube is used. One type is the so-called "cesium" tube, in which the cathode, a silver surface, is oxidized very carefully, and a layer of cesium is deposited over the oxide. Under optimum conditions these vacuum phototubes will deliver about 30 microamp/lumen.

The kind of photosensitive material used for the cathode, the method of application, and the type of glass used for the envelope all affect the color response of the phototube. Commonly used phototubes have a color response somewhat similar to that of the human eye. Phototubes can be made to have other spectral responses; the wavelength for maximum sensitivity increases in the same order as the atomic numbers of the alkali earth metals, and the relative emission decreases as the atomic number increases.[1]

The types of photocells described above are *photoemissive* (the only true electron tube type) in which

$$\tfrac{1}{2}mv^2 = hf - P,$$

where m is mass of the electron, v is velocity of the emitted electron, h is Planck's constant, f is frequency of the incident light, and P is energy required by the electron to leave the surface of the cathode (work function).

If $P = hf$, the initial velocity of the emitted electron is zero, and therefore a definite frequency f must exist for each photosensitive material, below which no emission can occur, no matter how intense the light.

If this threshold frequency is f_0, then

$$\tfrac{1}{2}mv^2 = h(f - f_0).$$

The existence of such a threshold frequency has been proved experimentally.[1]

The *electron multiplier* or *photomultiplier* tube (p. 239) combines a photoemissive cathode with a series of elements called *dynodes* in which cascaded secondary emission takes place. In one commercial electron multiplier tube, type 1P21, an electron multiplication of over 7.5×10^6 is attainable for 150 v/dynode stage.

The *photoconductive* cell is not an emitter of electrons; it has been thought of as a light-sensitive resistor. Materials such as cadmium sulfide and cadmium selenide have a high resistance in the dark, decreasing enormously when illuminated. The cadmium sulfide type is sensitive to daylight and fluorescent light, has a response time of approximately 100 millisec, and is relatively stable to temperature

---

[1] *Electronic Engineering Handbook*, edited by R. R. Batcher and W. Moulic, Electronic Development Associates, New York, New York, 1944.

changes. The cadmium selenide type is sensitive to incandescent, neon, and infrared light, with a response time of 10 millisec and a relatively large temperature sensitivity. When hermetically sealed, such cells have good stability and life. In conjunction with a small battery, they are used, as photographic exposure meters, etc.[1]

The *photovoltaic* or *barrier-layer* cell, also not a true emitter of electrons, consists, in one type, of an oxidized copper plate carrying a thin, transparent conductive layer over the oxide. The oxide layer is sensitive to light, generating an open-circuit voltage up to 0.5. Cells of this type have been used as light-intensity or photographic exposure meters, and are capable of providing an output of 175 microamp/lumen in sunlight.

Photoetching. This is a method of producing small, intricate shapes on metal or semiconductors by a photographic and chemical method. Such shapes are sometimes required for use as electron tube elements or other structures, and the method is applicable where conventional machining would be difficult or impossible. One procedure follows:[2]

1. The design is drawn several times the size of the finished piece on bristol or illustration board with India ink. This is photographed down to the desired size in sharp focus on an extremely fine-grained film.

2. Prepare a blank of the metal or material to be etched. Lap and polish it, finishing with $\frac{1}{2}$ micron grid-size diamond paste. Immerse in a dilute etchant, suitable to the material, only long enough to remove a few microns of the work-strained surface. Rinse, degrease in trichlorethylene and acetone, and dry.

3. The polished piece is then coated with a thin layer of an acid-resistant lacquer or varnish.[3] This material is handled and applied only in artificial light; avoid daylight or ultraviolet light. After the photographic stencil of step 1 is dried under a heat lamp, it is held in close contact with the work piece, preferably by vacuum, and is exposed to an arc lamp. The stencil is removed and the piece is immersed in a suitable developer such as Kodak Photo Resist Developer. After the stencil is removed from the developer, a few drops of a dye are applied to make the developed image visible.

4. The resist is washed away under a stream of tepid distilled water. Only those areas are removed which were under the dark parts of the stencil. The work may now be dried with filter paper and inspected in full daylight—under a microscope, if required. If satisfactory, the work is baked for a few minutes at a temperature under 100°C to harden the resist.

5. The piece is immersed in an etchant suitable to the material. Any amount can be dissolved away, but frequent inspection is necessary if a specific depth is called for.

6. The piece is thoroughly rinsed in running water and distilled water. A metal deposit can now be applied (if required in the case of semiconductors) by plating or evaporation. The remaining resist is removed by immersion in 2-ethoxyethyl acetate for 10 minutes, plus gentle swabbing.

---

[1] See "Design Considerations in Selecting Photoconductive Cells," General Electric Company (Electronics), Owensboro, Kentucky, 1962.

[2] Eastman Kodak Company, Graphic Reproduction Division, Rochester 4, New York. Data from the Kodak pamphlet, "Etching, Chemical Milling, and Plating with Kodak Metal-Etch Resist," 1959.

[3] Kodak Photo Resist.

Photomultiplier tube (see p. 432; also ELECTRON MULTIPLIER, p. 239).

Physisorption. The removal of gases in a vacuum tube or vessel by means which are of the nature of entrapment or entrainment. The actions of mechanical and diffusion pumps constitute physisorption, as do those of cryopumps, cold-traps, and, to some extent, getter-ion pumps, especially in connection with the noble gases which cannot be removed by ordinary chemical getters, although some metals can entrap gases by adsorption gettering, which is an example of physisorption (where no chemical action such as oxidation or reduction is involved). *Cf.* CHEMISORPTION, p. 199, and DESORPTION, p. 224.

Picein wax.[1] A black wax of low vapor pressure, useful for some temporary seals in vacuum applications. It is soluble in benzol and turpentine, but is unaffected by alcohol and short immersion in chromic-sulfuric cleaning fluid. The softening point of this wax is about 50°C, and it liquefies at 80°C. Another variety liquefies at 105°C. Picein repels moisture and is a very good electrical insulator, equal to amber if not overheated. It is a good adhesive (although without high strength) on clean surfaces, and can be used for sealing mica windows to metal and for closing small leaks in room-temperature vacuum systems.

A sample of this wax exhibited a vapor pressure of 2.5×10^{-7} torr at room temperature, and after being heated *in vacuo* to 123°C (just past the liquefying point), at which temperature the vapor pressure was 5×10^{-5} torr, the pressure dropped with temperature to reach 1.8×10^{-7} torr at 25°C.[2]

Pickles for metal. Any chemical solutions or mixtures which are used to remove oxides, scale, rust, or stains from metal surfaces. Pickling usually removes a small amount of the metal. (See pp. 3–18.)

Pierce gun. In the electron gun (Figs. 121, 122; see also pp. 130, 239) as used in cathode-ray tubes or electron microscopes, the beam is normally focused after the

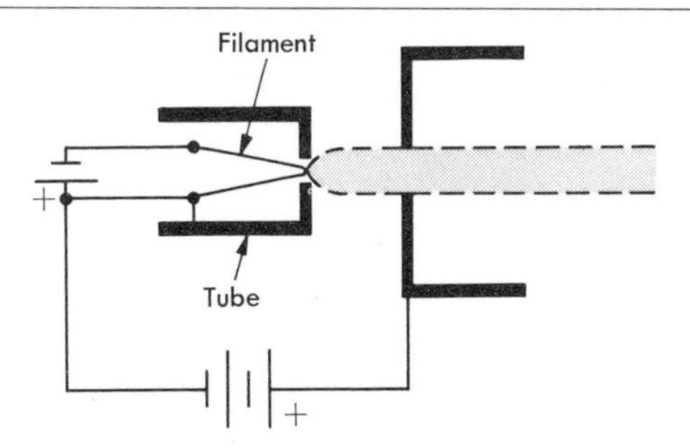

FIG. 121. The small currents required in an electron microscope can be supplied by a gun in which a hairpin filament, a tube at the same potential as the filament, and an accelerating electrode are arranged as shown. Electrons from the hottest part of the filament (the sharp end) travel in paths at first divergent and then more or less parallel through the apertures. This beam can then be focused by additional apertures or "lenses" (electrostatic focusing) or by magnets (magnetic focusing). (See also, "Magnetic Focusing of Electron Beams," J. T. Mendel, *Proc. I.R.E.*, **43**, 327, 1955.)

[1] Supplied by Schrader & Ehlers Company, 239 Fourth Avenue, New York, New York, and also by the Minneapolis-Honeywell Corp.

[2] *Tube Laboratory Manual*, second edition, edited by F. Rosebury, Research Laboratory of Electronics, Massachusetts Institute of Technology, Cambridge, Massachusetts, 1956. See also p. 140 of this text.

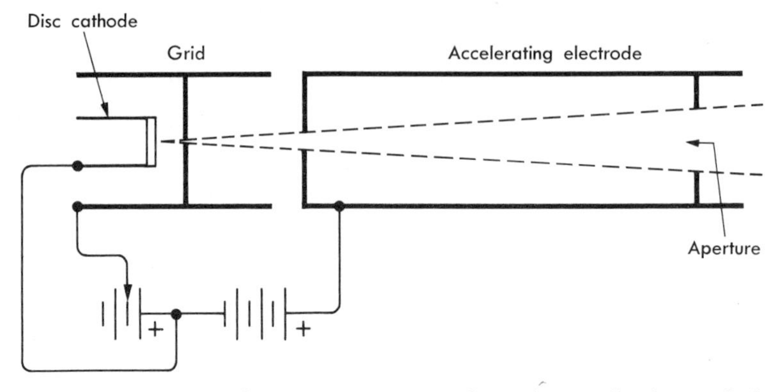

FIG. 122. Cathode-ray tube guns are arranged as shown. In front of the oxide-coated cathode there is an aperture called the grid, or modulating electrode, which is negative with respect to the cathode and controls the electron current. The electron beam then passes through the apertures (the accelerating electrode has up to screen voltage applied to it) which control the width of the emergent beam. (See also, "Magnetic Focusing of Electron Beams," J. T. Mendel, *Proc. I.R.E.*, **43,** 327, 1955.)

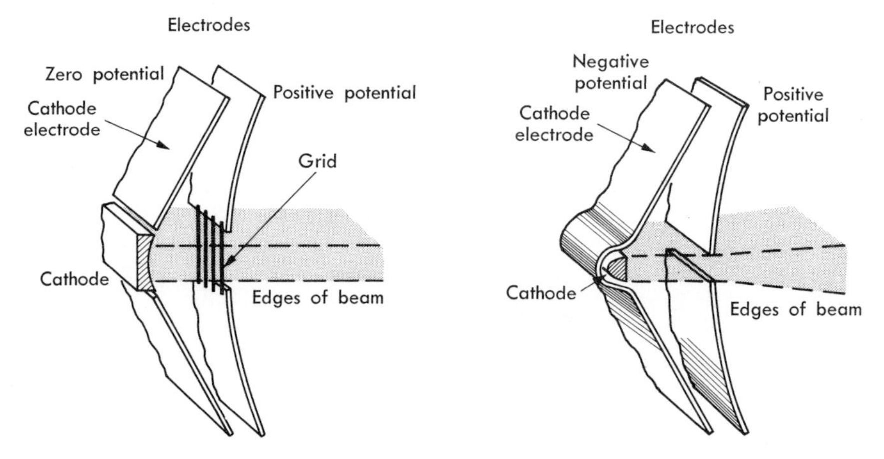

FIG. 123. An electron gun using rectilinear electron flow. (Refer to Fig. 10.5, p. 172, of J. R. Pierce's book.)

FIG. 124. A two-dimensional electron gun using rectilinear electron flow. (Refer to Fig. 10.6, p. 172, of J. R. Pierce's book.)

electrons leave the electrodes shown, and this is done by additional apertures irises or lenses) or by magnetic fields.[1]

The Pierce gun,[2] on the other hand, produces a well-focused beam of high current at low voltage. In general, the cathode is spherically concave to form a converging

[1] H. Moss, "Engineering Methods in the Design of the Cathode-Ray Tube," *J. Brit. I.R.E.*, **5,** 204–223, 1945; "The Electron Gun of the Cathode-Ray Tube," Part 1, *ibid.*, **5,** 10–22, 1945; Part 2, *ibid.*, **6,** 99–129, 1946.

[2] Data on the Pierce gun are excerpted from *Theory and Design of Electron Beams*, J. R. Pierce, D. Van Nostrand Company, Inc., New York, New York, 1949, with the permission of the publisher.

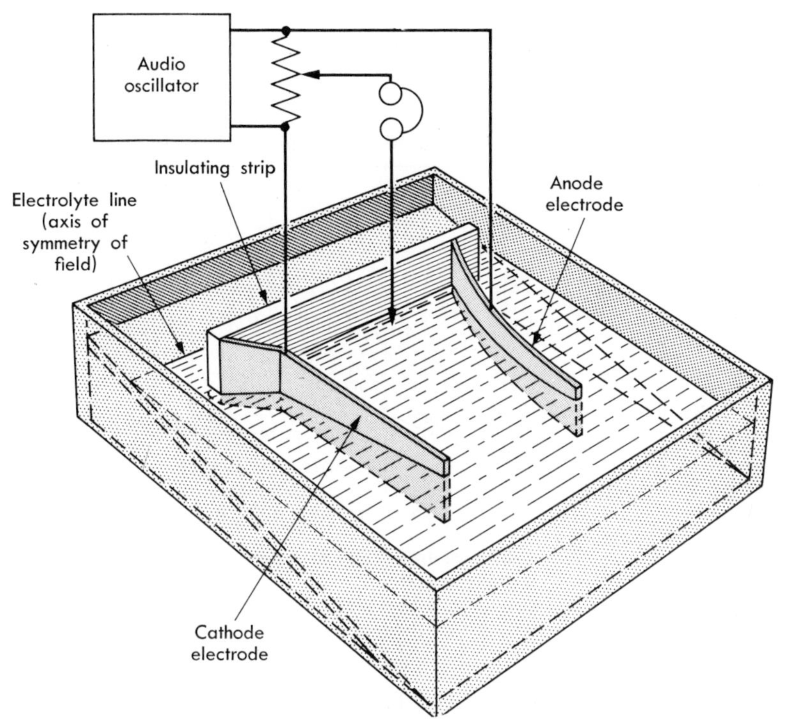

FIG. 125. Use of an electrolytic tank in obtaining equipotentials for rectilinear flow which is axially symmetrical. (Refer to Fig. 10.7, p. 174 of J. R. Pierce's book.)

cone of electron flow. The cathode electrode (Figs. 123, 124) is shaped to aid in focusing the beam. Many configurations are possible, and use is made of an electrolytic tank (Fig. 125) with an oscillator and detecting device to study experimentally the analogous behavior of large models.

According to Pierce, parallel electron flow can exist adjacent to a charge-free region, the boundaries between the flow and the charge-free region being in the form of planes. To realize such a flow in a certain region, electrons may enter and leave the region through two parallel grids, to which are joined electrodes corresponding to equipotential surfaces.

Consider the case of electrons entering the charge-free region from a cathode forming one boundary and giving space-charge-limited emission (pp. 229, 338), in which the gradient is zero at zero potential. The shape of the equipotentials in the curves (Fig. 126) is independent of the absolute magnitude of the potentials involved and of the units in which distance is measured. In this figure, potential is indicated in terms of an arbitrary potential V assigned to one equipotential surface. The potential of the cathode is taken as zero and the distance is measured in arbitrary units, with the origin located at the edge of the cathode. It will be seen that the zero potential surface is a plane which meets the edge of the cathode ($x = y = 0$), making an angle of 67.5° with the normal to the cathode (the x-axis). Figure 123 shows how a plane cathode with a zero-potential electrode and a positive

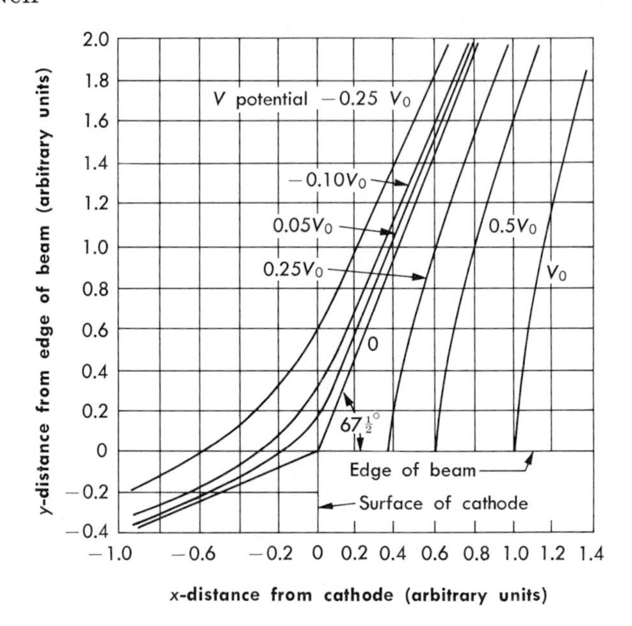

FIG. 126. Equipotentials outside the boundary between rectilinear electron flow from a cathode.

potential electrode (from the curves, Fig. 126) may be combined to give a parallel beam of electrons.

In Fig. 124 both positive and negative equipotential electrodes are used in producing the beam. In the structure shown, the beam leaves the second (positive) electrode through a slit rather than through a grid. When the width of the slit is considerably less than the cathode-anode spacing, the electron flow between the cathode and anode will be practically the same as though a grid were present. However, the beam emerging from the slit will be divergent because of the lens action of the slit. The focal distance will be practically equal to the focal length of the lens formed by the slit.

The same considerations can be applied to circular elements. Figure 127 shows how the shape of an emergent electron beam can be changed by varying the ratio of cathode-to-anode radii of curvature.[1, 2]

Pinch (same as PRESS, see p. 450).

Pinch-off and Pinch-off seal (see COPPER TUBING SEAL, p. 119).

Pirani gauge.[3] Two physical principles are involved in the operation of the Pirani vacuum gauge, which is essentially a thermal conductivity device.

(1) A metal wire or ribbon increases in electrical resistivity when heated.

(2) The thermal conductivity of a gas is a function of the pressure. In high

---

[1] J. R. Pierce, *op. cit.*

[2] See "The Effect of the Anode Aperture on Potential Distribution in a 'Pierce' Electron Gun," K. L. Brown and C. Süsskind, *Proc. I.R.E.*, **42**, 598, 1954.

[3] M. von Pirani, "Selbstzeigendes Vakuum—Messinsinstrument," Deutsch, *Phys. Gesell.*, Verh., **8**, 24, 1906.

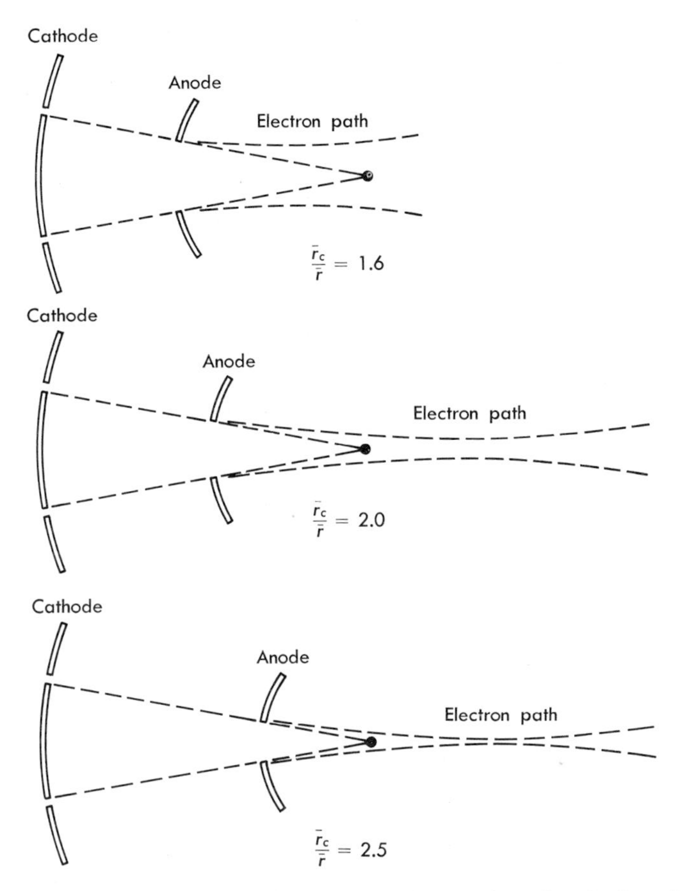

FIG. 127. The emerging electron beam for various ratios of cathode radius to anode radius. $\bar{r}_c$ is the radius of curvature of the cathode, r is the radius of curvature of the anode.

vacuum, a heated body loses heat only by *radiation,* but when gas is present heat is lost by radiation and *conduction.*

It has been found that the maximum effect of heat loss by conduction (in a gas) occurs, in general, at or below red heat. If a wire or filament in a vacuum system is supplied with a constant electric heating current, it will have a certain resistance at a given gas pressure. If the pressure is increased, i.e., if gas is admitted to the system, the filament will lose heat to the gas and will therefore become cooler, as a consequence of which its resistance will decrease. If the gas is pumped out of the region of the filament, the wire will become hotter and the resistance will increase.

The simplest and most accurate form of Pirani gauge circuit is one in which two identical filaments are used. One of these is mounted in a high-vacuum, sealed-off tube; the other is placed in the system whose pressure is to be measured. These are electrically connected in a simple Wheatstone bridge circuit.[1] When the pressure

[1] Model 516, NRC Equipment Corp., Newton 61, Massachusetts.

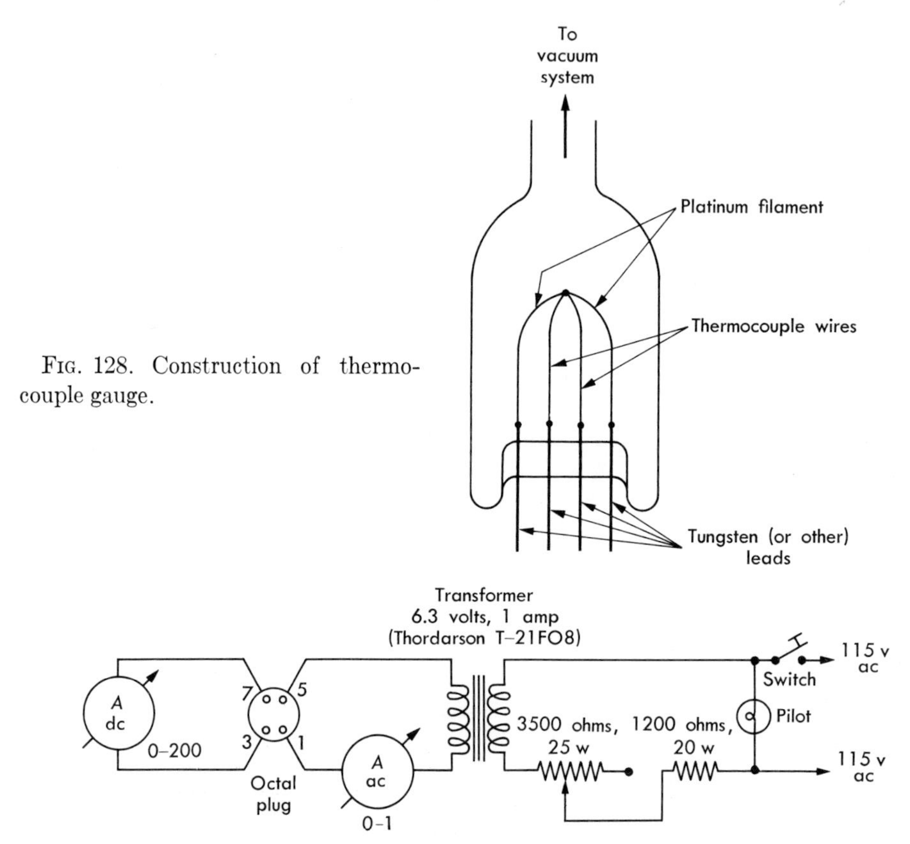

FIG. 128. Construction of thermocouple gauge.

FIG. 129. Simple circuit for use with NRC Type 501 thermocouple gauge.

in the system is equal to that in the high-vacuum tube, there will be a balance, and the indicator will read zero. As the pressure increases, the resistance of the filament in the vacuum system will decrease and the bridge will become unbalanced. Such a device is calibrated with a McLeod gauge (pp. 348 *et seq.*) and can be made direct reading for a given gas. Since the thermal conductivities of the various gases have somewhat different values, the gauge will require calibration for each.

Other circuits are sometimes used. A single filament, supplied with a constant current, will have a voltage drop across it depending on the resistance. Or if a constant voltage is supplied, the current will vary with the pressure.

Thermocouple gauge.[1] A modification of the Pirani gauge, the thermocouple gauge, which is continuous reading, utilizes a simple electrical circuit, retains its calibration fairly well, and is relatively foolproof. The construction of such a gauge is shown in Fig. 128.

Gauges of this type are commercially available from several concerns. One of these, the NRC Type 501[2] thermocouple gauge, has been used successfully in the circuit shown in Fig. 129. This control circuit is available from the manufacturer,

[1] G. C. Dunlap and J. G. Trump, *Rev. Sci. Instr.*, **8**, 37, 1937.

[2] NRC Equipment Corp., Newton 61, Massachusetts.

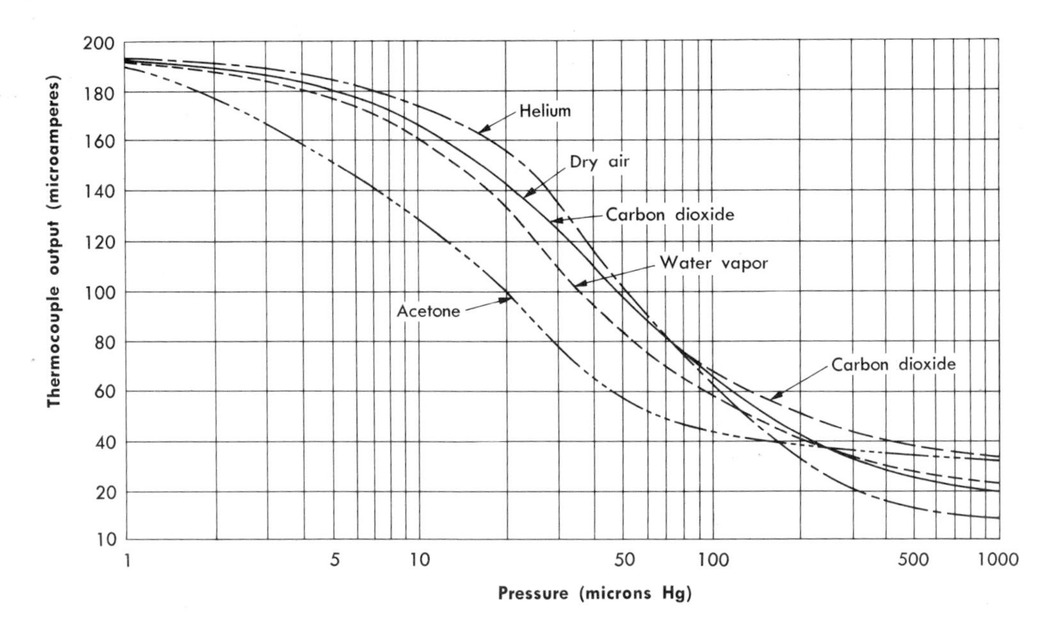

FIG. 130. Calibration curve of thermocouple vacuum gauge for various gases (NRC Equipment Corp.).

who also makes a protective device for use with this gauge which will operate a control circuit when the pressure in the gauge exceeds a chosen preset limit in the range 500–2 microns Hg.

A typical calibration curve for various gases, as indicated by the NRC 501 gauge, is shown in Fig. 130.

Other thermocouple gauges are made by Consolidated Electrodynamics Corporation, Rochester Division, Rochester 3, New York; Hastings-Raydist, Inc., Hampton, Virginia; Radio Corporation of America, Tube Department, Harrison, New Jersey (Type 1946); George E. Fredericks Company, Bethayres, Pennsylvania; Vacuum Tube Products Company, Inc., Oceanside, California; Vacuum-Electronics Corporation, Plainview, Long Island, New York; and others.

Planck's constant. When radiant energy (light, X-rays, cosmic rays, infrared, etc.) impinges upon any substance with sufficient energy, it can liberate electrons or energy. Also, heated solids emit electrons or energy in amounts depending on their temperature. The energy emitted is in the form of discrete "chunks" or *quanta,* rather than in a continuous stream. These quanta have the magnitude $e = h\nu$, where ν is the frequency of the incident radiation, and h is *Planck's constant,* which is universal for all substances and has the value

$$6.62 \times 10^{-27} \text{ erg·sec}$$

or

$$4.13 \times 10^{-15} \text{ ev·sec.}$$

The quantum or *photon* is associated with the emission of energy always in integral multiples, i.e., the energy exists as $h\nu$, $2h\nu$, $3h\nu$, etc., and never as 0.5 $h\nu$ or 2.4 $h\nu$.

Since ν, the frequency of the radiation, is equal to c/λ where λ is the wavelength in Angstrom units (10^{-8} cm), and c is the velocity of light (3×10^{10} cm/sec), therefore

$$\lambda = \frac{3 \times 10^{18}}{\nu} \quad \text{or} \quad \nu = \frac{3 \times 10^{18}}{\lambda}.$$

If we let h, the energy of the radiation quantum, be equal to V electron volts, then

$$V = \frac{3 \times 10^{18} h}{\lambda},$$

and

$$V\lambda = 3 \times 10^{18} h = 12{,}398,$$

where V is in electron volts and λ is in Angstrom units.

The conservation of energy can be expressed as

$$\tfrac{1}{2} m v_{\max}^2 = h\nu - W,$$

where $v_{\max}$ is the maximum speed of emitted electrons, ν is the frequency of incident radiation in cycles/sec, and, W is the work required to remove an electron from the substance (different for different substances).

The work required to eject an electron from a substance is equal to the threshold frequency ν_0 (i.e., the minimum frequency of radiation which will liberate a quanta, electron, photon) multiplied by Planck's constant h. This quantity is known as the work function ϕ of the substance:

$$\phi = \nu_0 h \text{ (or } h\nu_0\text{)},$$

where ν is in cycles/sec.

Plasma. Ionized gases in discharge tubes or devices are composed in general of electrons, as negative carriers, and positive ions. Any negative ions present quickly recombine with the positive ions. When the concentration of ions and electrons is approximately equal and high, a condition of *plasma* is said to exist. Such a condition is found in the *positive columns* of the glow and arc discharges.

The plasma region is practically field-free. It is highly conducting and therefore has a low voltage drop. In this respect it begins to resemble a metal.

In a plasma, the positive ion temperature is usually higher than that of the gas itself; the electron temperature may be very much higher. The temperatures of both kinds of particles are increased by the applied electric field. Even though the energy gained by the electrons from the field may be greater because of their higher mobility, their very small mass precludes the giving up of all but small amounts of energy to the neutral particles with which they collide, but the positive ions, on the other hand, will increase the gas temperature because they are of comparable size to the neutral gas particles.[1]

---

[1] "Electrical Discharges in Gases," F. M. Penning, Macmillan Co., pp. 23, 56, New York, 1957. See also "Controlled Fusion Research—An Application of the Physics of High Temperature Plasmas," R. F. Post, *Proc. I.R.E.*, **45,** 134, 1957.

Plastics. Though rather a loose designation, the word plastics is used to describe materials, usually synthetic in structure, which are moldable or formable into intricate shapes at moderately elevated temperatures, have fair to excellent strength-to-weight ratio as compared to metals, are usually electrical nonconductors (though many plastics can be made conductive by the addition of carbon or metallic powders, etc.), have considerably lower thermal conductivity than metals, and have a wide range of other properties, such as transparency to opacity, flexibility to rigidity, hardness to sponginess.

Most modern plastics, although often produced in pure form, can be compounded with fillers and/or plasticizers and with other plastics and rubbers. Fillers include such substances as cellulose, paper, cloth, wood-flour, asbestos, glass fibers, mica, clays, ceramics, etc.

The variety and range of properties exhibited by today's plastics are too extensive to cover in a work of this nature. For detailed information, the reader is referred to the literature (see bibliography below).

A few plastics have been used in vacuum applications, either as structural parts or to effect seals. The vapor pressures of some plastic materials will be found on pp. 139–141. Epoxy resins (p. 194) have been used as satisfactory vacuum seals up to 100°C. Acrylics[1] have been used at room temperature as window-closures for demountable vacuum systems, with Neoprene (p. 387) or Teflon O-rings. Teflon (p. 513) has been used as electrical insulation and structural components in vacuum.

Plastics—Bibliography

Modern Plastics Encyclopedia, Breskin Publications, Inc., New York, New York, 1958.

Handbook of Chemistry and Physics, forty-first edition, Chemical Rubber Publishing Co., Cleveland, Ohio; pp. 1533–1551, 1959–60.

"Vapor Pressures of Plastic Materials," N. Jensen, *J. Appl. Phys.,* **27,** 1460, 1956.

Engineering Properties and Applications of Plastics, G. F. Kinney, John Wiley & Sons, Inc., New York, New York, 1957.

"Technical Data on Plastics," Manufacturing Chemists· Association, Inc., New York, New York, 1957.

"Materials Selector Issue," *Materials in Design Engineering,* **52,** pp. 12–28, 35, 187–229, mid-November, 1960.

Cellulosics, W. D. Paist, Reinhold Publishing Corporation, New York, New York, 1958.

"The New Polyethylenes," M. W. Riley, *Materials in Design Engineering,* **48,** 98, July, 1958.

"Engineer's Guide to Plastics" (a review), M. W. Riley, *Materials in Design Engineering,* **49,** 103, February, 1959.

A Concise Guide to Plastics, H. R. Simonds, Reinhold Publishing Corporation, New York, New York, 1957.

Epoxy Resins, I. Skeist, Reinhold Publishing Corporation, New York, New York, 1958.

Vinyl Resins, W. M. Smith, Reinhold Publishing Corporation, New York, New York, 1958.

[1] See Plexiglas, p. 446.

Plate. That element in an electron tube to which the most positive emf is connected, and which attracts electrons. The anode or ultor. It may be any shape, including that of a cylindrical or oval tube, a solid button, or a flat plate.

Plate current. The passage of electrons to the anode or plate of a tube produces a current which is controlled by (1) the emission and space-charge surrounding the cathode, (2) the potential on the grid, (3) the potential on the anode, and (4) within certain limits, the spacing and configuration of the various elements of the tube (see p. 132). The plate current is proportional to the emission of the cathode and to the degree of positive polarity of the grid. (See EQUIPOTENTIAL LINES, p. 244.)

Plate resistance (see p. 547).

Plating (see ELECTROPLATING, pp. 23 *et seq.*).

Platinizing. This is a chemical process for obtaining a finely divided platinum (black) surface on smooth platinum electrodes used in the measurement of the conductivity and pH of liquids. The procedure is given on p. 32.

Platinizing on glass and ceramics (see below, p. 445).

Platinum. One of the noble metals. It is white, lustrous, very malleable, and ductile. It can be welded at red heat and does not oxidize at high temperatures, although it volatilizes at about 1300°C. It is attacked by the halogens, cyanide, sulfur, and caustic alkalies. It is insoluble in hydrochloric and nitric acids, but it dissolves in a mixture of these (aqua regia) to form chloroplatinic acid, H_2PtCl_6.

Platinum has the following properties:

Atomic weight	195.09
Atomic number	78
Specific gravity	21.4
Melting point (°C)	1770
Boiling point (°C)	4530
Thermal conductivity (cgs)	0.17
Specific heat at 20°C (cal/gm/°C)	0.0324
Resistivity (microhm-cm) at 0°C	9.8
at 20°C	10.6
Coefficient of resistivity 0–100°C approximately	0.003923
Coefficient linear expansion (20–100°C per °C $\times 10^{-6}$)	10.2
Ultimate tensile strength (psi) (annealed) at room temperature	18,000
at 1000°C	4500
Elongation (annealed) %	40
Hardness (annealed) VHN (gold, silver are 25)	39
Modulus of elasticity (psi $\times 10^6$)	22
Reflectivity, % at 450 mμ	55
at 550 mμ	60–65
at 750 mμ	71

The slow volatilization of platinum at temperatures above 1300°C can be minimized, when using the metal as an electrical heating element or thermocouple, by embedding it in a nonsiliceous ceramic such as alumina. The volatility appears to be associated with circulating air.[1, 2]

Platinum wire is used as the element in precision resistance thermometry because of its stability. The ratio of resistance of pure platinum, as between 0° and 100°C, is $R_{100}/R_0 < 1.3910$. Any impurity lowers this ratio. In the making and winding of resistance thermometers, the platinum must be mounted strain-free.

Platinum finds use in experimental electron devices as a substitute for nickel where high temperatures are encountered. It is often used as a "flux" (pp. 87, 253) for spot-welding tungsten to tungsten or to molybdenum and other refractory metals. It can also be used as a braze material for the refractory metals in hydrogen or vacuum.

Platinum is used as a cladding for molybdenum first grids in high-power electron tubes having thoriated tungsten emitters, such as those used in pulsed operation. Bare molybdenum grids can become coated with evaporated thorium from the emitter, and under conditions of elevated temperature, *grid emission* occurs, i.e., electrons are emitted from the grid. This can lead to excessive heating and destruction of the tube. Platinum has a much lower emission (higher work function—see pp. 236, 570) than molybdenum in the presence of thorium, but because platinum by itself is too soft and expensive to be a practical structural material for grids, the molybdenum can be coated with a 25%-by-weight layer of platinum. This has been done by a method involving an outer tube of platinum with an inner close-fitting core of molybdenum. The wire thus formed is drawn down through dies to the size desired under carefully controlled conditions so as to obtain a uniform and complete contact between the metals. Such platinum-clad grids can be operated at 1400°C with a power dissipation of 10 w/cm^2.[3]

Platinum has also been used as a cathode base for oxide-coated emitters in small long-life amplifying tubes.[4]

Platinum-to-glass seals. Satisfactory glass-to-metal seals can be effected with platinum. Soft glass, particularly lead glass, which "wets" platinum more easily than soda-lime glass, and platinum have about the same coefficient of expansion. In the process of results. Thin-walled platinum tubing can be sealed into Pyrex glass. Because of the sealing platinum wires into glass, the wire should be "beaded" (p. 163) for best softness of the metal, it yields with movements of the glass. The platinum tubing should have a wall thin enough to allow this.[5] (See also pp. 488, 489.)

Platinum coating on glass and ceramics. Glass and ceramics can be coated with a thin layer of platinum to provide a conductive layer, or one upon which other metals

---

[1] J. E. Priddis, *Platinum Metals Rev.*, **2,** 38, 1958.

[2] H. E. Bennett, "Noble Metal Thermocouples," Johnson, Matthey & Company, Ltd., London (1956); pp. 30–32.

[3] A. K. Snell, "The Use of Platinum in High Power Thermionic Valves," *Platinum Metals Review,* **4,** 82, 1960. Such wire is obtainable from J. Bishop & Company, Malvern, Pennsylvania, and Johnson, Matthey & Co., Ltd., London.

[4] E. M. Wise, "The Platinum Metals," International Nickel Co., Inc., New York, New York, 1953. See also same author, "The Platinum Metals," *J. Electrochem. Soc.*, **97,** 62C, 1950.

[5] E. L. Wheeler, *Scientific Glassblowing,* Interscience Publishers, Inc., New York, New York, 1958.

can be electroplated. Vacuum-tight seals may be produced in this way. Two formulas for platinizing of glass and ceramics are given by Wheeler:[1]

Formula A	*Parts by volume*
1. Platinic chloride, pure	1
(This is prepared by evaporating a 10% solution to dryness.)	
2. Moisten with a few drops of absolute alcohol.	
3. Grind in an iced mortar with lavender oil	10
(Add the oil gradually in small quantities.)	
4. Add Burgundy pitch or ordinary rosin to attain the desired consistency.	

Formula B	*Parts by volume*
1. Collodion in methyl alcohol, 6% solution	3
2. Chloroplatinic acid in denatured alcohol, 6% solution	3
3. Denatured alcohol	3
4. Bismuth chloride	1
(The bismuth chloride is made from a 5% solution of bismuth chloride in denatured alcohol to which 5% hydrochloric acid is added. The solution is stored and diluted to the proper proportions just before use.)	
5. When applied to glass or ceramic (with a brush or by any means) and heated to about 300°C, the collodion chars and completely volatilizes, leaving a film of bright platinum.	

Platinum and Platinum alloys for brazing (see list on pp. 176 *et seq.*).
Platinum-platinum alloy thermocouples (see THERMOCOUPLES, pp. 525 *et seq.*).
Platinum plating (see p. 32).
Platinum, vapor pressure of (see p. 147).
Plexiglas.[2] This thermoplastic is light, optically transparent, water-white, easily moldable and machinable, and susceptible of a high polish. It has fairly low water absorption (0.2 to 0.4% in 24 hours) and electrical properties as follows:

Volume resistivity (ohm-cm)	$>10^{15}$
Dielectric strength, short time (volt/mil)	450–500
Dielectric constant, 60 cycles	3.5–4.5
10^6 cycles	2.7–3.2
Dissipation factor, 60 cycles	0.05–0.06
10^6 cycles	0.02–0.03
Arc resistance	no track

[1] E. L. Wheeler, *Scientific Glassblowing,* Interscience Publishers, Inc., New York, New York, 1958.

[2] Rohm & Haas Company, Philadelphia 5, Pennsylvania. Data on Plexiglas reproduced by permission.

Other properties:

Specific gravity	1.18–1.19
Thermal conductivity, (cgs)	$4–6 \times 10^{-4}$
Coefficient of thermal expansion per °C $\times 10^{-6}$	50
Specific heat (gm-cal/gm/°C)	0.35
Refractive index	1.485–1.500
Transmittance, luminous, 0.125 in. (%)	91–92
Haze (%)	1–2
Water absorption, 24 hr (%)	0.2–0.4
Flammability, 0.125 in. (in/min)	0.5–2.5
Modulus of elasticity in tension ($10^5 \times$ psi)	3.5–5.0
Tensile strength ($10^3 \times$ psi)	6–10
Elongation in 2 in. (%)	2–7
Hardness, Rockwell, M-scale	90–102
Impact strength, Izod notched (ft-lb)	0.4–0.5
Modulus of elasticity in flexure ($10^5 \times$ psi)	3.5–5.0
Flexural strength ($10^3 \times$ psi)	12–17
Compressive yield strength, 0.1% offset ($10^3 \times$ psi)	10–14
Hot-forming temperature, Type I (°C)	120–160
Type II (°C)	140–170
Heat resistance: maximum service temperature (°C)	
Type I	60–70
Type II	80–90
Heat distortion temperature Type I (°C)	66–77
Type II (°C)	88–99

Chemical resistance: resistant to weak acids, alkalies, and aliphatic hydrocarbons. Not resistant to esters, ketones, aromatic hydrocarbons, concentrated acids, and alkalies.

Vapor pressure: see p. 141.

LUCITE has the same properties as Plexiglas. Both are classed as *acrylic* plastics.

Plumber's solder. A solder containing 67% lead and 33% tin (nominally 2 parts lead, 1 part tin) and having a melting point of 275°C, a specific gravity of 9.4, and a thermal expansion coefficient of 25×10^{-6} in/°C.

Polyethylene and polypropylene. These are widely used thermoplastic materials classed as *polyolefins,* i.e., high-molecular-weight polymers of aliphatic hydrocarbons. Polyethylene and polypropylene are polymers of ethylene and propylene, respectively.

These plastic materials are very inert, being resistant to most acids, alkalies, salts, solutions, and water at ordinary temperatures. They are not resistant to strong oxidizing acids, such as nitric, chlorosulfonic, and fuming sulfuric. Aromatic, aliphatic, and chlorinated (halogenated) hydrocarbons (e.g., trichlorethylene, carbon tetrachloride) cause some swelling at room temperature. Organic acids, essential oils, and halogens are absorbed by or diffused through the polyolefins. For short-term exposure (up to 24 hours), these plastics will withstand almost any chemical at room temperature. At elevated temperatures oxidation by air and oxidizing substances can take place. Long exposure to sunlight or ultraviolet light hastens the oxidation, with consequent embrittlement.

TABLE OF POLYPHENYL ETHERS

FLUID	MOLECULAR WEIGHT	EVAPORATION TEMPERATURES AT				ULTIMATE PRESSURES TRAP TEMPERATURE		LOWEST BLANK-OFF PRESSURE WITH 25°C TRAP (THIS INVESTIGATION)			
		10 mm	1 mm	0.1 mm	0.01 mm	25°C	5°C	G-1	G-3	PMC	NRC
2-ethylhexyl sebacate (Narcoil-20)	426	264°C	215°C	175°C	149°C	1.3×10^{-7}	7×10^{-9}	2.5×10^{-6}	7×10^{-8}	—	—
bis(m-phenoxy-phenyl) ether	354	284	228	182	153	2.0×10^{-7}	1.3×10^{-8}	2.5×10^{-6}	—	—	—
m-bis(m-phenoxy-phenoxy) benzene	447	342	285	238	200	3.0×10^{-10}	1.0×10^{-11}	2×10^{-8}*	4.5×10^{-10}	4×10^{-9}†	4×10^{-9}
mixed pentaphenyl ethers	447	345	285	234	193	1.7×10^{-9}	5×10^{-11}	2×10^{-8}*	15×10^{-9}†	—	—
bis-m(m-phenoxy-phenoxy phenyl ether)	539	374	323	276	236	8.5×10^{-13}	2×10^{-14}	2×10^{-8}	—	—	—

Notes:

* Pressures as low as 1.5×10^{-9} were recorded in a special one-stage pump.

† Pressures of 2×10^{-9} were registered for a few minutes after outgassing the ionization gauge.

G-1: Air-cooled single-stage glass pump.

G-3: Air-cooled three-stage glass pump.

PMC: Consolidated Vacuum Corp., PMC 1440 diffusion pump.

NRC: NRC Equipment Corp., HS-1500 diffusion pump.

Properties of Polyethylene

Coefficient of thermal expansion per °C × 10^{-5}	12.5–20.9
Refractive index	1.51–1.54
Specific heat	0.53–0.55
Water absorption, 24 hr (%)	<0.01
Flammability (in/min)	1.0
Modulus of elasticity in tension (10^5 × psi)	0.20–0.27
Tensile strength (10^3 × psi)	0.9–5.5
Elongation in 2 in. (%)	25–725
Hardness, Shore scale	D45–D70
Impact strength, Izod notched (ft-lb) (high density)	1.0–3.0
Brittleness temperatures (°C)	<−20–<−73.5
Stiffness in flexure (10^3 × psi)	10–70
Shear strength (10^3 × psi)	1–4.5
Volume resistivity (ohm-cm)	10^{17}–10^{19}
Dielectric strength, short time (volts/mil)	480
Dielectric constant	2.3
Dissipation factor	<0.0005
Bulk factor (for fabrication)	1.6–2.2
Compression molding pressure, high density (10^3 × psi)	1.0–3.5
Compression molding temperature, high density (°C)	150–230
Injection molding pressure, low density (10^3 × psi)	2–10
Injection molding pressure, high density (10^3 × psi)	5–22
Injection molding temperature, low density (°C)	120–180
Injection molding temperature, high density (°C)	135–343
Mold shrinkage (in/in)	0.01–0.05
Softening point, low density (°C)	68
Softening point, high density (°C)	82–110

These plastics are obtainable in various densities ranging in specific gravity from 0.910 to 0.97. They have a thermal conductivity of 0.19 Btu/hr/ft²/°F/ft. Other properties are tabulated above.

Some of the polyethylenes can be used in vacuum at room temperature (see pp. 139, 140).

Polyphenyl ethers.[1] Several fluids, under this and related names are useful in high vacuum because of their exceptional stability. The isomer mixture, bis(phenoxy-phenoxy) phenyl ether, has a vapor pressure at 25°C of about 10^{-9} torr, and yields vacuum approaching 10^{-9} torr in the unrefrigerated condensation pump. Applied to gaskets, valves, and joints, or as a coating to large inside metal surfaces, they enable ultrahigh vacuum conditions to be induced rapidly and economically on any desired scale of operation.

The table on p. 448 gives a summary of the performance of several of the specially purified ethers, as compared with 2-ethyl hexyl sebacate (Narcoil −20).

---

[1] K. C. D. Hickman, "High Vacuum with the Polyphenyl Ethers," *Trans. Am. Vacuum Soc.*, 8th Ann. Symp. (1961), 307–314, Pergamon Press, London, 1962.

Porous metals. Metals sintered from powders are available[1] which might find uses in electron tube and vacuum devices, as matrices for cathode and other materials, as gas dispersion media, and as gas-leak devices, etc. Various metals and alloys are produced, including nickel, Monel, stainless steel types 304, 309, 316, 347, 410, and 446, Carpenter #20 alloy, Haynes #25 alloy, platinum, gold, silver, tantalum, aluminum, and other metals. The mean pore sizes range from 5–165 microns, with 20 and 35 the most common. These metals are obtainable in sheet form 0.010 inch–0.25 inch thick, or more, and in sizes 18 inches × 48 inches, which can be blanked, sheared, rolled, and, to some extent, drawn and spun. They can also be readily machined, although precautions, such as filling the surface with a soluble resin before machining, should be taken to prevent smearing over of the particles by the tool.

The technique of producing porous metals can also be applied to Teflon and other plastics.[2,3]

Positive ions (see p. 302).

Positive ion bombardment (see pp. 101, 167).

Powder metallurgy. Many metals can be fabricated by a technique which involves pressing the metal in powder form and then subjecting it to a heat treatment just below the melting point. At this temperature the metal particles weld or *sinter* together. Some refractory metals, such as tungsten, molybdenum, tantalum, etc., are ordinarily manufactured in this way more or less by necessity, although zone refining and the growing of single crystals can be done subsequently to produce metals of very high purity. The sintered ingots are subjected to further treatment, such as rolling, pressing, or calendering while hot, in order to achieve a density very close to that of theoretically solid metals (see SINGLE CRYSTALS, p. 485). These refractory metals must, of course, be heat-treated in a protective atmosphere suitable to the material (other than air), such as hydrogen for tungsten and molybdenum, and vacuum for tantalum, columbium, zirconium, etc.

Brass, bronze, and iron, as well as other common metals and alloys, can be produced in porous form by powder metallurgy (see POROUS METALS, above) for various applications. Sintered bronze and iron can be impregnated with oil and used as self-oiling bearings for rotating machinery.

Press (Pinch, British). That part of a glass vacuum tube through which the electrical and supporting leads are sealed. Examples of various types of presses are shown in Fig. 10. In the laboratory, the tungsten or other wires are held in position in a graphite or stainless steel jig made from a piece of solid round stock, which is formed as shown in Fig. 131, the holes being spaced and drilled to the proper depth. The wires are first beaded (p. 163) then inserted in the jig. A piece of glass tubing is flared and placed in the position shown at (b) then rotated in the glass lathe while heating. When the glass has reached the plastic temperature, the lathe is stopped and the flared tubing is pressed down over the beaded wires as shown in (c) and (d). The operation can more efficiently be done on machines especially designed for this purpose[4,5] in which the pressure for sealing—stages (c) and (d)—is applied while the jig and the tubing are rotating.

---

[1] Micro Metallic Division of Pall Corporation, Glen Cove, New York.

[2] Porous Plastic Filter Co., Glen Cove, New York.

[3] J. B. Campbell, "Porous Metal Sheet," *Materials & Methods,* **41**, 98, 1955.

[4] Eisler Engineering Company, Newark, New Jersey.

[5] Kahle Engineering Company, Union City, New Jersey.

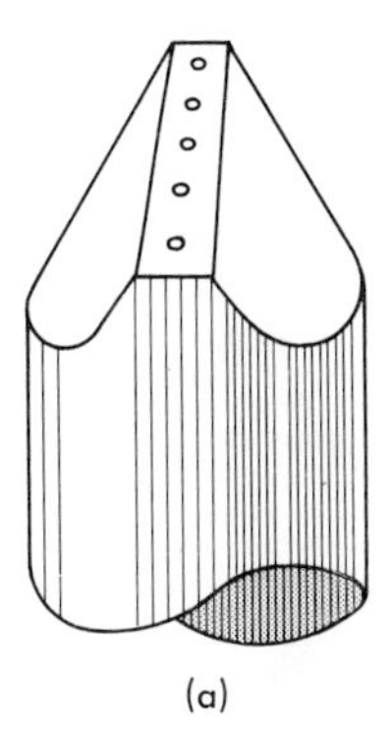

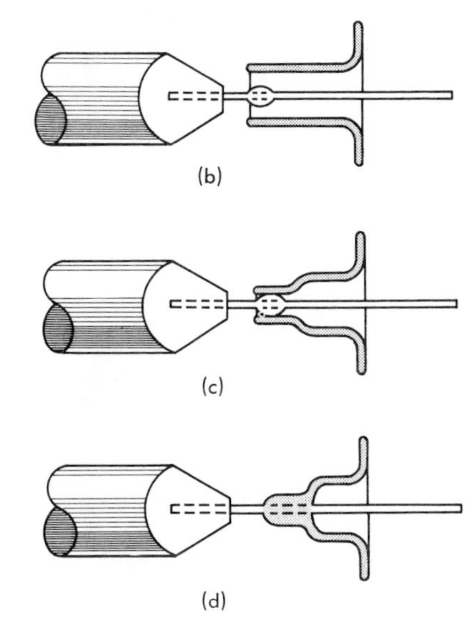

FIG. 131. Jig and steps in forming tube press.

Pressure measurements (see BAYARD-ALPERT GAUGE, p. 162; IONIZATION GAUGE, p. 303; MANOMETERS, pp. 347 *et seq.*).

Pressure units, conversion table (see p. 218).

Protective gases for tube assembly (see ATMOSPHERE, PROTECTIVE, p. 160).

Pumps, vacuum (see DIFFUSION PUMPS, pp. 227, 228; EJECTOR PUMPS, pp. 231, 232; FOREPUMPS, p. 253); see also ION PUMPING, pp. 106, 108). Various kinds of pumps and pumping systems are used in the laboratory and on an industrial scale for vacuum processing. These pumps can be described on the basis of three quantities:

(1) The pressure at the exhaust end of the pump, i.e., at the point where the pumped gases are discharged.

(2) The lowest pressure (highest vacuum) of which the pump is capable under proper operating conditions. This is usually given in microns or mm Hg (1 mm = 1 torr[1]), or sometimes, for very large industrial pumps, in inches of mercury.

(3) The rate of speed (see pp. 455–456) of pumping (exhaust, evacuation) expressed in unit volume per unit time (e.g., liters/sec or liters/min).

Under category (1) there are three general types, as follows:

(a) Those which can discharge the gas extracted from a vessel directly into the atmosphere (see FOREPUMP, p. 253). These are known as forepumps or mechanical pumps[2] and exist in single and compound stages. Such pumps cannot alone attain very low pressures.

(b) Those which can operate efficiently *only* when the pumped gases are discharged into a space or vessel which is *below* atmospheric pressure, e.g., into an operating forepump described under (a). The pumps under (b) include *boosters* (p. 168), *diffusion pumps* (pp. 227, 228), and *ejector pumps* (p. 231), all of which

---

[1] After Evangelista Torricelli, 17th century physicist. Standard atmospheric pressure at sea level and 0°C is 760 mm (approximately 30 inches; i.e., the weight of the earth's atmosphere at sea level will support a column of mercury 760 mm in height.

[2] Also called backing pumps.

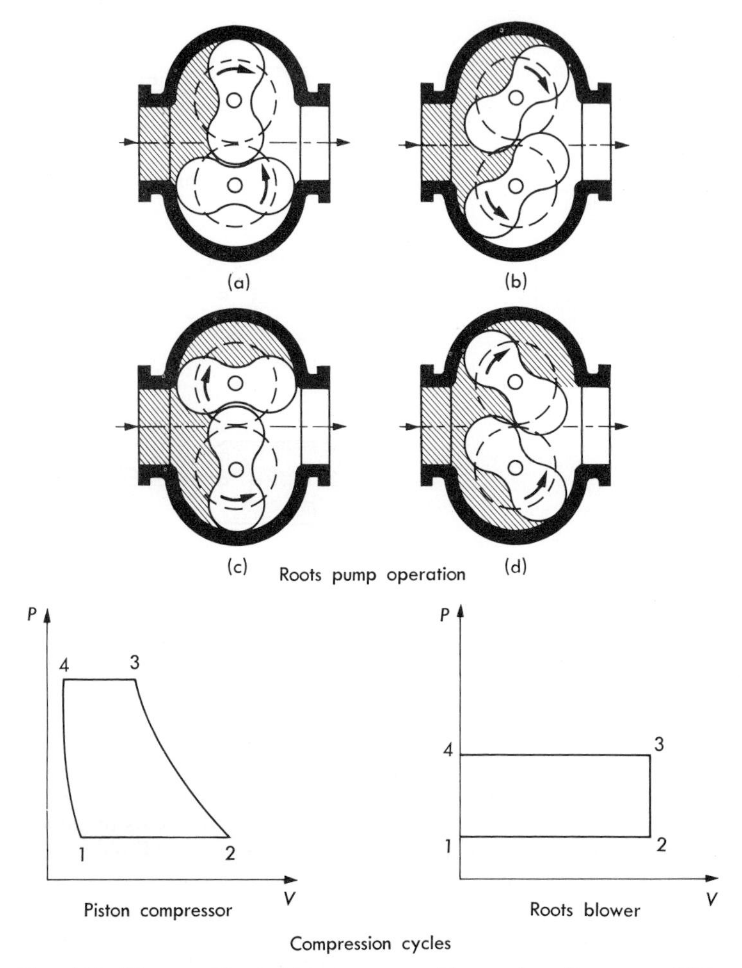

FIG. 132. Heraeus-Roots blower pump. (See explanation on p. 453.)

are sometimes called *vapor pumps*. With the combination of forepump and some type of vapor pump, quite low pressures can be obtained. Vapor pumps can be made in single or compound stages, and some types of diffusion pumps are fractionating, i.e., the pump fluid partially purifies itself of decomposition products by a distillation process which occurs during the pumping.

(c) Those which operate by ionic, chemical (getter), or refrigerant pumping or combinations of these (see pp. 108, 109, 110). Ionic and chemical pumps initially operate in a low pressure created by the pumps in category (a), or a combination of (a) and (b).

Many vacuum systems include a cold trap (pp. 211, 212, 250) or cold finger, which can be refrigerated by anything from cold or ice water or brine, through solid CO_2 ("dry ice") with acetone or other depressants, liquid nitrogen, to liquid helium, etc. Mechanical refrigeration is also used with Freon or other evaporants. This cold zone traps and removes those gases or vapors which condense at temperatures above that of the refrigerant, and therefore can be said to act as a pump. Getter-ionic pumping, once started with conventional pumps, does not usually require the presence of pumps in category (a) and (b). In fact, the efficient operation of getter-ion pumps can be interfered with by them. Very low pressures can be obtained with various combinations of pumps in this class.

Miscellaneous pumps. An intermediate type of pump is that of Heraeus-Roots[1] in which two close-meshing impellers (Fig. 132) are driven at high speed in an evacuated housing. The impellers or pistons do not actually touch one another, and they run in a dry, oil-free environment so that backstreaming (pp. 110, 161) of oil is avoided. Such pumps can be used on moderate-to-large vacuum systems as a species of booster, and are designed to be preceded by a conventional backing pump of the oil-vane type. [See (a) above.]

Method of operation of Roots blower pump.[1] The rotors move in opposition to each other, as indicated in Fig. 132, being synchronized by gears mounted on the rotor shafts. The gas to be pumped enters the inlet and fills the shaded area of (a). With further rotation, this gas flows into the shaded space in (b) between the rotors and the chamber wall. The volume of gas entrapped is shown in (c). Further movement of the rotors, as in (d), vents the gas into the outlet or forepressure side of the pump. At this point air from the outlet, which is at higher pressure, flows in until the pressure is equalized. The volume of pumped gas between the rotor and the chamber wall is then discharged. It will be seen that for each complete revolution of the drive-shaft, the pumping cycle described above occurs four times.

Although the Roots pump can operate against atmospheric pressure, such practice is not recommended. For discharge into a conventional forepump of adequate capacity, the amount of power required for the Roots pump is reduced. Also the heating due to gas-friction is much less, so that danger of seizing of close-tolerance parts in an unlubricated machine is minimized.

The *molecular pump* was first described by Gaede.[2] It consisted of a cylinder rotating at high velocity inside a small-clearance casing (stator). Intake and exhaust ports are installed at the ends of a recess at one sector of the stator. At pressures somewhat below atmospheric (viscous flow), the rotor drags gas from one port to the other in the recessed sector, thus creating a difference in pressure. At lower pressures (molecular flow) the molecules of gas tend to follow the movement of the rotor. In working pumps of this kind the rotor has a number of slots or fins which can be connected in series to amplify the effect.

A modification[3] of this pump has a conventional compound mechanical pump connected to its high-pressure port. The maker claims an ultimate pressure of 1×10^{-8} torr with a pumping speed of 140 liters/sec. These pumps do not use any fluid and are therefore inherently capable of clean, vapor-free operation.

The *water aspirator,* or water-jet suction pump, is attached to an ordinary faucet, and the stream of water passing through an orifice draws vapors with it. Such a pump is obviously limited in its range by the vapor pressure of water, which at

---

[1] Consolidated Vacuum Corporation, Rochester 3, New York.

[2] W. Gaede, *Ann. Physik.*, **41**, 337–380, 1913.

[3] The "Turbo-Molecular" pumping system of Welch Scientific Company, Chicago, Illinois, Bulletin 1377A, 1961.

0°C is 4.6 torr, and at 10°C is 9.2 torr. The water aspirator can be followed by a refrigerant trap to attain pressures below the vapor pressure of water, and is sometimes used to evacuate desiccators, etc.

The *Toepler pump* (Geissler-Toepler pump) is fundamentally the same as that used by Toricelli in his famous experiment. In this pump (see Fig. 133), a mercury column acts as a piston, drawing in gas from the vessel E being exhausted and opening and closing the valve G. This pump is normally made of glass and operates as follows:

The mercury reservoir R is in the upper position, then it is lowered to open the valve G and thus allow gases in E to enter B. The tubing below B is of barometric length. On the upward "stroke," the gas in B is isolated from E and forced through the tubing into the atmosphere at M. On the downward stroke again, the pressure in E is lowered by expansion of the gas into B.

There are two major disadvantages of the Toepler pump: (1) Since it is operated manually, by raising and lowering the reservoir R, the pumping speed is extremely slow. (2) Because of the very slow speed, it is difficult with a Toepler pump to attain in actual practice pressures below about 0.01 micron. This type of pump is useful, however, for the transferring of gas samples from one vessel to another.

Other forms of the Toepler pump are described by E. Bessel-Hagen,[1] A. Stock,[2] and E. Grimsehl.[3] G. Urry and W. H. Urry[4] describe an automatic Toepler pump of improved design in which the mercury motion is controlled by a switching relay activated by electrodes so placed that at the ultimate of its stroke, the air

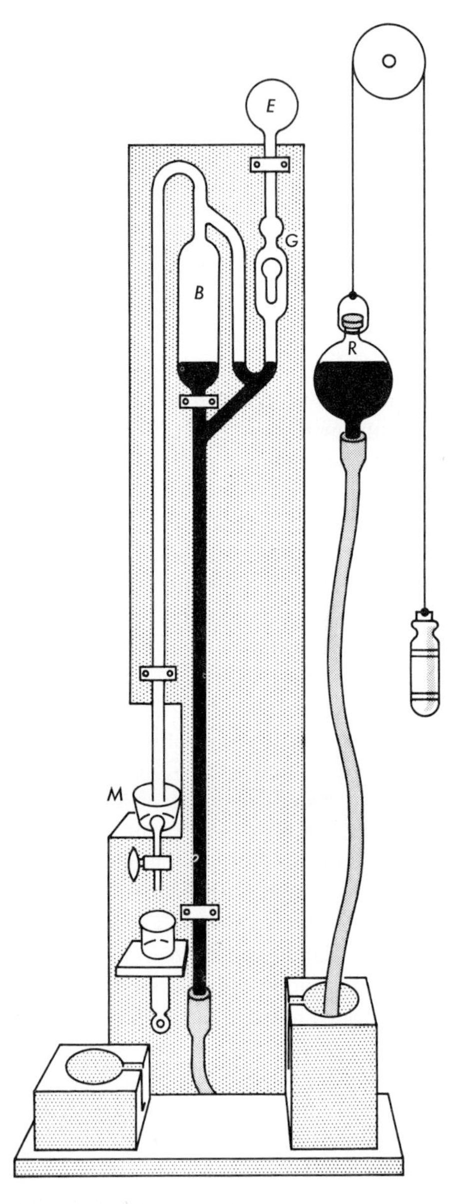

FIG. 133. The Toepler pump. (After Dushman.)

[1] E. Bessel-Hagen, *Wied. Ann.*, **12**, 425, 1881.
[2] A. Stock, *Ber. deut. chem. Ges.*, **38**, 2182, 1905.
[3] E. Grimsehl, *Physik. Z.*, **8**, 762, 1907.
[4] G. Urry and W. H. Urry, *Rev. Sci. Instr.*, **27**, 819, 1956 (with references).

leak to the lower mercury reservoir is closed and an oil vacuum pump is started to evacuate it, and at the bottom of the stroke the vacuum pump is stopped and the air leak opened to allow the mercury to rise in the piston chamber. Pumping action is effected by two glass valves with conically ground seats in series in the gas inlet and outlet tubes.

A modification of the Urry and Urry Toepler pump is described by Vrátný and Graves.[1] In this design means are provided to reduce splashing and surging, and to reduce arcing of the contacts in the cycle reversal.

Pump speed[2] is the rate at which a pump can remove gases from a vessel or system, expressed in unit volume per unit time, as liters per minute or per second.

The speed of a vacuum pump, S (liters/sec), is given by the formula:

$$S = \frac{V}{t} \log_e \frac{(P_1 - P_0)}{(P_2 - P_0)}$$

where V is volume of the system being evacuated, in liters, P_1 is initial pressure of the system, P_2 is terminal pressure of the system, P_0 is ultimate pressure of the pump [see quantity (2) on p. 451].

Conductance, or the pumping speed of connecting tubing in a vacuum system G, is given by (for pressures below atmospheric):

$$G = \frac{r^3}{L} \frac{1}{(1 + 8r/3L)} \sqrt{\frac{T}{300} \frac{29}{M}} \text{ liters/sec,}$$

where r is radius of the tubing in mm, L is length of tubing in mm, T is temperature of the gas in °K, M is molecular weight of the gas (air = 29). For room temperature, and converting to dimensions in inches, the formula appears as:

$$G = 80 \frac{d^3}{H + 4d/3} \text{ liters/sec,}$$

where d is diameter in inches, H is length in inches.

The overall pumping speed of a system is given by:

$$\frac{1}{S_t} = \frac{1}{S_1} + \frac{1}{S_2} + \frac{1}{S_3} \cdots \frac{1}{S_n},$$

when S_t is speed of the entire system (liters/sec); S_1, S_2, S_3, etc. are speeds of the individual conductances of the components. For example, note the configuration of the system illustrated in Fig. 134. Let the pump have a speed G_1 of 20 liters/sec, the tubing A have a conductance G_2 of 20 liters/sec, and the tubing B a conductance G_3 of 2 liters/sec; then,

$$S_t = \frac{1}{\frac{1}{20} + \frac{1}{20} + \frac{1}{2}} = \frac{1}{0.05 + 0.05 + 0.5} = \frac{1}{0.6} = 1.66 \text{ liters/sec.}$$

[1] F. Vrátný and B. Graves, *Rev. Sci. Instr.*, **30,** 597, 1959.

[2] See *Scientific Foundations of Vacuum Technique,* second edition, S. Dushman, p. 186, John Wiley & Sons, Inc., New York, 1962. Also see "Rate of Exhaust through a Tube or Orifice," J. Rothstein, *Rev. Sci. Instr.*, **29,** 243, 1958.

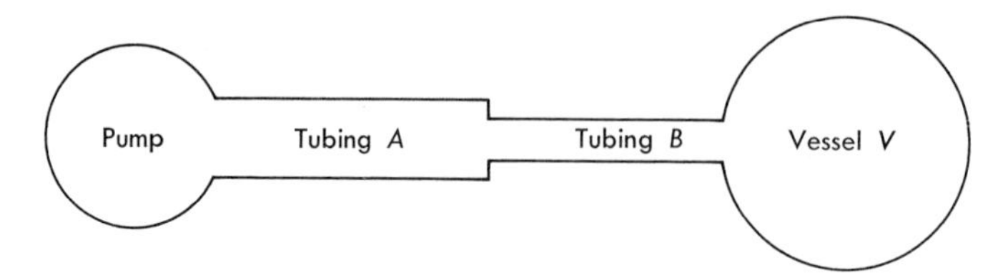

FIG. 134. Illustrating pump speed formulas.

In making calculations of the pumping speed of a vacuum system, consideration must be given to bends and constrictions in the tubing, cold traps, baffles, and the like. These are considered as impedances which will reduce the overall speed. For very small diameter tubulations or constrictions (leaks, etc):

$$S = \frac{Q}{P},$$

where S is speed of the system in liters/sec, Q is flow or leak rate in micron-liter/sec,[1] P is pressure in microns. For example, where $Q = 10^{-3}$ micron-liter, and the pressure $P = 10^{-3}$ microns (10^{-6} torr), the speed $S = 1$ liter/sec.

The shortest possible time needed to exhaust a given volume to a stated pressure is:

$$t = \frac{V}{S} \log_e \frac{P_1}{P_2},$$

where t is *pumpdown time* in seconds, V is volume of the system in liters, S is speed of the system in liters/sec, P_1 is initial pressure, P_2 is terminal pressure. For example, where $V = 100$ liters and $S = 10$ liters/sec,

$$P_1 = 10^{-2} \text{ torr} \quad \text{and} \quad P_2 = 10^{-7} \text{ torr};$$

$$t = \frac{100}{10} \log_e \frac{10^{-2}}{10^{-7}}$$

$$= 10 \log_e 10^5 \ (\log_e 10^5 = \log_{10} 10^5 \cdot 2 \cdot 3)$$

$$= 10 \cdot 5 \cdot 2.3 = 115 \text{ sec.}$$

This formula does not take account of the presence of water vapor, adsorbed vapors, and other volatile contaminating materials present on the walls of the vessels or in the system. The actual pumpdown time must be determined by experiment, although the formula is a guide as to what to look for. This comment indicates the desirability of not letting down or opening a vacuum system to the air when it is being shut down, but of admitting a *purge gas* such as dry nitrogen, helium, argon, etc., so that the adsorption of water vapor and other condensible materials by the walls of the system is minimized.

Purge gas. An inert or noncombining gas used to remove or purge air from a furnace retort, vacuum system, or vessel. Thus dry nitrogen can be used to purge a hydrogen

---

[1] Sometimes called **Throughput.**

furnace which has been shut down and is open to the air. The subsequent admission of hydrogen can be done without danger of explosion. Purge gases can be used in a vacuum system, as mentioned on p. 456, to minimize the adsorption of water vapor and other contaminants which are likely to exist in ordinary air. In glassblowing operations, dry nitrogen, forming gas (p. 160), argon, etc., can be introduced to protect easily oxidizable metals from the heat.

Pyrometer, optical (see p. 244).

Quartz. A natural mineral, silicon dioxide (SiO_2), found in two forms: sand[1] and rock crystal. Both types are used in making *fused quartz* (vitreous silica, silica glass, quartz glass, fused silica), which is produced in clear, glasslike, and translucent (fused silica) forms, the latter having a satiny appearance caused by the inclusion of many bubbles during manufacture. Rock crystal or crystalline quartz occurs in nature, sometimes in crystals as large as 20 inches in diameter. It has approximately a hexagonal shape with pyramidal ends. A good grade of crystal quartz is extremely clear, water-white, and transparent, and it has unique optical[2] and piezoelectrical properties.

Both crystal and fused quartz are chemically (see below) and thermally resistant, although crystal quartz exhibits a form of crystal breakdown known as "twinning" in the neighborhood of 500°C, which, however, does not affect some of its properties.

Quartz has an extremely low coefficient of thermal expansion, being 1/34 that of copper, 1/17 that of platinum, 1/7 that of Pyrex glass, and 1/9 that of tungsten (see the table below).

Other properties of crystal and fused quartz are given in the following table.[3,4]

PROPERTIES OF CRYSTAL AND FUSED QUARTZ

PROPERTY	CRYSTAL QUARTZ (ORIENTATION TO OPTICAL AXIS)		FUSED QUARTZ (CLEAR)
	⊥	‖	
Specific gravity (gm/cc)	2.65	2.65	2.20
Hardness, Mohs' scale	6.3–7.0	6.3–7.0	4.9
Crushing strength, (psi × 10^3)	320	348	284
Tensile strength of ¼-inch rod (psi × 10^3)	—	—	7
fibers	—	—	43–116

(cont.)

[1] Sand contains occluded gases and some impurities which may be volatile.

[2] Crystal quartz has an extremely high coefficient of transmission of ultraviolet light. Fused quartz has very nearly the same (approximately 90% transmission at 2100 AU). (Pyrex #7740 has zero transmission at 2700 AU.) Quartz also has superior transmission in the region of 30,000–40,000 AU of the infrared.

[3] General Electric Company, "Fused Quartz Catalog Q-6," 1959.

[4] Linear expansion data from *Handbook of Physics and Chemistry,* forty-first edition, Chemical Rubber Publishing Co., Cleveland, Ohio, 1960.

Properties of Crystal and Fused Quartz (*Cont.*)

Property	Crystal Quartz (Orientation to Optical Axis)		Fused Quartz (Clear)
	⊥	‖	
Modulus of compression (psi × 10^3)	—	—	604
Modulus of rigidity (psi × 10^3)	—	—	4344
Modulus of elasticity (Young's) (psi × 10^3)	—	—	4418
Average coefficient of thermal expansion (cm/cm/°C × 10^6 20–320°C)	16.9	9.6	0.55
Increase in length per unit length at temperature (°C)			
0–80	13.37	7.9 (Benoit, 1887)	
−191 to +16	—	— (Henning, 1907)	0.256
0–30	—	— (Chappius, 1903)	0.42
0–100	—	— (Scheel, 1907)	0.50
0–800	—	— (Randall, 1910)	0.546
0–1200	—	— (Randall, 1910)	0.585
Thermal conductivity (cgs)	0.0170	0.0320	0.0033
Specific heat, (gm-cal/gm/°C at 20°C)	0.18	0.18	0.18
Melting point (°C), approximately	—	—	1756
Softening point (°C)	—	—	1667
Strain point (°C)	—	—	1070
Electrical resistivity (ohm-cm) 500 volts, 25°C	—	—	$>1 \times 10^{19}$
Dielectric constant	4.2–4.7	4.5–5.0	4.1
Dielectric loss factor (%) at 10,000 volts and 994 kc/sec	—	—	0.0009
Power factor (%) at 10,000 volts and 994 kc/sec	—	—	0.00023
Surface leakage, width of path (amp/cm) at 500 volts, 1 cm spacing between electrodes			
50% relative humidity	—	—	1 to 5 × 10^{-11}
90% relative humidity	—	—	2 to 5 × 10^{-7}
Dielectric strength, (volts/mil), thickness at 50°C, $\frac{1}{4}$-inch sample	—	—	410
	ϵ	ω	
Index of refraction, NaD	1.553	1.544	1.458

Fused quartz can be drawn into fine fibers by various methods.[1] These fibers exhibit almost perfect elasticity up to the breaking point. Quartz fibers smaller than 2.5 microns (9.8×10^{-5} in) have been produced. Such fibers are used as suspension, torque, or spring elements for electrometers, microbalances, light-pressure indicators, etc.

Quartz is attacked by hydrofluoric acid at room temperature, and fused quartz is attacked by phosphoric acid at temperatures over 300°C. Hydrogen has some reducing effect on quartz at high temperatures so that flames containing hydrogen tend to cause some surface effect which is mistaken for devitrification, but which is actually a deposit of silicon hydride partly oxidized into silicon and silica.

Fused quartz is permeable in thin sections to neon, hydrogen, and helium. The permeability increases with temperature and pressure. Fused quartz also absorbs or adsorbs water vapor to some extent, an effect which is noticeable in quartz fibers, whose strength and elastic properties are adversely affected by water vapor adsorption.

The relative expansion coefficients of various materials compared to fused quartz (arbitrarily set at 1) is given in the following table:[2]

Material	Coefficient	Material	Coefficient
Fused quartz	1	Tantalum	11
Carbon	2	Flint glass	14
Pyrex glass	6	Graphite	14
Porcelain	6	Plate and crown glass	16
Tungsten	9	Platinum	17
Hard glass	10	Cast iron	18
		Copper	34

Following is a table showing various conditions for fused quartz at elevated temperatures:[2]

1000°C May be used continuously with no change in physical properties.

1150°C May be used continuously or intermittently with life limitation variable as affected by other conditions in the process.[3] Devitrification is generally gradual, with corresponding strength loss.

1250°C Intermittent use still practical but dependent on modifying conditions present.[3]

1350°C Short life may be expected with approximately 50% strength loss in 4 hours, with other conditions ideal.

[1] N. J. Tighe, "Fused-Quartz Fibers," NBS Circular No. 569, U.S. Government Printing Office, Superintendent of Documents, Washington 25, D.C., 1956. Includes an excellent bibliography.

[2] Amersil Quartz Division, Engelhard Industries, Inc., Hillside 5, New Jersey.

[3] Appreciable attack may be expected if the silica is in contact with alkalies, some metallic oxides, alkaline phosphates, sodium tungstate, and molybdate. Phosphoric acid will attack silica above 300°C, and hydrofluoric acid at all temperatures.

The continuous operation of *evacuated* fused quartz vessels above 800°C is not generally recommended. They may, however, be used with a hydrogen atmosphere, although precaution should be taken for earlier than normal breakdown when tempratures exceed approximately 900°C. The rate of diffusion of gases such as hydrogen, helium, deuterium, and neon are accelerated with temperature increase.

Radiation heating. A hot body radiates heat whether it is in the atmosphere or in other gases, or in a vacuum. Other bodies nearby, at lower temperatures, will absorb some of this heat, and their temperature will thus be raised. If gases are present, these will also be heated, and some of this heat will be transmitted by thermal *conduction,* as well as by radiation, to solid bodies in the vicinity. In a vacuum, practically all the heat is transmitted to nearby bodies by radiation alone, the amount depending on the degree of vacuum.

Radiation heating is distinct from induction heating (see pp. 45, 51, 221, 222) and heating by electron or ion bombardment (see p. 167 and 417, respectively). The heating of a glass envelope by a hot tungsten filament in a high-vacuum tube is an example of radiation heating. The bottle-brazing procedure described on pp. 39–40 is an example of radiation and conduction heating in hydrogen.

Radiation (heat) shields. Bodies can be protected from direct radiation of heat (from an emitter) by the interposition of a metal sheet, cylinder, or other shape. Two interposed shields are more effective than one, since the second reflects some of the heat absorbed by the first, which is then acting as an emitter.

Metals vary slightly in their heat-reflective efficiency in the infrared region. The percentages of normally incident radiation reflected by the polished surfaces of copper, gold, iron, steel, nickel, platinum, silver, tungsten, aluminum, molybdenum, rhodium, tantalum, stellite, and stainless steels are all well over 90% at wavelengths above 9 microns (90,000 Angstroms). (See HEAT SHIELDS, p. 291.)

Refrigerant. A substance used for cooling and, in vacuum parlance, for condensing vapors such as water, carbon dioxide, oil, etc., in a system.

René 41 Alloy (now called **CM-R 41 Alloy**[1]). A high-nickel, vacuum-melted alloy which can be heat-treated for very high tensile and elastic properties at elevated temperatures. It has the following composition:

Carbon	0.06–0.12	Boron	0.003–0.010
Silicon	0.50 max.	Cobalt	10.00–12.00
Manganese	0.50 max.	Molybdenum	9.00–10.50
Iron	5.00 max.	Titanium	3.00–3.30
Chromium	18.00–20.00	Aluminum	1.50–1.60
		Nickel	balance

CM-R 41 has good resistance to oxidation at temperatures up to and including 982°C. After 100 hours' exposure in slow-moving air, the intergranular penetration of oxide was less than 0.001 inch per side on the sample tested.

---

[1] Cannon-Muskegon Corporation, Muskegon, Michigan. All data on CM-R 41 Alloy are reproduced from the Corporation's literature by permission.

The emissivity of CM-R 41 at various temperatures is:

°F	°C	Emissivity
825	440	0.41
900	482	0.43
945	508	0.45
1025	551	0.47

Density	0.296 lb/in^3
Specific gravity	8.19 gm/cc
Electrical resistivity	820 ohm-mil-ft (68°F)
	13.66 microhm-cm (20°C)
Specific heat	0.108 gm-cal/gm/°C

CM-R 41 has a very critical heating and cooling rate because the alloy will age-harden at temperatures between 650°–980°C. This age-hardening phenomenon occurs if the piece is held in this range for more than 4 seconds. Note the typical air-cooled and water-quenched data for mill-annealed material.

The following is a summary of machinability data for CM-R 41:

Type of tool—high-speed steel (M-3)
Speeds—20 sfpm, 30 sfpm max.
Positive rake—10°
Relief—10°
Side cutting edge—45°
Face cutting (on work)—50°
Depth of cut—0.200 inch
Feed—0.004 inch–0.005 inch
Cutting fluid—water-base

It is recommended that a test of the hardness of the piece be made. If a reading in excess of 40 Rockwell C is found, the material should be heat-treated at 1080°C for one hour and oil-quenched.

Because of the presence of titanium and aluminum in CM-R 41, hydrogen-furnace-brazing is not feasible, but vacuum-brazing with high nickel materials can be done. The metal surface should be thoroughly clean before any brazing procedure.

Heat treatment of CM-R 41. Use one of the following:

1. Furnace-anneal at 1080°C ± 10°C, with rapid quench.
2. Solution-treat at 1066°C for 30 minutes; air-cool. Then age at 760°C for 16 hours and air-cool.
3. Solution-treat at 1177°C for 30 minutes; air cool. Then age at 900°C for 4 hours, and air-cool.

Procedure 2 is used to obtain maximum tensile and yield strengths.

Procedure 3 is used to obtain maximum stress-rupture strengths.

Resistance brazing. By the insertion of a thin foil or sheet of some lower-melting metal or alloy between the two members to be joined, a spot-welding machine can sometimes be used to effect a braze with protective atmospheres or liquids. This can also be done on a larger scale with heavy-duty machines. A modification of this process is that in which the work, e.g., a copper magnetron body, can be brazed by setting it up between two blocks or cylinders of graphite. A continuous current is passed through this sandwich from a spot-welding transformer, thus resistance-heating the graphite to incandescence. This heat is transferred to the work by direct conduction.

Resistance thermometer. All metals undergo a change in electrical resistivity with temperature, the change being known as the temperature coefficient of resistivity, which is defined as the ratio of the change of resistance in a wire due to change of temperature of 1°C to its resistance at 0°C. In most common metals and alloys, this change is positive, i.e., the resistance increases with temperature.

Pure nickel exhibits a large temperature coefficient (0.006 at 20°C), and platinum has a somewhat lower value (0.003 at 20°C).

A typical resistance thermometer is constructed by mounting a thin wire, strain-free on a ceramic form, in such a way that the wire is in minimal contact with the form (the employment of flutes or grooves is suggested). The total resistance of this wire will change appreciably with small changes in temperature, and this change in resistance can be applied in various modifications of the Wheatstone bridge[1] to indicate and control the temperature of cryostats, ovens, furnaces, etc. Resistance thermometers made of nickel wire are suitable for use up to about 500°C in air, and up to 1000°C in hydrogen, and those of platinum wire can be used up to 1000°C in air.[2, 3] These and other materials can also be used as resistance thermometers at low temperatures (i.e., below room temperature and down to cryometric regions.

Thermistors (semiconducting materials) can also be used as sensitive resistance thermometers; some of them have much larger coefficients than metals over limited ranges.[3]

Resistance welding (see SPOT WELDING, p. 493).

RF or Radio frequency heating (see INDUCTION HEATING, pp. 45, 51, 221, 222, 231).

Rhenium (Re). The following material is condensed from WADC Technical Report No. 54–371 on "Investigation of Rhenium," Battelle Memorial Institute, June, 1954. Also see "Rhenium Data Sheet" of Chase Brass & Copper Company, Waterbury 20, Connecticut, March, 1956.

Rhenium is a refractory metal sometimes used in place of tungsten for heaters and filaments in electron tubes. It can be spot-welded, and hydrogen- or vacuum-fired for outgassing. Rhenium has the following properties:

Atomic number	75
Atomic weight	186.31
Density, or specific gravity (gm/cc)	21
Melting point (°C)	3180 ± 20
Boiling point (°C)	5900
Vapor pressure, solid, at 2250°C	2.61×10^{-9} atm, 3.4×10^{-6} mm Hg
Vapor pressure, solid, at 2725°C	7.37×10^{-7} atm, 9.7×10^{-4} mm Hg
Electrical resistivity (microhm-cm) at 20°C	19–21
Linear coefficient of thermal expansion, in/in, 0–1000°C	6.8×10^{-6}
Spectral emissivity	0.36–0.42

[1] "Design of Simple Resistance Thermometer Bridges," R. D. Goodwin, *Rev. Sci. Instr.*, **29,** 497, 1958.

[2] See "A Platinum Resistance Thermometer for High Temperatures," W. Obrowski, *Platinum Met. Rev.* (London), **4,** 102, 1960; also "A High Temperature Thermoregulator," F. Rosebury, *Rev. Sci. Instr.*, **24,** 398, 1953.

[3] "Thermistor Thermometer Bridge," K. S. Cole, *ibid.*, **28,** 326, 1957.

Thermionic emission:
Work function, ev 4.80
Maximum secondary-electron emission coefficient 1.4

The oxidation resistance of rhenium is good at room temperature and up to 600°C, but the metal oxidizes rapidly above that temperature, with the formation of a volatile oxide. Its resistance to the water cycle effect is much superior to that of tungsten. Rhenium exhibits good resistance to molten tin, zinc, aluminum, silver, and copper, but dissolves in molten nickel and iron.[1]

Although rhenium is quite ductile and malleable, it shows a very high anomalous surface hardness, which makes drilling, filing, and other machining operations difficult. This is thought to be due to an extremely high rate of surface work-hardening. Machining operations can be done with carbide tools with slow speeds and feeds, or the metal can be formed with ultrasonic or electric-spark tools. Grinding is also feasible.

It is possible that small amounts of impurities are responsible for the anomalous surface-hardness of rhenium, and that when purer materials (e.g., single crystals) are available, these will be found more tractable. (*Cf.* tungsten-rhenium thermocouples, pp. 531, 536.)

Rhodium. A silver-white metal of the platinum group which has good corrosion resistance and high hardness, and is therefore used as an electroplate on base metals (see p. 464).

Rhodium is also used as an alloying element with platinum to make thermocouples, 10% and 13% Rh alloys being common (THERMOCOUPLES, pp. 530 *et seq.*).

The properties of rhodium are:

Atomic weight	102.91
Atomic number	45
Melting point, (°C)	1985
Boiling point, (°C)	4500
Density, or (specific gravity) (gm/cc)	12.5
Coefficient of linear expansion per °C $\times 10^{-6}$ at 20°C	8.3
Thermal conductivity cgs at 20°C (cgs)	0.21
Electrical resistivity (microhm-cm) at 0°C	4.1
Electrical resistivity (microhm-cm) at 20°C	4.5
Temperature coefficient of resistivity, 0–100°C	0.0044
Annealed hardness (similar to Brinell: 10-mm ball, 3000-kg load)	
cast	147
annealed	144
50% RA	401
Tensile strength, annealed (psi $\times 10^3$)	80
Modulus of elasticity in tension (psi $\times 10^6$)	50
Reflectivity at 550 $\mu\mu$ (%)	79
at 450 $\mu\mu$ (%)	78
at 750 $\mu\mu$ (%)	80
Specific heat at 0°C	0.058

[1] "Investigations of Rhenium," Eleventh Quarterly Progress Report, Battelle Memorial Institute, to Aeronautical Research Laboratory, WADC, March, 1955.

Rhodium imparts increased hardness and also increased corrosion resistance to alloys with platinum. Alloys containing more than 20% Rh are virtually immune to attack by aqua regia and the 10% Rh alloy is resistant to attack by free wet chlorine. The 10% alloy, having a higher electrical resistance and a higher melting point than those of pure platinum, is useful as a winding for high-temperature laboratory furnaces.

Rhodium plating.[1] Most common metals can be rhodium-plated directly, except steel and aluminum, which are attacked by the strongly acid bath unless a dense, nonporous undercoating of silver or nickel is previously applied. In any event, the undercoating of silver or nickel is usually applied to all metals.

Because of the high cost of rhodium, electrodeposits over 0.002 inch are not common. However, the hardness and corrosion resistance of thin, nonporous rhodium electroplates are such that 0.00001 inch will protect a silver surface from tarnish, although heavier deposits are required for wear resistance (0.001 inch).

Deposits of silver, copper, or nickel of not less than 0.001 inch on steel and not less than 0.0015 inch on aluminum are required as adequate undercoats for rhodium plating. Where high temperatures are to be encountered, nickel plating is preferred.

Very great care must be taken to ensure thorough cleaning before plating, or poor adhesion may result. When thick deposits of rhodium are required, the base metal should be etched in an appropriate bath. An anodic etch in cyanide is suitable for silver, while a ferric chloride and hydrochloric acid solution is used for nickel, which can also be treated by a cathodic procedure in 10% (volume) sulfuric acid at 20–25 amp/ft^2 for 30 seconds. Etched work is to be transferred to the rhodium bath without rinsing and with as little delay as possible.

The table below gives the range of concentration of the constituents in rhodium-plating baths. Rhodium sulfate is used with free sulfuric acid.

GENERAL TYPE OF APPLICATION	MINIMUM THICKNESS ON SIGNIFICANT SURFACES (IN.)	RECOMMENDED RHODIUM CONTENT (GM/LITER)	RECOMMENDED MINIMUM H_2SO_4 CONTENT (ML/LITER)
Tarnish protection only	0.000015	2	20
Reflectors	0.000025	2	20
Light mechanical loading and infrequent use	0.0001	4	20
Medium mechanical loading	0.0002	4	20
Heavy mechanical loading	0.0004	10	50
Very heavy loading conditions in special applications only	0.0008	10	50

Pinholes in the deposits are avoided by tapping the work rack occasionally to dislodge gas bubbles, or a mechanical device could be set up to do this at intervals of about 20 to 30 seconds.

[1] "Rhodium Plating to Specification," R. R. Benham, British Ministry of Aviation Report, *Process Specification DTD 931*. Excerpt reproduced by permission.

See also "Data and Directions for Electroplating with Rhodium," Engelhard Industries, Inc., Chemical Division, Newark 2, New Jersey, 1961.

These baths use a nonconsumable anode, and this can be platinum or a rhodium-platinum alloy. This requires that the bath be replenished frequently, and chemical analyses should be made to determine the rhodium content. The best practice calls for replenishment before the rhodium content of the bath has fallen by 10%. A good plan is to add replenisher solution after each job.

These baths deposit about 0.00025 inch of rhodium in 1 to 1½ hours. Temperature is 30–50°C and current density is 5–20 amp/ft².

Organic contamination in the bath can be minimized by the use of activated charcoal (see p. 149).

Electrodeposited rhodium is extremely hard (800 to 900 Vickers, or 65 to 67 Rockwell C).

Richardson formula, equation or constant (see ELECTRON EMISSION FORMULAS, p. 236).

R-Monel (see p. 382).

Rodar alloy. This is a glass-sealing alloy manufactured by the Wilbur B. Driver Company, Newark, New Jersey. Its composition and properties are given below:

Composition, %	Ni 29, Co 17, Mn 0.3, Fe balance
Density, or specific gravity (gm/cc)	8.36
Melting point (°C)	1430 approximate
Linear coefficient of thermal expansion per °C × 10⁻⁶:[1]	
30–200°C	4.33–5.30
30–300°C	4.41–5.17
30–400°C	4.54–5.08
30–450°C	5.03–5.37
30–500°C	5.71–6.21
Tensile strength (psi)	65,000–150,000
Yield strength, 0.2% offset (psi)	50,000 average
Elongation in 2 inches (%)	30
Thermal conductivity (cgs) at 20–100°C	0.05
Electrical resistivity (ohm-cmf) at 68°F	294
(microhm-cm) at 20°C	48.4
Magnetic attraction	strong
Curie temperature (°C)	440

This alloy matches the expansivity of thermal shock-resistant glasses such as Corning 7052 and 7040. It produces a permanent vacuum-tight seal with simple oxidation procedure (*cf.* KOVAR, pp. 322–338) and resists attack by mercury. Rodar is readily machined and fabricated, and can be welded, soldered, and brazed. It is available in the form of bar, rod, wire, strip, and tubing (*cf.* also THERLO, pp. 58, 520).

Rodine inhibitor (see pp. 8, 9, 292).

Roughing pump. A vacuum pump which discharges gases directly into the atmosphere and is used as a backing pump for diffusion and other types of secondary pumps. (See FOREPUMP, p. 253, also pp. 451 *et seq.*)

Roughing valve. In Fig. 18, p. 76, valve C, so-called because it can be used to rough-down (forepump) the bell-jar or vessel. The headgate valve A is closed until the

---

[1] As determined from cooling curves, after annealing in hydrogen for 1 hour at 900°C and for 15 minutes at 1100°C.

pressure is down to a value appropriate to the diffusion pump. Also, a roughing valve is any valve between a forepump and a diffusion pump. (See also HEADGATE VALVE, p. 290, and BYPASS VALVE, p. 189.)

Rubber (see also pp. 387, 390). The use of natural rubber in vacuum systems (as hose, gaskets, etc.) is restricted in favor of more suitable materials such as chloroprene synthetic rubber (Neoprene, p. 387) for gaskets and O-rings, and a polyvinyl chloride (Tygon, p. 560) for vacuum tubing or hose. Natural rubber gives off volatile vapors, and tends to be porous. The vapor pressures of both Neoprene and Tygon are adequately low at room temperature, and they are nonporous. Silastic or Silicone rubbers are also used with success in demountable systems (see pp. 223, 407; see also VITON, p. 567).

Sag in tungsten or molybdenum filaments. Filaments and heaters will sag to a considerable degree if unsupported. Although the expansion coefficient is small, the high temperature of operation makes expansion a factor to be considered. For example, a tungsten wire 10 inches long heated to 2500°C will expand about 0.1 inch. In addition, because the metal becomes very ductile at high temperatures, its own weight might cause it to exceed the yield point, and thus a degree of irreversible stretching or deformation will occur. To minimize these effects, a long or helical filament should be supported in several places, and this can be done by using tungsten hooks sealed into glass, or otherwise mounted on ceramic. A method for reducing the tendency of tungsten filaments to sag is suggested on p. 87.

Sapphire, synthetic. A very pure form of aluminum oxide (Al_2O_3). It is similar in composition to natural sapphire, ruby, and corundum, the colors of which are imparted by small amounts of impurities.

The following material is taken from "A Summary of Available Data on the Physical Properties of Synthetic Sapphire," by R. A. McFarlane.[1]

The physical properties of synthetic sapphire make it valuable for special applications where conventional materials are inadequate. Sapphire has high transmission in the ultraviolet, visible, and infrared spectra, and windows can be made which are mechanically strong and wear-resistant. In optical systems the low dispersion of sapphire and its low susceptibility to abrasion make it valuable for outside elements of lenses subject to severe mechanical abuse. A loss of transmission of not more than 3% is encountered when the material is heated to 440°C, and transmission properties in the infrared region are useful up to 1500°C. Sapphire is superior to other infrared transmitting materials, which scratch or fracture readily or have high reflection losses.

The low dielectric loss, high resistivity, mechanical strength, and freedom from outgassing have led to the use of sapphire for output windows of high- and low-power microwave tubes, and for insulators and support rods of internal tube structures. The ability of sapphire to make vacuum seals to metal, ceramics, glass,[2] and even to sapphire offers many possibilities to the tube designer.

A small amount of chromium added to sapphire produces ruby. The paramagnetic resonance of the Cr^{+++} ion in the crystal lattice is used for microwave maser[1]

[1] Reproduced by permission of the Adolf Meller Company, Sapphire Products Division, Providence, Rhode Island.

[2] See p. 284.

amplifier applications. Available data indicate a resonance bandwidth of approximately 50 Mc/sec. for very small amounts of chromium doping, increasing to about 570 Mc/sec., with a higher doping of approximately 1% chromium in aluminum sites. The chromium impurity in "pink" ruby is less than 0.1%, in "standard" ruby, between 0.1% and 0.5%, and in "dark" ruby, greater than 0.5%.

Ruby is being used for the active material in a laser[1] from which a highly monochromatic beam of red light can be obtained with an effective source temperature of approximately 10^{10}°K. Single crystal cylinders are generally employed, and slow-grown material is available to provide greater crystal uniformity.

Where special applications require accurate crystal orientation, a precision of 0.5° can be achieved by optical methods and 0.01° by X-ray techniques.

The physical properties of synthetic sapphire are given below:

Chemical formula . . . . Al_2O_3
Molecular weight 101.94
Crystal class . . . . hexagonal system—rhombohedral classification
Specific gravity (gm/cc) 3.98
Water absorption . . . . nil
Solubility: Sapphire is insoluble in water and in common acids and alkalies to approximately 1000°C. It is not attacked by hydrofluoric acid below 300°C
Hardness . . . . Mohs' scale: 9
Knoop scale: 1525–2000
depending on orientation (1000-gm indenter)
Bulk modulus (psi) 300,000
Young's modulus (modulus of elasticity): Measurements were made by flexure. The angle indicated is that between the *C*-axis and the axis of the bar. Values obtained are, in general, lower than those obtained in either tension or compression. See Fig. 135.

Angle, degrees	Modulus (psi)
30	5.5×10^7
45	5.1×10^7
60	5.0×10^7
75	5.6×10^7

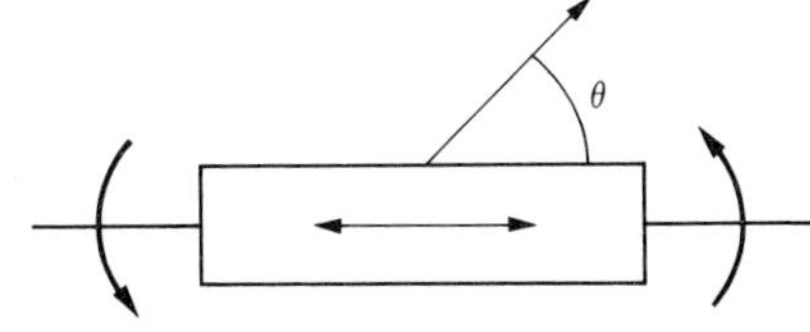

FIG. 135. Orientation of axes.

Modulus of rigidity: This constant was measured in torsion and depends upon crystal orientation. The minimum value quoted is 2.15×10^7 psi.
Modulus of rupture (maximum bending stress): This is a function of crystal orientation; refer to Fig. 135.

Angle, degrees	Modulus (psi)
30	100,000
45	78,000
60	65,000
75	94,000

Melting point (°C) . . . . 2040 ± 10
Specific heat, 91°K 0.0249
291°K 0.1813

[1] See Lasers and Masers, p. 339.

Linear coefficients of thermal expansion (in direction indicated):

Temperature range (°C)	$\|\|C$-axis	60° to C-axis (values are $\times 10^{-6}$/°C)	$\perp$ C-axis
20–50	6.66	5.8	5.0
20–500	8.33	7.7	7.70
20–1000	9.03	8.4	8.31
20–1500	—	9.0	—

Thermal conductivity: This appears to be little affected by orientation. There is experimental indication that it is very slightly lower along the A-axis (90°) than along the C-axis (0°).

Temperature	Thermal conductivity (cgs units)
2.5°K	0.08
4.2°K	0.28
20°K	8.4
35°K	16.0
77°K	2.3
200°K	0.21
0°C	0.11
100°C	0.060
300°C	0.039
500°C	0.026
700°C	0.020
900°C	0.018

Optical properties: refractive index (ordinary ray at 24°C):

WAVELENGTH (μ)	REFRACTIVE INDEX	WAVELENGTH (μ)	REFRACTIVE INDEX	WAVELENGTH (μ)	REFRACTIVE INDEX
0.26520	1.8336	0.64385	1.7655	2.4374	1.7278
0.28035	1.8243	0.706519	1.7630	3.2432	1.7044
0.28936	1.8195	0.85212	1.7588	3.2666	1.7036
0.29673	1.8159	0.89440	1.7579	3.303	1.7023
0.30215	1.8135	1.01398	1.7555	3.3293	1.7015
0.3130	1.8091	1.12866	1.7534	3.4188	1.6982
0.33415	1.8018	1.36728	1.7494	3.5078	1.6950
0.34662	1.7981	1.39506	1.7489	3.70	1.6875
0.361051	1.7945	1.52952	1.7466	4.258	1.6637
0.365015	1.7936	1.6932	1.7437	4.954	1.6266
0.39064	1.7883	1.70913	1.7434	5.1456	1.6151
0.404656	1.7858	1.81307	1.7414	5.349	1.6020
0.435834	1.7812	1.9701	1.7383	5.419	1.5973
0.54607	1.7708	2.1526	1.7344	5.577	1.5864
0.576960	1.7688	2.24929	1.7323		
0.579066	1.7687	2.32542	1.7306		

Heat capacity:

Temperature (°K)	Heat capacity (abs. joules/deg·mole)
50	2
100	13
200	52
300	79
600	112
900	122
1200	127

In the visible region of the spectrum, the refractive index for the ordinary ray can be written:

$$N_0 = 1.74453 + \frac{101.0}{\lambda - 1598},$$

where λ is the wavelength in Angstroms. The refractive index for the extraordinary ray is approximately 0.008 less than that for the ordinary ray.

The temperature coefficient of the index of refraction is approximately $+13 \times 10^{-6}/°C$ at room temperature for the visible spectrum. It averages $+20 \times 10^{-6}/°C$ at the shorter wavelengths and $+10 \times 10^{-6}/°C$ near 4 microns.

Reciprocal dispersion:

$$\text{nu value} = \frac{N_D - 1}{N_F - N_C} = 72.2,$$

where

$$\lambda_D = 0.5893\mu, \qquad \lambda_F = 0.6563\mu, \qquad \lambda_C = 0.4861\mu.$$

Optical transmission: Sapphire has useful transmission from 0.15μ to 6μ. In the visible region, losses result primarily from reflection at interfaces. If no internal absorption occurs, the transmittance of a plane-parallel plate can be expressed as a function of the refractive index N:

$$T = \frac{2N}{N^2 + 1},$$

where internal reflections are considered.

At wavelengths shorter than 0.3μ, internal absorption results in an additional decrease of transmission:

Wavelength (μ)	Transmittance of 1-mm plate (%)
0.28	79
0.22	72
0.20	66
0.18	53
0.16	34
0.15	21

In the infrared region, transmission is maintained out to approximately 4 microns. At longer wavelengths, internal absorption decreases transmission:

Wavelength (μ)	Transmittance of 0.94 mm plate (%)
3.0	92
5.35	84
6.3	34

The coefficient of absorption at a wavelength of 5.35 microns is 1.9 cm^{-1} and at a wavelength of 6.3 microns is 7.6 cm^{-1}. Overall transmittance calculations must include Fresnel reflection losses:

$$T = \frac{(1 - r)^2 e^{-\alpha X}}{1 - r^2 e^{-2\alpha X}},$$

where T is the ratio of transmitted-to-incident light intensity; r is the surface reflection coefficient given in terms of the refractive index of the window material N,

$$r = \frac{(N - 1)^2}{(N + 1)^2}$$

where α is the coefficient of absorption, and X is the thickness of the window.

Electrical properties of synthetic sapphire are as follows: Volume resistivity (indicated values are order-of-magnitude only).

Temperature (°C)	Resistivity (ohm-cm)
500	10^{11}
1000	10^{9}
1500	10^{5}
2000	10^{3}

Te value: The temperature at which a 1-cm cube has a resistance of 1 megohm = 10^6 ohms:

1231°C parallel to C-axis
1214°C perpendicular to C-axis.

Dielectric strength at 60 cycles: 480,000 volts/cm, 1200 volts/mil.

Dielectric constant:

Temperature (°C)	Electric field relative to C-axis	
	Perpendicular	Parallel
20	9.35	11.53
100	9.43	11.66
300	9.66	12.07
500	9.92	12.54
700	10.26	13.18

These values are valid for frequencies from 10^4 to 9×10^9 cps. For frequencies below 10^4 cps, the dielectric constant increases slightly with temperatures above 400°C. Below 400°C no frequency dependence is apparent.

Loss tangent: At low frequencies the loss tangent is a very strong function of temperature. Over the audio range, it can be represented within a factor of 2 by:

$$\tan \delta = \frac{A}{2 \log_{10} (f/100)} 10^{(16 - \log_{10}(f/100)) - T/2000},$$

where f is the frequency (cps), T is the temperature (°C),

$$A = 2.4 \times 10^{-6} \text{ for the field} \perp C\text{-axis}$$
$$= 1.9 \times 10^{-6} \text{ for the field} \parallel C\text{-axis.}$$

The above equation summarizes measurements made from 200°C to 600°C.

At 8.5 kMc/sec the loss tangent is less sensitive to temperature, and measurements made in the temperature range 20°C to 700°C can be represented to within 10% by:

$$\tan \delta = 2.8 \times 10^{-5} \times 10^{T/800} \text{ field} \perp C\text{-axis}$$
$$= 8.5 \times 10^{-5} \times 10^{T/2000} \text{ field} \parallel C\text{-axis.}$$

No anomalous values at lower temperature have been reported.

(The material presented in this report on synthetic sapphire is based on published and unpublished measurements of M. W. P. Strandberg, who made the ruby data available; A. R. Von Hippel, the Linde Company; Maletson, Murphy, and Rodney;[1] and Ballard, McCarthy, and Wolfe.[2])

Sapphire-to-metal seals. Bonding of synthetic sapphire to 42% nickel-iron or to Kovar (p. 322) can be made by the "active-metal" process described for ceramics on p. 67. A detailed procedure for making such seals is given by Omley.[3]

Saturation (see pp. 228, 338).

Schottky effect (see pp. 228, 250).

Schulz-Phelps (or Schulz) Gauge.[4] This is an ionization gauge in which the electron paths are relatively short and well-defined and do not change appreciably with pressure. It is useful in the range of pressures above that in which conventional ionization gauges are insensitive. A typical pressure range for the flat plate type (Fig. 136) is one millimeter down to 10^{-5} torr. The dimensions of the components of the construction shown are: electron and ion collectors, $\frac{1}{2}$ inch $\times$ $\frac{3}{8}$ inch, spaced $\frac{1}{8}$ inch apart; filament 0.005 inch tungsten wire spaced midway between the plates. The electron collector could be replaced by a $\frac{1}{8}$ inch $\times$ $\frac{1}{2}$ inch tungsten ribbon 0.0004 inch thick for easier outgassing. Commercial gauges of this type are available.[5, 6]

---

[1] *J. Opt. Soc. Amer.*, **48**, 72, 1958.

[2] Report 2389–11–S, Willow Run Laboratory, University of Michigan, January, 1959.

[3] "Sapphire-to-Metal Seals," H. A. Omley, paper presented in a panel discussion at a meeting of the Electronics Division of the American Ceramics Society, Philadelphia, Pennsylvania, April, 1960.

[4] "Ionization Gauges for Measuring Pressures up to the Millimeter Range," G. J. Schulz and A. V. Phelps, *Rev. Sci. Instr.*, **28**, 1051, 1957.

[5] Type I.G. 100, Eitel-McCullough, Inc.

[6] Type V.T. 191, Tung-Sol Electric, Inc.

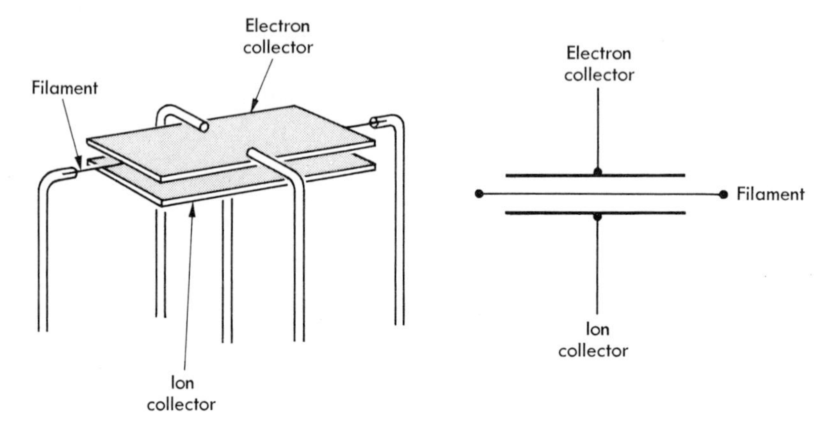

FIG. 136. Schulz-Phelps gauge for the measurement of relatively high pressures (millimeter to 10^{-5} torr range). Operating potentials: ion collector (grounded), 0 volt; electron collector, +120 volts; filament, +60 volts (for dimensions see p. 471).

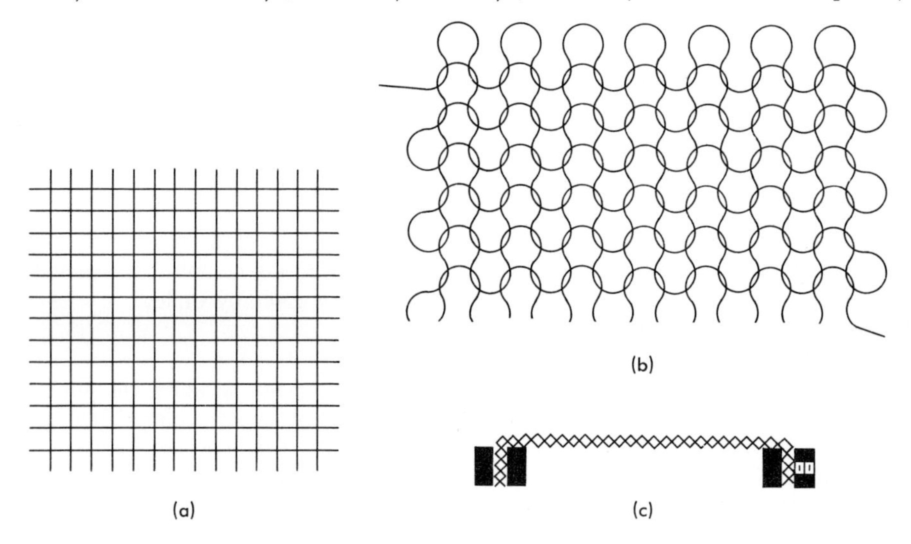

FIG. 137. Woven and knitted mesh and a suggested method of mounting to form a grid. (a) Woven mesh. (When the spacing is not uniform but forms a regular pattern, e.g., three wires close together, then a space, then another three, etc., the mesh is called "twilled.") (b) Knitted mesh. (c) Mounted grid. Section through "embroidery rings" for mounting.

It should be noted that the press mounting for the various electrodes in this gauge should have long leakage paths in order to minimize spurious leakage currents.

Screens, metal. Woven and knitted metal mesh is available in fine wires 100/in or more. Tungsten, molybdenum, and other metals are obtainable (see below).

A photo- or electroforming process is used (see below) to make flat perforated metal screens in a number of metals. These can be made extremely fine and with intricate patterns not feasible by machining.

Woven refers to a mesh in which the wires run at right angles in a warp and a woof, as in Fig. 137(a), while *knitted* describes a mesh which is a continuous wire looped upon itself, as in (b). The *woven* mesh is only slightly resilient, the *knitted* material is very much more so.

A circular screen for electron tube use is made by assembling the mesh tautly between two metal (e.g., stainless steel) rings, in the manner of using embroidery or darning hoops [Fig. 137(c)], and spot welding it in several places. The two metal rings should have enough clearance between them to provide a tight fit for the mesh. Threaded holes or tabs for mounting should be provided in the outer ring previous to assembly.

The knitted material, if under slight tension, will sag little or not at all when heated, since the loops can change shape slightly to compensate for increased wire length. On the other hand, the woven mesh wires are essentially straight, so that some bulging or sag will occur during heating. While the woven mesh can be cut in any direction without too much danger of fraying at the edges, the knitted material is best mounted and spot-welded on its frame before cutting, because raveling may take place.[1]

Knitted meshes of 0.001 inch tungsten wire with 30–35 openings per inch (90% transmission in single layer), as well as other sizes and metals, are available from the Metex Electronics Corporation, Clark, New Jersey.

Woven tungsten mesh up to 1 inch wide of 0.0008 inch wire, 100 to the inch both ways, is available from the R. G. Buser Silk Corporation, Paterson, New Jersey.

Electroformed mesh of various metals, including tungsten 100 lines per linear inch, up to 4 inches square (6 inches square for stainless steel, nickel, copper, and silver) is available from the Buckbee-Mears Company, St. Paul, Minnesota. This company also makes special intricate shapes too difficult or expensive to produce by other means.

Screws. Machine screws are much used in assembling electron tubes and devices. Metal screws should always be fired in vacuum or hydrogen before assembly. It is well to keep in mind that the mating threads of fired screws (nuts, threaded holes), being superclean with no trace of oil or grease, tend to gall or seize. Therefore if disassembly is contemplated, loose fits are indicated in threading.

Screws of molybdenum or tantalum are sometimes required, and since these are not commonly available commercially, they can be made by any competent machinist, following the directions for machining these metals.

Tables of standard sized screws will be found in many handbooks and catalogs. Below, for convenience, is a list of very small ("jeweler's") sizes which are not usually included in the standard tables. (Small screws are also obtainable in millimeter sizes.)

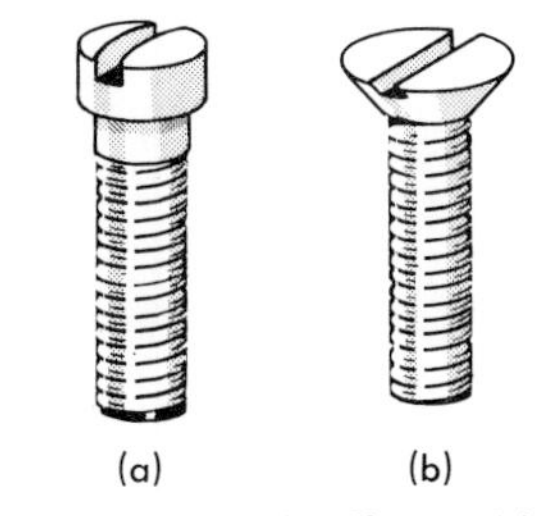

FIG. 138. Small machine screws.

[1] Tungsten mesh can be formed to a shape, e.g., hemispherical, by stretching it tightly and evenly over a preoxidized stainless steel form, clamping down the edges, and firing in tank hydrogen for 15–30 minutes at 950°C. It can then be removed from the form and mounted on a metal ring by spot-welding, in the same manner as the grid shown in Fig. 137(c).

Instrument Head (oval modified fillister)

SIZE	THREADS PER INCH	DIMENSIONS MAJOR DIAMETER	PITCH DIAMETER	MINOR DIAMETER	PITCH	DEPTH OF THREAD	HEAD DIAMETER	HEIGHT OF HEAD	DEPTH OF SLOT	WIDTH OF SLOT	TAP DRILL	BODY DRILL
000	120	0.034	0.0286	0.0260	0.00833	0.00400	0.056	0.031	0.014	0.012	#71 (0.026)	#63 (0.037)
00	90	0.044	0.0403	0.0326	0.01111	0.00721	0.068	0.038	0.014	0.023	#65 (0.035)	#55 (0.052)
0	80	0.060	0.0519	0.0438	0.01250	0.00812	0.090	0.050	0.022	0.025	3/64 (0.047)	#51 (0.067)
1	72	0.073	0.0640	0.0550	0.01389	0.00902	0.111	0.062	0.024	0.027	#53 (0.059)	#47 (0.078)
2	56	0.086	0.0744	0.0628	0.01786	0.01160	0.132	0.073	0.029	0.030	#50 (0.070)	#42 (0.093)
3	48	0.099	0.0855	0.0719	0.02083	0.01353	0.153	0.084	0.035	0.032	#47 (0.078)	#37 (0.104)
4	40	0.112	0.0958	0.0795	0.02500	0.01624	0.174	0.096	0.040	0.034	#43 (0.089)	#31 (0.120)

Flat Head (82°)

SIZE	THREADS PER INCH	DIMENSIONS MAJOR DIAMETER	PITCH DIAMETER	MINOR DIAMETER	PITCH	DEPTH OF THREAD	HEAD DIAMETER	HEIGHT OF HEAD	DEPTH OF SLOT	WIDTH OF SLOT	TAP DRILL	BODY DRILL
000	120	0.034	0.0286	0.0260	0.00833	0.00400	0.061	0.016	0.007	0.012	#71 (0.026)	#63 (0.037)
00	90	0.044	0.0403	0.0326	0.01111	0.00721	0.089	0.024	0.010	0.013	#65 (0.035)	#55 (0.052)
0	80	0.060	0.0519	0.0438	0.01250	0.00812	0.110	0.030	0.012	0.020	3/64(0.047)	#51 (0.067)
1	72	0.073	0.0640	0.0550	0.01389	0.00902	0.136	0.038	0.016	0.023	#53 (0.059)	#47 (0.078)
2	56	0.086	0.0744	0.0628	0.01786	0.01160	0.161	0.046	0.019	0.027	#50 (0.070)	#42 (0.093)
3	48	0.099	0.0855	0.0719	0.02083	0.01353	0.187	0.054	0.022	0.031	#47 (0.078)	#37 (0.104)
4	40	0.112	0.0958	0.0795	0.02500	0.01624	0.213	0.061	0.025	0.035	#43 (0.089)	#31 (0.120)

Seal-off of tubes (see also pp. 110, 119). In sealing off glass tubes from the pumps, the glass at the constriction should be heated gently at first to drive off occluded gases. The indications of the ionization or other vacuum gauge should be used as a guide in determining the rate of seal-off speed.

Seals, rotary vacuum (see p. 385 *et seq.*).

Seals, vacuum:

Ceramic-to-metal—p. 67.
Copper gasket—pp. 117, 309.
Glass-to-glass, glass-to-metal—p. 54.
Glass-to-Kovar—pp. 58, 325 *et seq.*
Glass-to-molybdenum—pp. 58, 281.
Glass-to-copper (Housekeeper)—p. 63 (see also p. 282).
Glass-to-sapphire—p. 284.
Glass-to-stainless steel (Housekeeper)—p. 64.
Knife-edge, metal—pp. 309, 320.
Metal tubing—p. 119.
Mica-to-metal seals—p. 374.
Motion seals—pp. 383 *et seq.*
Silver chloride—p. 481.
Step-type—p. 117.
O-ring seals—p. 407.
Metal O-rings—p. 408.
Metal X-rings—pp. 408, 571.
Solder glass—pp. 486 *et seq.*
Tungsten-to-glass—pp. 58, 61, 559.

Sealvac "A" alloy (see the table on p. 58).

Seam welding. A type of spot welding, usually done automatically, in which the seam (lap, etc.) is run between electrode-rollers, to which the welding current is applied in pulses as the work is fed at a continuous rate. This produces a "stitching" weld which is not ordinarily gas-tight, although an overlapping technique can be used to make it so. (See SPOT WELDING, p. 493.)

The term seam welding is also applied to continuous welds done with the various forms of arc equipment and to electron beam welding. This type of weld can be made vacuum-tight.

Secondary electrons (see also ELECTRON MULTIPLIER, p. 239).

When electrons strike a surface, secondary electrons are often emitted. However, these secondary electrons cannot be distinguished from such primary electrons as are reflected upon striking the surface, and the reflected electrons are included in measurements of secondary emission. The emission increases with increasing energy of the primary electrons to a maximum for primary energies of several hundred volts and then decreases with increasing energy of the primary electrons. The maximum number δ of secondary electrons emitted per incident primary electron is given in the table on p. 476, together with the corresponding primary energy for a number of carefully outgassed metals. The value of δ for well-cleaned surfaces generally lies between 1.0 and 1.5 The voltage at which δ is equal to unity is given in the table below. The number of secondary electrons emitted is decreased by heating and outgassing the surface, and is increased by the presence of electropositive impurities. Without special cleaning δ may reach

4, and on low-work-function surfaces as many as 10 secondary electrons may be emitted per incident primary electron. The secondary electrons are emitted in random directions and with velocities corresponding to only a few volts, even for primary electrons of thousands of volts of energy. When the secondary emission of an insulator under the influence of electron bombardment is greater than the number of incident primary electrons, a positive charge is built up on the surface of the insulator. Such an active spot, established by high-energy primary electrons, may be heated to a high temperature. As the positive charge is built up, more and more electrons may be attracted to the active spot. If the active spot is on the glass wall of a vacuum tube, the glass may be softened and the tube may be destroyed.[1]

This table shows the number of secondary electrons δ emitted per primary electron striking metal.[2]

ELEMENT	MAXIMUM		VOLTAGE FOR $\delta = 1$
	δ	VOLTS	
Aluminum	1.90	220	35
	—	—	45
Gold	1.14	330	160
Copper	1.32	240	100
	—	—	220
Iron	1.30	350	120
	—	—	183
Magnesium	—	—	80
Molybdenum	1.30	360	120
	1.15	600	280
Nickel	1.30	460	160
Platinum	—	—	250
Tungsten	1.45	700	200
	1.40	630	240

Selenium. A nonmetallic element in the sulfur family. It is very volatile (melting point 220°C, boiling point 688°C) and poisonous to life as well as to oxide-coated cathodes, so that metals containing appreciable amounts of selenium should not be used in electron tubes at any elevated temperature. Type 303 stainless steel contains a minimum of 0.07% selenium (or sulfur).

The vapor pressure of selenium is close to that of cadmium, being approximately 3 microns Hg at the melting point and 1 mm Hg at 350°C.

Selenium is used in certain types of photoconductive cells (*cf.* p. 433) because the electric conductivity of the gray form increases with the intensity of light impinging upon it.

---

[1] From *Gaseous Conductors*, J. D. Cobine, p. 112, Dover Publications, New York, New York, 1958. Reproduced by permission of the publisher.

[2] A. v. Engel and M. Steenbeck, *Elektrische Gasentladungen, ihre Physik u. Technik*, **1**, p. 111; also J. J. Thomson and G. P. Thomson, "Conduction of Electricity through Gases," **2**, p. 191. Both references are as given by J. D. Cobine in *Gaseous Conductors*, Dover Publications, New York, New York, 1958.

Silastic rubber, silicone rubbers.[1,2] These are synthetic elastomers which can be obtained in the form of sheet, O-rings, molded parts, tubing and sleeving, sponge, and insulation on wire and cable, in Shore Durometer hardnesses ranging from 25 to 80. These materials, in general, can withstand greater temperatures than other synthetic rubbers, the range being from −84°C to +315°C (various formulations have different temperature properties). The silicone rubbers have good electrical properties, resistance to compression set, aging, ozone and ultraviolet light, and good chemical and oil resistance. The silicone rubbers can be used as gaskets, O-rings, and other mechanical sealing parts. The vapor pressure is about 1×10^{-6} torr at room temperature. Porosity of these rubbers to gases is somewhat higher than that of Neoprene. New silicone rubber for use as gaskets or O-rings should be handled cleanly; cleaning, if necessary, should be done only with a mild detergent and water, with thorough rinsing. Use no solvents.[3]

The dielectric strength of the silicone rubbers ranges from 150 to 450 v/mil. The dielectric constant at 1 Mc is from 3 to 8. The power factor at 1 Mc is from 0.001 to 0.045, depending on the color and fillers (fillers used are alumina, glass, mica, ceramics, diatomaceous earth, zirconium orthosilicate, Fiberglas, and silica flour).

The Silicones have no corrosive action on metals.

Formulations with Teflon and other materials imparting special properties are obtainable.

Sil-fos (see p. 183, item 123).

Silica (see QUARTZ, pp. 457 *et seq.*).

Silicon. This semimetallic element has the following properties:

Color	silvery-white (crystalline)
Atomic weight	28.06
Atomic number	14
Melting point (°C)	1420
Boiling point (°C)	2600
Specific gravity (gm/cc) at 20°C	2.42

Silicon is a constituent of quartz, sand, and most rocks. It is used as an alloying element with copper (silicon bronze) and with ferrous and other metals, where it imparts hardness. The pure element (or with controlled amounts of trace impurities) is used in the manufacture of transistors and crystal diodes (semiconductors).

Silicon, vapor pressure of (see p. 148).

Silicone pump oils (see p. 401).

Silicone rubbers (see SILASTIC, p. 477).

Silicone stopcock (or vacuum) greases. The Dow-Corning Corporation, Midland, Michigan, makes two vacuum greases: (1) a grease serviceable from −40°C to +200°C, with fairly low vapor pressure and good resistance to chemicals; and (2) a heavier grease for sealing high-vacuum systems. It must be remembered that silicone greases are more resistant to solvents than other petroleum or organic-base

---

[1] Silicone Products Department, General Electric Co., Waterford, New York.

[2] Silicones Division, Union Carbide Corp., Tonawanda, New York.

[3] See "Mass Spectrometer Studies of High Vacuum Materials," J. R. Sites and R. Baldock, U.S. Atomic Energy Commission Report No. ORNL-1405, 1952.

greases and consequently are more difficult to remove from places that are not easily accessible.

Silver (Ag). A lustrous, white metal which, when pure, has the following properties:

Atomic weight	107.880
Atomic number	47
Melting point (°C)	960.5
Boiling point (°C)	1955+
Specific gravity, density at 20°C (gm/cc)	10.49
Electrical resistivity (microhm-cm)	1.59
Electrical conductivity, IACS, % pure copper	105.2[1]
Specific heat (gm-cal/gm/°C)	0.0562
Thermal conductivity (cgs)	1.0
Linear coefficient of thermal expansion, in./°C, 0–100°C	1.9×10^{-5}
Young's modulus, psi	10.3×10^{6}[2]

Silver of high purity (fine silver) runs at least 999.0 parts Ag per 1000[3] and is often 999.3, or even more. Below are listed the principal impurities in a typical analysis:

	Typical %	Maximum %		Typical %	Maximum %
Copper	0.05	0.09	Silicon	<0.001	0.002
Lead	0.004	0.04	Tin	none	
Bismuth	<0.001	0.01	Zinc	none	
Iron	0.001–0.003	0.005	Gold	trace	
Manganese	<0.001	0.003	Palladium	trace	
Nickel	<0.001	0.002	Selenium	0.0002	
Magnesium	<0.001	0.002	Tellurium	0.0002	

Silver is 20% heavier than copper and nickel, twice as heavy as zinc, four times as heavy as aluminum, nine-tenths the weight of lead, a little over one-half that of gold and tungsten, and a little less than one-half that of platinum.

High-fineness silver designates metal of 999.5 parts Ag per thousand, or higher; some runs 999.7 to 999.9.

Fine silver may contain, besides the impurities listed, small amounts of oxygen or hydrogen. Silver containing O_2, like electrolytic or tough pitch copper (see pp. 35, 219), is subject to hydrogen embrittlement. Deoxidized grades of silver are available.

Fine silver can be obtained in the form of bars, grain, sheet, strip and foil, wire, rod, tubing, powder, and flake.[4]

Silver can be cast by conventional methods but should be protected during melting by a covering layer of charcoal, or the process should take place in hydrogen or an inert gas. Complete deoxidation is attained by the addition of lithium or phosphorus to leave a residue of less than 0.01%.

---

[1] Very high-purity silver may measure up to 108%. Cold work lowers the conductivity of silver more than it does that of copper. (See the table on p. 479.)

[2] This low value means that silver is inherently a "limber" metal. It deflects far with low loads and springs back far when the load is released.

[3] Data on silver on pp. 478 to 480 inclusive are by permission of Handy & Harman, 850 Third Ave., New York 22, New York.

[4] Handy & Harman, 850 Third Avenue, New York 22, New York.

Fine silver can be hot- or cold-worked and extruded, rolled, swaged, or drawn. Between anneals, it can be cold-rolled or cold-drawn to a considerable extent. The heat generated in cold-working may be sufficient to cause silver to "self-anneal" so that if a maximum of hardness by cold-working is desired, the metal should not be worked so rapidly or continuously as to cause appreciable temperature rise (see tables of reduction by drawing and annealing temperatures below).

Silver is extremely ductile but also weak in tension. More and lighter reductions are required for silver than for brass and copper. On the other hand, the metal work hardens less, and thus more working between anneals can be done.

High-purity silver may self-anneal at room temperature. The presence of very small amounts of impurities will raise the annealing temperature greatly. The recommended annealing temperature for fine silver is from 200°–430°C. Higher temperatures do not soften it further to any extent but do cause loss in ductility and a condition known as "orange peel" surface, which is due to excessive grain growth. Higher temperatures also may cause pieces in contact to stick or weld together; this is more pronounced in thin sheet or sections and fine wires so that the lower temperatures (nearer to 200°C) are sufficient for light-gauge material.

Fine silver does not form a visible oxide during annealing in air; hence, pickling is unnecessary. However, the silver does dissolve oxygen upon heating; therefore, metal that has been annealed in air should not be subsequently heated in hydrogen because surface embrittlement occurs, with the possibility of blistering.

Annealed fine silver is difficult to machine because of its softness; if machining is planned, the piece should be cold-worked as much as possible. For turning, drilling, milling, reaming, etc., a lubricant such as lard oil is useful. The machining properties of silver are approximately the same as those of lead-free brasses.

Silver can be soldered and brazed without difficulty by conventional methods. It can also be welded by inert-gas arc-welding techniques.

PROPERTIES OF 0.091-INCH FINE SILVER WIRE VERSUS REDUCTION BY DRAWING

REDUCTION (%)	NUMBERS (HARD)	TENSILE STRENGTH (PSI)	ELONGATION IN 2 IN. (%)	HARDNESS, ROCKWELL 15T	ELECTRICAL CONDUCTIVITY (PERCENT OF COPPER)
Annealed	0	25,900	50	14	102.8
10.2	$\frac{1}{2}$	29,000	34	52	102.2
20.0	1	33,300	13	59	101.0
37.0	2	40,600	5	66	99.7
48.6	3	43,200	5	68	99.5
60.0	4	45,000	4	70	99.4
68.5	5	46,900	4	71	98.4
74.0	6	49,200	4	71	98.1

(*Note:* The hardness values were obtained on longitudinal sections made by filing flat faces parallel with the axis of the wire. Hardness values from tests on cylindrical wire surfaces may be erroneous. Hardness values on sheet and strip having the same percentage reductions are approximately the same as those obtained on flat faces filed on wire.)

PROPERTIES OF 0.091-INCH FINE SILVER WIRE VERSUS ANNEALING TEMPERATURE

TEMPERATURE (°C)	TENSILE STRENGTH (PSI)	ELONGATION IN 2 IN. (%)	TEMPERATURE (°C)	TENSILE STRENGTH (PSI)	ELONGATION IN 2 IN. (%)
RT	43,200	5	482	24,550	52
204	40,300	10	538	24,300	43
260	27,500	43	593	24,750	44
316	25,500	52	649	25,350	39
371	25,200	55	704	25,800	32
427	25,000	54			

(*Note:* Figures shown in the tables are typical values which may vary in other samples having different amounts and kinds of impurities.)

Silver alloys. Common alloys of silver with copper are as follows:

(1) *Coin silver.* Ag 90%, Cu 10%; solidus[1] temperature 779°C, liquidus[1] temperature 870°C.

(2) *Sterling* (or standard) *silver.* Ag 92.5%, Cu 7.5%; solidus temperature 810°C, liquidus temperature 890°C. Sterling silver, used for coinage in Great Britain and widely used for silverware, is a hardenable silver alloy.[2] Its ductility is decreased after hardening. Properties of annealed and hardened sterling silver are as follows:

CONDITION	TENSILE STRENGTH (PSI)	YIELD POINT (PSI)	ELONGATION IN 2 IN. (%)
Annealed (650°C for 30 minutes and quench)	37,400	19,680	42
Age-hardened (325°C for 30 minutes)	43,400	30,000	26

(3) *Jewelry silver.* Ag 80%, Cu 20%; solidus temperature 779°C, liquidus temperature 820°C.

(4) *Silver-copper eutectic.* Ag 72%, Cu 28%; solidus and liquidus temperatures identical—779°C. This alloy is much used as a braze material for OFHC copper and other metals and alloys in a hydrogen-atmosphere process. See p. 36.

Other silver alloys used as braze materials will be found in the tables on pp. 176–186.

[1] The terms solidus and liquidus correspond to freezing and melting point, respectively. While some metals and alloys have identical solidus and liquidus temperatures (pure metals, some simple binary eutectics), many alloys have a plastic or "puddly" stage, these being useful where brazing to obtain a heavy fillet is desired. The sharp-melting-point metals generally flow freely at the melting temperature.

[2] "The Science of Dental Materials," third edition, revised 1947, E. W. Skinner, the W. B. Saunders Company, Philadelphia, Pennsylvania.

Silver chloride seals. Windows of glass, mica, rock salt, quartz, calcium fluoride, and other materials can be sealed vacuum-tight to metal by cementing them with silver chloride. This material, which comes in sheets up to 0.050 inch thick[1] has a melting point of 455°C.[2, 3]

The silver chloride wets rock salt and silver, but glass surfaces must be heated to the softening point to achieve a good bond. This is true for soft glasses; Pyrex and other hard glasses do not require heating to the softening temperature but can be platinized (see p. 445), in which case a temperature of 500°C is adequate.

If the silver chloride has been stored for some time, spots or stains of silver sulfide may appear on the surface. These can be carefully scraped off with a razor blade. After it is cut to the shape desired, the silver chloride is degreased and then pressed between filter paper to flatten it, if required.

The parts are assembled with the silver chloride in place, and the assembly is placed in an oven at room temperature and slowly raised to 500°C. The rate of temperature rise will differ with the materials being cemented—about 50°C per hour is average. Hold at 500°C for five minutes and then allow to cool, preferably overnight in an insulated oven.

Silver chloride reacts with iron and copper to form volatile chlorides which are harmful in a vacuum system.

Any material which does not melt below 500°C can be sealed with silver chloride. Extreme cleanliness must be observed in the assembly procedure.

Silver chloride seals can be demounted by the use of a hot wire applied to the joint. A coating of silicone or other *opaque* compound or lacquer should be applied to the outside of the joint to prevent contact with copper or iron, and to prevent solarization, since silver chloride is light-sensitive.

Silver-copper eutectic (see p. 480).

Silver-lead alloy (see p. 342).

Silver magnesium-nickel alloy.[4] A hardenable high-silver alloy which has the composition: Ag, 99.5–99.7%, Ni, 0.2%, and Mg, 0.3–0.1%. This alloy is hardened by an internal oxidation process which involves heating in air (see below). When thus treated, it has permanent hardness, low creep rate, very high corrosion resistance and thermal and electrical conductivities.

The alloy is soft, like fine silver or copper in the annealed condition, and can be stamped, drawn, bent, spun, and otherwise formed. In its oxidation-hardened condition, the tensile properties at room temperature are similar to those of hard-rolled coin or sterling silver, and at elevated temperatures, the hardness and strength are considerably higher than those of hard-rolled silver-copper alloys since the latter will anneal but the silver-magnesium-nickel alloy will not. The alloy should not be plastically shaped or deformed after hardening.

The high hardness and strength of the hardened alloy are accompanied by restricted ductility under high stress at elevated temperatures. Parts that are to be stressed when hot should be designed for known safe limits.

---

[1] Courtesy of Handy & Harman, 850 Third Avenue, New York 22, New York.

[2] R. Frank and R. L. Stow, *Rev. Sci. Instr.*, **25,** 514, 1954.

[3] M. H. Greenblatt, *ibid.*, **29,** 738, 1958.

[4] Handy & Harman, 850 Third Avenue, New York 22, New York, by whose courtesy the material in this section is provided.

The following table gives approximate values taken from a single sample of oxidation-hardened Type A and Type B alloys[1] at elevated temperatures.

TEMPERATURE (°C)	ULTIMATE STRENGTH SHORT-TIME TEST (PSI)	STRESS (PSI) TO CAUSE RUPTURE IN: 2 HOURS		100 HOURS	
		TYPE A	TYPE B	TYPE A	TYPE B
260	45,000–50,000	30,000	31,000	22,000	26,000
400	—	19,000	19,000	14,000	12,000
427	35,000–45,000	—	—	—	—
538	—	9,000	10,000	6,000	6,000
650	12,000–20,000	—	—	—	—
760	10,000–14,000	—	—	—	—
816	—	1,000	—	800	—

Note that the two types of silver-magnesium-nickel alloys have very similar stress-to-rupture values. During the stress-to-rupture tests, furthermore, it was observed that the creep rates on both types were exceptionally low (in relation to the stresses involved). Thus, it would seem that the limiting factor in design would likely be stress-to-rupture and not creep strength. There are not yet sufficient data to define precisely the creep rates at various stresses and temperatures. They are a fraction of those of copper.

At stresses higher than the indicated stress-to-rupture values for the various temperatures, the hardened alloy *fractures* rather than *creeps;* or, conversely, stresses that would ordinarily be expected to cause *creep* will cause fracture instead. This is why special attention should be given to designing for proper stresses; the parts, once made and hardened, will not plastically accommodate design errors or loose production tolerances, as is the case with more ductile materials.

The maximum practical hardening effect is attained with about 0.3% magnesium. More than this results in increasing brittleness without appreciable increase in strength. On the other hand, a lower magnesium content provides lower strength but increased ductility and less susceptibility to brittle hot fracture. The stress level in a low magnesium alloy at elevated temperature is lower than in an alloy with the higher magnesium content. The tabulation below gives some properties of Type A and Type B annealed and cold-rolled alloys:

PROPERTY	ANNEALED	50% COLD-ROLLED
Hardness—Rockwell	58–65 (15T)	50–60 (30T)
Ultimate strength (psi)	28,000–34,000	50,000–55,000
Elongation in 2 in. (%)	30–40	6–8
Electrical conductivity (% IACS)	75	70

[1] The ultimate strengths of oxidation-hardened alloys are:
Type A—65,000–70,000 psi
Type B—60,000–65,000 psi
Other types are available from the manufacturer.

Some properties of oxidation-hardened Type A and Type B alloys at room temperature are given below:

PROPERTY	TYPE A	TYPE B
Hardness, Rockwell (30T)	63–68	58–63
Ultimate strength (psi)	65,000–70,000	60,000–65,000
0.2% yield strength (psi)	53,000–58,000	45,500–50,500
Elastic limit (psi)	43,000–48,000	37,500–42,500
Elongation in 2 inch (%)	5–15	13–21
Modulus of elasticity (psi)	11×10^6	11×10^6
Electrical conductivity (% IACS)	75	75

(*Note:* Except for the modulus of elasticity and the electrical conductivity, the properties are linearly proportional to the magnesium content.)

The electrical conductivity of silver-magnesium-nickel, like that of most other metals, decreases with temperature, approximately as follows:

TEMPERATURE (°C)	ELECTRICAL CONDUCTIVITY (% IACS) (TYPE A)
25	75
100	67
200	55
260	50

The alloy is available in the form of strips, circles, blanks, rod, wire, and tubing.

Annealing. Any of the conventional forming or metalworking techniques can be applied to the alloys in their annealed condition. If annealing is required between operations, the piece is heated to 370°C for 15 to 30 minutes in air. Temperatures in excess of this value will result in superficial hardening and a checked surface on further working.

Hardening. The curves in Fig. 139 show the *minimum* times for complete oxidation-hardening of silver-magnesium-nickel Type A *strip.* The time at temperature can be extended moderately without detrimental effect. Since the hardening time varies as the square of thickness, the hardening time for strip of greater thickness than shown in Fig. 139 may be conveniently approximated by multiplying the time for half the thickness in question by 4, e.g., desired hardening time at 800°C for 0.120-inch thick stock would be 28 hours, since the time for 0.060-inch stock is 7 hours. Wire will harden in one-half to three-quarters of the time needed for strip of the same gauge. Lower magnesium alloys harden in shorter times, in direct proportion to the magnesium content.

Hardening is to be done in freely circulating air; i.e., closed boxes or muffles are not to be used. The pieces should not be overlapping or piled on one another. Also the metal must be free of dirt and residual oil or grease on the surface. A direct gas-fired furnace is not suitable for this operation since the combustion products are deficient in oxygen.

The 800°C temperature is to be used only on parts which are not to be hot-stressed. The best combination of strength and ductility is obtained at the 735°C temperature.

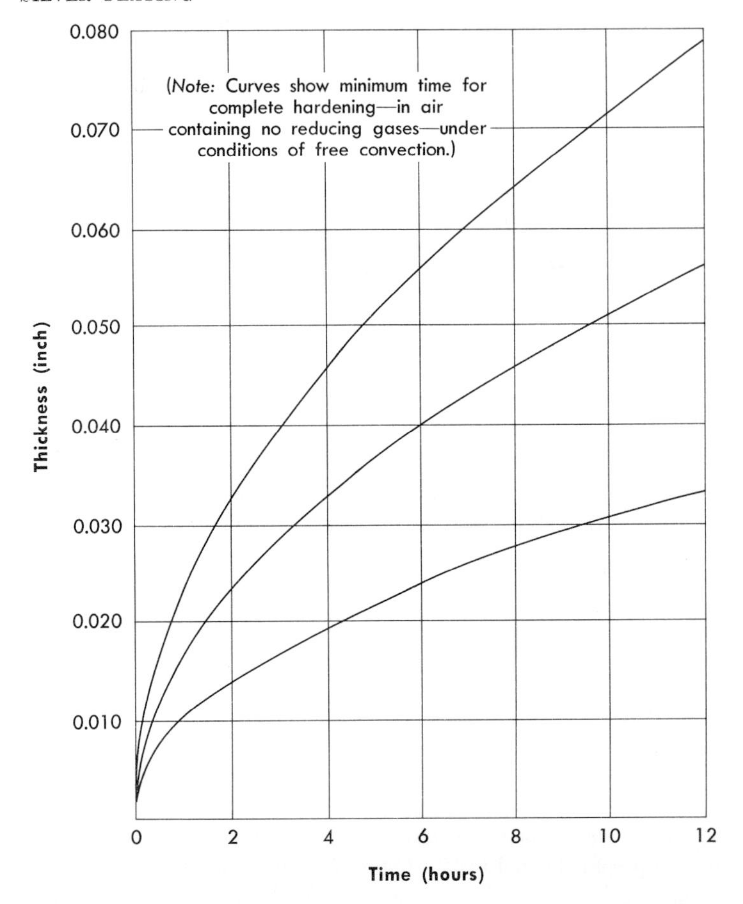

FIG. 139. Oxidation-hardening curves for Type A Ag-Mg-Ni.

The hardened alloy should not be heated in an atmosphere containing hydrogen because embrittlement will result. Hydrogen-furnace-brazing of the hardened alloy is therefore not feasible.

Torch-brazing is possible with any of the standard silver-brazing alloys, in conjunction with an active flux.[1] Soft-soldering with lead-tin solders is also feasible. In either brazing or soldering, high stresses (e.g., as applied by jigs or fixtures) should be avoided.

Corrosion resistance. The alloy has a corrosion resistance similar to that of fine silver. It tarnishes on exposure to sulfur and sulfur compounds.

Uses. In addition to its uses as electrical contacts, high thermal and electrical conductivity springs, and other types of low-contact resistance parts, silver-magnesium-nickel has been used with some success to make dynodes for electron- or photomultipliers (see p. 239).

Silver plating (see pp. 32, 33).

Silver-plating copper in hydrogen-furnace brazing (see p. 36).

---

[1] Handy-Flux," Handy & Harman, 850 Third Avenue, New York 22, New York.

Silver, vapor pressure of (see the table on p. 146).

Single crystals. Refractory metals, such as tungsten, molybdenum, vanadium, columbium, and tantalum, can be obtained in the form of large single crystals which have high purity and virtually no porosity. They can be worked at significantly lower temperatures than those required for other forms of these metals.

In vacuum applications, outgassing and leakage, as well as cold emission, are greatly minimized by the use of single-crystal metals.

Tungsten single crystals can be worked into shapes at temperatures more than 500°C lower than those needed for either powder metallurgy or vacuum-arc cast tungsten. Also, the brittleness caused by grain boundary films or envelopes of oxides has been eliminated because single-crystal tungsten contains no grain boundaries. This allows swaging and rolling to be done at lower temperatures. Such items as threaded bolts can be made from the material, using standard carbide-tipped tools at room temperature (see below).

Cylindrical crystals are available in diameters up to 1 inch. The metal crystals have been made in lengths up to 12 inches.

The following table gives some of the properties of these single crystals.[1]

METAL	CRYSTAL STRUCTURE	MELTING POINT (°C)	VICKERS HARDNESS (300 GM)	DENSITY*
Tungsten (W)	bcc	3370	367	19.259
Molybdenum (Mo)	bcc	2625	192	10.2
Vanadium (V)	bcc	1735	189	6.0
Columbium (Cb)	bcc	2415	107	8.57
Tantalum (Ta)	bcc	2996	119	16.6
Molybdenum disilicide ($MoSi_2$)	Tetragonal	2030	1097	6.24

* This value agrees with the theoretical density to within $\pm$ 0.02 gm/cm^3.

Single-crystal tungsten has an electrical resistivity of 4.25 microhm-cm at 0°C, compared with the commonly reported value of 5.5 microhm-cm for sintered and worked tungsten. The relative resistivity at various temperatures is:

Temperature (°K)		4.2	77	190	273	400
Relative resistivity-$R_t/R_{273°K}$		0.00241	0.116	0.663	1.	1.6
Temperature (°K)	600	800	1000	1200	1400	1600
Relative resistivity-$R_t/R_{273°K}$	2.6	3.8	5.0	6.4	7.7	9.1

Single crystal tungsten can be turned with a Carboloy No. 883 AR-6 tool. Stock can be removed at the rate of 0.050 inch–0.070 inch at a speed of about 175 rpm, with a feed of 0.0019 inch per revolution.

[1] Linde Crystal Products, Division of Union Carbide Corporation, New York 17, New York, 1960.

Sintering. (see POWDER METALLURGY, p. 450). The term sintering can also apply to semimetallic and nonmetallic materials such as silicon, boron, ceramics, etc.

Solder glass. The following data, by courtesy of the Corning Glass Works, describes several types of solder glasses which can be used for making successful vacuum-tight joints in glass-to-glass, glass-to-metal, metal-to-metal, and ceramic seals.

Pyroceram Brand Cement #45 is a finely powdered glass of special composition which, when held in suspension by a low viscosity vehicle, may be applied to a sealing area by dipping, pressure flow, or brush. When properly applied and fired, it will join codes 1710, 1720, and 1723 glass, tungsten, molybdenum, and other glasses, metals, or ceramics of suitable thermal expansion for the geometry of the seal.

The uncured cement, after complete evaporation of the vehicle, is chalky and does not render a satisfactory seal. However, when the green seal is fired directly according to prescribed schedules, a change in material occurs. The glass develops a partially crystalline structure which results in a devitrified glass seal which is much stronger and harder than the original glass.

The strong seals made with Pyroceram Brand Cement #45 are not only *vacuum-tight* but also offer unique thermal properties. The glass fires at 750°C; then after firing, it is serviceable up to more than 700°C. This permits high bake-out temperatures required in many power-, microwave-, and cathode-ray tubes.

Preliminary Properties

Vitreous stage:	
Thermal expansion $\times 10^{-7}$/°C	40
Softening point	644°C
Devitrified stage (fired 1 hour at 750°C):	
Thermal expansion (25–625°C) $\times 10^{-7}$/°C	42.4
Viscosity at 700°C	10^{13} poises
Modulus of rupture at room temperature	9,000 psi
at 500°C	12,000 psi
at 700°C	10,000 psi
Dielectric constant	6.5 range
Log resistivity ohm-cm	
at 250°C	13.2
at 350°C	11.4
Seals at	750°C
Serviceable to	700°C
Density (cullet)	3.3 (approximate)

INSTRUCTIONS FOR SEALING MATERIALS WITH PYROCERAM BRAND CEMENT #45

Pyroceram Brand Cement #45 is a thermal-setting solder glass which will join Code 1723 alumino-silicate glass to itself, tungsten, molybdenum, and other glasses or metals of suitable thermal expansion for the geometry of the seal. The steps to be followed to obtain a strong vacuum-tight seal are: (1) Preparation, (2) Applications, (3) Sealing Schedule.

1. *Preparation*

a. Surface preparation—Clean both parts by scrubbing gently with lint-free paper soaked with acetone or other solvent. All grease, oil, and organic or inorganic material must be removed. If the preglazing technique is to be used, and if the glass has a ground surface, it is important for maximum strength to acid-fortify glass by three 15- to 20-second dips in about 50% hydrofluoric acid, with intermediate and final scrubbing to remove film formed.

b. Suspension preparation—Use a 250-ml beaker or a small custard cup and a small stainless steel spatula to mix only enough frit and nitrocellulose-amyl acetate vehicle for the job in hand. The consistency of the mixture will be determined by the method of application to the surface and what the individual prefers.

2. *Application*

a. Frit application—The suspension may be applied to one or both sealing surfaces by extrusion from a small pipette or a polyethylene squeeze bottle, or applied with a stirring rod or brush. In many cases the seal area can be dipped in a thinner slurry, but good stirring is essential to prevent particle segregation. Thoroughly dry the applied frit before firing. The dried suspension has considerable green strength and will withstand assembling and alignment without loss of material. There is considerable shrinkage during firing, and it is best to have the parts arrive at their final state of proximity during the actual sealing operation, at which time the excess frit is extruded to form a fillet. The object's own weight is often sufficient to accomplish this.

b. Preglaze—When it is desirable to seal in a neutral or reducing atmosphere, it is necessary to preglaze one or both parts. In preglazing, the solder glass is heated enough to become glassy, forming a continuous surface, but not enough to devitrify. Pyroceram Brand Cement #45 can be preglazed at 660°C for 10 minutes. The heating and cooling rate should be 3° to 5°C per minute.

If the solder glass is applied as a suspension in nitrocellulose-amyl acetate, the preglazing must be carried out in an oxidizing atmosphere. When it is desirable to preglaze a readily oxidizable metal, the frit must be suspended in pure amyl acetate and the firing done in a vacuum at no more than 600°C.

Expansion characteristics of the glassy vitreous material are quite different from those of the final devitrified material. Since the latter is the basis for selection of the sealing glass, it is possible for the expansion mismatch in the glassy state to result in cracking. If the cracks are confined to the solder glass, they will fire out during sealing with no ill effects. However, a slower heat rate during final sealing may be necessary to prevent heat-shock breakage. Sintering may be the solution if this problem is encountered.

Sintering is a partial preglazing which can be done at a lower temperature (about 600°C), but contamination of the porous material formed must be guarded against in subsequent operations.

3. *Sealing*

a. General—The sequence of events during a sealing operation leading to a strong vacuum-tight joint are summarized as follows: The solder glass melts, maintaining a sufficiently low viscosity long enough to allow the excess glass to flow out of the interface and form a fillet. During this stage, there is wetting of the substrate by the solder glass and mutual interaction to form a good bond. Devitrification of the solder glass to a mixture of crystals and a harder glass then takes place, to result in a final state with higher softening point than that of the original solder glass.

b. Firing—Since most items involve such complicated factors as lead wires, phosphors, etc., it is often necessary to make the final seal under neutral or reducing atmospheres; however, it is not possible to fire the frit directly in a reducing atmosphere. Preglazing will condition the solder glass to a state where effects of a reducing atmosphere during sealing are minimized.

Pyroceram Brand Cement #45, a thermal-setting solder glass, should be sealed at 750°C for 1 hour, with heating and cooling rates of 3° to 5°C. Trial may show that in some special cases somewhat lower or higher temperatures and/or slower heating and cooling may produce better results.

c. Temperature control—*It is very important that all parts of a joint be at the same temperature when the glass devitrifies.* It will help to muffle samples against direct radiation from the heating elements. *Absolute knowledge of the temperature at the joint area, not just in the furnace area, is essential.* All the above temperatures refer to the actual temperature at the joint.

(*Note:* The volume of Pyroceram Brand Cement #45 is approximately twice that of Pyroceram Brand Cement #95.)

Pyroceram Brand Cement #95 is a finely powdered glass of special composition which, when held in suspension by a low viscosity vehicle, may be applied to a sealing area by dipping or pressure flow. The uncured seal, after complete evaporation of the vehicle, is chalky and does not render a satisfactory seal. However, when the green seal is fired directly and according to prescribed schedules, a change in the material occurs. The glass develops a partially crystalline structure which results in a devitrified glass seal much stronger and harder than the original glass.

Pyroceram Brand Cement #95, in addition to providing a mechanically excellent seal, also offers unique thermal properties. The glass fires at a relatively low (400 to 450°C) range, permitting heat-sealing of material likely to deform at temperatures of 500°C and over. However, the crystalline seal is serviceable in use at temperatures up to 450°C.

Pyroceram Brand Cement #95 will seal materials in the thermal-expansion range of 85 to 110×10^{-7} cm/cm/°C. Glass-to-glass, metal-to-metal, and ceramic-to-ceramic seals, or combinations of these, may be made. Some suggested seals are:

Metals	Glasses	Ceramics
Chrome-iron, stainless steel	Most lime glasses	Forsterite
Platinum	Most electronic glasses	Steatite
Sylvania #4 alloy		
50% nickel alloys		
Dumet		

Certain seal geometries will enable other materials to be sealed.

Physical properties

Young's modulus	6.66×10^6 psi
Shear modulus	2.62×10^6 psi
Poisson's ratio	0.27
Modulus of rupture at 25°C	6000. (approximate)

(*cont.*)

Physical properties (cont.)

Modulus of rupture at 425°C	1500. (approximate)
Density	6.5 (approximate)

Electrical properties

Log dc resistivity	at 250°C	8.550		
	at 350°C	7.030		
		100 cycles	1 kc	100 kc
Loss tangent	at 25°C	0.0058	0.0064	0.0094
	at 230°C		0.11	0.0057
	at 373°C			0.15
Dielectric constant	at 25°C	21.2	21.0	20.4
	at 230°C		23.4	22.2
	at 373°C			25.2

Loss factor = loss tangent × dielectric constant

Chemical properties—solubility

Solution	Time	Percent weight loss
10% sulfuric acid	4 hours	0.1
10% hydrofluoric acid	4 hours	0.3

No loss in weight in humidity chamber (90% relative humidity, 50°C).

Pyroceram Brand Cement is not recommended for applications involving prolonged immersion in nitric acid, sodium hydroxide, or boiling water.

Pyroceram Brand Cement #89 is a finely powdered glass of special composition which, when held in suspension by a low viscosity vehicle, may be applied to a sealing area by dipping or pressure-flow. The uncured seal, after complete evaporation of the vehicle, is chalky and does not render a satisfactory seal. However, when the green seal is fired directly and according to prescribed schedules, a change in the material occurs. The glass develops a partially crystalline structure which results in a devitrified glass seal much stronger and harder than the original glass.

Pyroceram Brand Cement #89, in addition to providing a mechanically excellent seal, also offers unique thermal properties. The cement fires at a low temperature range of 400°C to 450°C, depending on sealing time. This permits the joining of materials likely to deform at temperatures much above 450°C. However, the crystalline seal is serviceable in use for temperatures up to 425°C.

Pyroceram Brand Cement #89 will seal materials in the thermal expansion range of 80 to 92×10^{-7} cm/cm/°C. Glass-to-glass, metal-to-metal, and ceramic-to-ceramic seals, or combinations of these, may be made. Some suggested seals are:

Metals	Glasses	Ceramics
Driver-Harris 152 Alloy Platinum Sylvania #4 Alloy 50% nickel alloys Dumet	Many electronic glasses, such as 9010, 0120, and 0122	Forsterite Steatite

Certain seal geometries will enable other materials to be sealed.

Physical properties

Young's modulus	7.4×10^6 psi
Shear modulus	3.0×10^6 psi
Poisson's ratio	0.25
Modulus of rupture at 25°C	6000. (average)
Modulus of rupture at 400°C	4800. (average)
Density (after sealing)	6.3

Electrical properties

Log dc resistivity at 250°C 8.6; at 350°C 7.05

		100 cycles	1 kc	100 kc
Loss tangent	at 25°C	0.0061	0.0091	0.011
	at 230°C	—	—	0.014
	at 373°C	—	—	0.250
Dielectric constant	at 25°C	20.6	20.4	19.8
	at 230°C	—	23.7	21.8
	at 373°C	—	—	25.6

Chemical properties—solubility

Solution	Time	Percent weight loss
10% sulfuric acid	4 hours	0.1
10% hydrofluoric acid	4 hours	0.3

No loss in weight in humidity chamber (90% relative humidity, 50°C).

APPLICATION OF PYROCERAM BRAND CEMENT #89 AND #95

General information

1. Pyroceram Brand Cement is normally prepared for flow application to the sealing area by preparing a suspension of glass in a low viscosity vehicle containing nitrocellulose in amyl acetate. The application can be accomplished with either a simple glass pipette, polyethylene squeeze tube, toothpaste-type tube, or similar device. Application may also be performed by the dipping technique. For production operations, special machinery has been designed for flowing solder glass onto television tube-sealing edges. This principle can be easily modified for other applications.
2. In general, it is recommended that the seal be made by firing the green state directly. In the case of television bulbs, the weight of either panel or funnel is sufficient to cause the excess softened sealing glass to flow out of the interface and form a fillet prior to setting up thermally. For smaller, lighter items, it might be necessary to apply some pressure to achieve the same results.
3. Pyroceram Cement is not recommended for the kind of operation in which the seal areas are coated and fired to glaze the frit prior to assembly and sealing of parts. Unless the preglazing temperature and time are carefully controlled, the glass may set up too far to make a satisfactory seal. When preglazing is essential, a relatively thin application must be made—by flow techniques or the dip method—to prevent cracking and crawling. The coated surface should be heated rapidly (5 to 10°C/min) to 390°C, held for 10 minutes, and then cooled as rapidly as the size and geometry of the article will allow.

Application

1. *Surface preparation*—Clean both parts by scrubbing gently with lint-free paper or cloth soaked with acetone, isopropanol, or other suitable solvent. All grease, oil, fingerprints, and organic or inorganic material must be removed or they will interfere with the seal.
2. *Suspension preparation*—The type of application and the amount of spreading desired determine the weight ratio of glass to vehicle. For hand-tube application, a ratio of 12 to 1 is usually satisfactory. Lower ratios draw up into the tube more readily but show a greater tendency to spread out too far on the seal area. Use a 250-ml beaker or small custard cup and a small stainless steel spatula to mix only enough material to complete the job at hand. In general, the mixture is usable over a period of four or six hours if kept in a closed container to prevent evaporation. Where evaporation causes the mixture to become too thick, add a small amount of amyl acetate. Storage for longer periods may result in a rubber-like set which is difficult to break and which prevents normal handling.

   The container holding the ground glass must be tightly closed. Prolonged exposure to air may result in a change in its suspension characteristics.

   The vehicle also must be kept tightly stoppered, since evaporation of the solvent will affect suspension characteristics.
3. *Application*—One method is to flow or extrude under slight pressure applied by mouth from a Pyrex Brand No. 7101 pipette, with tip cut to within $\frac{3}{4}$ inch from the bulb. The suspension may also be applied from a suitable polyethylene squeeze bottle, toothpaste tube, or a small paintbrush or spray gun.

   The suspension is somewhat thixotropic (catsuplike) and shows a tendency to cling to the pipette wall, but gentle tapping or shaking will cause it to run down toward the orifice.

   The sealing glass may also be dip-applied, using a less viscous suspension than for flow application. At least two dips, with partial drying between each dip, are required. The first dip produces a thin coating. A second dip will result in a much greater suspension pickup. The dip application method has the advantage of providing a naturally formed nonre-entrant seal fillet.
4. *Suspension drying*—To prevent darkening of the sealing glass, it is recommended that it be thoroughly dried before firing. This can be accomplished by several hours of air-drying in a well-ventilated area or by oven-drying at 115°C for 15 to 30 minutes. A bank of heat lamps, arranged to bear on the frit, works very well. When oven-dried, the operation should be carried out in a furnace other than the one in which the seal is made.

Sealing

1. *Heating rates*—When the green frit is fired directly, the heating rate can be whatever the item being sealed can take; 10 or 15°C/min to the sealing temperature are representative rates. Rates more than 20°C/min are not recommended because devitrification may set in before a good seal is obtained.
2. *Fusing*—The normally recommended schedule for solder glass calls for 60 minutes at 440°C, but 90 to 120 minutes at 425° may be adequate, and approximately 30 minutes at 455°C can also be used. In general, the temperature should be held within these limits.

3. *Cooling rate*—The rate of cooling will depend on the size and geometry of the ware being sealed, as well as on the expansion match between frit and material being sealed. In general, the optimum cooling rate should be determined experimentally, but it can usually be somewhere between 3 and 15°C/min. Slower rates can, of course, be used.
4. *Additional thermal processing*—In those cases in which the sealed item must undergo further thermal processing, the best schedule must be determined experimentally, and maximum rates will again be dictated by size, geometry, and expansion mismatch. In such cases, temperatures above 425°C should be used with caution, since it is possible to overdevitrify the sealing frit.

Miscellaneous

1. *Salvage operations*—Acid-resistant stainless steel, glass, and ceramic parts can be salvaged after sealing by immersion in 10% nitric acid, preferably at 50°C to 60°C. For certain seal shapes, salvage can be accomplished faster by first immersing the seal in the nitric acid bath to dissolve the outside solder glass fillet, followed by a thermal shock using an outside heat source; this will usually separate the parts.
2. *Cleaning*—Application equipment is readily cleaned by rinsing several times with acetone to remove the nitrocellulose. The remaining glass frit can then be flushed away with water, rinsed with acetone, and dried. The sealing glass which adheres to the inside of glass pipettes can be dissolved away, after acetone washing, with 10% nitric acid.
3. *Precaution*—The vehicle, being a suspension of a very small amount of nitrocellulose in amyl acetate, is flammable and extremely volatile. Normal precaution in its use calls for having adequate ventilation and not working near open flames. The use of acetone as a cleaner also requires precaution due to its flammability and possible toxic effects if its fumes are breathed in quantity.

   Since the solder glass has a high percentage of lead oxide, it is recommended that *special precaution* be exercised while mixing and using this material. A few simple rules can lessen any danger of lead poisoning:
   (a) Wear a respirator while handling the powdered glass.
   (b) Wash hands thoroughly, especially under the nails, after working with the solder glass paste or powder.
   (c) Since the glass could be carried home in work clothes, the use of a laboratory coat is recommended, and the coat should be left at the work location.
   (d) Never eat, drink, or smoke after working with the solder glass in paste or powder form without first washing hands thoroughly.

Soldering and brazing. These two terms are used more or less interchangeably, with the following reservations: soldering may be either soft or hard; i.e., *soft soldering* generally refers to the joining of parts (normally metal) with a filler metal or alloy of very much lower melting point. The soft solders usually have as constituents lead, tin, zinc, bismuth, antimony, cadmium, or various combinations of two or more of these elements. Hard-soldering applies to the joining of parts with metals or alloys having much higher melting points than soft solders (see the table on pp. 175–187 for a list of brazing filler metals useful for vacuum devices) and is alternatively called *brazing* because the early workers used alloys of copper and zinc with a blowpipe.

The term *soldering* may mean the joining of metals by the use of a molten metal or alloy of *any* melting point below that of the parts being joined, while *brazing* (or hard-soldering) usually denotes operations restricted to relatively high-melting-point solders.

Welding, in the strict sense, refers to the joining of metals by fusion of the parent metals themselves and/or by the addition of a filler rod or wire which resembles the parent metals in composition, melting point, and expansion coefficient.

Space charge (see pp. 229, 338).

Sparker. The Tesla coil. This is a device which generates very high frequencies at high voltage, usually with very minute currents. An ordinary iron-core induction coil is coupled through a condenser and spark gap to a second induction coil with an air or nonmagnetic core and a second spark gap. Strong corona discharges occur in the neighborhood of a point or probe connected to the secondary winding of the air-core transformer, and these can initiate or establish glow discharges of various kinds in partially evacuated glass tubes approached by the probe. The character of the discharge changes markedly with pressure and kind of gas, and this phenomenon is utilized in estimating partial vacua down to about 10^{-4} torr and in hunting for leaks in vacuum systems. (See p. 134.)

Specific heat. The ratio of the amount of heat required to warm a given mass of the substance between two temperatures to the amount similarly required for water in a given temperature range (usually 15°C):

$$s = \frac{H}{m(t_2 - t_1)}.$$

We let s stand for specific heat or thermal capacity, H for the number of calories necessary to raise m, which is the number of grams (weight) of the substance, from t_1, a lower temperature, °C, to t_2, a higher temperature, °C.

The common units for s are: British thermal unit (Btu) (mean) per pound per °F, and the gram-calorie (gm-cal) (mean) per gm per °C. These are equal, i.e.,

$$1 \text{ Btu/lb/°F} = 1 \text{ gm-cal/gm/°C}.$$

A less common unit is the joule per gram per °C, and this has the following equivalences:

$$\begin{aligned} 1 \text{ joule/gm/°C} &= 0.2389 \text{ gm-cal (mean)/gm/°C} \\ &= 0.2389 \text{ Btu (mean)/lb/°F}. \end{aligned}$$

The specific heat coefficient is a factor in calculating heat transfer in induction heating (see p. 52).

Spot welding. If a heavy current at low voltage is passed through a small area in two pieces of sheet metal or wire in contact for a short time, local fusion can occur and the two members may be welded together at this "spot." The interval of current passage should be short in order to minimize oxidation, which would interfere with the consummation of a good weld; it is therefore obvious that the metals to be joined should be clean and free of scale, grease, rust, tarnish, and other contamination.

Spot-welding machines may be of the so-called ac variety, in which a simple step-down transformer (e.g., 50 : 1 ratio) is controlled by a simple mechanical or electrical timing device so that pulses down to perhaps one cycle can be passed through the work. These machines range from light-duty, air-cooled bench models suitable for a wide variety of vacuum tube work to large industrial machines with water-cooled electrodes, for welding heavy sections. Portable models are also available (extensively used in automobile factories), and the bench models can be fitted with "tweezer" or plier-like electrodes on flexible cables for working in places which cannot be brought to the fixed welder.

The electrodes are commonly pure copper, shaped to accomplish the work in hand. For some types of critical work, tungsten or tungsten alloy electrodes are used.

Another kind of spot-welding machine is the condenser-discharge or stored energy type in which a variable bank of large-capacity condensers is discharged through the electrodes. The timing is electronically controlled and is capable of very short pulses (down to a few microseconds) so that this type of machine is suitable for welding very fine wires, thin foil, or materials such as semiconductor crystals which can be easily destroyed by heat. Copper or tungsten electrodes are also used in this type of welder.

Although spot welding is usually done in the air, protective atmospheres can be used. The arrangements for providing such atmospheres can be simple or fairly elaborate. A common procedure in the vacuum tube laboratory when small work is handled is to apply a drop or two of some liquid just prior to applying the welding current. Mixtures of alcohol and water are often used. Such liquids not only provide a kind of protective atmosphere but also produce a cooling effect.

Spot (or resistance-welding, as it is sometimes called) is inherently capable of producing a joint which is both mechanically and electrically sound.[1] This is especially true of welds made between like metals (with some reservations, e.g., tungsten to tungsten and molybdenum to molybdenum, etc.) and of welds between similar metals such as nickel to copper-nickel alloys (copper and nickel alloy in all proportions), and of compatible metals which have closely similar melting points.

Unless welding currents, intervals, pressures, and types of electrodes are chosen very carefully, the spot-welding of copper to copper or copper to any other metal (the same applies to silver) is difficult because of the high heat conductivity of copper (and silver), which results in carrying heat away from the weld site so rapidly that fusion does not occur, even though the other metal may have a lower melting point than the copper. Nickel-clad copper has been used to make satisfactory welds. Good joints between copper and silver parts can be made by using a small piece of low-melting silver solder foil (e.g., Easy-Flo) as a flux. Strictly speaking, this is a braze rather than a weld.

The welding of tungsten to tungsten and of molybdenum to molybdenum is also likely to be difficult because (a) these metals have fairly high heat and electrical conductivity, (b) their melting points are very high, and (c) they tend to oxidize easily at temperatures far below the fusion point. Their heat conductivity can be minimized as a factor by using high currents for very short pulses, and this also tends to reduce the effect of (b) and (c).

---

[1] See "High-Density Electronic Packaging-Resistance Welding," P. J. Gray, R. Steingerwald, and P. N. James, *Electronic Design,* **9,** 44, May 24, 1961.

Tantalum can be spot-welded with considerable facility, even though its melting point is very high. This is owing to its lower thermal and electrical conductivity, as a consequence of which the heat generated by a moderate current is contained in a small area and is sufficient to cause fusion. Where easy bonds are to be made between tungsten and tungsten, tungsten and molybdenum, or molybdenum and molybdenum, it is often expedient to sandwich a thin piece of tantalum between the two members (see FLUXES, pp. 87, 253), or if the joint is not to be subjected to high temperatures, a thin piece of nickel can be used in the same way.

In all spot- or resistance-welding machines, the electrical conductors and contacts between the power source and the electrodes must imperatively be of the lowest possible resistance. The reason for this is obviously that since the voltages are low and the currents high, even a small resistance will result in a large voltage drop, which one cannot afford. Special attention should be paid to "tweezer" and plier welding tools in which relatively long flexible cables are used. Such cables should preferably be composed of a large number of very small copper strands, and the end lugs should be silver-soldered rather than soft-soldered. Electrodes and all lug connections must be bolted tightly and kept clean.

It is sometimes expedient to use spot-welding electrodes of different materials where welds between metals of different heat conductivities are required.[1]

Simple spot-welding implies the fusion at a single small site. Variations of this are *projection welding,* in which electrodes of much larger area are used, one of the work pieces having one or more projections jutting out of its surface in contact with the other piece. These projections are stamped or punched.

Seam-welding is accomplished by passing the current through wheel or roller electrodes in pulses of definite duration while the work is being moved along continuously or intermittently. Seam welds can be either overlapping or not, depending on the type of motion and duration of pulse; the overlapping seam weld can be gas- or vacuum-tight if properly done.

Butt-welding is a procedure in which the two members (e.g., wires[2] or strips) are joined endwise. The work pieces are each held in a clamp-electrode, the current is applied, and the two pieces are pushed slightly together as fusion takes place and forms an "upset nugget."

In *flash-butt welding* most of the heating occurs by reason of an arc produced by pulling the work pieces slightly apart after contact, then slowly moving them together as metal is burned away. At the point of maximum fusion the two pieces are forced together, and the upset nugget is formed.

Seam-, butt-, and flash-butt welding all require some degree of automation in addition to the automatic timing needed for all spot-welding operations.

In welding components in electron tubes, utmost cleanliness is generally to be observed. The welding area should be air-conditioned and protected from drafts. Critical jobs should be done in a dry-box or behind a shield so that the operator's breath does not impinge on the work.

---

[1] Tungsten and various tungsten-copper alloys are used as electrodes for some applications.

[2] Butt-welding of wires is a useful technique for making press- or stem-leads for vacuum tubes. A composite lead can thus be made in which, for example, a short piece of tungsten (for the glass-sealing section) is joined at either end to a nickel wire, one of which (the outside lead) may be stranded.

It is often mandatory to hold the components in special jigs or fixtures while spot-welding is being performed. The welding operation will always produce some movement of the parts (thermal expansion, displacement due to fusion and pressure, etc.) and fixtures must be used when close dimensional tolerances are to be held. Jigs and fixtures must be kept clean and should preferably be made of nonvolatile materials. Removing an electron-tube assembly from a *brass* fixture where some friction is encountered might result in small particles of brass (containing zinc, lead) adhering to the assembly, with harmful consequences to oxide-coated cathodes.

Spraying and spray equipment. *Oxide coating for cathodes* (see pp. 96–98). The application of sprayed material to a nickel base is usually done to a thickness of about 0.003 inch, although coatings down to 0.001 inch and up to 0.007 inch or more have been used. These measurements can be made on test pieces by means of an optical micrometer or by special gauges. For production work the unsprayed cathode is weighed, the thickness of coat is initially determined and then weighed (after thorough drying), and the weight difference is used as a basis for evaluating samples picked at random from the batch.

The DeVilbiss[1] type CH or CV spray gun is commonly used for hand-spraying procedures. This gun is used with a No. 90 air-cap and a type F fluid tip and needle. Other makes and types of guns[2] can also be used, although the adjustments and settings will be different.

With the DeVilbiss gun, a line air pressure of approximately 80 psi is used, with the regulator supplying air or gas to the gun being set at 30 to 35 psi. Unless the compressed air is scrupulously filtered to remove water, oil, dust, and other contaminants, dried, water-pumped nitrogen at 80 psi pressure should be used. Oil-pumped nitrogen may also be used if tests indicate the absence of oil.

The needle setting on the spray gun is given as the number of turns from a closed position. If an index line does not appear on the body and the screw, such a line should be scribed. Some wear will be suffered by the needle-fluid tip so that adjustments will be required from time to time. Normal settings will be approximately from one-half to two turns open.

A ring on the air-cap of the DeVilbiss gun is imprinted with numbers from 0 to 20. The setting of this ring determines the proportion of air or gas admitted to the side nozzles, and this in turn determines the amount of air available for "fanning." Fanning regulates the spray coverage and, to some degree, the rate of drying of the coating. Settings range from 10 to 18 for most normal operations.

In hand spraying, the gun is held from three to seven inches from the cathode, measured from the fluid tip to the center of the cathode when the gun is pointing directly at the cathode. Passes are made by rotating the hand so that the angle made by the gun nozzle with the work is approximately 45° at each end of the pass. The number of such passes will depend on (a) the thickness of coating required, and (b) the area to be covered (or, if several pieces are being sprayed together, the length of travel). Anything up to 40 or 50 passes may be required. The speed of the passes will have to be determined by experiment, since all other factors are involved. A value of about two seconds for a single one-way pass is average.

---

[1] The DeVilbiss Company, Toledo, Ohio.

[2] American Brake Shoe Co., Kellogg Division, Rochester 9, New York; also Paasche Air Brush Co., Newton, Massachusetts.

If too many passes are made consecutively, the coating may cake or drip. To overcome this, drying passes are made after every few spraying passes, and this is done by pulling the trigger only part way, thus opening the atomizing air outlet but not retracting the needle from the fluid tip.

A good indication of the spray pattern and character can be obtained by directing the gun at a sheet of dark paper or other surface. The width and coverage of the spraying can then be adjusted to suit. If the pattern is blotchy or irregular, this means that the fluid tip or air-cap of the gun is dirty or worn, or that the air passages are plugged.

Spraying is usually done by starting at one end of the pass so that the spray impinges on the work while the gun is moving. Spraying is continued beyond the work to assure complete coverage. The gun must be held firmly and the pass made at as uniform a rate as possible, all strokes being at the same rate. When several cathodes are to be sprayed in consecutive order, the spray bottle should be shaken between sprayings to keep the material in suspension. Some operators find it advantageous to hold a finger over the air-cap while firing the gun for a short interval; the gas bubbles thus provide a good agitation of the fluid. Before using the gun again, and indeed before any spraying on cathodes, operate the gun to fill the fluid tube and to see that the stream is in order.

Spraying is to be done in an approved spray booth. Since the spray constituents are both toxic and highly flammable, an efficient exhaust blower is to be provided, with an explosion-proof motor and controls. The lighting in the spray booth, which should be adequate, must also be explosion-proof. A baffle-plate should be installed in the booth to prevent strong drafts. The booth and baffles are to be kept clean by the use of a wire brush and an air hose to drive the loosened material up the duct; be sure the blower is running.

The sprayed cathodes are to be dried for one to three minutes on the rack or fixture in an air oven at 80°–90°C, or with radiant heating elements.

Nickel cathode bases must be properly cleaned and fired before spraying. See pp. 12, 98.

It is very important to keep the spray gun clean. This is best done *immediately* after each job by removing the fluid jar and replacing it with one containing clean acetone, and then firing the gun into the booth 10 to 20 seconds *after* all traces of the cathode spray have disappeared. For the removal of stubborn deposits, the gun assembly can be cleaned with acetone in an ultrasonic device.

Insulation (Alundum) coating for tungsten and molybdenum heaters (see pp. 81–84). The remarks regarding the spraying of oxide cathode material above apply in general to the spraying of Alundum, with exceptions and additions as discussed below.

Guns and spray booths used for oxide-cathode coatings must not be used for heater insulation coatings, and vice versa.

Sheet molybdenum boxes or boats are to be provided for drying and firing the sprayed heaters. These are fitted with molybdenum liners bent in such a way that the heaters cannot roll or move while being processed. Only a few heaters should be placed in the boat to avoid contact of the coated pieces with each other. The boats can be used as bare metal or they can be coated with the same material and fired (see p. 84). If the coating becomes chipped or discolored, the boat should be recoated and refired. Boats not in use should be kept covered and in a clean, dry storage area.

Sputtering.[1] A negatively charged electrode (e.g., a cathode of any kind) in a partially evacuated device can be bombarded with positive ions which cause ejection of metal particles from the electrode. This is called sputtering; it results in a gradual disintegration of the cathode surface. The particles are deposited on nearby surfaces, and, if on glass, will eventually build up a dark layer.[2]

The intensity of sputtering is dependent on the kind of metal of the cathode, the gas, the gas pressure, the energy and current density of the incident ions, and the cathode temperature. The amount of material sputtered is given to a fair approximation by:

$$m = K(V_c - V_o),$$

where m is mass of material sputtered per second,

K is a gas constant ($\sqrt[4]{\text{atomic weight of the gas}}$),

V_o is a metal constant (350–550 volts—usually about 450),

V_c is energy of the incident positive ions (cathode drop of the glow discharge used as a source of positive ions).

It is believed[3] that the phenomenon of sputtering is an evaporation of the metal caused by the very high local temperatures at the point of positive-ion impact.

The sputtering process[4] is useful for the deposition of very thin semitransparent, electrically conducting films of metal onto various substrates (bases); these are employed for optical and for various other purposes, including the making of resistors (deposition on glass, mica, ceramics, etc.). Sputtered films have been made as thin as 5μ.[5] Films 30μ thick are found to be very uniform and can withstand a pressure of 8 torr. Substrate materials include cellulose acetate, which can be dissolved in acetone after deposition.[6]

Because of the formation of a thin layer of oxide on aluminum, magnesium, and zinc, these metals disintegrate but slowly under positive-ion bombardment so that sputtering is consequently somewhat inhibited. On the other hand, cadmium, silver, and lead are among the metals which sputter freely.

For a high cathode drop, the amount of sputtered material is proportional to the discharge current. As the mass of the impinging positive ions increases, sputtering increases.

It has been found[7] that the product of the mass of sputtered material, the gas pressure, and the distance between cathode and anode is a constant:

$$C = mpD,$$

where m is the amount of sputtered material (mg/amp-hr), p is gas pressure (mm Hg), D is cathode-anode distance (cm).

---

[1] *Gaseous Conductors*, J. D. Cobine, Dover Publications, New York, New York, 1958

[2] See also p. 194.

[3] A. v. Hipple, *Ann. Physik*.

[4] H. F. Fruth, *Physics*, **2**, 280, 1932.

[5] K. Lauch and W. Ruppert, *Physik. Z.*, **27**, 452, 1926.

[6] F. Joliot, *Ann. Physik*, **15**, 418, 1931.

[7] A. Güntherschulte, *Z. Physik*, **38**, 575, 1926.

For a silver cathode in hydrogen, the constant C equals $0.863V_c$. Güntherschulte gives the sputtered amount of various cathode metals (μgm/amp-sec).[1]

Magnesium	2.5	Nickel	18
Tantalum	4.5	Iron	19
Chromium	7.5	Tin	55
Aluminum	8	Carbon	73
Cadmium	8.9	Copper	84
Manganese	11	Zinc	95
Molybdenum	16	Lead	110
Cobalt	16	Gold	130
Tungsten	16	Silver	205

SPUTTERING—BIBLIOGRAPHY

"Summary of Technical Papers on Thin Film Deposition and Ultra High Vacuum Techniques," Edwards High Vacuum, Inc., Grand Island, New York, New York, 1961.

G. Papp, *Rev. Sci. Instr.*, **30,** 911, 1959.

J. P. Reames, *ibid.*, **30,** 834, 1959.

G. Papp, *ibid.*, **30,** 911, 1959.

K. E. McCulloh, *ibid.*, **31,** 780, 1960.

Vacuum Deposition of Thin Films, L. Holland, John Wiley & Sons, Inc., New York, New York, 1956.

Trans. Am. Vacuum Soc., 10th Ann. Symp., Part II, pp. 309–503 (36 papers by various authors), Macmillan Company, New York, 1963.

Sputter-ion pumps. See GETTER-ION PUMPS, p. 108.

Stainless steels. The ferrous corrosion-resistant alloys of interest to electron tube and vacuum vessel designers are those containing chromium as the important alloying element plus, in many instances, nickel.

The *austenitic* stainless steels contain chromium and nickel, with small amounts of other elements such as carbon, manganese, silicon, phosphorus, sulfur (or selenium) and sometimes molybdenum, titanium, columbium, tantalum, and zirconium. The most widely used stainless steels for tube or vacuum work are the so-called nonmagnetic or 18–8 types (the chromium-nickel ratio). Actually, as will be seen by an examination of the tables on pp. 500–506, the composition of the austenitic stainless steels varies somewhat from the 18–8 values. Also the magnetic properties of these steels at room temperature are not zero but a small figure which will be sensitive to the amount of cold-working. In general, severe cold-working can result in raising the magnetic permeability of curie point (p. 231) of some of these alloys to a marked degree.

The 18–8 steels cannot be hardened by heat-treatment but only by cold-working. Note that an exception is type 17–7PH, which contains about 1% aluminum. Cold-formed pieces of 17–7PH are hardened by heating for one hour at 480°C, which results in a Rockwell C hardness of 47 to 52. The annealed hardness of 17–7PH is Rockwell B 78 to 92; cold-rolling produces a hardness of C 38–44. For the soft-annealed alloy, the hardening process consists of two steps: (a) heating to 760°C

[1] *Ibid.*, **36,** 563, 1926. See also *Scientific Glassblowing,* E. L. Wheeler, Interscience Publishers, Inc., New York, New York, 1958, pp. 214–216.

TABLE OF DATA AND PROPERTIES OF STAINLESS STEELS[1] (AUSTENITIC GRADES)[2,3]

TYPE NO.	APPROXIMATE COMPOSITION PERCENT[4]										ANNEALING PROCEDURES (TEMPERATURE °C FOR MAXIMUM SOFTNESS)	FORMABILITY, ETC.
	Cr	Ni	C MAX	Mn MAX	P MAX	S MAX	Si MAX	Mo MAX	Zr MAX	OTHER		
302	17–19	8–10	0.15	2.0	0.045	0.03	1.0	—	—	—	1090: air-cool light sections, water-cool heavy sections	Good; frequent anneals for drastic forming operations.
303	17–19	8–10	0.15	2.0	0.20	(or Se) 0.15	1.0	Mo or Zr 0.60		—	1065: water-quench	Fair; not suitable for severe cold-forming operations.
304	18–20	8–12	0.08	2.0	0.045	0.03	1.0	—	—	—	1090: air-cool light sections, water-quench for heavy sections	Good; frequent anneals for drastic forming operations.
305	17–19	10–13	0.12	2.0	—	—	1.0	—	—	—	980–1070: air-cool or water	Has low work-hardening rate thus more suitable for spinning, deep-drawing, cold-heading than **302** or **304**.
316	16–18	10–14	0.08	2.0	0.045	0.03	1.0	2–3	—	—	1090: air-cool for light sections, water-quench for heavy sections	Fair; anneal frequently for drastic forming operations.
321	17–19	9–12	0.08	2.0	0.045	0.03	1.0	—	—	Ti 5 × C min	1040–1070: air-cool for light sections, water-quench for heavy. Ti content makes it difficult to braze in hydrogen	Good; anneal frequently for drastic forming operations.
347 **348**	17–19	9–13	0.08	2.0	0.045	0.03	1.0	Cb-Ta 10×C max	Ta 0.10 max	—	1090: air-cool for light sections. Water-quench for heavy sections. Cb, Ta content makes it difficult to braze in hydrogen.	Can be hardened somewhat more than other types by cold-working.

TABLE OF DATA AND PROPERTIES OF STAINLESS STEEL (AUSTENITIC GRADES) (*Cont.*)

TYPE NO.	MACHINABILITY AND PROCEDURES	WELDABILITY AND PROCEDURES	SCALING TEMPERATURE (°C) (MIN. IN AIR)	CORROSION RESISTANCE	PHYSICAL PROPERTIES: MODULUS OF ELASTICITY TENSION (1000 PSI)	PHYSICAL PROPERTIES: MODULUS OF ELASTICITY TORSION (1000 PSI)	PHYSICAL PROPERTIES: ELECTRICAL RESISTIVITY (μOHM-CM 25°C)
302	Good. Use heavy feeds, low speeds, sharp tools, and coolants.	Good. Use Type **308** electrodes. Anneal after welding in dry H_2.	900	Superior	28	12.5	72.0
303	Excellent. (This is free-machine grade.) Use heavy feeds, sharp tools. Machine at 60–75% speed used for mild steel.	Not recommended for welding.	900	Good	28	—	72.1
304	Good. Same as for **302.**	Good. Use Type **308** electrodes. Anneal after welding in dry H_2.	900	Superior	28	12.5	72.0
305	—	—	900	Excellent	29	—	72.0
316	Fair. Use heavy feeds and speeds about 50% those for mild steel. Keep tools sharp and rigid.	Good. Use Types **316, 317** electrodes.	900	Excellent	28	—	72.4
321	Same as for **316.**	Good. Use Type **347** electrodes.	900	Superior	28	—	72.0
347, **348**	Same as for **316.**	Good. Use Type **347** or **348** electrodes.	900	Superior	28	—	73.0

[1] Data by courtesy of Crucible Steel Company, Pittsburgh, Pennsylvania.
[2] Austenitic stainless steels are not hardenable except slightly by cold-working thin sections.
[3] Austenitic stainless steels are practically nonmagnetic when fully annealed, having magnetic permeabilities of 1.01 to 1.02 (room temperature at 200H). Cold-working produces a slightly magnetic condition.
[4] In all cases the balance is iron.

(*Cont.*)

TABLE OF DATA AND PROPERTIES OF STAINLESS STEEL (AUSTENITIC GRADES) (*Cont.*)

TYPE NO.	SPECIFIC HEAT	SPECIFIC GRAVITY (GM/CC)	THERMAL CONDUCTIVITY		LINEAR COEFFICIENT OF THERMAL EXPANSION IN./°C AT TEMPERATURES INDICATED						MELTING POINT RANGE (°C)	TENSILE STRENGTH (RT, 1000 PSI)	YIELD STRENGTH (RT, 1000 PSI) (0.2% OFFSET)
			AT 100°C	AT 540°C	0–100°C	0–315°C	0–540°C	0–650°C	0–815°C	0–930°C			
302	0.12	7.94	9.4	12.5	17.3	17.8	18.4	18.7	—	—	1400–1420	85–90	35–40
303	C.12	7.92	9.4	12.5	17.3	17.8	18.4	18.7	—	—	1400–1420	90	35
304	0.12	7.94	9.4	12.5	17.3	17.8	18.4	18.7	—	—	1400–1450	85	30–35
305	0.12	7.9	9.4	12.4	17.3	—	—	—	—	—	1400–1455	75	25
316	0.12	7.91	9.3	12.4	16.0	16.2	17.6	18.6	20.0	—	1370–1400	85–90	35–40
321	0.12	7.89	9.3	12.7	16.8	17.1	18.5	19.3	—	0–980°C: 20.1	1230–1430	85–90	35
347, **348**	0.12	8.02	9.2	12.5	16.6	17.1	18.6	19.1	20.0	—	1370–1430	90–95	40–45

TYPE NO.	IZOD IMPACT RESISTANCE (FT-LB)	HARDNESS NUMBERS (ANNEALED)		COLD BEND (DEGREES)	ELEVATED TEMPERATURE PROPERTIES SHORT TIME TENSILE STR. (1000 PSI)					CREEP DATA: STRESS FOR CREEP RATE OF 0.0001%/HR (1000 PSI)				
		SHEET STRIP PLATE	BAR (1-INCH ROUND)		700°C	815°C	930°C	1040°C	1090°C	540°C	590°C	650°C	700°C	815°C
302	110	$80R_B$	$81R_B$	180	37.5	22.0	12.0	6.5	5.5	17.0	12.0	7.0	4.0	1.2
303	80	$87R_B$	$87R_B$	180	37.5	22.0	12.0	6.5	5.5	17.0	12.0	7.0	4.0	1.2
304	110	$80R_B$	$82R_B$	180	37.5	22.0	12.0	6.5	5.5	17.0	12.0	7.0	4.0	1.2
305	85 min.	$90R_B$ max.	—	180	—	—	—	—	—	—	—	—	—	—
316	100	$85R_B$	$84R_B$	180	46.5	27.0	18.5	—	—	25.0	18.2	12.7	7.9	2.8
321	100	$80R_B$	$84R_B$	180	36.5	22.0	15.0	—	—	18.0	13.0	8.0	4.5	0.85
347, **348**	100	$85R_B$	$84R_B$	180	40.5	24.0	14.5	10.0	—	19.0	14.0	8.2	4.6	1.5

TABLE OF DATA AND PROPERTIES OF STAINLESS STEELS (MARTENSITIC AND FERRITIC GRADES)*

TYPE NO.	APPROXIMATE COMPOSITION PERCENT (see footnote[4] on page 501)									ANNEALING PROCEDURE ANNEAL TEMPERATURE (°C)	HARDENING AND TEMPERING PROCEDURE
	Cr	Ni	C MAX	S MAX	Mn MAX	Si MAX	P MAX	Mo	Zr		
403 (martensitic)	11.5–13	—	0.15	0.03	1.0	0.5	0.04	—	—	840; furnace-cool for better machinability, air-cool from 790°C	Air-cool from 1010°C or oil-quench from 955°C. Temper above 595°C. Avoid tempering range 430°–595°C.
410 (martensitic)	11.5–13.5	—	0.15	0.03	1.0	1.0	0.04	—	—	Same as for **403.**	Same as for **403.**
416 (martensitic)	12–14	—	0.15	0.15	1.25	1.0	0.06	0.06 or	0.06	Same as for **403, 410**	Same as for **403, 410**
420 (martensitic)	12–14	—	over 0.15	0.03	1.0	1.0	0.04	—	—	Soak at 870°C for 6 hours, furnace-cool. Cycle-anneal by heating to 870°C, hold 2 hours, cool to 705°C, hold 4 hours, air-cool. Machinability is improved by annealing at 760°C.	Oil-quench from 980°–1040°C. Large sections to be preheated at 680°C. Temper above 595°C. Avoid tempering range 430°–595°C.
431 (martensitic)	15–17	1.25–2.5	0.02	0.03	1.0	1.0	0.04	—	—	Normalize slowly from 870°C; reheat to 650°C for 10–12 hours, air-cool.	Cool rapidly from 980°–1070°C (air- or oil-quench). Avoid tempering range 430°–595°C. Temper above 595°C.
440A (martensitic)	16–18	—	0.6–0.75	0.03	1.0	1.0	0.04	max 0.75	—	Same as for **420.**	Oil-quench from 1010°–1040°C. Preheat large sections to 790°C. Avoid tempering range 430°–590°C.
440C (martensitic)	16–18	—	0.95–1.2	0.03	1.0	1.0	0.04	max 0.75	—	Soak at 900°C for 6 hours; furnace-cool. Cycle-anneal at 870°C, 2 hours, cool to 705°C; hold 4 hours, air-cool.	Same as for **440A.**
430 (ferritic)	14–18	—	max. 0.12	0.03	1.0	1.0	0.04	—	—	790°–840°C; air- or water-quench. For much better machinability, semianneal at 680°C and air-cool.	Can be hardened slightly only by cold-working thin sections.

* The martensitic types are hardenable by heat-treatment as given. The ferritic grade **430** can be hardened only by cold-working. Both grades are magnetic at all times at room temperature.

(Cont.)

TABLE OF DATA AND PROPERTIES OF STAINLESS STEEL (MARTENSITIC AND FERRITIC GRADES) (*Cont.*)

TYPE NO.	ATTAINABLE HARDNESS R_C	FORMABILITY	MACHINABILITY	WELDABILITY	SCALING TEMPERATURE °C (IN AIR)	CORROSION RESISTANCE
403	38–47	Good	Fair; see under "Annealing Procedure." Machining speed about 55% that for mild steel.	Weldable with **410** electrodes. Preheat to 150°C (min.) and postheat (anneal) at 705°C. Furnace-cool 25°–50°C/hr to 590°C. Air-cool.	680	Fair
410	38–47	Good	Same as **403.**	Same as **403.**	680	Fair
416	32–45.5	Fair for gradual cold-working. Not suitable for severe cold-working operations.	Same as **403, 410,** except that machining speed of 85% that for mild steel can be used.	Not recommended for welding.	680	Fair
420	51–54.5		Same as **403, 410,** except that machining speed of 40% that for mild steel can be used.	Weld with **420** electrodes. Preheat to min. of 205°C and postheat (anneal) at 705°C for 8 hours. Air cool.	650	Fair
431	40.5–47		Same as **403, 410,** except that machining speed of 50% that for mild steel can be used.	Weld with **431** electrodes. Preheat to minimum of 150°C and postheat (anneal) immediately after welding at 650°C; air-cool.	870	Good
440A	44		Same as for **420.**	Use **440A** electrodes. Preheat and postheat same as for **431.**	760	Fair
440C	51		Same as for **420.**	Use **440C** electrodes. Preheat and postheat same as for **431.**	760	Fair
430*	23		See under "Annealing Procedure." Machining speed of 55% that for mild steel can be used.	Use **308** or **430** electrodes. Preheat to minimum of 150°C; cool to below 120°C, then post heat (anneal) at 760°C–815°C for minimum of ½ hour (to 4 hours) plus 1 hr/in of thickness.	870	Good

Table of Data and Properties of Stainless Steel (Martensitic and Ferritic Grades) (*Cont.*)

Type No.	Mod. of Elasticity (1000) psi (ann)		Elec. Resistivity at 25°C (μohm-cm)	Spec. Heat	Spec. Gravity gm/cc	Thermal Conductivity		Linear Coefficient of Thermal Expansion					Melting Point Range (°C)
	Tension	Torsion				at 100°C	at 540°C	0–100°C	0–315°C	0–540°C	0–650°C	0–815°C	
403	29.0	11.0	56.9	0.11	7.7	14.4	16.5	9.9	10.1	11.5	11.7	—	1480–1530
410	29.0	11.0	56.9	0.11	7.7	14.4	16.5	9.9	10.1	11.5	11.7	—	1480–1530
416	29.0	10.5	56.8	0.11	7.75	14.4	16.5	9.9	10.1	11.5	11.7	—	1480–1530
420	29.0	11.7	54.8	0.11	7.75	14.4	—	10.2	10.8	11.7	12.2	—	1455–1510
431	29	—	72	0.11	7.77	11.7	—	11.7	12.1	—	—	—	1430–1480
440A	29	—	59.9	0.11	7.75	14.0	—	10.1	10.8	—	—	—	1370–1510
440C	29	—	59.9	0.11	7.75	14.0	—	10.3	10.8	—	—	—	1370–1480
430*	29	—	59.9	0.11	7.72	13.1	15.2	10.4	11.0	11.4	11.9	12.4	1430–1510

Type No.	Tensile Strength (1000 psi)		Yield Strength (0.2% offset 1000 psi)		Izod Impact Resistance (ft-lbs)		Hardness, R_B (annealed)		Cold Bend (degrees)	Elevated Temperature Properties, Short Time Tensile Strength (1000 psi at temperature °C)						
	Sheet	Bar	Sheet	Bar	Sheet	Bar	Sheet	Bar		540°	590°	650°	700°	760°	815°	930°
403	65	75	35	45	—	90	80	82	180	44.5	33.0	22.0	13.5	9.0	—	—
410	65	75	35	45	—	90	80	82	180	44.5	33.0	22.0	13.5	9.0	—	—
416	—	75	—	40	—	90	80	82	180	44.5	33.0	22.0	13.5	9.0	—	—
420	—	95	—	50	—	—	—	89	180	—	—	—	—	—	—	—
431	—	125	—	95	—	50	—	102	—	—	—	—	—	—	—	—
440A	—	105	—	60	—	—	—	96	—	—	—	—	—	—	—	—
440C	—	110	—	65	—	—	—	98	—	—	—	—	—	—	—	—
430*	75	75	45	40	—	40	80	84	180	39.0	29.0	20.5	14.0	—	6.5	3.5

* Type 430 is ferritic; the other grades are martensitic.

(*Cont.*)

Table of Data and Properties of Stainless Steel (Martensitic and Ferritic Grades) (*Cont.*)

TYPE NO.	CREEP DATA: STRESS FOR CREEP RATE OF 0.0001%/HR AT TEMPERATURES GIVEN °C 1000 PSI			
	540°	590°	650°	700°
403	9.2	4.2	2.0	1.0
410	9.2	4.2	2.0	1.0
416	9.2	4.2	2.0	1.0
420	—	—	—	—
431	—	—	—	—
440A	—	—	—	—
440C	—	—	—	—
430	8.5	4.3	2.2	1.3

for $1\frac{1}{2}$ hours, followed by air- or water-cooling to 15°C or below; and (b) heating to 480°–590°C for about 1 hour, followed by air-cooling to room temperature. This results in a hardness of Rockwell C 40 to 45, the lower temperatures under (b) producing the higher hardness values. Typical figures are:

CONDITION	REDUCTION (%)	BRINELL HARDNESS	TENSILE STRENGTH (1000 PSI)	ELONGATION IN 2 IN. (%)
Annealed(*)	—	170	95	68
Cold-rolled	8	230	125	40
Cold-rolled	16	270	143	30
Cold-rolled	23	295	160	20
Cold-rolled	32	315	175	15
Cold-rolled	40	330	190	10
Cold-rolled	47	335	205	3
Cold-rolled	55	340	220	2

* Composition: 18.5% Cr, 8.2% Ni, 0.11% C, balance Fe.

The 18–8 stainless steels can be annealed after cold-working by heating to temperatures as shown in the table. If this heating is done in air, a film of green chromium oxide is formed on the surface; this can be removed by the processes given on pp. 9, 14, 22. Annealing can be done in dry hydrogen[1] (see pp. 41–51), in which case the metal will have a bright finish and will be suitable for vacuum-tube work without further processing. If, however, dry-hydrogen-fired stainless steel is to be used where corrosion resistance is a requirement, the metal will require

[1] Except for types 347 and 348, which contain columbium and tantalum. Both react with hydrogen to form hydrides and may produce serious embrittlement. In any event the presence of the hydride prevents a bright finish and interferes with the "wetting" of braze materials so that poor brazing results can be expected with these alloys.

passivation[1] or the formation of a very thin, invisible chromium oxide film on the surface, which is the corrosion-resistant agency. If the annealing is done in ordinary tank hydrogen, a light film of the green oxide will appear, and this is a useful property when the metal is to be used for brazing jigs (see p. 37) and for heater or filament mandrels (see pp. 82, 83) because it prevents other metals in contact from sticking.

There is some indication that when very highly polished 18–8 stainless steel is dry-hydrogen-fired (whether for annealing, outgassing, or brazing), a microscopic egg-shell surface becomes apparent. This is probably the result of entrapment of gases or volatile decomposition products of and by the buffing materials, which are then subsequently expanded to produce the tiny blisters on the surface. Where a high polish is required, such as for high-voltage electrodes, it would be better to hydrogen-fire first and polish afterward, using only the cleanest technique and materials possible. see p. 429).

The austenitic stainless steels can easily be brazed,[2] using the procedure given on pp. 41–51. Stainless steels *welded* by the heliarc process can be dry-hydrogen-fired above 1000°C after welding to anneal and obtain a bright finish. This firing will remove all but the heaviest scale. Vacuum or shielded inert gas arc or electron beam[3] welding can be used to get a scale-free joint.

In general the procedures for handling the other types of stainless steel (martensitic, ferritic) will be similar to those for the austenitic types, except that some of the martensitic types are hardenable by heat treatment, notably types 403, 410, 416, 420, 430, 431, 440A, and 440C, which are magnetic and contain little or no nickel. Heat treatment and properties of these alloys are given in the table on pp. 503 *et seq.* The data for this table has been furnished by courtesy of the Crucible Steel Company of America, Pittsburgh 30, Pennsylvania.

Stannic oxide conductive coating for glass (see p. 207).

Static seal. A seal in which none of the members moves. This term is often applied to O-ring or gasket seals and distinguishes such seals from those in which one of the mating members slides and/or rotates. See pp. 117, 118, 309, 407–415; also *cf.* p. 383.

Stay time. The time elapsing between the last processing step for the getter in a tube and the seal-off.[4]

Steel. There are many types of steel (that is, iron-carbon or iron-iron carbide alloys), a few of which are described below.

Cold-rolled steel is not any particular type; the term usually designates the low-carbon steels such as AISI types C1010, C1015, C1018, C1020, C1025, and others. All of these have good-to-excellent machinability and forming qualities in the cold-worked condition and are suitable for use in vacuum tubes if their high magnetic permeability can be tolerated (in general their residual magnetism is low) and if the finished parts are properly handled. (See also pp. 116, 209.)

These steels are not corrosion-resistant and must be kept in a clean, dry area or container after cleaning. To prepare steel components for vacuum-tube use, they

---

[1] See p. 428.

[2] With exceptions as noted in the footnote on p. 506.

[3] See p. 234.

[4] "Residual Gas Pressure in Electron Tubes," H. J. Schütze and H. W. Ehlbeck, *Vacuum* (Br), **10,** 1/2, p. 5, 1960.

can be cleaned (if rusty or scaly from heating or welding), by one of the processes given on p. 8 *et seq*. Or if they are freshly machined, degreasing (p. 7) is sufficient. The parts are then to be vacuum-fired (p. 75) at 900°–1000°C, or dry-hydrogen-fired according to the procedure for stainless steel given on pp. 41–51.

Low carbon steels are not hardenable to any extent by heat treating and cannot be hardened much more than about 10–12% by cold-working. They can, however, be surface-hardened by carburizing,[1] which is accomplished by heating the metal to above the transformation temperature (about 600°C) while it is in contact with a carbon-rich material such as charcoal or coke.

Wet-hydrogen-firing or air-firing steel causes the formation of a blue or blue-gray oxide film which prevents the sticking of tungsten or molybdenum when steel mandrels are used for firing heaters in ordinary or wet hydrogen. The oxide film, however, is not adequate to prevent the adherence of brazing materials, so that oxidized *stainless steel* (see p. 37) should be used for making brazing jigs and fixtures.

Cold-rolled steel can be furnace-brazed with various high-temperature alloys in the same manner as that used for stainless steel (see pp. 41–51).

Tool steels (drill-rod, ground-stock, and certain other proprietary brand-name steels) are alloys containing greater amounts of carbon than cold-rolled steel has, together with other elements introduced to obtain a wide variety of properties. These alloys are, in general, not as easily machined and formed as the low carbon or mild steels, but they can be heat-treated to obtain various degrees of hardness and temper, making them useful for the fabrication of tools, punches, dies, mandrels, and the like.

Iron and steel are not attacked by mercury. All the iron and steel alloys (except the austenitic stainless steels: 18–8 or 300 series) are strongly magnetic. The high-carbon (tool) steels have, as a rule, a high magnetic retentivity, or residual magnetism, when hardened, but their use as permanent magnets has largely been replaced by the Alnico and other special magnetic formulations.

High-speed steels can be used for machining metals at high speeds; some of them operate up to dull red temperatures.

Steel, stainless (see STAINLESS STEEL, pp. 499 *et seq.*).

Sterling silver (see p. 480).

Sticking coefficient, Sticking factor, Sticking fraction. Of the particles in a low-pressure environment (whether pump-fluid, etc., due to backstreaming, or evaporated material from heated bodies), not all are condensed or deposited on the cool walls of the chamber. The ratio of the number of particles sticking to the walls to the total number *striking* the walls per unit area is called the sticking coefficient.[2]

Sticking vacuum. So-called because the mercury appears to adhere to the glass in a McLeod gauge (p. 348). This is generally the lowest possible pressure readable on this type of gauge, about 10^{-6} torr under good conditions.

Stop-off lacquer. A cellulose or nitrocellulose lacquer used for limiting areas of electroplates. It is often colored a bright red for identification and visibility. The lacquer

---

[1] Also known as "case hardening."

[2] The coefficient varies with the kind of gas. More molecules will adhere to areas of small dimensions (orifices) so that in baking vacuum systems, these areas will require particular attention. In this connection, heating tapes are useful.

Sylvania Alloys

ALLOY NO.	COMPOSITION (PERCENT)	TENSILE STRENGTH (1000 PSI) ANNEALED	TENSILE STRENGTH (1000 PSI) HARD	YIELD STRENGTH (1000 PSI) ANNEALED	ELONGATION (PERCENT) ANNEALED	SPECIFIC GRAVITY (GM/CC)	RESISTIVITY (OHM-MIL-FT)	COEFFICIENT OF LINEAR EXPANSION/°C $\times 10^{-6}$
4	Ni 41.5–42.5 Cr 5.4 –5.9 Mn 0.15–0.25 C 0.07 max Si 0.15–0.30 S 0.025 max Al 0.10–0.20 P 0.025 max Fe balance	80 min	—	40 min	30	8.12	565 microhm-cm 94.2	7.4(0°–100°C)
42	Ni 41–43 Mn 0.75–1.25 C 0.15 max Si 0.30 max S 0.020 max P 0.02 max Fe balance	70 min	120–160	50 min	28	8.12	420 microhm-cm 70.0	9.53(20°–500°C)
52	Ni 51 Fe balance	70 min	120–160	50 min	25	8.25	260 microhm-cm 43.2	9.5(20°–500°C)
55	Cr 27–30 Mn 1.0 max C 0.16 max P 0.04 max Fe balance	90 min	—	70 min	23	7.67	433.4 microhm-cm 72.2	9.9(20°–500°C)

can be applied by brush or spray and is easily removed after plating by rinsing the parts in acetone or other suitable solvent. See p. 25.

Stop-off in brazing (see pp. 37, 358).

S.T.P. or **STP.** Standard Temperature and Pressure, i.e., 0°C and 760 mm Hg (or 1 atmosphere). See GAS LAWS, p. 265.

Straightening tungsten wire (see p. 86).

Strains in glass and Detection of (see pp. 285, 287).

Stresses in glass-to-metal seals, etc. see pp. 55–62, 269–274, 289).

Stripping. This term refers to the removal of electroplates, etc., from base metals and also to the removal of plastic insulation from copper or other wires. Solutions for accomplishing these tasks are described on pp. 33–35.

Strontium. This element is of importance in electron tube technology because its oxide is almost always mixed with the oxide of barium in approximately equal proportions as constituents of the materials in oxide-coated cathodes (see pp. 96–97).

Substrate. Literally, an underlayer. The base upon which something is applied or deposited. Thin films of metal and other materials can be deposited by evaporation or bombardment (see DEPOSITION, p. 224, and SPUTTERING, p. 498) upon the surfaces of metals, glass, ceramics, plastics, etc., which thus become substrates.

Svea metal. This is a pure form of ingot iron of European origin, similar to ARMCO IRON (p. 307).

Sylvania alloys. Some of the Sylvania alloys are tabulated on p. 509. The Sylvania No. 4 (Sealmet #4) is a glass-sealing metal suitable for bonds with soft glasses such as Corning 001, 012, and 8160. Driver-Harris Alloy No. 14 and Carpenter Alloy No. 426 have the same composition, although their expansion coefficients and thermal conductivities are given as slightly different.

Tantalum.[1] A refractory metal much used in experimental and high-power electron tubes and in other vacuum and chemical equipment. In pure form tantalum has the following properties:

Atomic number	73
Atomic weight	180.9
Melting point (°C)	2996 ± 50
Vapor pressure at 1727°C or 2000°K (torr)	9.52×10^{-11}
Specific heat (gm-cal/gm/°C) at 20°C	0.036
Thermal conductivity, 0–100°C (cgs)	0.130
Lattice type	body-centered cubic
Lattice constant, Kx units (A)	3.296
Density or specific gravity (gm/cc)	16.6
Density (lb/in³)	0.601
Coefficient of linear expansion/°C, 0–100°C	6.5×10^{-6}
Heat of sublimation (cal/gm-atom) at 0°K	$185.5 \pm 0.3 \times 10^3$
Heat of combustion (cal/gm)	1380
Electrical resistivity (microhm-cm): at 18°C	12.4
at 1000°C	54
at 1500°C	71
Temperature coefficient of electrical resistivity/°C, 0–100°C	$3.8–10^{-3}$

[1] Much of the material on tantalum is taken from the literature of the Fansteel Metallurgical Corporation, North Chicago, Illinois. Reproduced by permission.

Average apparent electron work function (ev)	4.10
Average apparent + ion work function (ev)	10.0
Electron emission (ma/cm^2) at 2000°K	19.5
at 1500°K	4.7×10^{-3}
at 1273°K	1×10^{-5}
Magnetic susceptibility (cgs)	$+0.93 \times 10^{-6}$

Mechanical properties:

Tensile strength, annealed sheet (psi)	50,000
annealed wire (psi)	100,000
Elongation in 2 inches (%) annealed sheet	35
annealed wire	11
Hardness, Rockwell E, annealed sheet	80–95
Young's modulus of elasticity (psi $\times 10^6$)	27

Machinability index: like cold-rolled steel with CCl_4 coolant.
Coefficient of friction: galls against itself and other metals.

Because tantalum reacts with hydrogen at elevated temperatures, components for electron tubes made of this metal must be outgassed in high vacuum (pressures of 10^{-6} torr or lower). Vacuum outgassing is most rapidly accomplished at 2000°C, although temperatures as low as 1800°C can be used for longer times. The major contaminants of tantalum are oxygen, carbon, nitrogen, and hydrogen. If both oxygen and carbon are present (which is likely to be the case if the metal has been handled without due regard for cleanliness), a reaction between them takes place in the neighborhood of 1600°C with the liberation of carbon monoxide. Raising the temperature to 1800°C removes whichever constituent is present in the smaller amount. Very small traces of oxide can be eliminated only at temperatures in excess of 2000°C, and this is true also for nitrogen. Hydrogen can be removed by vacuum-outgassing at 650°C. All outgassing procedures must be preceded by thorough chemical cleaning or degreasing in fresh solvents.

Because of its affinity for gases, tantalum can act as a *getter*. This phenomenon occurs over a temperature range of 700° to 1200°C, with the maximum in the neighborhood of 1000°C. When heated, a completely degassed tantalum component will, therefore, absorb gases from other parts of a vacuum tube and hold them to a greater or lesser extent at temperatures below 1200°C. At 1500°C the metal begins to evolve any absorbed gases, with complete elimination only at temperatures in excess of 2000°C.

Tantalum is very inert chemically at and somewhat above room temperature, so that strong reagents may be used to clean it. Aqua regia or hot chromic-sulfuric cleaning fluid (p. 5) is used to remove foreign contaminants originating from tools, handling, etc., without attack on the tantalum itself. Grit-blasted tantalum components (clean steel grit should be used rather than sand because of the difficulty of removing silica particles embedded in the surface) are to be cleaned in the same way to remove and dissolve grit particles. In designing tantalum parts, avoid pockets and unsealed overlaps because of the difficulty in flushing away entrapped chemicals used for cleaning.

Because of its very high melting point and low vapor pressure, exceeded only by those of tungsten and rhenium, tantalum tube elements can be operated at high temperatures. This makes it useful in such locations as those close to high-temperature tungsten filaments, as well as for cathodes emitting by electron bombardment (pp. 101, 167) and for high heat-dissipation anodes. Steel-grit-blasted anodes can be operated safely up to 25 watts per square inch of anode surface.

Tantalum is easily spot-welded in air without harmful oxidation if the timing is limited to one cycle. If the welding is done under water, or water and alcohol mixtures, 3 to 10-cycle timing may be used. For tantalum sheet of 0.004-inch to 0.006-inch thickness, a current flow of approximately 2000 amperes at 1.5 to 2.0 volts is required, so that heavy copper leads and tight, clean connections on the welder are imperative. Current measurements are to be made when the equipment is warm, i.e., when the coils and leads have their highest electrical resistance. Tantalum can be spot-welded easily to nickel and platinum and, without too much difficulty, to tungsten and molybdenum. In some cases nickel or platinum as a flux (p. 253) can be used for making welds between tungsten or molybdenum and tantalum.

In designing tubes with tantalum components which are to be outgassed by induction during processing, bear in mind the high temperatures required for such outgassing. This demands that low-temperature materials (oxide-coated cathodes, copper, nickel, stainless steel, and even platinum, in some cases) cannot be used near the tantalum element without danger of evaporation or destruction.

Tantalum can be brazed to itself and to other metals (nickel, stainless steel, copper, tungsten, molybdenum, iron, etc.) if the braze material contains nickel and if the process is carried out in a vacuum at a pressure not higher than 10^{-6} torr. Brazes between tantalum and tantalum, tantalum and tungsten, and tantalum and molybdenum or other refractory metals can be made with pure nickel (melting point 1435°C) with a molybdenum-nickel alloy (Mo 46.5%, Ni 53.5%, melting point 1320°C), a palladium-nickel alloy (Pd 30%, Ni 70%, melting point 1320°C), various copper-nickel alloys (cupro-nickels), and others. The selection of a braze alloy depends on the kind and shape of the metals to be brazed and the method of heating. In brazing tantalum to nickel or stainless steel, for example, a gold-nickel braze alloy[1] (Au 82%, Ni 18%, melting point 960°C) has been found to make strong bonds and to wet the tantalum, as well as the other metal, with considerable facility.

The use of tantalum hydride in making metal-to-ceramic seals by the "active metal" process is discussed on p. 67.

The vapor pressure of tantalum, as mentioned above, is extremely low. The table on p. 148 gives the vapor pressure values at various temperatures.

Tantalum is a ductile metal which can be formed by any of the standard procedures used for mild steel. All forming operations are done at room temperature, since heating does not increase tantalum's ductility. In fact, the absorption of oxygen or other gases at higher temperatures may cause embrittlement. The steel dies used for blanking or punching should have a clearance of about 6% of the thickness of the metal being worked. Tantalum has a greater tendency to seize or gall than mild steel so that the use of a light oil or trichloroethane is recommended. Ampco metal (No. 21 or 22), beryllium copper, and certain low-melting alloys can be used for forming tantalum, and rubber against metal can be used for the pneumatic or hydraulic forming of parts such as diaphragms.

---

[1] Premabraze #130 VTG, Handy & Harman Company, New York, New York; also Nioro, Western Gold & Platinum Company, Belmont, California.

In the deep-drawing of tantalum, only fully annealed metal is to be used. Work-hardening is slow in tantalum and begins to appear at the top rather than at the deepest part of the draw. Draws of a depth up to the diameter can be made in one pass, although if more than one drawing operation is to be done, the first pass should not exceed 50% of the diameter.

Where several severe forming or very deep drawing operations are to be performed, intermediate anneals are required, and these should be done at temperatures of not less than 1100°C in high vacuum.

Tantalum spins with relative facility by standard techniques. Thorough cleaning should follow all forming operations to remove tool particles, lubricants, and other foreign materials.

Machining of tantalum is done readily with high-speed steel tools kept sharpened with as much positive rake as the strength of the tool point will stand. Turning speeds of less than 100 surface feet per minute will cause the metal to tear. Recommended coolants are carbon tetrachloride or trichloroethane.

Teflon. This names two general types of fluorocarbon plastics which have many technical and commercial uses. The TFE (tetrafluoroethylene) plastic exists in several forms, but the FEP (fluorinated ethylene-propylene) type, with significantly different though related properties, is produced at present in one form. Teflon TFE is usually fabricated by a kind of "sintering" technique in which the basic powder is aggregated into dense, coherent shapes at normal temperatures. Uniform pressure is applied to the unheated TFE material, which is then strengthened by heating to 370°–380°C, whereupon the resin particles coalesce and then are cooled to below 327°C. At slightly above this temperature, the TFE resin enters into a gel state, which is not conducive to melt flow, as a consequence of which preforming, sintering, and postforming are the techniques most commonly used.

FEP resin, on the other hand, exhibits a melt flow much like that of other thermoplastic resins and can thus be processed in conventional plastic molding and extruding equipment. Shapes that are very difficult or impossible to mold with Teflon TFE resins can often be achieved easily with Teflon FEP.

A marked change in volume of 1.0–1.8% occurs for TFE resins in the "transition zone" from 18.3°C to 25.0°C. Parts which have been machined on either side of this zone will change dimensions if permitted to go through the zone. For this reason, final operating temperature of a precision part must be accurately known. Teflon FEP plastics do not exhibit this peculiar transition-expansion characteristic.

Teflon TFE resins have high strength, toughness, and self-lubrication at low temperatures. Both the TFE and FEP types are useful down to −265°C, and are flexible down to −79°C.

The thermal conductivity of Teflon 1 (TFE) is 1.7 ± 0.3 (Btu/ft^2-sec)/(°F/in); for Teflon 100X (FEP), 1.4 ± 0.3.

The heat distortion temperatures (obtained by ASTM D 648) for Teflon 1 and for Teflon 100X are as follows:

Type	Stress (psi)	Heat distortion temperature (°C)
TFE Teflon 1	66	123
TFE Teflon	264	56
FEP Teflon 100X	66	70
FEP Teflon	264	51

Parts made from Teflon fluorocarbon resins exhibit "elastic memory," i.e., they tend to return to their original dimensions after a deformation, but the process of recovery may take a long time. A fabricated part which creeps or deforms over a period of time under stress will recover its original shape when stress is removed and the part is raised to sintering temperature (p. 513). However, partial recovery will take place at lower temperatures; the recovery to be expected at any given temperature is substantially complete within 15 minutes, but extent of recovery increases with increased temperature.

For example, a TFE filament 4 inches long, stretched to a length of 12 inches, and heated to 100°C, recovers to approximately 11 inches within 15 minutes and then remains essentially unchanged. A similar piece heated to 200°C recovers to 10 inches. The first piece, after additional heating to 200°C, recovers further to 10 inches. When heated to 350°C both pieces return to their original 4-inch length.

Some indication of the vacuum or outgassing properties of Teflon materials may be obtained by examining their decomposition rates at elevated temperatures. This is shown in the following table:

TEMPERATURE (°C)	RATE OF DECOMPOSITION (PERCENT PER HOUR)			
	FEP TEFLON 100X	FEP TEFLON 6, 30	TFE TEFLON 1, 5, 7	
	INITIAL	INITIAL	INITIAL	STEADY STATE
232	0.004	0.0001 to 0.0002	0.00001 to 0.00005	1×10^{-11}
260	0.001	0.0006	0.0001 to 0.0002	1×10^{-9}
316	0.02	0.005	0.0005	0.000002
371	0.3	0.03	0.004	0.0009

A maximum service temperature of 260°C for TFE resins and 204°C for FEP resins is recommended for most applications. Adequate ventilation is required where fabrication temperatures above 340°C are encountered.

The rate of decomposition of the fluorocarbon resins appears, in many cases, to decrease with continual exposure. A very low, fairly steady decomposition rate for parts made of TFE resins Teflon 1, 5, and 7 is established after less than 1% of the material has decomposed.

The tables following give some of the mechanical and electrical properties of fluorocarbon resins.

The resistance of TFE resins to weathering and ultraviolet light is excellent. The permeability of molded Teflon sheet is comparable to that of Neoprene and butyl rubber.

Machining Teflon resins: Rods, tubes, billets, and other shapes of Teflon should be stress-relieved before machining, especially when working to close tolerances. Stress-relieving or annealing is done by heating the material above its service temperature, but below 328°C for TFE and 260°C for FEP. The piece is then cooled slowly. Annealing for 1 hour per inch of thickness is adequate. It may be necessary to rough-machine the piece to within 0.015 inch–0.030 inch and then reanneal to eliminate the stresses introduced by the tool.

Mechanical Properties of Fluorocarbon Resins

Property	TFE Teflon 1	Filled[1] TFE Teflon 1	FEP Teflon 100x
Fatigue resistance (23°C)			
cycles to failure at stress			
(psi) of 1000	$>2 \times 10^7$	—	$>7 \times 10^6$
1400	$>7 \times 10^6$	—	$>7.2 \times 10^6$
1450	12,000[2]	—	1300
1500	1200[2]	—	960
Impact strength, tensile,			
($ft\text{-}lb/in^3$) at 23°C	320	—	1020
($ft\text{-}lb/in^3$) at −54°C	105	—	365
Izod (ft-lb) at 23°C	2.9	—	Sample bends
at −54°C	2.3	—	2.9
Hardness: Rockwell-R	58	—	25
Durometer-D	52	—	59
Durometer-A	98	—	96
Friction properties:			
max. PV values, P (psi)			
V (ft/min)			
continuous use	1000	10,000	600
intermittent use	3000	20,000	1000
Sliding tape weight loss[3]			
Average weight loss (gm/in^2)	0.337	—	0.174
Revolving disk weight loss[4]			
Cumulative weight loss (mg)			
10 test cycles	0.35	—	0.30
50 test cycles	1.65	—	0.60
100 test cycles	2.2	—	1.0
500 test cycles	5.7	—	3.9
1000 test cycles	8.9	—	7.5
2000 test cycles	13.4	—	13.2
Tape length required to abrade through wire coating[5]			
Average tape length, in			
Heat aging: none	—	76	107
Heat aging: 96hr at 150°C	—	78	94
Heat aging: 500hr at 150°C	—	98	118
Heat aging: 96 hr at 200°C	—	84	87

[1] A 25% glass-fiber-filled TFE Teflon 1. [2] Yielded, but did not break.

[3] Armstrong abrasion test (ASTM D 1242–56). This test measures abrasion resistance of flat surfaces by drawing abrasive tape, under load, over test specimens at a slip rate of 100 in/min. With #320 abrasive under a 15-lb. load, weight loss was measured after 200 revolutions (1 hour 40 minutes).

[4] Taber abrasion test. This test measures abrasion resistance of a flat surface by rotating a 4-inch diameter specimen disk beneath an abrasive under load. A 1000-gm load was used on a Calibrase wheel No. CS-17F.

[5] Tape abrasion test (MIL-T-5438). This test measures abrasion resistance of wire coatings by drawing, under load, a clean abrasive cloth tape of continuous length across the test wire until the coating is worn through. A 1-pound load on No. 400 grit was used on a coating thickness of 0.015 inch.

ELECTRICAL PROPERTIES OF FLUOROCARBON RESINS

PROPERTY	TFE	FEP TEFLON 100X
Volume resistivity (ohm-cm)	$>10^{19}$	$>10^{19}$
Surface resistivity (ohm-cm)	$>10^{17}$	$>10^{17}$
Dielectric strength (volt/mil) at 60 cycle, short-time test		
Thickness 0.100 inch	500	—
Thickness 0.010 inch	2000	—
Thickness 0.001 inch	4000	—
Dielectric strength[1] (volt/mil) short-time test, 1-inch electrode in silicone oil		
at 38°C	900	—
at 150°C	850	—
at 260°C	800	—
Dielectric strength (volt/mil) 40-second test, $\frac{1}{16}$-inch breakdown path, $\frac{3}{4}$-inch electrode with $\frac{1}{8}$-inch edge radius		
at 100 cy	600	—
at 1 kc	470	—
at 10 kc	390	—
at 100 kc	340	—
at 1 mc	310	—
at 10 mc	140	—
at 100 mc	150	—
Dielectric constant		
60 cycles to 60 mc	2.1	2.1
3000 mc	2.1	2.1
Dissipation factor		
60 cycles to 60 mc	>0.0003	0.0003
3000 mc	>0.0003	0.0006 (at 50 Mc; see below)
Effect of frequency on dissipation factor at 23°C[2]		
at 100 cy	—	0.0003
at 1 kc	—	0.0002
at 10 kc	—	0.0002
at 100 kc	—	0.0005
at 1 mc	—	0.0007
at 50 mc	—	0.0006
Arc resistance	Will not track	Will not track

1 ASTM D 149-55 T.
2 ASTM D 150-54 T.

Ordinary twist drills may be used for drilling, but special drills designed for plastics are recommended for production work. Conventional reamers produce holes with good finish and accurate dimensions. Because of localized thermal expansion, however, cuts made with a fixed reamer tend to be undersize, and expansion reamers may be preferred.

Teflon resins can be threaded and tapped with ordinary tools. Turning, facing, and boring operations are done in a lathe.

TYPICAL ELECTRICAL PROPERTIES OF REINFORCED TFE PLASTICS

MATERIAL	THICKNESS (INCHES)	DIELECTRIC[1] STRENGTH (VOLT/MIL)	DIELECTRIC[2] CONSTANT	DISSIPATION FACTOR	VOLUME[3] RESISTIVITY (OHM-CM)	SURFACE RESISTIVITY (OHM/SQUARE UNIT)
Unfilled	0.07	400	2.1	0.0002	1.89×10^{19}	10^{17}
15% milled glass fiber	0.05	250	2.4	0.0006	5.0×10^{14} dry 6.7×10^{8} wet	2.9×10^{13} dry 4.0×10^{12} wet
35% milled glass fiber	0.05	230	2.8	0.0019	1.25×10^{15} dry 1.78×10^{8} wet	2.4×10^{13} dry 6.1×10^{12} wet
50% quartz	—	—	3.65	0.008	—	—
15% graphite	0.06	—	—	—	2.44×10^{6}	1×10^{5}
35% graphite	0.06	—	—	—	2.44×10^{6}	1×10^{5}
15% copper	0.06	—	—	—	2.44×10^{6}	1×10^{5}

[1] ASTM D 149-55 T.
[2] ASTM D 150-54 T.
[3] ASTM D 257-57 T.

TEMPERATURE CONVERSION CHART*†

−459.4 to 0			0 to 100						100 to 1000					
C		F	C		F	C		F	C		F	C		F
−273	**−459.4**		−17.8	**0**	32	10.0	**50**	122.0	38	**100**	212	260	**500**	932
−268	**−450**		−17.2	**1**	33.8	10.6	**51**	123.8	43	**110**	230	266	**510**	950
−262	**−440**		−16.7	**2**	35.6	11.1	**52**	125.6	49	**120**	248	271	**520**	968
−257	**−430**		−16.1	**3**	37.4	11.7	**53**	127.4	54	**130**	266	277	**530**	986
−251	**−420**		−15.6	**4**	39.2	12.2	**54**	129.2	60	**140**	284	282	**540**	1004
−246	**−410**		−15.0	**5**	41.0	12.8	**55**	131.0	66	**150**	302	288	**550**	1022
−240	**−400**		−14.4	**6**	42.8	13.3	**56**	132.8	71	**160**	320	293	**560**	1040
−234	**−390**		−13.9	**7**	44.6	13.9	**57**	134.6	77	**170**	338	299	**570**	1058
−229	**−380**		−13.3	**8**	46.4	14.4	**58**	136.4	82	**180**	356	304	**580**	1076
−223	**−370**		−12.8	**9**	48.2	15.0	**59**	138.2	88	**190**	374	310	**590**	1094
−218	**−360**		−12.2	**10**	50.0	15.6	**60**	140.0	93	**200**	392	316	**600**	1112
−212	**−350**		−11.7	**11**	51.8	16.1	**61**	141.8	99	**210**	410	321	**610**	1130
−207	**−340**		−11.1	**12**	53.6	16.7	**62**	143.6	100	**212**	413.6	327	**620**	1148
−201	**−330**		−10.6	**13**	55.4	17.2	**63**	145.4	104	**220**	428	332	**630**	1166
−196	**−320**		−10.0	**14**	57.2	17.8	**64**	147.2	110	**230**	446	338	**640**	1184
−190	**−310**		− 9.4	**15**	59.0	18.3	**65**	149.0	116	**240**	464	343	**650**	1202
−184	**−300**		− 8.9	**16**	60.8	18.9	**66**	150.8	121	**250**	482	349	**660**	1220
−179	**−290**		− 8.3	**17**	62.6	19.4	**67**	152.6	127	**260**	500	354	**670**	1238
−173	**−280**		− 7.8	**18**	64.4	20.0	**68**	154.4	132	**270**	518	360	**680**	1256
−169	**−273**	−459.4	− 7.2	**19**	66.2	20.6	**69**	156.2	138	**280**	536	366	**690**	1274
−168	**−270**	−454	− 6.7	**20**	68.0	21.1	**70**	158.0	143	**290**	554	371	**700**	1292
−162	**−260**	−436	− 6.1	**21**	69.8	21.7	**71**	159.8	149	**300**	572	377	**710**	1310
−157	**−250**	−418	− 5.6	**22**	71.6	22.2	**72**	161.6	154	**310**	590	382	**720**	1328
−161	**−240**	−400	− 5.0	**23**	73.4	22.8	**73**	163.4	160	**320**	608	388	**730**	1346
−146	**−230**	−382	− 4.4	**24**	75.2	23.3	**74**	165.2	166	**330**	626	393	**740**	1364
−140	**−220**	−364	− 3.9	**25**	77.0	23.9	**75**	167.0	171	**340**	644	399	**750**	1382
−134	**−210**	−346	− 3.3	**26**	78.8	24.4	**76**	168.8	177	**350**	662	404	**760**	1400
−129	**−200**	−328	− 2.8	**27**	80.6	25.0	**77**	170.6	182	**360**	680	410	**770**	1418
−123	**−190**	−310	− 2.2	**28**	82.4	25.6	**78**	172.4	188	**370**	698	416	**780**	1436
−118	**−180**	−292	− 1.7	**29**	84.2	26.1	**79**	174.2	193	**380**	716	421	**790**	1454
−112	**−170**	−274	− 1.1	**30**	86.0	26.7	**80**	176.0	199	**390**	734	427	**800**	1472
−107	**−160**	−256	− 0.6	**31**	87.8	27.2	**81**	177.8	204	**400**	752	432	**810**	1490
−101	**−150**	−238	0.0	**32**	89.6	27.8	**82**	179.6	210	**410**	770	438	**820**	1508
− 96	**−140**	−220	0.6	**33**	91.4	28.3	**83**	181.4	216	**420**	788	443	**830**	1526
− 90	**−130**	−202	1.1	**34**	93.2	28.9	**84**	183.2	221	**430**	806	449	**840**	1544
− 84	**−120**	−184	1.7	**35**	95.0	29.4	**85**	185.0	227	**440**	824	454	**850**	1562
− 79	**−110**	−166	2.2	**36**	96.8	30.0	**86**	186.8	232	**450**	842	460	**860**	1580
− 73	**−100**	−148	2.8	**37**	98.6	30.6	**87**	188.6	238	**460**	860	466	**870**	1598
− 68	**− 90**	−130	3.3	**38**	100.4	31.1	**88**	190.4	243	**470**	878	471	**880**	1616
− 62	**− 80**	−112	3.9	**39**	102.2	31.7	**89**	192.2	249	**480**	896	477	**890**	1634
− 57	**− 70**	− 94	4.4	**40**	104.0	32.2	**90**	194.0	254	**490**	914	482	**900**	1652
− 51	**− 60**	− 76	5.0	**41**	105.8	32.8	**91**	195.8				488	**910**	1670
− 46	**− 50**	− 58	5.6	**42**	107.6	33.3	**92**	197.6				493	**920**	1688
− 40	**− 40**	− 40	6.1	**43**	109.4	33.9	**93**	199.4				499	**930**	1706
− 34	**− 30**	− 22	6.7	**44**	111.2	34.4	**94**	201.2				504	**940**	1724
− 29	**− 20**	− 4	7.2	**45**	113.0	35.0	**95**	203.0				510	**950**	1742
− 23	**− 10**	14	7.8	**46**	114.8	35.6	**96**	204.8				516	**960**	1760
− 17.8	**0**	32	8.3	**47**	116.6	36.1	**97**	206.6				521	**970**	1778
			8.9	**48**	118.4	36.7	**98**	208.4				527	**980**	1796
			9.4	**49**	120.2	37.2	**99**	210.2				532	**990**	1814
						37.8	**100**	212.0				538	**1000**	1832

*Reprinted by permission of *Metal Progress.*
†Albert Sauveur type of table. Look up reading in **middle column**; if in degrees centigrade, read Fahrenheit equivalent in right-hand column; if in degrees Fahrenheit,

−459.4 to 0			1000 to 2000						2000 to 3000					
C		F	C		F	C		F	C		F	C		F
−273	−459.4		538	1000	1832	816	1500	2732	1093	2000	3632	1371	2500	4532
−268	−450		543	1010	1850	821	1510	2750	1099	2010	3650	1377	2510	4550
−262	−440		549	1020	1868	827	1520	2768	1104	2020	3668	1382	2520	4568
−257	−430		554	1030	1886	832	1530	2786	1110	2030	3686	1388	2530	4586
−251	−420		560	1040	1904	838	1540	2804	1116	2040	3704	1393	2540	4604
−246	−410		566	1050	1922	843	1550	2822	1121	2050	3722	1399	2550	4622
−240	−400		571	1060	1940	849	1560	2840	1127	2060	3740	1404	2560	4640
−234	−390		577	1070	1958	854	1570	2858	1132	2070	3758	1410	2570	4658
−229	−380		582	1080	1976	860	1580	2876	1138	2080	3776	1416	2580	4676
−223	−370		588	1090	1994	866	1590	2894	1143	2090	3794	1421	2590	4694
−218	−360		593	1100	2012	871	1600	2912	1149	2100	3812	1427	2600	4712
−212	−350		599	1110	2030	877	1610	2930	1154	2110	3830	1432	2610	4730
−207	−340		604	1120	2048	882	1620	2948	1160	2120	3848	1438	2620	4748
−201	−330		610	1130	2066	888	1630	2966	1166	2130	3866	1443	2630	4766
−196	−320		616	1140	2084	893	1640	2984	1171	2140	3884	1449	2640	4784
−190	−310		621	1150	2102	899	1650	3002	1177	2150	3902	1454	2650	4802
−184	−300		627	1160	2120	904	1660	3020	1182	2160	3920	1460	2660	4820
−179	−290		632	1170	2138	910	1670	3038	1188	2170	3938	1466	2670	4838
−173	−280		638	1180	2156	916	1680	3056	1193	2180	3956	1471	2680	4856
−169	−273	−459.4	643	1190	2174	921	1690	3074	1199	2190	3974	1477	2690	4874
−168	−270	−454	649	1200	2192	927	1700	3092	1204	2200	3992	1482	2700	4892
−162	−260	−436	654	1210	2210	932	1710	3110	1210	2210	4010	1488	2710	4910
−157	−250	−418	660	1220	2228	938	1720	3128	1216	2220	4028	1493	2720	4928
−161	−240	−400	666	1230	2246	943	1730	3146	1221	2230	4046	1499	2730	4946
−146	−230	−382	671	1240	2264	949	1740	3164	1227	2240	4064	1504	2740	4964
−140	−220	−364	677	1250	2282	954	1750	3182	1232	2250	4082	1510	2750	4982
−134	−210	−346	682	1260	2300	960	1760	3200	1238	2260	4100	1516	2760	5000
−129	−200	−328	688	1270	2318	966	1770	3218	1243	2270	4118	1521	2770	5018
−123	−190	−310	693	1280	2336	971	1780	3236	1249	2280	4136	1527	2780	5036
−118	−180	−292	699	1290	2354	977	1790	3254	1254	2290	4154	1532	2790	5054
−112	−170	−274	704	1300	2372	982	1800	3272	1260	2300	4172	1538	2800	5072
−107	−160	−256	710	1310	2390	988	1810	3290	1266	2310	4190	1543	2810	5090
−101	−150	−238	716	1320	2408	993	1820	3308	1271	2320	4208	1549	2820	5108
− 96	−140	−220	721	1330	2426	999	1830	3326	1277	2330	4226	1554	2830	5126
− 90	−130	−202	727	1340	2444	1004	1840	3344	1282	2340	4244	1560	2840	5144
− 84	−120	−184	732	1350	2462	1010	1850	3362	1288	2350	4262	1566	2850	5162
− 79	−110	−166	738	1360	2480	1016	1860	3380	1293	2360	4280	1571	2860	5180
− 73	−100	−148	743	1370	2498	1021	1870	3398	1299	2370	4298	1577	2870	5198
− 68	− 90	−130	749	1380	2516	1027	1880	3416	1304	2380	4316	1582	2880	5216
− 62	− 80	−112	754	1390	2534	1032	1890	3434	1310	2390	4334	1588	2890	5234
− 57	− 70	− 94	760	1400	2552	1038	1900	3452	1316	2400	4352	1593	2900	5252
− 51	− 60	− 76	766	1410	2570	1043	1910	3470	1321	2410	4370	1599	2910	5270
− 46	− 50	− 58	771	1420	2588	1049	1920	3488	1327	2420	4388	1604	2920	5288
− 40	− 40	− 40	777	1430	2606	1054	1930	3506	1332	2430	4406	1610	2930	5306
− 34	− 30	− 22	782	1440	2624	1060	1940	3524	1338	2440	4424	1616	2940	5324
− 29	− 20	− 4	788	1450	2642	1066	1950	3542	1343	2450	4442	1621	2950	5342
− 23	− 10	14	793	1460	2660	1071	1960	3560	1349	2460	4460	1627	2960	5360
− 17.8	0	32	799	1470	2678	1077	1970	3578	1354	2470	4478	1632	2970	5378
			804	1480	2696	1082	1980	3596	1360	2480	4496	1638	2980	5396
			810	1490	2714	1088	1990	3614	1366	2490	4514	1643	2990	5414
						1093	2000	3632				1649	3000	5432

read centigrade equivalent in left-hand column. Values as printed in "Bethlehem Alloy Steels."

Various techniques have been developed for attaining special surfaces on TFE and FEP parts to which conventional adhesives will bond. Good bonding strengths can be achieved with adhesives in bonding to glass, steel, aluminum, copper, ceramics, and plastics. Although parts made of TFE or FEP Teflons will withstand high temperatures, the maximum temperature of the adhesive may limit the application and should be established beforehand.[1]

Tellurium copper. The addition of small amounts of tellurium to copper makes that metal more easily machinable. Tellurium is an element in the lead group, and since it has a higher vapor pressure (10^{-5} torr at 250°C) than lead, the use of tellurium copper in making vacuum devices should be restricted to those which are not to be heated.

Temperature conversion chart (see pp. 518–519).

Therlo alloy. A cobalt-nickel-iron alloy for sealing to hard or thermal shock-resistant glasses. It matches Corning glasses 7052 and 7040 in expansivity from 80°C to the anneal point. Permanent vacuum-type seals are produced with a simple oxidation procedure. Therlo is resistant to mercury. It is readily machined and can be welded, soldered, and brazed.

Thermal conductivity. The rate of transfer of heat by conduction through a substance; also called *heat conductivity*. If the two opposite faces of a rectangular solid are maintained at temperatures t_1 and t_2, the heat conducted across the solid section a and thickness d in a time T will be:

$$Q = \frac{K(t_2 - t_1)aT}{d}.$$

The letter K is a constant depending on the nature of the substance, designated as the specific thermal or heat conductivity; Q is often given in calories (or gm-cal); t_1 and t_2 are in °C; a is in cm^2, and d is in cm. Another commonly used unit for thermal conductivity is the British thermal unit (Btu)/hr/ft^2 (or in^2) for a temperature gradient of 1°F/ft (or in.). These units are converted as follows:

1 Btu/ft^2-sec for a temperature gradient of

$$1°\text{F/in} = 1.2404 \text{ gm-cal } (15°\text{C})/\text{cm}^2/\text{sec}$$

for a temperature gradient of 1°C/cm^2.

1 gm-cal (15°C)/cm^2/sec for a temperature gradient of

$$1°\text{C/cm} = 0.8062 \text{ Btu (mean)}/\text{ft}^2\text{-sec}$$

for a temperature gradient of 1°F/in.[2]

A nomograph for determining the thermal conductivities of a number of metals and alloys has been worked out by R. L. Peters.[2] The table on pp. 521–525 gives the thermal conductivities for some metals and alloys. The data was gathered from manufacturers and reduced to a single comparative unit (cgs).[3]

---

[1] The foregoing material on Teflon is excerpted from "New Design Data for Teflon," by L. H. Gillespie, D. O. Saxton, and F. M. Chapman, *Machine Design*, January 21, 1960 and February 18, 1960. Reproduced by permission. The original paper should be consulted for additional data.

[2] R. L. Peters, *Materials in Design Engineering*, **55,** 90–91, 1962.

[3] The cgs (centimeter-gram second) unit may be abbreviated (cal/cm^2-sec)/(°C/cm).

Thermal conductivities of some metals and alloys

Thermal conductivity is given in cgs units: gram-calories of heat transmitted per second through a plate 1 cm thick across an area of 1 cm^2 when the temperature difference is 1°C.

Other physical properties of the metal will be found on the page number given in the last column. Explanation of superscript numbers is on p. 525.

Metal or Alloy	Temperature (°C)	Thermal Conductivity	Page no.
Advance[1] (Cu 55 percent, Ni 45 percent)	100	0.059	150
Alchrome[2] (Fe-Cr-Al alloy: heating elements)	25	0.045	
Allegheny #42[3] (glass-sealing alloy)	25	0.036	58
Allegheny #4750[3] (glass-sealing alloy)	25	0.037	56
Aluminum, commercially pure (#1100 alloy)	−160	0.514	152
	+20	0.570	
	300	0.640	
	400	0.760	
	600	1.01	
A Nickel (Nickel 200)[4]	0–100	0.142	388
	600	0.088	
Armco Iron[5] (ingot iron, magnetic material)	0–100	0.167–0.175	307
Balco[2] (Ni 70 percent, Fe 30 percent; ballast resistor elements)	25	0.069	
Beryllium	100	0.385	
Beryllium copper #25[6] annealed	0–100	0.255–0.310	163
Bismuth	18	0.019	166
Brass, red (Cu 85 percent, Zn 15 percent) wrought	0–100	0.374	
Brass, yellow (Cu 70 percent, Zn 30 percent) wrought	0–100	0.286	
Carpenter stainless #20, #20Cb[7]	100	0.049	
Cast iron, ductile	0–100	0.072	
Cast iron, gray	0–100	0.105	
Ceramvar[2] (Fe-Ni-Co alloy, alumina-to-metal seals)	20	0.040	197
	600	0.057	
Cerrobend[8] (fusible alloy)	0–100	0.045	
Chromax[1] (Ni-Cr-Fe heating element alloy)	100	0.031	
Columbium (Niobium)	25	0.13	215
Constantan (see also Advance) (Cu 55 percent, Ni 45 percent)	0–100	0.053	
Copper, 99.9%	100	0.908	219
	100–540	0.902	
	100–840	0.858	
Cupron[2] (Cu 55 percent, Ni 45 percent) (see Advance, Constantan)	25	0.056	
Cupro-Nickel, (Ni 10 percent)	25	0.115	
CM-R Alloy (see René-41 Alloy)			

(Cont.)

Metal or Alloy (*Cont.*)	Temperature (°C)	Thermal Conductivity	Page no.
D-H #14[1] (Ni 42 percent, glass-sealing alloy)	100	0.032	56
D-Nickel (Nickel 211)[4]	0–100	0.097–0.114	394
Dumet (core Ni 42 percent, Fe 58 percent; cladding Cu 20–30 percent of total weight, glass-sealing material)	25	0.04 (approx.)	230
Duranickel (Alloy 301)[4]	0–100	0.043–0.047	395
E-Nickel (Alloy 212)[4]	0–100	0.098–0.114	395
Evanohm[2] (precision-resistance alloy) . .	0–100	0.030	
Fernico[9] (glass-seal alloy similar to Kovar, see page 322 *et seq.*)	25	0.046	58
Ferrovac-E (vacuum-melted pure Fe)[10] .	25	0.20	366
Fine silver (99.9 + Ag)	0–100	0.98–1.00	478
Gold, pure (24K) annealed	0–100	0.700	
Haynes Stellite #25[11] wrought	25	0.22	
Illium-G[12]	0–100	0.029	
Inconel (Alloy 600)[4]	0–100	0.035	294
Inconel-X (Alloy X-750)[4]	100	0.037	296
Indium	20	0.057	297
Ingot iron[5]	20	0.175	307
Invar[13] (low-expansion Fe-Ni alloy) . .	0–100	0.025	299
Invar, free machining[1], [9], [5], [3], [7] . .	0–100	0.032	
Iridium	0–100	0.139	
Iron (see Armco, Ferrovac-E, Ingot iron)			
Iron, wrought	0–100	0.142	
Iron, gray (cast)	0–100	0.105	
Kanthal DR[14]	25	0.045	310
Karma[1] (high-resistance alloy)	0–100	0.030	
K-Monel (Alloy K-500)[4]	0–100	0.044	382
KR-Monel (Alloy K-501)[4]	0–100	0.044	383
Kovar (Ni-Fe-Co glass-sealing alloy)[15] . .	30	0.0395	322
	300	0.0485	
	400	0.053	
	500	0.0585	
Lead, commercially pure	−160	0.092	342
	+ 18	0.083	
	100	0.082	
Lohm (Ni 6 percent, Cu 94 percent, low-resistance alloy)[1]	100	0.250	
Magnesium	0–100	0.376	
Manganin (Cu-Mn-Ni precision-resistor alloy)	18	0.0519	347
	100	0.0631	
	−160	0.035	
Mercury	0	0.0148	364
	17	0.0197	
Molybdenum	0–100	0.306	377

Metal or Alloy (*Cont.*)	Temperature (°C)	Thermal Conductivity	Page no.
Monels: Regular Monel (Alloy 400)[4] . .	100	0.059	382
	538	0.090	
R-Monel (Alloy R-405)[4] . . .	21	0.056	382
	538	0.080	
Monel Alloy 411[4] cast	816	0.093	
Nichrome[1] (Ni-Cr-Fe resistance alloy) . .	0–100	0.026	388
Nichrome V[1] (Ni 80 percent, Cr 20 percent, resistance-heater alloy)	0–100	0.029	388
Nickel, pure (Nickel 270)[4]	21	0.223	293
Nilvar[1] (*cf.* Invar) 293 (low-expansion alloy)	100	0.026	396
Nimonic alloy #75 (Ni-Cr)	0–100	0.029	
Niobium (see Columbium)			
Niromet #42 (Ni-Fe glass-sealing alloy)[2] .	20–100	0.038	397
Niromet #46 (Ni-Fe glass-sealing alloy)[2]	20–100	0.027	397
Niron[2] (Ni-Fe glass-sealing alloy) . . .	20–100	0.029	397
Ni-Span-C (Alloy 902[4]) annealed (constant-elasticity alloy)	0–100	0.031	
OFHC copper (See Copper)			
Palladium	0–100	0.166	425
Permalloy[3] (Ni-Fe-Mo magnetic alloy) .	0–100	0.079	
Permanickel (Alloy) 300[4]	0–100	0.136	395
Phosphor bronze, Type A (5 percent Sn) annealed	0–100	0.164	
Platinum, commercially pure, annealed . .	0–100	0.158	444
René-41 (CM-R) Alloy[9]	204	0.025	460
	427	0.032	
	649	0.039	
	760	0.043	
	982	0.051	
Rhodium	0–100	0.208	463
Rodar[2] (Ni-Fe-Co glass-sealing alloy—see Kovar, page 322)	20–100	0.050	58
Silver, fine (99.9 percent)	0–100	0.98–1.00	478
Silver, sterling (Ag 92.4 percent, Cu bal.) .	0–100	0.855	480
Silver, coin (Ag 90 percent, Cu bal.) . . .	0–100	0.845	480
Soft solder (50–50)	0–100	0.105	
Soft solder (60–40)	0–100	0.112	
Stainless steel #201, 202	0–100	0.038	
Stainless steel #301, 302, 303, 304, 304L, 316, 316L, 317	0–100	0.037	499
	650	0.050	
Stainless steel #321, 347, 348	100	0.037	500
	650	0.047	
Stainless steel #309	100	0.036	
	650	0.043	

(*Cont.*)

Metal or Alloy (*Cont.*)	Temperature (°C)	Thermal Conductivity	Page no.
Stainless steel #310	100	0.032	
	650	0.043	
Stainless steel #330	0–100	0.031	
Stainless steel #410	100	0.058	503
	650	0.066	
Stainless steel #430	0–100	0.062	503
Stainless steel #431	100	0.047	503
Stainless steel #440A	100	0.056	503
Stainless steel #442	100	0.050	
Stainless steel #446	100	0.048	
	650	0.056	
Stainless steel, precipitation hardening, #17–4PH	0–100	0.042	
Stainless steel, precipitation hardening, #17–7PH	0–100	0.040	499
Steel, low and medium carbon: AISI C1010, 1015, 1018, 1020, 1025, 1030, 1035, annealed	100	0.108–0.124	507
Steel, medium and high carbon: AISI C1040, 1045, 1055, 1060, 1070, 1080, 1095, annealed	100	0.108	
Steel, free-cutting, medium and high carbon, annealed	100	0.108	
Steel, nitriding: #135, 135 Mod., "N," "EZ,"	100	0.120	
Steel, low alloy, #13XX	100	0.108	
Steel, low alloy, #23XX, hardened	100	0.153	
Steel, low alloy, #25XX, hardened	100	0.139–0.155	
Steel, low alloy, #40XX	100	0.108	
Steel, low alloy, #41XX, hardened	100	0.099	
Steel, low alloy, #43XX, hardened	100	0.087	
Steel, low alloy, #46XX	23	0.108	
Steel, low alloy, #48XX	25	0.104	
Steel, low alloy, #51XX	0–100	0.108–0.136	
Steel, low alloy, #61XX	100	0.108	
Steel, low alloy, #86XX, 87XX	50	0.087	
Steel, low alloy, #82XX, 94XX	100	0.108	
Stellite #25[11] (Fe-Cr-W-Ni alloy) wrought	25	0.022	
Svea metal (see Ingot iron)			
Sylvania #4 (Ni 42 percent glass-sealing alloy) [16]	100	0.032	56
Tantalum[17]	17	0.126–0.130	510
Therlo[1] (Fe-Ni-Co glass-sealing alloy; see Kovar, page 322)	50	0.034	520
	100	0.035	
	500	0.042	

Metal or Alloy (*Cont.*)	Temperature (°C)	Thermal Conductivity	Page no.
Tin	0	0.153	540
	100	0.145	
Titanium, unalloyed	0–100	0.040	541
Titanium alloys	100	0.016–0.029	543
Tophet-A[2] (*cf.* Nichrome IV) (Ni-Cr resistance-heating elements)	20	0.033	545
Tophet-C[2] (Ni-Fe-Cr resistance-heating elements)	20	0.032	(*cf.* Nichrome)
Tungsten	0–100	0.472	548
Waspalloy (vacuum-melted high Ni alloy)	20–815	0.027–0.054	370
Zinc	0–100	0.254	573
Zirconium	0–100	0.059	576
No. 42 Alloy (Ni 42 percent, Fe bal.) glass-sealing alloy, annealed	0–100	0.036	58
No. 49 Alloy (Ni 49 percent, Fe bal.) glass-sealing alloy, annealed	0–100	0.042	
No. 142 Alloy[1] (glass-sealing alloy)	100	0.039	
No. 146 Alloy[1] (glass-sealing alloy)	100	0.037	
No. 152 Alloy[1] (glass-sealing alloy)	50	0.034	
No. 200 Alloy[1] (see Kanthal DR, Alchrome)			
No. 902 Alloy[4] (see Ni-Span-C)			

[1] Driver-Harris Co., Harrison, New Jersey.
[2] Wilbur B. Driver Co., Newark, New Jersey.
[3] Allegheny-Ludlum Steel Corp., Brackenridge, Pennsylvania.
[4] International Nickel Co., Huntington Alloy Division, New York, New York.
[5] Armco Steel Co., Middletown, Ohio.
[6] The Beryllium Corp., Reading, Pennsylvania.
[7] Carpenter Steel Corp., Reading, Pennsylvania.
[8] Cerro Sales Corp., New York, New York.
[9] General Electric Co., Schenectady, New York.
[10] Crucible Steel Co., Pittsburgh, Pennsylvania.
[11] Haynes Stellite Division, Union Carbide Corporation, Kokomo, Indiana.
[12] Stainless Foundry & Engineering, Inc., Milwaukee, Wisconsin.
[13] S. A. de Commentry-Fourchambault et Decazivillle (Aciéres d'Imphy).
[14] The Kanthal Corp., Stamford, Connecticut.
[15] The Carborundum Corp., Latrobe, Pennsylvania and Niagara Falls, New York.
[16] Sylvania Division of General Telephone & Electric Corp., New York, New York.
[17] Fansteel Metallurgical Corp., North Chicago, Illinois.

Thermocouples. If two wires of unlike metals or alloys are joined together firmly at one end, and this junction is heated or cooled, a small voltage (emf) will appear at the open ends. This emf is a function of the temperature difference and of the kinds of metals used. Any junction, such as a weld, braze, solder, and screw- or clamp-held

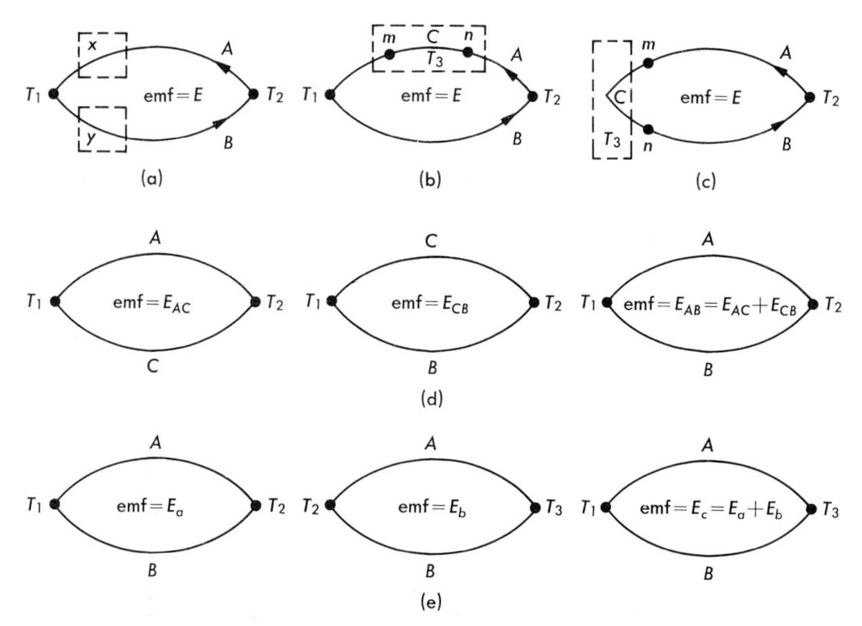

FIG. 140. Illustrating the laws relating to thermocouples.

pieces (if dissimilar, are in clean, tight contact), will exhibit this phenomenon[1] to some extent. If current is passed through such a junction, heating or cooling, depending on the direction of the current and the kinds of metals, takes place.[2] Related to these two effects is that in which a reversible heat absorption occurs when an electric current flows in a homogeneous conductor in which there is a temperature gradient.[3]

There are certain definite laws relating to thermocouples. These are as follows:

(1) An electric current will not flow in a single homogeneous metal by the application of heat alone. As a consequence of this, if a junction of two different metals is at a temperature T_1 and another junction is at temperature T_2, the thermal voltage that appears is in no way dependent on any temperature gradient or distribution along the conductors. In Fig. 140(a), the emf (voltage) is not affected by the temperatures at x and y so long as the two dissimilar conductors A and B are homogeneous.

[1] The Seebeck effect: T. J. Seebeck, *Gilb. Ann.*, **73,** 115, 430, 1823; *Pogg. Ann.*, **6,** 1, 133, 253, 1826; *Abt. d. Konigl., Akak. d. Wiss. Berlin,* p. 265, 1822–23.

[2] The Peltier effect: J. C. A. Peltier, *Ann. Chim. Phys.*, second series, **56,** 371, 1834. See: *Temperature, Its Measurement and Control,* A.I.P., N.B.S., N.R.C.; section on "Thermoelectric Thermometry," W. F. Roeser. Published by Reinhold Publishing Co., Inc., New York, New York, 1941. A bibliography on thermopiles and thermocouples is obtainable from the U.S. Department of Commerce, Office of Technical Services (OTS), Washington 25, D.C.: SB-430 "Thermopiles and Thermocouples," August, 1960.

[3] The Thomson effect: Sir W. Thomson (Lord Kelvin), *Proc. Roy. Soc.*, London, **VII,** May, 1854; *Phil. Mag.*, July, 1854; *Trans. Roy. Soc.*, Edinburgh, **21,** 123, 1857; *Trans. Edinb. Soc.*, **21,** 153, 1847; *Math. Phys. Papers,* **1,** 232, 266, 1882.

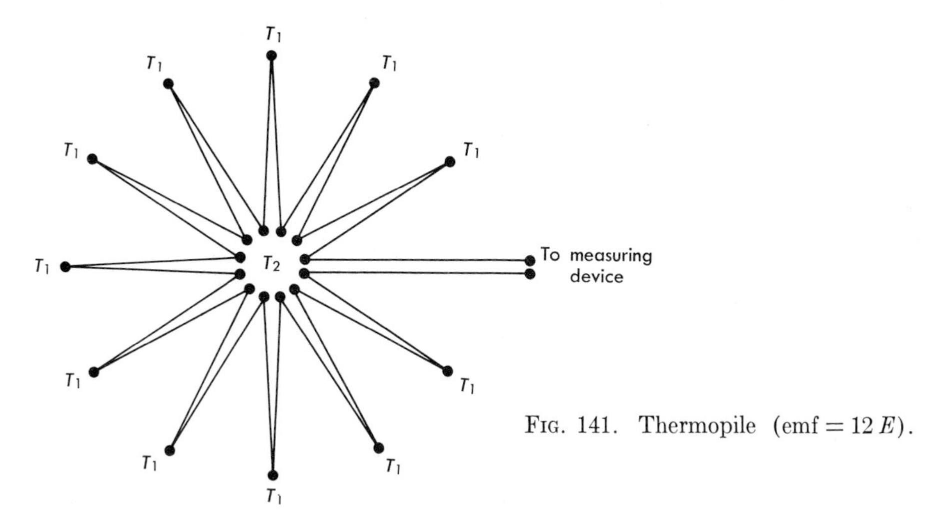

FIG. 141. Thermopile (emf $= 12\,E$).

(2) If a third dissimilar homogeneous metal conductor C is introduced, as shown in Fig. 140(b), so long as the temperatures at the two new junctions m and n are the same, and the conductor C has a uniform temperature T_3 over its entire length, there will be no change in the emf. As a corollary to this and to (1), so long as m and n are at the same temperature, the conductor C [Fig. 140(c)] may extend into a region of entirely different temperature T_3 without changing the emf of the circuit. That is:

$$E_{AC} + E_{BC} = E_{AB}.$$

Therefore, if the thermal emf properties of two metals A and B are known with respect to a third or reference metal C, the combined emf of the two metals A and B is the algebraic sum of their emfs against the metal C [Fig. 140(d)].

(3) If the junctions of two metals, respectively at temperatures T_1 and T_2, exhibit a thermal voltage E_a, and at temperatures T_2 and T_3 generate a voltage E_b, the voltage (emf) produced when the junctions are at T_1 and T_3 will be $E_a + E_b$. This is illustrated in Fig. 140(e).

Thermocouples can be combined in series or in parallel. The series connection, called a *thermopile,* is illustrated in Fig. 141, while the parallel connection is shown in Fig. 142. In the case of the thermopile, the emfs at the junctions exposed to the temperature T_2 are additive when the reference junctions are at temperature T_1. In the parallel case, the emf produced would be the same as for a single junction. If the junctions are at various temperatures (assuming that they are alike and of equal

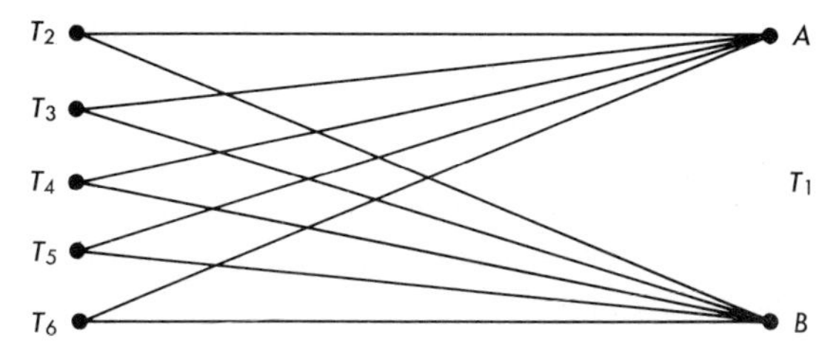

FIG. 142. Thermocouples in parallel (emf $= (E_2 + E_3 + E_4 + E_5 + E_6)/5$).

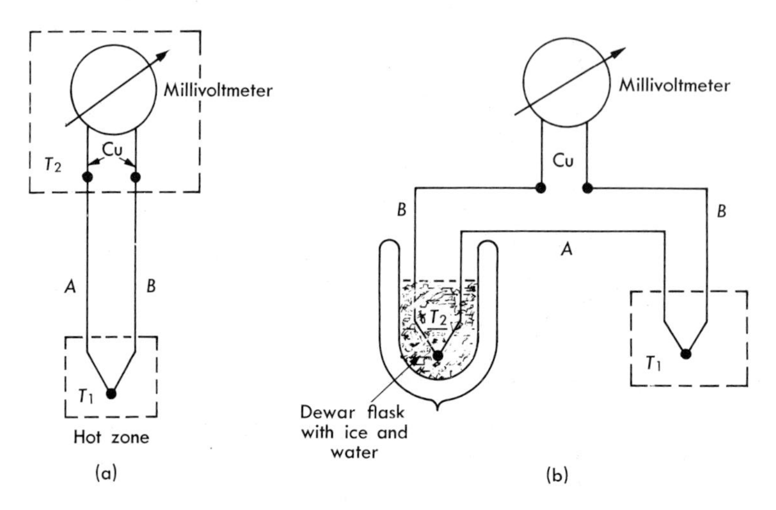

FIG. 143. Simple methods of using thermocouples.

resistance), the voltage generated will correspond to the mean of the temperatures of each of the couples.

If properly used, thermocouples can serve as very reliable and accurate thermometers. A simple thermocouple thermometer is shown in Fig. 143(a). In this case there is no temperature compensation, since the emf read on the millivoltmeter is the difference between T_1, the hot or cold zone, and T_2, room temperature. Because T_2 is not a constant quantity, allowance must be made for variations in it.

Figure 143(b) shows a method of providing automatic temperature compensation. In this case the reference junction T_2 is kept at constant temperature by immersion in a Dewar flask (Thermos bottle) partially filled with melting ice. Then T_2 will be equal to 0°C and the millivoltmeter will give a reading corresponding to true temperature above or below that reference point. Another temperature compensating method (not illustrated) is that in which the meter pivot suspension is a bimetallic spring which expands or contracts with temperature changes.

In these methods, the millivoltmeter (sometimes called a pyrometer) will be in error by a small amount whose magnitude will be in inverse proportion to the meter's internal resistance—within certain limits. This error cannot be completely eliminated because any such meter will require some energy to operate, and this "lost" energy is not read on the meter. The error is not serious when measuring high temperatures or large differences between T_1 and T_2, but it does become significant in the measurement of small temperature differences. A method of overcoming this error is shown in Fig. 144. The apparatus is called a *potentiometer* and involves the use of a *standard cell* of special construction whose voltage and voltage temperature coefficient are known to high precision. The voltage temperature coefficient is compensated for (usually manually) by means of a part of the standard cell coil. In this potentiometer, a local battery is adjusted, by means of the rheostat, to equal the voltage of the standard cell, balance being indicated on the galvanometer. The switch *SW* is of the momentary contact variety so that current is drawn for only very short intervals, and the same procedure is used in measuring the output of the thermocouple. When the galvanometer shows balance (usually zero center), no

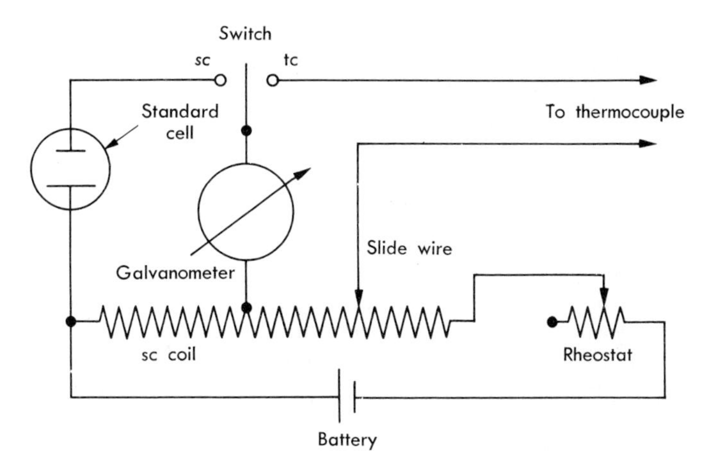

FIG. 144. Potentiometer for thermocouple use.

current is being drawn. If the compensated cold junction thermocouple arrangement of Fig. 143(b) is used, a very accurate and sensitive temperature-measuring device results.

Thermocouples for use in vacuum devices are to be chosen on the basis of (a) useful temperature range, (b) sensitivity, and (c) speed of response. Corrosion is, of course, not a factor in such applications. Metals and alloys with high vapor-pressures should be avoided where elevated temperatures and bake-out are scheduled.

The various thermocouple materials can be tabulated[1] in an order such that, at some specified temperature, each item in the list is thermoelectrically negative with respect to all those above it, and positive with respect to all those below it. The order may vary somewhat with the temperature at which the emf is observed. (The tabulation is given below.)

Thermocouple: thermoelectric series for selected metals and alloys. (The temperature at the top of each column is the observed temperature for the materials in that column, and has no relation to their position in the other columns.)

100°C		500°C		900°C	
Antimony	Palladium	Chromel-P	Cobalt	Chromel-P	Alumel
Chromel-P	Alumel	Nichrome	Alumel	Nichrome	Palladium
Iron	Nickel	Copper	Nickel	Silver	Constantan
Nichrome	Constantan	Silver	Constantan	Gold	(Adams)
Copper	(Adams)	Gold	(Adams)	Iron	—
Silver	Copel	Iron	Copel	Pt90, Rh10	—
Pt90, Rh10	Bismuth	Pt90, Rh10	—	Platinum	—
Platinum		Platinum		Cobalt	

[1] "Thermoelectric Thermometry," P. H. Dike, published by Leeds & Northrup Company, Philadelphia, Pennsylvania, 1954. The tables are reproduced by permission. See also "Thermoelectric Effects," F. E. Jaumot, Jr., *Proc. I.R.E.*, **46**, 538, 1958. This is a review paper with an excellent bibliography.

To form a sensitive thermocouple, choose a pair of materials well separated in the list and having higher melting points than the highest temperature to be encountered in service. They should also resist corrosion in the medium in which they are to be used, and should be homogeneous and not have too high an electrical resistivity. Actually, for general pyrometric use in air or other corrosive media at elevated temperatures, only a few materials can be used.

The range of emfs produced by most conventional couples in use is up to about 50 μv/°C. The tables on pp. 533–537 show the emf versus temperature values for some widely used combinations.

The speed of response is largely determined by the size of wire used for the two metals, and is greater with finer wires than with larger sizes. Also, where it is necessary to measure the temperature (in vacuum) of a small area, such as a cathode surface, a thermocouple made of very fine wires will give a more accurate reading than one of heavier wires because of its smaller heat conduction. But for use in oxidizing or corrosive atmospheres at high temperatures, as in furnaces and ovens where speed of response is not an important factor, the thermocouple should be made of heavy-gauge, corrosion-resistant material.

The list above shows that antimony and bismuth give a very high emf when formed into a couple (about 122 μv/°C), but since bismuth melts at 271°C, and because neither metal is easily drawn into wire, such a junction would be of little value to the vacuum technologist, to say nothing of the high vapor-pressure of both metals.

Platinum and platinum-rhodium alloy couples are widely used, although the metals are expensive and are also less sensitive than other types. However, these materials (noble-metal thermocouples) can be used at temperatures up to 1500°C in air (for short periods up to 1650°C) because they are highly resistant to oxidation and corrosion. The high purity obtainable with Pt/Pt90, Rh10 makes this combination an international standard for measuring temperatures between 630.5° and 1063°C (the freezing points of antimony and gold, respectively, which are used as calibration points). The actual emf values generated by an industrial Pt/Pt90, Rh10 thermocouple from a reputable source will agree with the values tabulated on p. 000 to within ± 0.25%. Exposure to high temperatures (up to 1600°C) may change the calibration at lower temperatures and should be checked after each such exposure. High temperatures and a reducing atmosphere such as hydrogen, even when the couple is inside a protecting ceramic tube, may cause additional departure, and thermocouples so exposed can be reconditioned by heating in air to 1200°–1300°C. This treatment anneals the metal and oxidizes impurities. If a bead of molten borax is allowed to flow down the heated wire, oxides and reduced metals are removed. Excess borax is dissolved in boiling distilled water. The clean thermocouple wire should not be handled with bare fingers because grease and salts from the skin produce contamination at high temperatures. For best results, only pure aluminum oxide tubes or insulators should be used with platinum thermocouples, and these should be replaced when they become discolored, either from evaporated metals or from other contamination.

Chromel-P-Alumel[1] thermocouples, tabulated on p. 535, are widely used in industrial and laboratory equipment because of their uniformity, corrosion resistance,

[1] Hoskins Manufacturing Company, Detroit 8, Michigan. Chromel-P is Ni 90%, Cr 10%; and Alumel is Ni 94%, Mn 3%, Al 2%, Si 1%.

sensitivity, and relative low cost (compared to platinum). Temperature versus emf values will be within ± 0.75% between 350° and 1260°C. Chromel-Alumel thermocouples can be used between −200° and +1260°C in air or in nonreducing environments. The alloys cannot be used at high temperatures in hydrogen, sulfur, or carbon monoxide atmospheres. For temperatures below −200°C, a junction of Chromel-X (Hoskins—Ni 64%, Fe 25%, Cr 11%) and a kind of Constantan known as Copel (Hoskins—Ni 45%, Cu 55%) is recommended.

Copper-Constantan junctions can be used in the range −260° to +350°C, the upper value being set by the rapid oxidation of copper at higher temperatures. The copper preferred for making these couples is OFHC (p. 219), which is very homogeneous. Constantan is a somewhat variable material, having the composition Cu 50–60%, Ni 50–53%. The table on p. 536 gives values obtained with a variety of Constantan having the composition Cu 57%, Ni 43%, with addition of small percentages of Mn, Fe, and some trace impurities such as C, Mg, Si, and Co. This is often designated as "Adams" Constantan.[1]

Iron-Constantan thermocouples are very widely used in oxidizing atmospheres up to 760°C and in reducing atmospheres up to about 980°C. The table on p. 534 gives the values for type "J" Fe/Constantan thermocouples as designated by the Instrument Society of America. There is also a "Y" type which has a slightly higher output. The multiplying factor for the "Y" type is as follows:

Temperature (°C)	Factor	Temperature (°C)	Factor
100	0.023	600	0.004
200	0.018	700	0.003
300	0.013	800	0.003
400	0.009	900	0.006
500	0.006		

Chromel-Constantan couples are corrosion-resistant and usable up to about 1090°C. They have high emf output and are sometimes used in place of Chromel-Alumel junctions.

Chromel-Gold 90%, Nickel 10% thermocouples. This combination has an even higher output than Chromel-Constantan, although its greater cost limits its usefulness.

Molybdenum-tungsten couples can be used in vacuum or in hydrogen up to about 2000°C. They cannot be used in air at elevated temperatures because both metals oxidize rapidly. The emf output is low and reverses polarity at about 600°C. (Some sources give the reversal temperature at about 1000°C.)

Tungsten-iridium (U.S. Patent No. 2,588,998) is said to make a junction usable up to 2100°C in vacuum or in a protective atmosphere such as helium or argon. A high emf output is obtained at high temperatures, although the thermoelectric power is negligible from 0° to 100°C so that no reference junction is required.

Tophel-Nial. These alloys are similar to Chromel-P and Alumel (Hoskins) and their characteristics and emf output are the same (p. 530).

Tungsten-tungsten 74%, rhenium 26%. This couple can be used up to 2800°C in vacuum, hydrogen, and inert gases such as nitrogen, argon, and helium, but it cannot be used in oxidizing or hydrocarbon atmospheres at high temperatures. The

[1] L. H. Adams, "Pyrometry", p. 165 (symposium published by A.I.M.M.E, 1920).

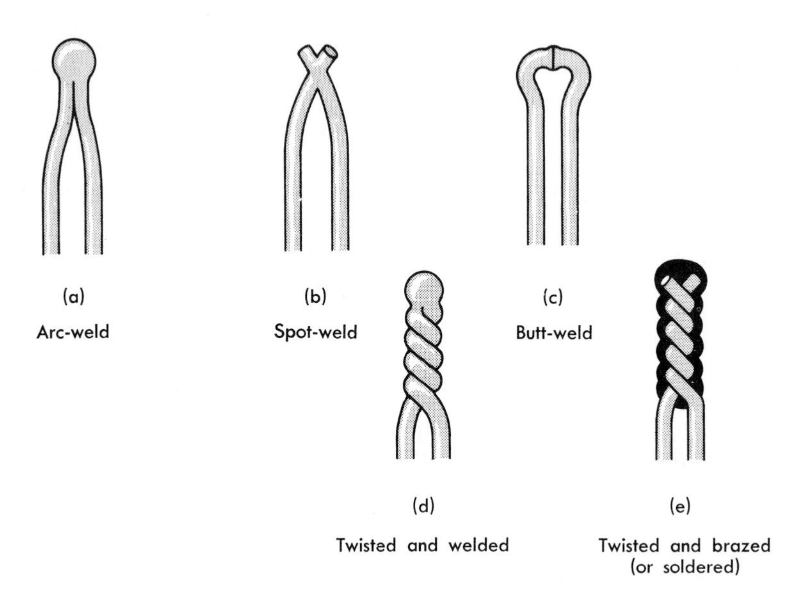

FIG. 145. Various methods of fabricating thermocouples.

elements have very high melting points (W 3400°C, Re 3167°C) and low vapor pressure at high temperatures. The calibration table on p. 536 applies to within ± 1%. Junctions are formed by inert-arc welding. Because the wires may become embrittled near the weld, they should not be bent or stressed after welding, and should be protected with suitable insulators which can act as supports during welding. Plain copper leads can be used as extension wires, since the output of this couple up to 100°C is very low.

Nickel-nickel 18%, molybdenum 82%[2] thermocouple can be used in reducing atmospheres (e.g., hydrogen, carbon monoxide, etc.) up to 1150°C. The calibration table for this combination is given on p. 537.

Platinum 70%, rhodium 30%$^{(+)}$ *versus platinum 94%, rhodium 6%*$^{(-)}$. This couple[3] has a considerably lower output than the platinum versus platinum 90%, rhodium 10% thermocouple. Output emfs of this combination are obtained from the table on Pt/Pt90, Rh10, by multiplying the emfs by a factor given in the table on p. 537.

Various other combinations are in use for specialized purposes; the list given here describes only the more common varieties.

Thermocouples can be made in several ways. For use in electron (vacuum) devices, an arc-, spot-, or butt-welding technique can be used, as illustrated in Fig. 145, (a), (b), and (c). Platinum thermocouples can be arc-welded without using any flux, or plain borax can be used in torch-welding to prevent the effects of a reducing flame which may embrittle the wires. In spot-welding, if copper electrodes are used,

[1] Engelhard Industries, Industrial Equipment Division, East Newark, New Jersey. W-W,26%Re is also obtainable from Hoskins Manufacturing Co., Detroit 8, Michigan.
[2] General Electric Company, Apparatus Department, Schenectady 5, New York.
[3] Thermo Electric Company, Inc., Saddle Brook, New Jersey.

any copper contamination should be removed by appropriate chemical treatment after the weld is made.

For furnace and oven thermocouples, the wires may be twisted together for a short distance at the end, and the junction made by welding or brazing, as shown in Fig. 145(d) and (e). In the case of the brazed (or soldered) junction (e), the presence of braze material between the elements does not introduce an error so long as the material is homogeneous and the temperature along it is uniform [*cf.* laws (2) and (3), p. 527.]

Thermocouples for use in vacuum can also be made by clamping, provided the metals are clean (e.g., preoutgassed) and the contact is tight.

In any case, wires for thermocouple use must be thoroughly clean at the junction site before any joining method is applied.

Thermocouples can also be placed in intimate contact with a metal object, either by welding or brazing, or by drilling a hole which is a tight fit, inserting the junction and peening over the edges of the hole. This technique is especially adaptable to the couples in Fig. 145(a), (d), and (e). Thermocouples can also be formed in which a single wire of one of the metals or alloys is welded, brazed, or clamped to a tube, sheet, or other solid shape of the other metal or alloy, and such a junction will operate well provided the thermocouple laws are observed.

The following tables give temperature-emf calibrations for various commonly used thermocouples.

Temperature-emf* for Platinum versus Platinum 90%, Rhodium 10% Thermocouples

°C	0	10	20	30	40	50	60	70	80	90
0	0	0.06	0.11	0.17	0.24	0.30	0.36	0.43	0.50	0.57
100	0.64	0.72	0.79	0.87	0.95	1.03	1.10	1.18	1.26	1.35
200	1.44	1.52	1.60	1.69	1.78	1.87	1.95	2.04	2.13	2.22
300	2.32	2.40	2.50	2.59	2.68	2.78	2.87	2.96	3.05	3.15
400	3.25	3.34	3.44	3.53	3.63	3.73	3.82	3.92	4.02	4.12
500	4.22	4.31	4.41	4.51	4.61	4.72	4.82	4.92	5.02	5.12
600	5.22	5.32	5.43	5.53	5.63	5.74	5.84	5.94	6.05	6.16
700	6.26	6.37	6.47	6.58	6.68	6.79	6.89	7.01	7.11	7.22
800	7.33	7.44	7.55	7.66	7.77	7.88	7.99	8.10	8.21	8.32
900	8.43	8.54	8.66	8.77	8.89	9.00	9.11	9.22	9.34	9.46
1000	9.57	9.68	9.80	9.92	10.03	10.15	10.27	10.38	10.50	10.62
1100	10.74	10.86	10.98	11.10	11.21	11.34	11.45	11.57	11.69	11.81
1200	11.94	12.05	12.17	12.29	12.41	12.54	12.65	12.77	12.89	13.01
1300	13.14	13.25	13.37	13.49	13.62	13.74	13.85	13.97	14.09	14.21
1400	14.34	14.46	14.58	14.70	14.82	14.94	15.06	15.19	15.31	15.42
1500	15.53	15.66	15.78	15.90	16.02	16.13	16.25	16.37	16.49	16.61
1600	16.72	16.84	16.97	17.09	17.20	17.31	17.43	17.56	17.67	17.78
1700	17.89	18.01	18.13	18.25	18.36	18.47	—	—	—	—

* Values in body of table are in millivolts.

Temperature-emf* for Platinum versus Platinum 87%, Rhodium 13% Thermocouples

°C	0	10	20	30	40	50	60	70	80	90
0	0	0.06	0.12	0.18	0.25	0.31	0.38	0.45	0.52	0.60
100	0.67	0.75	0.83	0.90	0.99	1.07	1.15	1.23	1.32	1.40
200	1.49	1.58	1.67	1.76	1.85	1.94	2.03	2.12	2.21	2.30
300	2.40	2.49	2.59	2.68	2.77	2.87	2.98	3.08	3.19	3.29
400	3.40	3.51	3.61	3.72	3.82	3.93	4.04	4.15	4.25	4.36
500	4.47	4.58	4.69	4.81	4.92	5.03	5.14	5.26	5.37	5.49
600	5.60	5.72	5.83	5.95	6.06	6.18	6.30	6.42	6.53	6.65
700	6.77	6.89	7.01	7.13	7.25	7.37	7.49	7.62	7.74	7.87
800	7.99	8.12	8.24	8.37	8.49	8.62	8.75	8.88	9.00	9.13
900	9.26	9.39	9.52	9.66	9.79	9.92	10.05	10.18	10.32	10.45
1000	10.58	10.72	10.85	10.99	11.12	11.26	11.40	11.54	11.67	11.81
1100	11.95	12.09	12.23	12.38	12.52	12.66	12.80	12.94	13.09	13.23
1200	13.37	13.52	13.66	13.81	13.95	14.10	14.25	14.40	14.54	14.69
1300	14.84	14.99	15.41	15.30	15.45	15.60	15.75	15.90	16.06	16.21
1400	16.36	16.52	16.67	16.83	16.98	17.14	17.30	17.46	17.61	17.71
1500	17.93	18.09	18.25	18.42	18.58	18.74	18.90	19.06	19.23	19.39
1600	19.55	19.71	19.88	20.04	20.21	20.37	—	—	—	—

* Values in body of table are in millivolts.

Temperature-emf* for Iron versus Constantan Thermocouples (Type "J")

°C	EMF	°C	EMF	°C	EMF	°C	EMF
−150	−6.50	200	10.78	550	30.22	900	51.83
−100	−4.63	250	13.56	600	33.11	950	55.00
− 50	−2.43	300	16.33	650	36.08	1000	58.17
0	0	350	19.09	700	39.16	1050	61.33
+ 50	2.58	400	21.85	750	42.32	1100	64.50
100	5.27	450	24.61	800	45.50	1150	67.67
150	8.00	500	27.39	850	48.70	1200	70.84

* Emf values are in millivolts.

Temperature-emf* for Chromel-P versus Alumel (Hoskins) Thermocouples†

°C	0	10	20	30	40	50	60	70	80	90
−200	−5.75	—	—	—	—	—	—	—	—	—
−100	−3.49	−3.78	−4.05	−4.32	−4.57	−4.81	−5.03	−5.24	−5.43	−5.60
(below) 0	0	−0.39	−0.77	−1.14	−1.50	−1.86	−2.21	−2.55	−2.87	−3.19
(above) 0	0	+0.40	0.80	1.20	1.61	2.02	2.43	2.85	3.26	3.68
+100	4.10	4.51	4.92	5.33	5.73	6.13	6.53	6.93	7.33	7.73
200	8.13	8.54	8.94	9.34	9.75	10.16	10.57	10.98	11.39	11.80
300	12.21	12.63	13.04	13.46	13.88	14.29	14.71	15.13	15.55	15.98
400	16.40	16.82	17.24	17.67	18.09	18.51	18.94	19.36	19.79	20.22
500	20.65	21.07	21.50	21.92	22.35	22.78	23.20	23.63	24.06	24.49
600	24.91	25.34	25.76	26.19	26.61	27.03	27.45	27.87	28.29	28.72
700	29.14	29.56	29.97	30.39	30.81	31.23	31.65	32.06	32.48	32.89
800	33.30	33.71	34.12	34.53	34.93	35.34	35.75	36.15	36.55	36.96
900	37.36	37.76	38.16	38.56	38.95	39.35	39.75	40.14	40.53	40.92
1000	41.31	41.70	42.09	42.48	42.87	43.25	43.63	44.02	44.40	44.78
1100	45.16	45.54	45.92	46.29	46.67	47.04	47.41	47.78	48.15	48.52
1200	48.89	49.25	49.62	49.98	50.34	50.69	51.05	51.41	51.76	52.11
1300	52.46	52.81	53.16	53.51	53.85	54.20	54.54	54.88	—	—

* Emf values are in millivolts.
† This table also applies to Tophel vs Nial (W. B. Driver).

Temperature-emf* for Copper versus Constantan Thermocouples

°C	0	10	20	30	40
−200	−5.54	−5.69	—	—	—
−100	−3.35	−3.62	−3.89	−4.14	−4.38
(below) 0	0	−0.38	−0.75	−1.11	−1.47
(above) 0	0	+0.40	0.80	1.20	1.61
100	4.28	4.75	5.23	5.71	6.20
200	9.29	9.82	10.34	10.90	11.46
300	14.86	15.44	16.03	16.62	17.22
400	20.87	—	—	—	—

°C	50	60	70	80	90
−200	—	—	—	—	—
−100	−4.60	−4.82	−5.02	−5.20	−5.38
(below) 0	−1.80	−2.14	−2.46	−2.77	−3.06
(above) 0	2.04	2.47	2.91	3.36	3.81
100	6.70	7.21	7.72	8.23	8.76
200	12.02	12.57	13.14	13.71	14.28
300	17.82	18.42	19.02	19.63	—
400	—	—	—	—	—

* Emf values are in millivolts.

Tungsten versus Tungsten 74%, Rhenium 26% Thermocouples*

°C	emf†	°C	emf†	°C	emf†	°C	emf†
100	0.333	800	8.888	1500	25.13	2200	36.88
200	1.250	900	10.83	1600	27.13	2300	38.13
300	2.200	1000	13.13	1700	29.13	2400	39.25
400	3.13	1100	15.63	1800	30.88	2500	40.25
500	4.38	1200	18.25	1900	32.50	2600	41.38
600	5.63	1300	20.75	2000	34.13	2700	42.25
700	7.13	1400	23.00	2100	35.50	2800	43.25

* No cold junction correction is required up to 20°C; above this temperature the corrections to be *added* are:

°C	Correction (millivolts)	°C	Correction (millivolts)	°C	Correction (millivolts)
25	0.050	55	0.141	85	0.274
35	0.077	65	0.180	95	0.312
45	0.108	75	0.218	100	0.333

† Emf values are in millivolts.

Platinum 70%, Rhodium 30%+ versus Platinum 94%, Rhodium 6%−* Thermocouples†

°C	FACTOR	°C	FACTOR	°C	FACTOR
100	0.10	700	0.40	1300	0.61
200	0.12	800	0.44	1400	0.63
300	0.19	900	0.48	1500	0.66
400	0.25	1000	0.51	1600	0.68
500	0.30	1100	0.55	1700	0.70
600	0.35	1200	0.59	—	—

* Thermo Electric Company, Inc., Saddle Brook, New Jersey.
† (The approximate output of this thermocouple is obtained by multiplying the values in the table for Pt versus Pt 90%, Rh 10%, p. 533, by the factor given below.)

Nickel versus Nickel 18%, Molybdenum 82% Thermocouples*

°C	EMF.	°C	EMF.	°C	EMF.
0	0	500	22.7	1000	49.7
100	4.3	600	27.6	1100	55.4
200	9.1	700	32.7	1200	61.3
300	13.9	800	38.2	1300	67.3
400	18.5	900	44.0	—	—

* General Electric Company, Apparatus Department, Schenectady, New York.

Thermocouple vacuum gauge (see pp. 136, 440). This is a vacuum gauge in which a sensitive thermocouple is bonded to a filament heated from a constant-current source. With changes in the pressure of gas surrounding the filament, the temperature will change, because heat losses due to gas conduction are a function of the gas density, within certain limits. As the gauge tube is evacuated, gas conduction losses decrease and the temperature increases, up to about 10^{-5} torr.

Thermocouples, vacuum. A vacuum thermocouple is a device in which a resistor with a sensitive thermocouple bonded to it is enclosed in an evacuated tube or bulb. The resistor is connected in an electrical circuit carrying current, and the thermocouple is connected to a suitable galvanometer or millivoltmeter. When any kind of current, dc and ac up to and beyond 10 Mc (10^7 cycles), flows through the resistor, the heating due to I^2R losses is sensed by the thermocouple. This makes a simple, convenient, and accurate means of measuring any kind of current in a universal meter. Since the meter is a D'Arsonval (dc) movement, the scale is linear and can be calibrated in terms of rms current. Enclosing the device in a vacuum makes it relatively insensitive to ambient temperature fluctuations, reduces the effect of gas (or air) conduction, and protects the elements against oxidation, corrosion, and damage.

One kind of vacuum thermocouple, designated as a radiation type, contains a very sensitive thermocouple strip but no filament. The strip is mounted in an evacuated glass bulb and is used in the so-called *radiation pyrometer* in which the

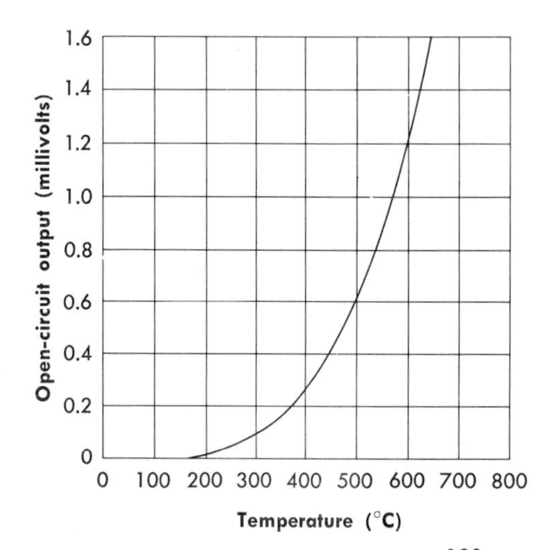

FIG. 146. Curve showing emf generated by a thermocouple placed 9 inches from an oxidized plate 3 inches in diameter.

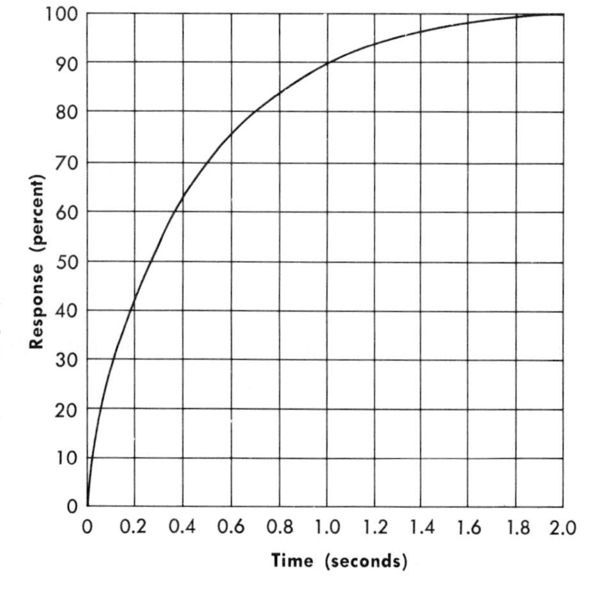

FIG. 147. Curve showing speed of response obtained when a thermocouple is used with a galvanometer having a free period of one-half second, and approximately critically damped.

radiant energy from a hot body impinges, at a distance, upon it. This radiant energy can be focused by lenses or mirrors, with appropriate correction. The output of this device is approximately 65 μv/°C, equivalent to 1100 μv when placed 15 cm from a 40-w filament lamp operating at 2527°C. The radiation pyrometer is useful for measuring high temperatures where conventional thermocouples or other types of temperature-measuring devices cannot be used because of (1) excess temperature, (2) corrosive environment, (3) rapid movement of the hot body (such as on conveyor belts, etc.), or (4) wherever it is inconvenient to attach a thermocouple. In this device the strip thermocouple is usually blackened on both sides to attain maximum heat absorption. Figures 146 and 147 show a typical emf-volts-temperature curve and a representative speed-of-response curve, respectively, for General Electric Company's type ZA-4 Radiation Vacuum Thermocouples.

Thermoelectron engine. This refers to a thermodynamic heat engine with no mechanical moving parts, in which the working fluid, an electron gas, receives heat at a high temperature, rejects heat at a lower temperature, and delivers useful electrical work to an external load. It is also a thermionic device in that the electron gas is produced by emission from a hot cathode *in vacuo* and by absorption or condensation of the electrons on a colder anode at a higher negative potential. The basic principle underlying this heat engine is that a calculable fraction of the electrons emitted from a heated cathode have sufficiently high emission velocity to overcome a retarding or repelling electrostatic potential barrier between cathode and anode *in vacuo*. These electrons, therefore, can change their high initial kinetic energy into useful potential energy at the colder anode. This potential energy can then be utilized by connecting the cathode and anode externally through a matched impedance load. Hence, this device uses a selection process which results in a large output voltage per unit cell as compared with the output of a thermoelectric generator per unit thermocouple.[1]

Thoria (Thorium oxide, ThO_2). This is a heavy, radioactive ceramic material which has the following properties:

Crystallography	isometric
Specific gravity (gm/cc)	9.7
Melting point (°C)	3030–3300
Boiling point (°C)	4400
Coefficient of linear expansion, (in/°C)	
25°–800°C	9.36×10^{-6}
25°–1100°C	10.98×10^{-6}
Thermal conductivity (cgs) hot pressed:	
38°C	0.033
93°C	0.029
150°C	0.027
Specific heat (gm-cal/gm/°C) at 25°C	0.06
Tensile strength (psi) at room temperature	14,000
Hardness, Mohs' scale	7.0
Compressive strength at room temperature (psi)	214,000
at 1000°C	51,000
at 1500°C	20,000
Young's modulus of elasticity (psi)	
at room temperature	2×10^7
at 1000°C	1.6×10^7
Modulus of rigidity (psi) at room temperature	6.6×10^6
Electrical resistivity	very high at room temperature but becomes relatively good conductor above 1000°C

Thoria should not be used in contact with carbon or other reducing agents at high temperatures. The material is slightly radioactive.

[1] "Analysis and Experimental Results of a Diode Configuration of a Novel Thermoelectron Engine," G. N. Hatsopoulos and J. Kaye, *Proc. I.R.E.*, **46,** 1574, 1958.

Thorium (Th). This metal is a constituent, to the extent of up to 1.5%, of thoriated tungsten (see p. 89) used as an emitter or cathode in electron tubes. The surface of the emitter is usually carbonized (covered with a layer of carbon) to prevent excessive evaporation of thorium.

The metal thorium is radioactive and has the following properties:

Atomic weight	232.05
Atomic number	90
Melting point (°C)	1845
Boiling point (°C)	>4500
Specific gravity (gm/cc)	11.3

Thorium getter. Pure thorium powder, after preliminary heating to 800°–1100°C in high vacuum, absorbs hydrogen, beginning at about 400°C. The absorption is quite rapid at 450°C.[1]

Three-halves power law (see pp. 238, 431).

Throughput. The quantity of gas flowing per unit time.

Throwing power in electroplating. When the piece being plated has an irregular shape, some parts of it are nearer to the anode than others, and therefore receive more current. It would seem that more metal would thus be plated on these nearer areas, and this would give an unsatisfactory result. However, this condition tends to remedy itself because: (1) where more metal is being drawn from the solution, a kind of depletion known as *concentration polarization* occurs, which is in opposition to the plating current; (2) for some types of plating baths, the cathode efficiency decreases as the current density increases, which results in less metal being deposited. Solutions in which these equalizing effects are well-pronounced are said to have good throwing power.

Tin (Sn). Pure tin has the following properties:

Atomic weight		118.7
Atomic number		50
Melting point (°C)		231.89
Boiling point (°C)		2260
Specific gravity (gm/cc)	gray	5.75
	rhombic	6.55
	tetragonal	7.31

Tin is an important constituent of many soft solders. Note that although the pure metal has a very low melting point (232°C), its boiling point is very high (2260°C), which makes it unique among metals. As would be expected from this phenomenon, tin has a very low vapor pressure (10^{-5} torr at 823°C, which is far above the melting point). This property makes tin useful as a solder or solder constituent for vacuum vessels, although the metal itself and some of its alloys (except those with lead as the equal or major element) tend to be hard and/or brittle.

---

[1] S. Dushman, *Scientific Foundations of Vacuum Technique,* second edition, p. 631, John Wiley & Sons, Inc., New York, New York, 1962.

Tin, stripping. Tin coatings can be stripped from steel by the use of the following chemical (nonelectrolytic) bath:

Sodium hydroxide NaOH	137 gm/liter or 16 oz/gal
Sodium chlorite (sodium hypochlorite NaClO)	22.4 gm/liter or 3 oz/gal

Tin coatings on brass and copper can be removed by immersion in the following chemical (nonelectrolytic) bath:

Ferric chloride $FeCl_3$	10–14 oz/gal or 75–105 gm/liter
Copper sulfate $CuSO_4$	18–21 oz/gal or 135–160 gm/liter
Acetic acid, glacial CH_3COOH	22–33 fluid oz/gal or 170–260 cc/liter

This solution may be reactivated by additions of hydrogen peroxide H_2O_2 to reoxidize the reduced iron.

Tin, vapor pressure of (see p. 148).

Tin oxide coating for glass (see TRANSPARENT CONDUCTIVE COATING FOR GLASS, p. 207).

Tin plating. Steel, copper alloys, and other metals can be coated with tin either by a hot-dipping process or by electroplating. In the former case the base metal is thoroughly cleaned and bright-pickled and immersed in a bath of molten tin. Common tin-dipping yields a coating of from 0.0008 inch to 0.002 inch. In the case of electroplating, formulas for two baths are given by the Metal & Thermit Corporation, New York, New York, as follows:

1. Potassium stannate $K_2Sn(OH)_6$	14 oz/gal or 105 gm/liter (Sn equivalent = 5.3 oz/gal or 39.5 gm/liter)
Potassium hydroxide KOH	2 oz/gal or 15 gm/liter
Temperature for use	150°–190°F
Cathode current density	30–100 amp/ft^2.
Voltage	4–8
Ratio of anode to cathode area	1.5:1
2. Sodium stannate $Na_2Sn(OH)_6$	14 oz/gal or 105 gm/liter (Sn equivalent = 5.6 oz/gal or 42 gm/liter)
Sodium hydroxide NaOH	1.25 oz/gal or 9.3 gm/liter
Temperature for use	140°–180°F
Cathode current density	6–30 amp/ft^2
Voltage	4–8
Ratio of anode to cathode area	1:1

During operation of both baths, the anodes must be covered with the typical yellow-green stannate film at all times. No film indicates the presence of stannite, which results in poor deposits. A brown or black film indicates passivity of the anode, in which case the bath will continue to operate until the stannate *in solution* is exhausted. No film at all is the more serious condition.

Titanium. This metal is of interest in vacuum technology both as a structural material and as a getter. It is light, strong, nonmagnetic, and highly resistant to corrosion.

Its general properties are listed below:

Atomic weight	47.90
Atomic number	22
Crystal structure: below 880°C	hexagonal close packed (alpha)
above 880°C	body-centered cubic (beta)
Transformation temperature (°C)	880 (1615°F)
Specific gravity (gm/cc)	4.54
Density (lb/in^3)	0.163
Melting point (°C)	1725
Boiling point (°C)	over 3000
Coefficient of linear expansion/°C, (in/in)	8.5×10^{-6}
Specific heat, (gm-cal/gm/°C)	0.13
Thermal conductivity, (cgs)[1] at 20°C	0.040
Electrical resistivity (microhm-cm) at 20°C	55–61
ohm-mil-ft at 68°F	370
Electrical conductivity, IACS (%)	3.1
Magnetism, paramagnetic; permeability	1.00005
Electrode potential	1.75
Tensile strength, annealed, commercially pure grades (psi)	$50–100 \times 10^3$
Yield strength, annealed, commercially pure grades (psi)	$40–80 \times 10^3$
Elongation in 2 inches, commercially pure grades, %	20–28
Modulus of elasticity, commercially pure grades, psi	$13–19 \times 10^6$
Hardness, Rockwell A, commercially pure grades	53–60
Impact strength, Charpy, 70°F	25–40

Titanium can be machined without much difficulty by the use of high-speed steel tools, although carbide-tipped tools give better results (Kennametal K-6, Carboloy 883, Firthlite HA, and others).

In turning, water-base coolants such as soluble oil or chemical fluids are recommended. Tools should be kept sharp and the work held rigidly.

Drilling can be done on titanium with ordinary high-speed steel drills. With a sharp drill the chips usually curl; as the drill wears, the chips become straighter and thicker, and begin to choke the flutes. In drilling deep holes withdraw the drill frequently for chip removal.

Tapping is best done on titanium to not more than a 65% thread. An active cutting oil such as chlorinated oil is recommended. In sizes under $\frac{1}{4}$ inch–20 a two-fluted tap is to be used; three-flute taps are used for larger threads. Relieving the land on the tap is often helpful.

Milling is somewhat difficult but can be done by "climb" milling instead of the conventional method. This requires great rigidity of machine and work and accurate alignment of cutters. There must be no backlash or lost motion in this type of milling. Cast-alloy cutters at lower speeds often give better results than carbide-tipped tools.

---

[1] See p. 520.

Reaming is best done with carbide-tipped reamers which have spiral flutes. Lack of concentricity results from too fast a feed in reaming.

Titanium bars can be cut on an abrasive wheel with water or a water-base cutting fluid. On bars 3 inches in diameter or larger, the stock should be rotated while cutting. The metal can be hacksawed with sharp high-speed steel alloy saws (300 BHN) having 4 to 6 teeth per inch, a positive feed, and high tension and set, at 60 to 70 strokes per minute, with feeds of 0.012 inch per stroke. The use of chlorinated oils is helpful in sawing.

Titanium can be formed by hydropressing and drawpressing operations. Slow working at high pressures is required because the metal resists sudden movements. Cold forming can be done at room temperature, although it is often helpful to heat the dies and the work to 250° to 430°C (500° to 800°F). The same considerations apply to spinning.

Welding of titanium can be done by seam, spot, resistance, flash, or inert-arc methods. Since the metal is very susceptible to embrittlement by absorption of oxygen, hydrogen, and nitrogen, special precautions must be taken to shield the weld area with an inert gas such as helium or argon.

Titanium has been successfully used as a braze material between copper and nickel, or copper and stainless steel. At 950°C, or thereabouts, the titanium forms a eutectic with copper which wets freely. This operation must be done in high vacuum.

Titanium is stress-relieved after working by raising it to a temperature of 540°C for 30 minutes. Full annealing is done at 600°–700°C. Heat-treating operations are best done in vacuum, although oxidizing atmosphere furnaces are used in industry with subsequent grit blasting or pickling in a 20–30% nitric acid, 2% hydrofluoric acid bath. Titanium should never be heat-treated in hydrogen because severe embrittlement and contamination result.

Gettering power of titanium: Titanium will absorb relatively large quantities of oxygen, nitrogen, carbon dioxide, carbon monoxide, hydrogen, and water vapor at temperatures above 650°C. The absorption of these gases is generally irreversible and causes embrittlement of the metal when used for structural purposes. However, this activity of titanium is extremely useful in vacuum tube work since a small amount of titanium evaporated (e.g., from a tungsten filament overwound with titanium wire) onto the walls of an evacuated vessel provides a pronounced pumping action (see p. 106 *et seq.*). The residual gases are trapped and held and thus removed from the vessel. When this action is combined with so-called ion-pumping, even inert gases such as helium can be trapped. The ionizing energy produces a metastable gas ion (see p. 160) and can be locked into the deposited titanium film.

Titanium alloys. Commercially pure titanium has the typical composition (major impurities): carbon, 0.05%; nitrogen, 0.03%; iron, 0.30%.[1] This grade is not hardenable by heat treatment, but can be hardened to some extent (53–60 Rockwell A) by cold-working.

A titanium-aluminum-vanadium alloy (Mallory-Sharon MST 6Al-4V; Dupont C-120 AV) is available which has the nominal composition: aluminum, 6%; vanadium 4%; titanium, balance. This alloy can be solution-heat-treated to obtain a fairly wide range of properties. The heat treatment consists of exposure to a

---

[1] Mallory-Sharon Titanium Corporation, Niles, Ohio; grade MST III.

temperature range of 760°–950°C, water quenching, and then aging 2 to 24 hours between 480° and 650°C. It has low creep and deformation rates up to 400°C.

A titanium-chromium alloy (Mallory-Sharon MST 3Al-5Cr) is produced which has the nominal composition: aluminum, 3%; chromium, 5%; titanium, balance. This alloy can be annealed to a Rockwell C hardness of 32 by heating to 870°C with forced cooling, or 700°–730°C with air cooling.

A titanium-aluminum-manganese alloy (Mallory-Sharon MST 4Al-4Mn) has the nominal composition: aluminum, 4%; manganese, 4%; titanium, balance. This alloy is suitable for forging applications and can be annealed to a Rockwell C hardness of 35 by heating to 700°C for 1 hour and air cooling.

Another alloy is available (Mallory-Sharon MST 8Mn; Dupont C-110M) containing 8% manganese. This material is suitable for forming operations and can be annealed to a Rockwell A hardness of 60 by heating to 680°C for 1 hour with forced cooling, or to 480°C and air cooling.

Titanium, cleaning of. A caustic molten salt-bath for descaling and cleaning titanium consists of:

Sodium hydroxide $NaOH$	88%
Sodium carbonate $NaCO_3$	3.25%
Sodium chloride $NaCl$	2.25%

plus small amounts of sodium sulfate (Na_2SO_4), sodium silicates, and iron oxides.

Operating temperature	427°C
Immersion time	10–15 minutes

Upon removal from this bath, the pieces are quenched in running water and then immersed in:

Sulfuric acid	10–15%
Water	balance

This is followed by a dip in:

Nitric acid HNO_3	10–15%
Hydrofluoric acid HF	0.25%
Water	balance
Operating temperature	60–66°C

(Do not exceed 82°C because this solution rapidly attacks titanium.)

This is followed by a thorough water rinse.

Descaling of titanium can also be accomplished by immersion in the following bath:

Nitric acid	8%
Hydrofluoric acid HF	2%
Water	balance

This is followed by a thorough water rinse.

Titanium hydride. Pure titanium reacts strongly with hydrogen at elevated temperatures, with the formation of titanium hydride, TiH. For this reason titanium and its alloys should not be heat-processed in a hydrogen furnace; all such treatment should be done in high vacuum.

Titanium hydride, in the form of a powder[1] mixed with a suitable vehicle, such as ethyl acetate or nitrocellulose lacquer, is used in the "active metal" method of making ceramic-to-metal seals. In this method, the properly fitting ceramic and metal parts are painted with the TiH mixture, with the braze material applied as powder, foil, or wire. The parts are heated in vacuum to brazing temperatures (See p. 67 *et seq.*)

Titanium-ion pumps (see GETTER-ION PUMPS, p. 109).

Tool steels (see p. 508).

Tophet alloys. These are nickel-chromium and nickel-chromium-iron electrical resistance alloys produced by the Wilbur B. Driver Company, Newark, New Jersey. The Tophet alloys are similar to the Nichrome alloys of the Driver-Harris Company.

Torch brazing (see p. 188).

Torr. A unit of negative pressure (vacuum) identical with the unit "mm of Hg." It is so named after Evangelista Torricelli, famous 17th century physicist who formulated many basic principles relating to vacuum.[2]

The following vacuum pressure notation has been proposed by J. A. Bennett, *Vacuum* (Br), **12**, p. 115, 1962:

millitorr (mtorr) = 1 micron (μ) = 10^{-3} mm Hg,
microtorr (μtorr) = 10^{-4} mm Hg,
nanotorr (ntorr) = 10^{-5} mm Hg,
picotorr (ptorr) = 10^{-6} mm Hg, etc.

Transconductance (see p. 546 *et seq.*).

Transite. A heat-resisting insulating material manufactured by the Johns-Manville Company, New York 16, New York. It is a hardboard compounded of certain proportions of asbestos fiber and portland cement, obtainable in various thicknesses and also as tubing, pipe, corrugated, and other structural shapes. Transite is useful for the construction of laboratory ovens, heat-resistant table tops, and the like. It can be sawed, drilled, and machined. Keep in mind that the abrasive nature of the material causes rapid wear on all tools.

Transite cannot be used inside vacuum devices because of its highly porous (gassy) nature and also because of the possible presence of certain organic binders which may decompose to gaseous constituents with heat.

Trap (see COLD TRAP, p. 211).

Trichlorethylene (or TRICHLOROETHYLENE). A chlorinated hydrocarbon fluid widely used as a solvent in ordinary and vapor-degreasing techniques. Some of its properties are as follows:

Boiling point (°C)	86.7
Distillation range (°C)	86–87.5
Flammability	nonflammable

Trichlorethylene is slightly soluble in water to the extent of about 0.1% by weight. The liquid and vapors are heavy. All degreasing of vacuum components with this solvent should be followed by an acetone rinse because the vapors of acetone, being more volatile than those of trichlorethylene, are easier to remove during pumping.

[1] Metal Hydrides, Inc., Beverly, Massachusetts.
[2] See E. Thomas, R. Servranckx, and R. Leyniers, *Vacuum*, (Br), **9**, 207, 1959.

Tube characteristics.[1] To permit the evaluation of a given tube without recourse to a graphical analysis of its characteristic curves, it is most useful to express the relationship between the grid and plate voltages and the plate current in the form of so-called *tube constants*. These tube constants are, strictly speaking, partial differential coefficients of the mathematical expression showing the plate current as a function of the plate and grid voltages. As will be seen, they are "constants" only under certain operating conditions. The three most common and most useful constants or factors are: The *amplification factor*, designated by the symbol μ and expressed by

$$\mu = -\frac{\partial e_b}{\partial e_c},$$

where the plate current, i_b, is constant. This could be stated to be *the ratio of the plate voltage change to the grid voltage change, which leaves the plate current unaffected*.

A grid voltage change is more effective in producing a plate current change than an equal plate voltage change, therefore μ, for some given small plate current change, is greater than unity for most tubes. In common triode types, μ values are from 3 to 100.

Although by definition these changes are assumed to be infinitesimal the following example will serve as an illustration. In a certain tube, the grid voltage is made one volt more negative. This reduces the plate current of the tube from 4 ma to 3 ma. With the grid voltage at its new value it is necessary to raise the plate voltage by 10 v in order to return the plate current to its original value of 4 ma. Thus in order to retain the plate current at a constant value of 4 ma a change in grid voltage one volt must be counteracted by a change in plate voltage of 10 volts. The amplification factor or μ of this tube is 10. It can be readily seen that the amplification factor is a measure of the relative effectiveness of the plate and grid potentials in controlling the plate current. Note that μ is a dimensionless ratio of two voltages.

In any electrical circuit, the current that flows is proportional to the voltage, the factor of proportionality being the *conductance* (reciprocal of resistance) of the circuit. In a vacuum tube, which can be considered as a two-mesh circuit, a change in grid voltage produces a change in plate current. The ratio of current change in the plate circuit (second mesh) to a voltage change in the grid circuit (first mesh) is the *transconductance* (or *mutual conductance*) of the tube.

The transconductance, symbol G_m, is expressed mathematically by:

$$G_m = \frac{\partial i_b}{\partial e_c}$$

where the plate voltage is constant.

This can be said to represent the ratio of a small change in plate current to the change in grid voltage causing it, under the condition that all other voltages remain constant. The transconductance of a tube is, therefore, determined by a

[1] The material under this heading is quoted verbatim from *The Electronic Engineering Handbook*, R. R. Batcher and W. Moulic, Electronic Development Associates, New York, 1945. Reproduced by permission of the publisher.

change in plate current per volt change in grid voltage. Its practical unit is the *micromho* (μmho).[1] Thus a tube whose plate current changes by one ma for a 1-volt change in grid voltage has a transconductance of 1000 μmhos.

The third important tube factor is the *dynamic plate resistance,* symbol R_p, in mathematical notation:

$$R_p = \frac{e_b}{i_b},$$

where the grid voltage e_c is constant. The dynamic plate resistance is the resistance of the plate circuit of the tube to small changes in plate current, and is the ratio of a small change in plate voltage to the variation in plate current produced by it. It should not be confused with the dc resistance of the tube, which is simply the total dc voltage across the tube divided by the total dc current through it. The dynamic, or ac plate, resistance can be considered as the internal resistance of a generator.

From the mathematical definitions of the tube factors given above it can be observed that the following relations exist among them:

$$\mu = R_p G_m \qquad R_p = \frac{\mu}{G_m} \qquad G_m = \frac{\mu}{R_p}.$$

All of these factors vary considerably with the plate current. Both the amplification factor and the transconductance decrease with plate current whereas the plate resistance increases with low plate current. These variations are due to the nonlinearity of characteristics because of electron space charge and saturation. (See Fig. 38, p. 132; also pp. 228, 338.)

In the above discussion the meaning of the various symbols is as follows: μ is amplification factor, e_b (or E_p) is plate voltage, e_c (or E_g) is grid voltage, G_m is transconductance or mutual conductance, i_b (or I_b, I_p) is plate current, R_p is plate resistance, ma is milliamperes, μmho is micromhos.

For a complete listing of definitions of terms relating to various kinds of tubes, see the following:

"IRE Standards on Magnetrons," Subcommittees on Power-Output High-Vacuum and Magnetron Tubes, C. E. Fay and G. A. Espersen, Chairmen, *Proc. I. R. E.*, **40,** 563, 1952.

"IRE Standards on Electron Devices: Definitions of Terms Relating to Microwave Tubes (Klystrons, Magnetrons, and Traveling Wave Tubes), 1956," P. A. Redhead, Chairman of Committee on Electron Tubes, *Proc. I. R. E.*, **44,** 346, 1956.

"IRE Standards on Electron Devices: Definition of Terms Related to Storage Tubes, 1956," Subcommittee on Storage Tubes, A. S. Luftman, Chairman, *Proc. I. R. E.*, **44,** 521, 1956.

"IRE Standards on Electron Tubes: TR and ATR Tube Definitions, 1956," Subcommittee on TR and ATR Tubes, K. Garoff, Chairman, *Proc. I. R. E.*, **44,** 1037, 1956.

"IRE Standards on Electron Tubes: Physical Electronics Definitions, 1957," Subcommittee on Physical Electronics, R. M. Matheson, Chairman, *Proc. I. R. E.*, **45,** 63, 1957.

---

[1] The *mho* is a reciprocal ohm equal to $1/R$.

"IRE Standards on Electron Tubes: Definition of Terms, 1957," Committee on Electron Tubes, P. A. Redhead, Chairman, *Proc. I. R. E.*, **45**, 983, 1957.

See also: "Principles of the Electrical Rating of High-Vacuum Power Tubes," E. E. Spitzer, *Proc. I. R. E.*, **39**, 60, 1951.

Tubes, processing and pumping of (see pp. 89, 98–104, 110).

Tungsten. A heavy refractory metal widely used in the electron tube industry for making filaments, heaters, electrodes (e.g., grids) of various kinds, and other components. It has the following properties:

Atomic number	74
Atomic weight	183.92
Atomic volume	9.5
Specific gravity at 20°C (gm/cc)	19.35
Density at 20°C (lb/in^3)	0.697
Melting point (°C) approximate	3400
Boiling point (°C) approximate (STP)	5900
Coefficient of linear expansion, 20°–590°C	4.6×10^{-6}
600°–1000°C	5.2×10^{-6}
(see table on p. 557)	
Specific heat, gm-cal/gm/°C at 20°C	0.034
at 1500°C	0.039
Thermal conductivity (cgs) at 0°C	0.399
Resistivity ($microhm\text{-}cm^3$) at 0°C	5.0
at 20°C	5.49
(see the table on p. 556)	
Electrical conductivity (% IACS)	31
Modulus of elasticity (kg/mm^2) approximate	40,000
Modulus of torsion (kg/cm^2)	1.45×10^6
Tensile strength	(see Fig. 148)

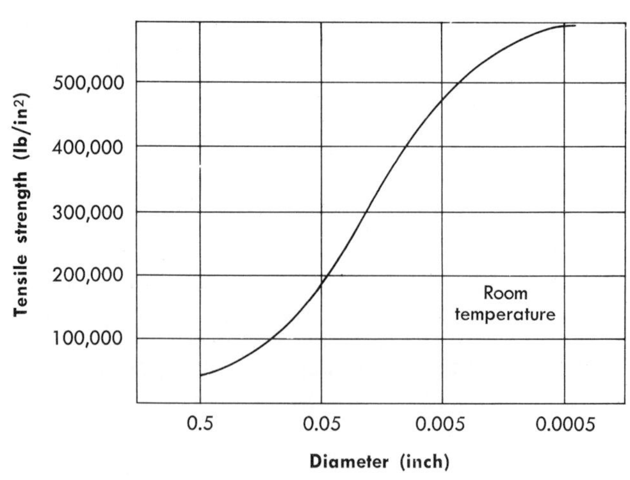

FIG. 148. Tensile strength of tungsten rod and wire.

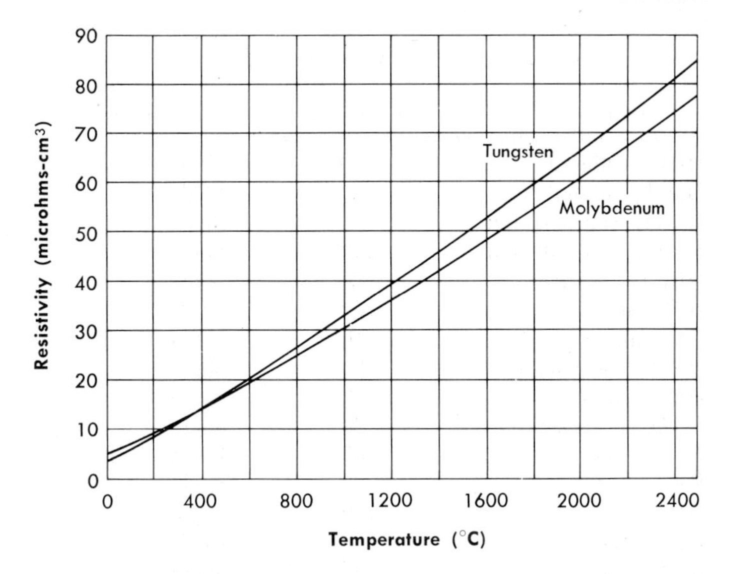

FIG. 149. Temperature versus resistivity characteristics of tungsten and molybdenum.

Tungsten is a powder-metallurgy product which has densities varying with the sintering temperature and the mechanical work done on it, as follows:

Presintered at 1400°C (gm/cc)	10–12
Fully sintered at about 3100°C	16.9–17.2
Swaged	17.2–19.2
Drawn	19.2–19.35

The electrical resistivity of tungsten wire increases rapidly with temperature. This is shown in Fig. 149.

To determine the resistance in ohms R of a given length and diameter of tungsten or molybdenum wire at a given temperature, multiply the resistivity (P) from the curve (Fig. 149) by the length (L) in cm, divided by the area or cross section (A) in cm^2:

$$P \frac{L}{A} \frac{\text{cm}}{\text{cm}^2}.$$

Pure tungsten is used as a cathode or direct emitter in many vacuum-tube applications (see pp. 86, 101, 235, 236). Although its electron emission level for a given temperature is low (higher work function), tungsten surfaces have some advantages over other types of cathodes:

(1) A pure tungsten emitter requires no activation other than outgassing.

(2) Tungsten is less affected by the presence of gases and contaminants than most other emitters (i.e., they are less easily "poisoned"), and can thus be used in gas-filled tubes and demountable systems.

(3) Tungsten is much less affected by mechanical shock than oxide-coated cathodes, and is little affected by ion bombardment.

CHEMICAL RESISTANCE OF TUNGSTEN[1]

REAGENT	TEMPERATURE °C	REACTION
H_2SO_4, diluted	20	None
H_2SO_4, diluted	100	Slight
H_2SO_4, concentrated	20	Slight
H_2SO_4, concentrated	110	Slow
HCl, concentrated	20	None
HCl, concentrated	100	Slight
HCl, diluted	110	Slight
HNO_3, concentrated	20	Slight
HNO_3, 25%	20	Slight
HNO_3, concentrated	100	Slight
Aqua regia	100	Fairly rapid
HF	20	Slight
HF	100	Slight
HF + HNO_3	20	Rapid
H_3PO_4, 10%	20	Slight
H_3PO_4, 10%	100	Slight
Cl, dry	—	Begins at 250°C
Br, dry	—	Begins at 250°C
I, dry	800	None
F, dry	20	Attacked
Air	20	None
Air	—	Oxidation begins at 400°C
H_2	—	None
O_2	—	Oxidation begins at 400°C
N_2	—	Nitriding begins at 2300°C
CO	—	Carburizing begins at 1400°C
CO_2	—	Carburizing begins at 1200°C
Water	20	None
Steam	700	Attacked
H_2S	20	None
H_2S	1200	Discolors
NH_4OH solution	20	None
NaOH, 10%	100	None
NaOH, fused	—	Rapid
S, dry	—	Attacked at red heat
C	—	Carburizing begins at 1200°C

[1] Fansteel Metallurgical Corporation, North Chicago, Illinois, 1951.

(4) The essentially clean nature of outgassed tungsten and its extremely low vapor pressure make it attractive for use in ultrahigh vacuum systems.

(5) Its very high melting point makes it possible to operate a tungsten emitter in a clean vacuum at very high temperatures, and thus realize the maximum emission of which it is capable.

(6) Tungsten can be annealed in hydrogen.

Some disadvantages in the use of tungsten must be noted:

(1) Its very refractory nature makes it difficult to form and machine, as compared with molybdenum, tantalum, and other refractory metals.

(2) Except in the form of thin wires or sheet, tungsten is not readily spot-welded to itself without special equipment and precautions, although welds to other metals (except molybdenum) can be accomplished without trouble. It is common practice in lamp manufacture to attach the tungsten filament to the press leads by a crimping or clamping method, rather than by spot-welding, especially in the case of the higher-wattage lamps. Welding at these points forms a eutectic which may have a lower melting point than either metal and thus can result in early failure.

Chemical resistance. Tungsten is fairly resistant to attack by chemical reagents, as shown in the table on p. 550.

Vapor pressure. The vapor pressure of tungsten is very low: 4×10^{-8} torr at 2200°C and 4×10^{-6} torr at 2500°C.[1] See the table on p. 148.

Some properties of tungsten, compared with those of copper, molybdenum, and nickel, are given in the table below. The properties of copper are assigned an arbitrary value of 100%.[2]

PROPERTY	COPPER	TUNGSTEN	MOLYBDENUM	NICKEL
Density	100	216	114	99
Thermal conductivity	100	42	37	23
Melting point	100	314	242	135
Electrical conductivity	100	31	36	14
Electrical resistivity	100	328	310	409
Coefficient of expansion	100	26	30	81
Modulus of elasticity	100	313	250	188

Because of its high melting point, tungsten is universally used as a filament in vacuum evaporation procedures. The metal to be evaporated, e.g., aluminum in the form of small pieces of wire, is placed on a tungsten filament which is then heated *in vacuo* to a temperature which vaporizes the aluminum. This is deposited on exposed adjacent work surfaces as a thin film (see p. 564). Silver, copper, gold, and other metals can be thus coated on various substrates, including plastics, glass, ceramics, and metals.

Tungsten heaters are widely used in small, indirectly heated, oxide-coated cathode radio-type tubes. The technique for designing and fabricating such heaters is discussed in detail on pp. 80–86.

---

[1] R. Kieffer and W. Hotop, "Pulvermetallurgie und Sinterwerkstoffe," Springer-verlag, Berlin, 1943.

[2] Fansteel Metallurgical Corporation, North Chicago, Illinois, 1951.

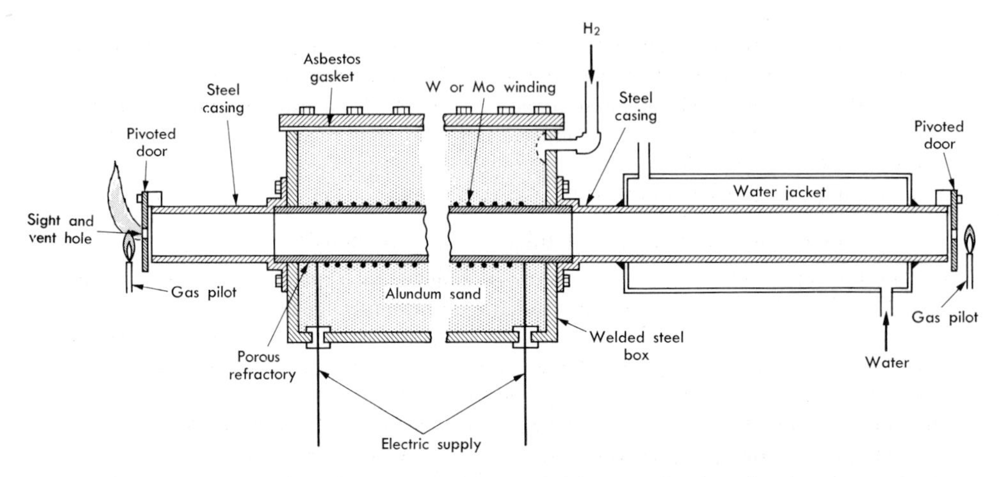

FIG. 150. High-temperature hydrogen muffle furnace for sintering heater coatings.

Since both tungsten and molybdenum are unaffected (except for reduction of oxides) by hydrogen at high temperatures, wires, ribbons, or plates of both these metals are used as heating elements in ceramic-muffle hydrogen furnaces.[1] Such an electrically heated muffle furnace (for firing the Alundum coatings on tungsten heaters (pp. 80–86), for metallizing ceramics in the "solid-state" (moly-manganese) process (p. 67), and for other purposes where temperatures up to 1800°C in a hydrogen atmosphere are required) is illustrated in Fig. 150. A porous refractory alumina muffle,[2] which has the tungsten or molybdenum wire wound on it, allows the hydrogen to pass freely through it, although it has adequate mechanical strength to withstand rough treatment in service. This wound muffle is mounted in a gas-tight, welded steel box with a bolted, asbestos-gasketed cover. The water-jacketed section is provided so that after heating, the work is cooled while still remaining in the hydrogen atmosphere, and can then be removed at or near room temperature without danger of oxidation.

Forming and fabricating tungsten. Since tungsten is a somewhat brittle metal, the danger of breaking or cracking is always present. Methods of forming and fabricating tungsten are given by Fansteel[3] as follows:

> Except for simple forming of fine wire in sizes up to 0.030 inch in diameter, tungsten should not be worked cold. Sheet up to 0.010 inch thick or wire up to 0.010 inch in diameter can be formed at a temperature of about 200°F (95°C). Up to 0.015 inch, the metal should be heated to 400°–500°F (200°–260°C). Tools and dies also should be heated. When forming material between 0.015 and 0.040 inch thick, the temperature should be increased to 1000°F (540°C). Thicker metal should be heated to 2400°–3000°F (1315°–1645°C).[4] Failure to heat

[1] In operating such a furnace, allow the hydrogen to flow long enough to fill the entire space before switching on the heating current, in order to protect the winding itself from oxidation.

[2] For example, Norton Company's (Worcester, Massachusetts) type RA 1139 Alundum.

[3] Fansteel Metallurgical Corporation, North Chicago, Illinois.

[4] In hydrogen.

tungsten to the proper temperature will almost invariably result in fracture, particularly in heavy stock.

Sharp bends should be avoided. A radius of at least twice the thickness (or diameter) of the material should be allowed.

Punching or shearing: The same general instructions given above for forming are applicable to blanking, punching, or shearing; that is, the metal should be worked hot. Punches, dies, and shear blades should be kept sharp to avoid lamination and cracking of the tungsten.

Sheet of 0.050 inch and thicker should not be sheared to finish dimensions, but should be sheared to within $\frac{1}{16}$ to $\frac{1}{8}$ inch of desired dimensions, then edge-ground.[1]

Dies of good hot-work steel will give fairly good results, but for long runs, tungsten carbide or Tantung[2] dies, with Tantung punches, are recommended.

Forging: Tungsten is not easily forged. Upsetting or heading operations are not recommended as a general practice. However, recent developments indicate that such operations might be accomplished with limited success. Swaging can be done when the material is well heated and not too much reduction in diameter is attempted at one heat. Hammer-forging is also possible under the same conditions.

Annealing: Tungsten cannot be annealed in the usual sense of the word. True annealing, or recrystallization, embrittles the metal to a point where it is very difficult to use or handle. However, parts which have been formed can be *stress-relieved,* which will help prevent cracking due to a stress condition. This operation is best done at 1000°C (1830°F),[3] the time at heat depending upon the thickness of the part. The recommended time at full heat for most parts is 20 to 30 minutes.

The rate of oxidation of tungsten is fairly slow at temperatures which can be attained without difficulty on a gas or electric hot plate. When higher temperatures are required, the metal should be heated in an atmosphere of hydrogen or dissociated ammonia. Tungsten pieces should be removed from this atmosphere for as short a time as possible for working, and if further working is necessary, they should be returned to the protective atmosphere immediately.

Joining, brazing, welding: Tungsten parts are best joined by riveting where this is feasible. If tungsten rivets are used, the riveting must be done hot. In some cases, however, molybdenum rivets can be used, and the work is much simpler because molybdenum rivets are much more easily worked. Tungsten can be brazed to itself and to a number of other metals, using copper, nickel, or other high-temperature brazing materials. The parts should be well cleaned (see below) and the brazing should be done in a reducing or inert atmosphere.[4]

Parts which are not too thick can be brazed on a spot- or seam-welder, using the same brazing materials, and using tungsten-faced electrodes.

Parts to be brazed in this manner should be thoroughly cleaned so that the use of a flux is not required. Torch brazing can be done, but is not recommended

---

[1] See p. 558.

[2] Tantung alloy, in the form of rods, bars, slabs or special shapes, is made by Vascoloy-Ramet Corp., Waukegan, Illinois. Tungsten carbide dies are also obtainable from this company.

[3] In hydrogen or dissociated ammonia. See paragraph following.

[4] Hydrogen, dissociated ammonia, or vacuum.

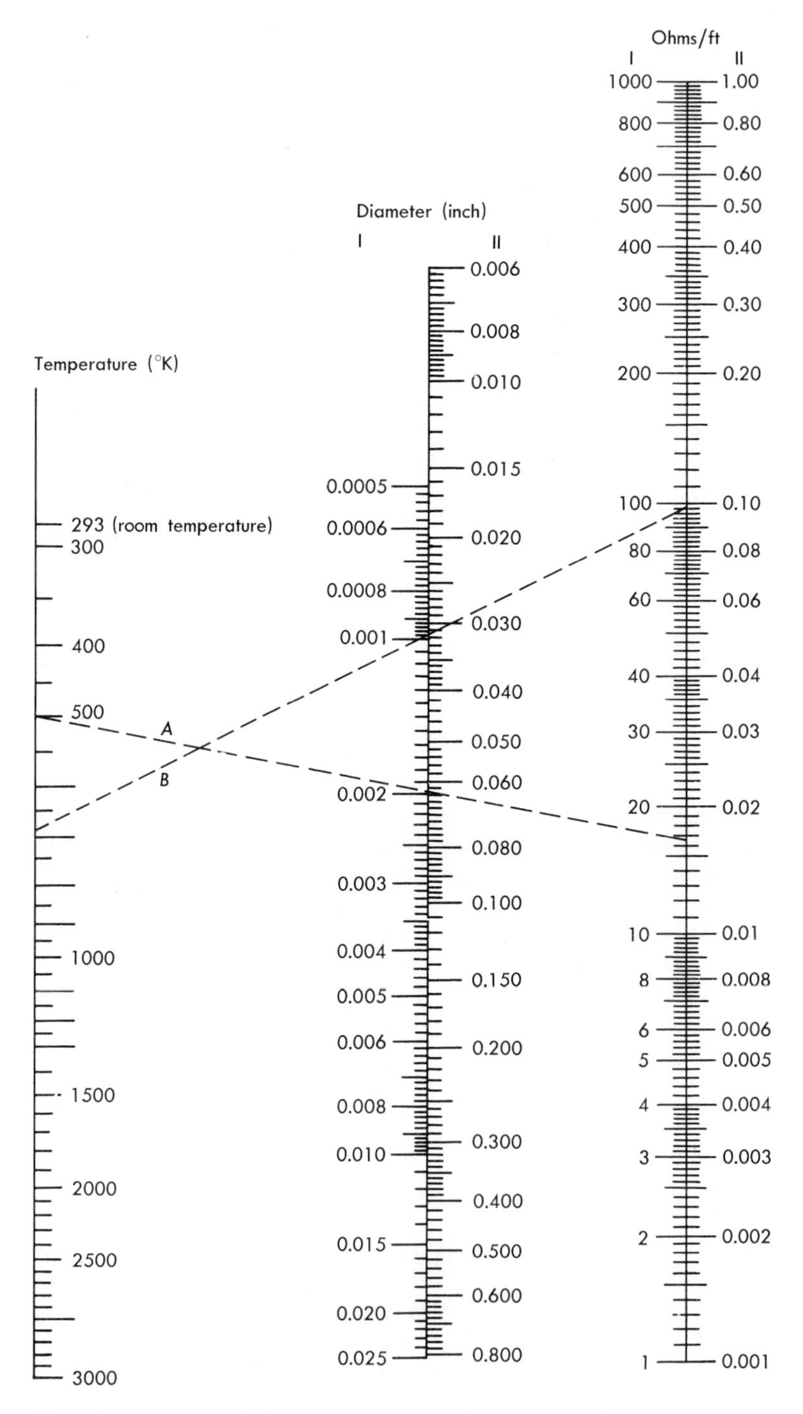

FIG. 151. Nomogram relating temperature, diameter, and resistance of tungsten wire. (*Cf.* nomogram on p. 80.)

because of the severe oxidation of the tungsten. With torch brazing, a flux must be used in order to ensure a good joint.

A high-temperature braze (or spot-weld) can be made by using tantalum foil approximately 0.001 inch thick as a brazing medium. This operation is done with spot- or seam-welding equipment, with the work immersed in water to prevent oxidation of the tantalum foil.

The spot-welding of tungsten to tungsten is difficult and uncertain in results, and is not recommended except in extreme cases where brazing with nickel or tantalum is not practicable.

Tungsten has been successfully welded to itself at Fansteel by adaptations of the inert-gas arc-welding process.

Cleaning, etching and grit-blasting: Tungsten parts which have been formed cold, or formed hot in a reducing atmosphere, can be degreased by conventional methods. When parts have been heated in an oxidizing atmosphere, however, there is always an oxide coating which may be identified by its yellow, brown, or blue appearance. These oxides may be removed by immersing the part in a bath of molten caustic soda (NaOH). The part should be immersed only for a few seconds, allowed to drain and cool, and then rinsed in hot running water. When doing this work the hazards of molten caustic must be kept in mind, and full safety precautions taken. It must be realized also that the caustic slowly attacks tungsten metal, and the parts should be exposed to the caustic for as short a time as necessary.

Tungsten can be acid-etched at room temperature with a mixture consisting of nine parts of 50% hydrofluoric acid[1] and one part of concentrated nitric acid. This should be followed with a rinse in running hot distilled water, or three dip-washes if running distilled water is not available.

Tungsten may be polished electrolytically for a bright finish using a 10% solution of sodium hydroxide (NaOH) as an electrolyte. (*Cf.* p. 17.)

Tungsten parts for electronic tubes are often blasted with steel grit to provide greater radiation surface. The recommended procedure is a blast of a few seconds with #90 steel grit at a pressure of 20 to 40 pounds followed by a thorough cleaning in hydrochloric acid to remove the iron particles. Sand, alumina, silicon carbide, or other abrasives should not be used because they become embedded in the tungsten and cannot be removed with any chemical treatment which would not also attack the metal.

Since the purpose of grit blasting is to increase the amount of surface per unit area, the blasting should be done in the manner which will produce fine "whiskers" rather than mere indentations on the surface. Sharp particles of grit will do this, while dull ones merely indent the surface. To achieve best results, the blasting nozzle should be held at an angle nearly tangential to the work rather than perpendicular to the surface.

Tungsten parts for electronic tubes are often "hydrogen-fired" before assembly into the tube. The purpose of this operation is to reduce oxides and make a chemically clean component. The operation also relieves cold-work strains and sets dimension (see pp. 82–84). The temperature range for hydrogen firing is

---

[1] Hydrofluoric acid is extremely corrosive and irritating to skin, eyes, and mucous membrane. Solutions containing it should be used only in an efficient chemical hood.

Some Properties of Tungsten

Temperature (°K)	(°C)	(1) Total Radiation (w/cm^2)	(1) Specific Resistance (microhm-cm)	(1) Hot Resistance Ratio (R_1/R_{293})	(5) Thermal Conductivity (cgs units)*
273	0	—	5.00	0.91	—
293	20	—	5.49	1.00	0.40
300	27	3.1×10^{-5}	5.65	1.03	—
400	127	2.0×10^{-3}	8.065	1.467	—
500	227	9.7×10^{-3}	10.56	1.924	—
600	327	3.0×10^{-2}	13.23	2.41	—
700	427	7.6×10^{-2}	16.09	2.93	—
800	527	0.169	19.00	3.46	0.29
900	627	0.322	21.94	4.00	—
1000	727	0.602	24.93	4.54	—
1100	827	1.027	27.94	5.08	—
1200	927	1.66	30.98	5.65	—
1300	1027	2.57	34.08	6.22	0.27
1400	1127	3.83	37.19	6.78	—
1500	1227	5.52	40.36	7.36	—
1600	1327	7.74	43.55	7.93	—
1700	1427	10.62	46.78	8.52	—
1800	1527	14.19	50.05	9.12	—
1900	1627	18.64	53.35	9.72	—
2000	1727	24.04	56.67	10.33	—
2100	1827	30.5	60.06	10.93	—
2200	1927	38.2	63.48	11.57	—
2300	2027	47.2	66.91	12.19	0.25
2400	2127	57.7	70.39	12.83	—
2500	2227	69.8	73.91	13.47	—
2600	2327	83.8	77.49	14.12	—
2700	2427	99.6	81.04	14.76	—
2800	2527	117.6	84.70	15.43	—
2900	2627	137.8	88.33	16.10	—
3000	2727	160.5	92.04	16.77	—
3100	2827	185.8	95.76	17.46	—
3200	2927	214.0	99.54	18.15	—
3300	3027	245.4	103.3	18.83	—
3400	3127	280.0	107.2	19.53	—
3500	3227	318.0	111.1	20.24	—
3600	3327	360.0	115.0	20.95	—
3655	3382	382.6	117.1	21.34	—

* (cal/cm^2—sec)/(°C/cm) see p. 520.

(3) THERMAL EXPANSION $\left(\frac{L_t - L_{293}}{L_{293}}\right) \times 10^{-3}$	(4) RATE OF EVAPORATION (GM/CM^2/SEC)	(1) VAPOR PRESSURE (MM HG)†	(1) LIGHT INTENSITY (LUMENS/WATT)	(1) ELECTRON EMISSION (AMP/CM^2)
—				
—				
—				
0.5				
1.0				
1.4				
1.8				
2.3				
2.8				
3.2	—	1.49×10^{-32}	6.93×10^{-4}	1.07×10^{-15}
3.6	—	9.15×10^{-29}	3.44×10^{-3}	1.52×10^{-13}
4.1	—	1.4×10^{-25}	1.26×10^{-2}	9.73×10^{-12}
4.6	—	6.14×10^{-23}	3.55×10^{-2}	3.21×10^{-10}
5.2	—	1.22×10^{-20}	8.99×10^{-2}	6.62×10^{-9}
5.7	1.69×10^{-22}	1.16×10^{-18}	0.199	9.14×10^{-8}
6.3	1.69×10^{-20}	6.32×10^{-17}	0.395	9.27×10^{-7}
6.9	9.90×10^{-19}	2.12×10^{-15}	0.724	7.08×10^{-6}
7.5	3.61×10^{-17}	4.74×10^{-14}	1.19	4.47×10^{-5}
8.1	8.83×10^{-16}	7.6×10^{-12}	1.94	2.28×10^{-4}
8.8	1.47×10^{-14}	1.0×10^{-11}	2.84	1.00×10^{-3}
9.4	2.01×10^{-13}	9.6×10^{-11}	4.08	3.93×10^{-3}
10.1	2.09×10^{-12}	7.4×10^{-10}	5.52	1.33×10^{-2}
10.8	1.82×10^{-11}	4.85×10^{-9}	7.24	4.07×10^{-2}
11.6	1.28×10^{-10}	2.64×10^{-8}	9.39	0.166
12.4	7.58×10^{-10}	1.28×10^{-7}	11.72	0.298
13.2	3.92×10^{-9}	5.4×10^{-7}	14.34	0.716
14.0	1.78×10^{-8}	2.15×10^{-6}	17.60	1.631
14.8	7.40×10^{-8}	7.4×10^{-6}	20.53	3.54
15.6	2.76×10^{-7}	2.25×10^{-5}	23.64	7.31
16.4	9.47×10^{-7}	6.9×10^{-5}	27.25	14.15
17.2	3.00×10^{-6}	1.88×10^{-4}	30.95	26.44
18.1	8.85×10^{-6}	4.6×10^{-4}	34.70	47.84
18.9	2.44×10^{-5}	1.13×10^{-3}	38.90	84.45
19.8	6.35×10^{-5}	2.56×10^{-3}	43.20	142.1
20.7	—	5.65×10^{-3}	47.15	233.2
21.6	—	1.15×10^{-2}	50.70	373.5
22.1	—	1.75×10^{-2}	53.10	479.9

† Theoretical; converted from dynes/cm^2.

usually 800°–1000°C (1470–1830°F), and the time is 10 to 30 minutes. Pure, dry hydrogen gas is recommended. Dissociated ammonia may be used if no further forming is to be done, but precautions must be taken to see that no free ammonia is present in the atmosphere. Fired parts must be cooled in the same protective atmosphere. Small parts are often loaded into trays or boats made of tungsten or molybdenum sheet.

Grinding and cutting tungsten: Tungsten is generally considered an unmachinable metal, and although it has been machined with very hard-cemented carbide or diamond-tipped tools, machining is not generally recommended.[1] For any finishing or cutting operations, the use of abrasive wheels is recommended.

In grinding tungsten, extreme care must be exercised to avoid localized heating, chipping, and cracking. For surface, cylindrical, or offhand grinding, light pressures, constant motion of the work, and the use of plenty of coolant are recommended.

Silicon carbide wheels are considered best for all types of grinding because they are relatively soft and wear down readily, which helps to prevent heat-checking. The wheel speeds recommended by wheel manufacturers are suitable for grinding tungsten. The desired finish will dictate the fineness of the grit. A 60-grit wheel, such as Norton #3860, is suitable for most grinding. Finer grits may be used for finer finishes, but wheels of a grit finer than 80 tend to load rapidly, which increases the danger of heat-checks.

For grinding very small pieces, an aluminum oxide, silicon-bonded wheel may be used, but extreme care must be exercised to avoid cracking the work.

The best method of cutting tungsten is with an abrasive wheel. Attempts to cut rod, or even wire, with shears or pliers almost invariably result in cracks which may travel for several inches in the material. Subsequent attempts to grind out these cracks often only make them worse. Wheels similar to Allison #15540 are recommended. The thickness of the wheel may be varied in proportion to that of the work. In cutting heavy bar or rod stock above $\frac{1}{4}$ inch thick, the wheel thickness should be about 0.040 inch. For lighter material, the wheel thickness can be reduced to as low as 0.025 inch, and, if very close tolerances are to be maintained and the operator is sufficiently skilled to avoid wheel breakage, a wheel 0.015 or 0.010 inch thick can be used.

Table of some of the properties of tungsten (pp. 556–557). From "Tungsten, Molybdenum and Special Alloys," Callite Tungsten Corp. (now Kulite Tungsten Corp.), Union City, New Jersey, 1945.

The reference numbers at the top of each column (in parentheses) refer to the following sources from which the data are taken:

(1) H. A. Jones and I. Langmuir
(2) A. G. Worthing
(3) C. J. Smithells
(4) C. Zwikker
(5) Sylvania Electric Products Co., Towanda, Pennsylvania, Bulletin CM 30, June, 1962.

---

[1] Single-crystal tungsten is more easily machinable than ordinary tungsten. See p. 485 for remarks on this material. (Editor)

Tungsten, annealing of heaters (see pp. 80 *et seq.*).
Tungsten, cleaning of (see pp. 11, 17, 555).
Tungsten, emission of (see pp. 235, 556, 557).
Tungsten, emitters (see pp. 86, 101).
Tungsten, thoriated, emitters (see p. 89).
Tungsten, vapor pressure of (see p. 148).
Tungsten, work function of (see p. 236).

Tungsten and molybdenum, vapor-phase deposition. This is a thermochemical process for the coating of these metals on copper, ferrous alloys, nickel, and other metals, as well as on ceramics, etc. Tungsten or molybdenum compounds (e.g., molybdenum pentachloride, tungsten hexachloride, and the carbonyls of the two metals) are melted, vaporized at reduced pressure (0.01 to 20 torr), and the vapor is then reduced on contact with the surface of the metal to be "plated," which is heated by induction or other means. The various processes have been summarized in a paper by H. W. Schultze: "Vapor-Phase Plating with Molybdenum and Tungsten," (American Society of Metals, 1959). Reprints of this paper are available from Climax Molybdenum Company, a division of American Metal Climax, Inc., 500 Fifth Avenue, New York 36, New York.

Tungsten filaments, life expectancy and luminosity of (see p. 90).
Tungsten filaments, minimizing sag in (see pp. 87, 466).

Tungsten-glass seal combinations (see also p. 58). Tungsten makes very satisfactory vacuum seals to glasses having closely similar expansion coefficients. In general, it can be stated that good seals can be made if the coefficients of expansion of the tungsten and the glass do not differ by much more than 1×10^{-6} in/in/°C. Glasses suitable for making such seals include the borosilicate or hard glasses. Corning[1] glasses in this category are listed below:

Glass No. (Corning)	Expansion (in/in/°C $\times 10^{-6}$)	Glass No. (Corning)	Expansion (in/in/°C $\times 10^{-6}$)
2405	4.3	7250	3.6
3320	4.0	7720	3.6
7050	4.6	9700	3.7
7052	4.6	9741	3.9

Even though a given glass has an expansion coefficient close to that of tungsten at a given temperature, it will have a different coefficient at another temperature. Tungsten, like most metals, has a more or less constant specific expansion up to the point of crystalline or phase change (which is beyond the glass-working range).

The glass of choice for making seals to heavy tungsten parts, or where higher stresses[2] due to heat or pressure are to be encountered, is Corning #3320. But #7720 can also be used. Seals to tungsten wires under 0.040 inch in diameter can

[1] Corning Glass Works, Corning, New York. (See pp. 267 *et seq.*)

[2] Because the relative expansion of a small wire is less than that of one of larger diameter, it is sometimes desirable to make presses for current-carrying leads with pairs or triplets of a small diameter wire which can then be paralleled. Even though doubling the diameter of a wire enables it to carry four times the current, for any given elevated temperature, a smaller wire sets up lower stresses in a glass seal, and may therefore be safely operated at a higher temperature than one of larger diameter.

be made to the other glasses listed. (A table of the safe electrical-carrying capacity of tungsten wires sealed into glass presses is given on p. 62.) In making seals to larger wires, a procedure known as "beading" is employed. This is mentioned on p. 163.[1] The glass used is #3320 or #7720, either of which is placed over the wire in the form of a small piece of tubing and fused to the metal at the sealing site by rotating and heating to redness. A good seal has a coppery or orange color, free from bubbles or striations, indicating that the tungsten oxide has been completely wetted by the glass.

For making good seals, both the tungsten and the glass must be clean and smooth. The tungsten can be cleaned by hydrogen-firing or by one of the chemical methods given on pp. 11, 17, 555. It should be free of scratches. The glass should be clear and free of bubbles and striae.[2]

A table giving the stresses in tungsten-glass and other metal-glass seal combinations will be found on pp. 56–59; also see p. 61.

Tungsten heaters (see pp. 80, 552).

Tungsten wire, straightening of (see p. 86).

Tygon. This is the trade name for a brand of vinyl plastic used widely as tubing in vacuum applications and for gas-handling where cleanliness is a requirement, in preference to rubber, which tends to be somewhat gassy and also slightly porous. The type of Tygon used for this purpose is designated as B44–3 by the manufacturer,[3] and it has the following properties:

Tensile strength (psi)		2200–2300
Elongation (%)		400
Hardness, Durometer; Shore A		68–75
Low-temperature flexibility;	brittle at	−40°C
	flexible at	−17.7°C
Maximum recommended operating temperature		82°C
High-temperature resistance		
	dry heat	102°C
	steam	30 minutes at 15 pounds
Color		Crystal clear
Odor		None
Taste		None
Toxicity		Nontoxic
Flammability		Self-extinguishing
Aging characteristics		Nonoxidizing
Chemical resistance:	strong acids	Good
	weak acids	Excellent
	strong alkalies	Fair
	weak alkalies	Excellent
	solvents—not resistant to ketones and esters; aromatic hydrocarbons produce swelling	

---

[1] See also pp. 450, 451.

[2] See *Scientific Glassblowing*, E. L. Wheeler, Interscience Publishers, New York, 1958; also: "Glass-to-Metal Seals," J. H. Partridge, *Soc. Glass. Tech.*, Sheffield, England; and *Materials Technology for Electron Tubes*, second edition, W. H. Kohl, Reinhold Publishing Co., New York, New York, 1959.

[3] The U.S. Stoneware Co., Akron 9, Ohio.

This material is available in the form of tubing in a wide variety of sizes, including heavy-walled types for vacuum work.

Like some types of rubber tubing, Tygon has a tendency to stick to clean surfaces with considerable tenacity, especially after long contact. When disconnecting Tygon tubing which has been for some time on glass or metal nipples or tubing, it is therefore often necessary to cut the tubing to remove it.

Ultimate pressure, ultimate vacuum. These terms designate the lowest pressure attainable in a vacuum system or by a vacuum pump; limiting pressure; blank-off pressure. (*Cf.* p. 455.)

The value of the ultimate pressure is determined by many factors, some of which are listed below:

structure of the pump or system used,
kind of oil or fluid used, and its purity and temperature,
length of pumping time,
condition of interior surfaces of pump or system—presence and quantity of contamination, whether or not parts have been previously outgassed by heating and for how long,
presence and kind of gasketing or sealing material used,
presence and effectiveness of baffling and/or cold-trapping,
presence and size of leaks,
amount and nature of backstreaming,

The ultimate pressure in a working vacuum system is also determined to a large extent by the *materials* in the system and their vapor pressures (and/or decomposition products, if any) at the temperature of operation.

Ultrahigh vacuum (see p. 110 *et seq.*).

Ultrasonics and ultrasonic cleaning. Some cleaning is effected when a component is dipped or immersed in an appropriate cleaning fluid, and the extent of this cleaning is increased by agitation. When the *frequency* of such agitation is raised to a high value (16 to 1000 kc/sec), removal of contamination from objects placed in the solution thus agitated reaches very high efficiencies,[1] especially at the higher frequencies.

The generators for producing this effect are available commercially. They operate either by feeding a synthetic piezoelectric ceramic (crystal) with electrical oscillations from a vacuum tube oscillator circuit, or by the *magnetostrictive* effect, in which a ferromagnetic element, magnetized parallel with its length, changes slightly in length following changes in the field.[2] In either case, the vibrations are transmitted directly or indirectly to a container or tank in which the fluid and the work to be cleaned can be suspended. Boxes or baskets may be used for this purpose.

In order to be called ultrasonic, the frequency must be 15 kc/sec or more. An effect known as *cavitation* is produced in the fluid. This is a microscopic but quite

---

[1] "An Ultrasonic System for Eliminating Contaminants from Electron Devices," D. E. Koontz and I. Amron, A.S.T.M. Special Technical Publication No. 246. Philadelphia, Pennsylvania, 1958.

[2] *The Electronic Engineering Handbook,* R. R. Batcher and W. Moulic, Electronic Development Associates, New York, New York, 1944. See also "Design of Nickel Magnetostriction Transducers," E. M. Wise; and "Magnetostriction," Development and Research Section; both papers published by International Nickel Company, New York, New York, 1957.

violent agitation produced by the rapid creation and collapse of large numbers of small vapor bubbles, as a consequence of which adhesive layers of contamination are removed from a work-piece immersed in the fluid.

Many types of cleaning fluids are used with the ultrasonic cleaning technique. Generally, the choice of a fluid will be dictated by the material of the work-pieces and by what kind of contamination is to be removed. Fluids used range from water with various amounts of wetting agents, soaps, detergents, and/or alkaline preparations, through solvents of all kinds, such as ketones (acetone, etc.), trichlorethylene, perchlorethylene, carbon tetrachloride, up to strong acid and alkali solutions for the removal of heavy scale, grease, paint, and the like.

Ultrasonic soldering and welding. Certain types of fluxless soldering can be done with ultrasonic equipment designed for this purpose. The process operates by cavitation (see above) produced in the molten solder, which tears off the oxide or other surface contaminant film that would ordinarily prevent bonding without flux. The solder itself is usually not heated appreciably by the ultrasonic energy, such heat being supplied from a separate source (resistance heating, etc). Materials such as silicon and germanium, as well as aluminum, magnesium, and the more commonly solderable metals—copper, silver, nickel, steel, etc.—can be thus soldered without the use of a contaminating flux.

Ultrasonic welding is a type of spot welding done at relatively low temperatures (sometimes even at room temperature), so that arcing, sputtering, and the oxidation usually associated with these phenomena are eliminated or minimized. The ultrasonic energy produces a solid-state bond without fusion. Metals such as tantalum, columbium, and palladium, as well as aluminum, stainless steel, copper, and brass can be joined in strong bonds by this technique. Welds between dissimilar metals are also feasible.

In both ultrasonic soldering and welding, it is usually necessary only to degrease the articles; no aftercleaning is required.

Unipotential cathode. This is an emitter of the indirectly heated type (see OXIDE-COATED CATHODES, pp. 96, 103; also HEATERS, pp. 80–86) in which the heater is either insulated electrically from the cathode or connected to it at only one point, so that the cathode itself is at a single voltage or potential over its entire surface with respect to the other elements in the tube. Ideally, a unipotential cathode should have a noninductive (bifilar, etc.) heater (see Fig. 21 on p. 83 for an example) in order to minimize the effect of a magnetic field surrounding the heater, which would not be completely shielded out by the cathode material, usually nickel. Unipotential cathodes are sometimes called *equipotential* cathodes.

Vacuum firing of tube components (see pp. 75 *et seq.*).

Vacuum gauges; vacuum measuring. Comparison of, p. 136; manometer types, pp. 347 *et seq.;* ionization gauges, pp. 162, 303–305, 348, 471–472; Pirani, pp. 348, 438; thermocouple, pp. 348, 440.

Vacuum-melted metals (see p. 366).

Vacuum-release valve (same as BLEEDER VALVE, p. 167).

Vacuum systems (see pp. 76, 99, 361).

Vacuum systems, shutting down (see p. 79).

Vapor versus gas (see GAS VERSUS VAPOR, p. 266).

Vapor pressure (see also pp. 138–148). All substances, no matter how inert and stable, are surrounded with a layer of vapor (molecules) of the substance, or of its components if it is not an element. The amount of vapor given off is a property of the substance and is also universally dependent on the temperature. (All substances give off more vapor at higher temperatures than at lower, until, at the boiling, or subliming, point, all the substance is converted into vapor.)

Vapor pressure of alloys.[1] According to the law of Raoult, which applies to dilute solutions, the vapor pressure of the solution is lower than that of the pure solvent by an amount which is proportional to the concentration of the solute. Let P_A and P_{AS} denote the vapor pressure of the pure solvent and solution, respectively, at any given temperature, and let x_B denote the molfraction of the solute present in the solution. Then according to Raoult's law:

$$\frac{P_A - P_{AS}}{P_A} = x_B = \frac{n_B}{n_A + n_B}, \tag{1}$$

where n_A and n_B denote the number of moles of solvent and solute, respectively. Since

$$x_A = \frac{n_A}{n_A + n_B}, \tag{2}$$

it follows from Equation (1) that the following relation should be valid:

$$a_A = \frac{P_{AS}}{P_A} = x_A, \tag{3}$$

where a_A is designated as the *activity* of A in the solution.

Applying these relations to a *binary* alloy in which one constituent A, which may be present in larger proportions, is by far more volatile than B, we may regard B as solute, and consequently the decrease in vapor pressure of A should be in accordance with Equation (1).

Furthermore, it follows, as a consequence of the application of the second law of thermodynamics, that corresponding to the decrease in vapor pressure of magnitude $P_A - P_{AS} = \Delta P_A$, there is an *increase* (ΔT_A) in the temperature at which the vapor pressure of the "solution" has a value of magnitude P_A. This increase is given by the relation:

$$\frac{\Delta T_A}{\Delta P_A / P_A} = \frac{R_0 T_A{}^2}{L_A}, \tag{4}$$

where R_0 is the molar gas constant ($= 1.9865$ cal/mole), and L_A is the heat of vaporization of A, in calories per mole.

From Equations (4) and (1), it follows that

$$\Delta T_A = \frac{R_0 T_A^2 x_B}{L_A} = C_A T_A^2 x_B, \tag{5}$$

where C_A is a constant characteristic of the "solvent" A.

These relations should be applicable to both the solid and liquid states of the alloys, provided that the value of n_B is small compared with that of n_A.

---

[1] S. Dushman, *Scientific Foundations of Vacuum Technique,* second edition, p. 710, John Wiley & Sons, Inc., 1962. Quoted by permission.

Evaporation of Metals for Vacuum Coating
(Consolidated Vacuum Corporation Bulletin 2-2/July, 1960)

METAL	MELTING POINT (°C)	EVAPORATION TEMPERATURE (°C) (vapor pressure = 10μ Hg	HEATING ELEMENTS	
			KIND OF FILAMENT	BOATS
Aluminum	658	996	W, Ta, helical coil	—
Antimony	630	678	Chromel, Ta, conical basket	Mo, Ta
Cadmium	321	264	Chromel, Cb, Ta, Mo, W, Ni, Fe conical basket	Mo, Ta
Carbon	3700 ± 100	2681	— *	—
Chromium	1900	1205	W, conical basket	-- †
Cobalt	1478	1649	Cb, W	—
Copper	1083	1273	Cb, Mo, Ta, W, conical basket	Mo, Ta†
Germanium	959	1251	Ta, Mo, W, conical basket	Mo, Ta
Gold	1063	1465	W, Mo, conical basket	Mo
Lead	328	718	Fe, Ni, Chromel, conical basket	Mo
Molybdenum	2622	2533	— *	—
Nickel	1455	1510	Heavy-gauge W helical coil	—
Platinum	1774	2090	Multistrand W wire twisted with Pt wire	—
Rhodium‡	1967	2149	W rod	—
Selenium	217	234	Chromel, Fe, Mo, Cb, conical basket	Mo, Ta
Silver	961	1047	Ta, Mo, Cb, Fe, Ni, Chromel, helical coil or W, conical basket	Mo, Ta†
Thorium	1827	2196	W, Mo, Ta, conical basket; Chromel, helical coil	Mo, Ta
Titanium	1727	1546	W, Ta, conical basket or helical coil; W wires twisted with Ti wire	—

* Since the melting point for this material is so high, it would be used as its own heating element.

† See also S. Tabata and M. Iwata, "Vacuum Evaporation of Copper, Silver, Tin, Iron and Chromium from a Titanium Carbide Heater," *Vacuum*, (Br) **11,** 36, 1961.

‡ "Vaporization of Iridium and Rhodium," M. B. Panish and L. Reif, *J. Chem. Phys*. **34,** 1915, 1961.

If, furthermore, both A and B in the pure state possess vapor pressures which are of the same order of magnitude, we should expect to observe a decrease in vapor pressure of A due to the addition of B.

In the discussion of particular illustrations of the above remarks, the composition of an alloy is spoken of in terms of *mol-fractions* rather than in terms of percent by weight. Let q_A denote the percent by weight of A, and q_B that of B, in a binary alloy. Then $q_A + q_B = 100$, and:

$$q_A = \frac{100x_A M_A}{x_A M_A + (1 - x_A)M_B} = \frac{100x_A M_A}{x_A(M_A - M_B) + M_B}, \tag{6}$$

where M_A and M_B denote the gram-molar (or gram-atomic) masses.

Also, given the percent by weight of each constituent, the mol-fractions can be deduced by means of the relation:

$$x_A = \frac{q_A/M_A}{q_A/M_A + (100 - q_A)/M_B} = \frac{q_A}{q_A + (100 - q_A)M_A/M_B}. \tag{7}$$

An illustration of the application of Equation (5) is found in the observation made by A. Schneider and U. Esch[1] on the rise in the boiling point of magnesium obtained by alloying it with different metals.

From the preceding discussion, it follows that at any given temperature the vapor pressure of each constituent in the alloy must be lower than that for the pure metal.

For example, iron at 1000°C has a vapor pressure of 10^{-6} torr, and that of manganese at the same temperature is about 10^{-2} torr. When alloyed, the vapor pressures were found to be: iron 9×10^{-7} torr and manganese 10^{-3} torr at the same temperature.

Iron at 1200°C has an approximate vapor pressure of 10^{-4} torr and nickel at the same temperature has a value of 3×10^{-5} torr. In an alloy containing 25% nickel, 75% iron, the vapor pressures were found to be: iron 7.5×10^{-5} torr, nickel 8×10^{-6} torr.

Vaporizable metals (see also pp. 36, 38, 39, 78, 247). All metals can be evaporated in vacuum if the temperature is high enough. Some metals are not commonly used in high-vacuum systems because of their very high vapor pressure at only slightly elevated temperatures; these include cadmium, zinc, lead, bismuth, and antimony. Other easily vaporizable metals are used in tubes where vapors of the metals are required for a supply of ions. Examples of such metals are mercury, cesium, sodium, potassium, rubidium, and lithium.

The evaporation temperatures for various metals used in vacuum evaporation or *coating* are given in the table on p. 564.

In evaporating metals, the surfaces upon which the deposit is to go must be exceptionally clean. In commercial vacuum-coating, surfaces which are not polished or which have irregularities are often lacquered with a type of synthetic lacquer from which all the solvent can be removed by baking or air-drying so as to prevent outgassing during the evacuation, which would cause bubbles or blisters.

---

[1] *Z. Elektrochem.*, **45**, 888, 1939.

Glass, plastics, and certain other materials can accept the evaporated metal directly, and need only to be cleaned in an appropriate way. A very high vacuum is not required for most vacuum-coating procedures; about 0.5 micron (5×10^{-4} torr is sufficient for aluminum. The aluminum is hung as small staples from a helical or stranded tungsten filament which is heated with current from a variable transformer. At about 660°C, the aluminum melts, and because of its ability to wet the tungsten, it coats the filament with a thin layer. When the temperature is raised to about 1000°C, the aluminum evaporates and is deposited on all nearby cooler surfaces in the line of sight. Masking can be done by placing the shields so that they receive the deposit instead of the work. The masks need not be in contact with the work pieces. Within a few seconds a deposited layer is formed on the work. Although this is only millionths of an inch thick, it provides a complete cover, and, in the case of glass and other smooth surfaces, is a mirror-bright surface.

After deposition, the pumps are shut down, air is admitted to the vacuum chamber, and the work can be removed.

Vee-rings. These are molded or machined Teflon rings serving somewhat the same function as O-rings (pp. 11, 117, 406, 407, 409, 410–415). Vee-rings are useful in reciprocating- or sliding-shaft-action vacuum seals. An example of the application of such rings is shown in Fig. 152. Two or more vee-rings are stacked such that only a low pressure applied by the nut is sufficient to force the lips of each ring tightly against the shaft and stuffing-box wall. The adapter rings are also Teflon, and the shaft is to have a very smooth finish, free of scratches and tool marks. The use of Teflon minimizes friction and eliminates "freezing" of the rings to each other and to the metal parts, even if the seal is not operated for a long time.

These Teflon vee-rings are available in a variety of sizes from any of the commercial Teflon processors licensed by the DuPont Company, or they can be made by machining from Teflon round stock (see p. 513).

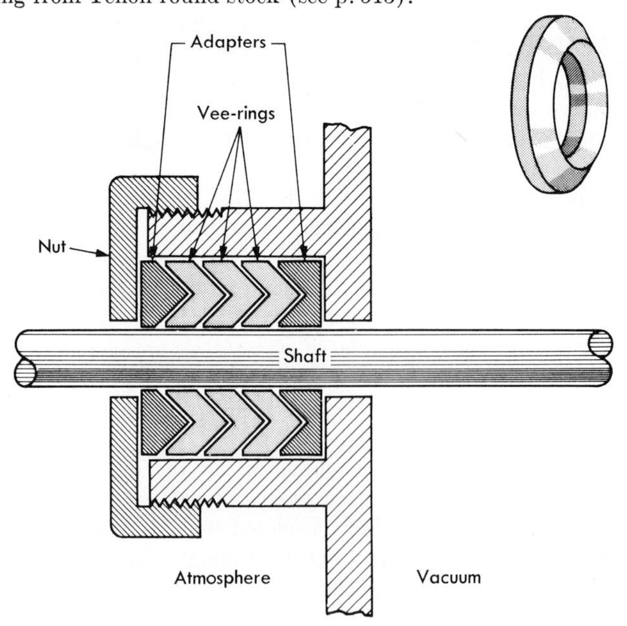

FIG. 152. Application of Vee-rings to sliding or rotating vacuum seal.

Viton. A synthetic rubber-like material (elastomer), chemically a linear copolymer of vinylidene fluoride and hexafluoropropylene. This material is processed[1] into O-rings and gasketing material useful for vacuum work. Viton has the following properties:

Molecular weight	60,000
Fluorine content	65% (approximate)
DC resistivity, (ohms-cm)	1.4×10^{14}
Dielectric constant	8.5
Power factor	2.5 percent
Dielectric strength (volts/mil)	500
Maximum service temperature for continuous use	370°C
Maximum service temperature for short-time use (with slight hardening)	480°C

Chemical resistance: resistant to H_2O_2, liquid fluorine, red fuming nitric acid, ozone, oxygen, petroleum oils, many solvents, fuels, some synthetic lubricants; also resistant to weathering

Viton compounds have the following mechanical properties:

Property	#V495–7	#V274–9	#77–545
Hardness, Shore A	70	88	72
Tensile strength (psi)	1640	1800	2160
Elongation (%)	200	140	195

The table below gives the results of ASTM heat tests performed on the hardness and mechanical properties exhibited by sheet material (O-rings will not show as high physical properties):

Property	#V495–7	#V274–9	#77–545
	168 hr at 204°C		72 hr at 204°C
Hardness, Shore A	75	88	72
Tensile strength (psi)	803	1070	1546
Elongation (%)	81	72	133
Volume change (%)	+2.8	+1.7	+4.4
Compression and heat test, 25% deflection, 70 hr at 121°C:			
% thickness	8.6	4.4	2.3
% deflection	24.1	17.7	9.4

No vapor pressure data are available on Viton at the present writing. However, the material has been successfully used as O-rings in vacuum systems. The DuPont

[1] By the Parker Seal Company, Cleveland 12, Ohio. The data on Viton are reproduced by courtesy of this company.

Company reports[1] very small weight loss for two Viton formulations:[2]

Elastomer	Pressure (torr)	Weight loss (%)
Viton C	1.8×10^{-9}	2.1
Viton D	2.0×10^{-9}	2.3

Addiss, Pensak, and Scott[3] report that Viton gaskets or O-rings, prebaked in vacuum at about 200°C for two to three days, essentially stopped losing weight. These baked rings, stored in a good desiccator until use, made possible pressures in a vacuum system of 3×10^{-8} torr with cold-trapping. These authors summarize the advantages of Viton seals in vacuum systems over other elastomers as follows: (a) Viton has practically the same flexibility, (b) hydrocarbon evolution, present in other sealing materials, is materially reduced, and (c) it is possible to bake a system employing Viton seals up to 250°C, thus greatly reducing gas evolution from the vacuum-vessel walls and leading to lower ultimate pressures.

Water cycle (see WATER VAPOR immediately following).

Water vapor. Water is constantly evaporating even from ice at very low temperatures (see table below) and is always present to a considerable degree in ordinary atmospheric air. It is one of the most pervasive contaminants bedeviling the vacuum technologist, since it not only exists in the gases that are to be removed but is particularly adherent to most of the materials used in tube construction. This condition is aggravated when the materials are subject to handling in high-humidity atmospheres. Baking at high temperatures and for long periods during evacuation is an effective way to remove water vapor, and it follows that ultrahigh vacuum cannot be achieved without doing so.

In general, the presence of water vapor in a tube, as with other gases, gives rise, under appropriate conditions, to ions which may have harmful physical effects on parts of the tube. In addition there are deleterious chemical effects, such as the "poisoning" of an active oxide cathode. In this case the water combines with the oxides to form hydroxides which have little or no emissive power. The reaction is not reversible, so that the presence of even small percentages of water vapor can permanently destroy the emission of a cathode. Pure tungsten is also adversely affected by the "water cycle," in which the tungsten is oxidized by the water, the products of this reaction evaporating below 1000°C (i.e., below operating temperature) with consequent loss of tungsten and the likelihood of early failure. Langmuir[4] notes that

> . . . water vapor coming in contact with an incandescent tungsten filament is decomposed, the oxygen combining with the tungsten and the hydrogen being evolved. The oxide distils to the walls of the vessel, where it is subsequently reduced to metallic tungsten by atomic hydrogen given off by the filament, water

---

[1] "Viton Reported Outstanding Vacuum Seal," *Elastomers Notebook* #104, February, 1962, E. I. duPont de Nemours & Co., Wilmington 98, Delaware.

[2] From a report by T. Carrell and R. Young in *Machine Design,* May 25, 1961.

[3] R. R. Addiss, Jr., L. Pensak, and N. J. Scott, *Evaluation of a New Fluoroelastomer as a Gasketing Material for High-Vacuum Systems,* Seventh National Symposium on Vacuum Technology Transactions, 1960, Pergamon Press, London, 1961.

[4] I. Langmuir, *Trans. A.I.E.E.,* **32,** 1893, 1913, as noted by S. Dushman in *Scientific Foundations of Vacuum Technique,* second edition, p. 647, John Wiley & Sons, Inc., New York, 1962.

vapor being simultaneously produced. The action can be repeated indefinitely with a limited quantity of water vapor. This produces darkening of a glass vessel because the amount of tungsten carried from the filament to the bulb can be many times greater than the chemical equivalent of the hydrogen produced, so the deposit on the bulb could not well be formed by simple attack of the filament by water vapor (in a single cycle).

Even in the absence of water vapor, the water-cycle may occur in the presence of a low pressure of hydrogen if traces of oxides are present on the filament (or the filament leads).

VAPOR PRESSURE OF WATER OVER ICE*		VAPOR PRESSURE OF WATER UP TO 100°C*	
TEMPERATURE (°C)	VAPOR PRESSURE (torr)	TEMPERATURE (°C)	VAPOR PRESSURE (torr)
—90	7×10^{-5}	+10	9.21
—80	4×10^{-4}	20	17.54
—70	1.9×10^{-3}	30	31.82
—60	8×10^{-3}	40	55.32
—50	2.9×10^{-2}	50	92.5
—40	9×10^{-2}	60	149.4
—30	0.286	70	233.7
—20	0.776	80	355.1
--10	1.95	90	526
0	4.58	100 (boiling)	760 (atmospheric)

* *Handbook of Chemistry and Physics*, forty-first edition, C. D. Hodgman, Editor in Chief. Chemical Rubber Publishing Co., Cleveland, Ohio, 1960. Reproduced by permission.

Water vapor glow discharge color (p. 213).

Watts nickel bath (see p. 29).

Willemite [Zinc orthosilicate (Zn_2SiO_4 or $2ZnO:SiO_2$)]. Willemite is used as a basis for fluorescent screens (phosphors) in cathode-ray tubes and the like, either alone or in combination with other materials. As ordinarily supplied, the zinc orthosilicate has a small addition of manganese (0.5–2.0%), and the screen employing it is designated by the tube manufacturers as Phosphor P-1. The material has a very high visibility, peaking at about 5250 Angstroms, as shown in the curve of Fig. 153, which represents spectral-energy emission characteristic of phosphor P-1 (Zn_2SiO_4:Mn) (Willemite). The color is yellowish-green and is well-suited for fluorescent screens which are to be observed visually.

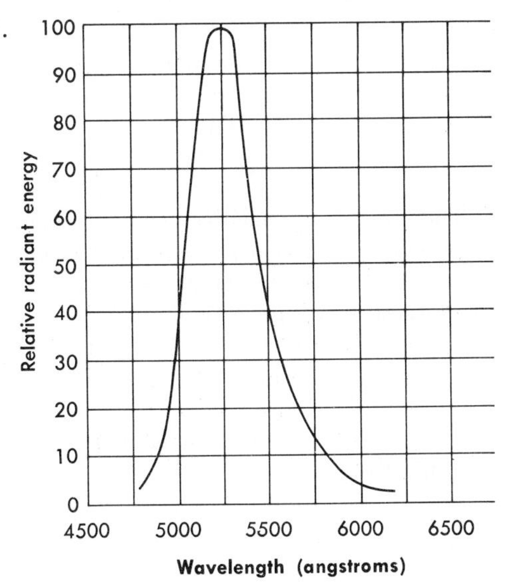

FIG. 153. Visible light emission of zinc orthosilicate phosphor.

For a discussion of the methods used in the laboratory for making a screen by settling out of an aqueous suspension, see p. 252.

Windows, vacuum. Many types of vacuum-tight "windows" have been devised for various purposes. A list of references to specific designs follows:

"Thin Glass Windows," A. Hemmendinger and A. P. Roensch, *Rev. Sci. Instr.*, **26,** 562, 1955.

"Vacuum-Tight Mica Window," F. Sterzer, *ibid.*, **28,** 208, 1957.

"Electron Permeable Window for Cathode-Ray Tube," J. Seehof, S. Smithberg, and M. Armstrong, *ibid.*, **29,** 776, 1958.

"Sealing a Calcium Fluoride Window to Glass," M. H. Greenblatt, *ibid.*, **29,** 738, 1958.

"Mica Window Assembly for Use at Bakeout Temperatures," A. R. Strnad, *ibid.*, **29,** 533, 1958.

"Reliable Optical Window for Cells Subject to Cycling of Temperature and Pressure," W. C. Waggener and A. M. Tripp, *ibid.*, **30,** 677, 1959.

"High-Power R. F. Window," K. C. Crebbin and D. F. Mosier, *ibid.*, **31,** 64, 1960.

"Thin Vacuum-Tight Mica Window Bakeable to 500°C," C. J. M. Anderson, *ibid.*, **31,** 898, 1960. (See p. 000.)

"Method for Determining Pinholes in Teflon," J. R. King and C. R. Gregory, Jr., *ibid.*, **32,** 89, 1961.

"A Versatile Metal-to-Dielectric Seal," P. C. Conder, H. Foster, and H. A. H. Boot, *J. Sci. Instr.* (Br) **38,** 134, 1961.

"High Power R-F Window Study Program," F. Johnson, L. T. Zitelli, and D. G. Dow, Final Technical Report RADC-TDR-63-510, prepared by Varian Associates for U.S. Air Force, Griffiss A.F.B., Rome, New York, November 1963. Available from U.S. Dept. of Commerce, O.T.S., Washington 25, D.C.

Wood's metal. There are various formulations for this low-melting point or "fusible" metal, one of which has the composition:

Bismuth	50%
Lead	25%
Tin	12.5%
Cadmium	12.5%

This alloy has a melting point of 65.5°C (and thus below boiling water). It is sometimes used as a soft solder for components which must not be exposed to heat. Its specific gravity is 9.7 gm/cc.

Work function (*cf.* pp. 235, 432–433, 442). To liberate an electron from a surface (of an emitter), a certain amount of energy is required, which is characteristic of the surface. When a quantity of electricity q is moved through a potential difference V, the work done equals qV. If the work done per electron is W_1, the electron charge is e, and the potential difference ϕ is required to supply an amount of energy equal to W_1, then

$$W_1 = \phi e,$$

and

$$\phi = \frac{W_1}{e} = \frac{k_0 b}{e} = 8.62 \times 10^{-5}\, b \text{ (volts)}.$$

The symbol ϕ ($= W_1/e$) is called the *work function* of the substance. A low value of ϕ indicates a large electron emission for a given temperature. The following table gives the *electron affinity* or work function of several substances:

SUBSTANCE	ϕ (VOLTS)	SUBSTANCE	ϕ (VOLTS)
Tungsten	4.52[1] [2]	Beryllium	3.10[2]
Platinum	4.4[1] 5.32[2]	Columbium	4.01[2]
Tantalum	4.3[1] 4.19[2]	Cerium	2.6[2]
Molybdenum	4.3[1] 4.15–4.44[2]	Cobalt	4.40[2]
Carbon	4.1[1] 4.0–4.84[2]	Chromium	4.60[2]
Silver	4.1[1] 3.09–4.31[2]	Cesium	1.81[2]
Copper	4.0[1] 3.85–4.55[2]	Hafnium	3.53[2]
Bismuth	3.7[1]	Iridium	5.3[2]
Tin	3.8[1]	Lanthanum	3.3[2]
Iron	3.7[1] 4.04–4.76[2]	Manganese	3.83[2]
Zinc	3.4[1]	Neodymium	3.3[2]
Thorium	3.4[1]	Palladium	4.99[2]
Aluminum	3.0[1]	Praeseodymium	2.7[1]
Magnesium	2.7[1]	Rhenium	5.1[2]
Nickel	2.8[1] 4.50–5.24[2]	Rhodium	4.80[2]
Titanium	2.4[1] 3.95[2]	Silicon	3.59–4.02[2]
Lithium	2.35[1]	Samarium	3.2[2]
Sodium	1.82[1]	Thorium	3.35[2]
Mercury	4.4[1]	Uranium	3.27[2]
Calcium	3.4[1] 2.24[2]	Vanadium	4.12[2]
Gold	4.0–4.58[2]	Zirconium	4.21[2]
Barium	2.11[2]		

[1] *The Radio Engineering Handbook*, K. Henney, Editor, McGraw-Hill Book Co., Inc. New York, New York, 1935.
[2] *Handbook of Chemistry and Physics*, forty-first edition, C. D. Hodgman, Editor in Chief, Chemical Rubber Publishing Co., Cleveland, Ohio, 1960. Reproduced by permission.

The work function of activated thoriated tungsten is approximately 2.0[1] and that of fully activated barium oxide/strontium oxide (normal "oxide-coating") is 1.5 or lower.

It must be remembered that even though many metals have lower work functions, tungsten can be heated to a much higher temperature than most others, and since the total emission is proportional to the square of the absolute temperature (Richardson's equation, p. 236), this metal appears favorably as an emitter in comparison with other materials, especially in view of its ruggedness and stability.

X-rings. These are metal O-ring-type seals, so-called because of their X cross section. They can be used as vacuum seals at bake-out temperatures in a properly designed

[1] W. E. Danforth, *Abstract of Summary of Bartol Cathode Work*, J. Franklin Inst., **248**, 449, 1949.

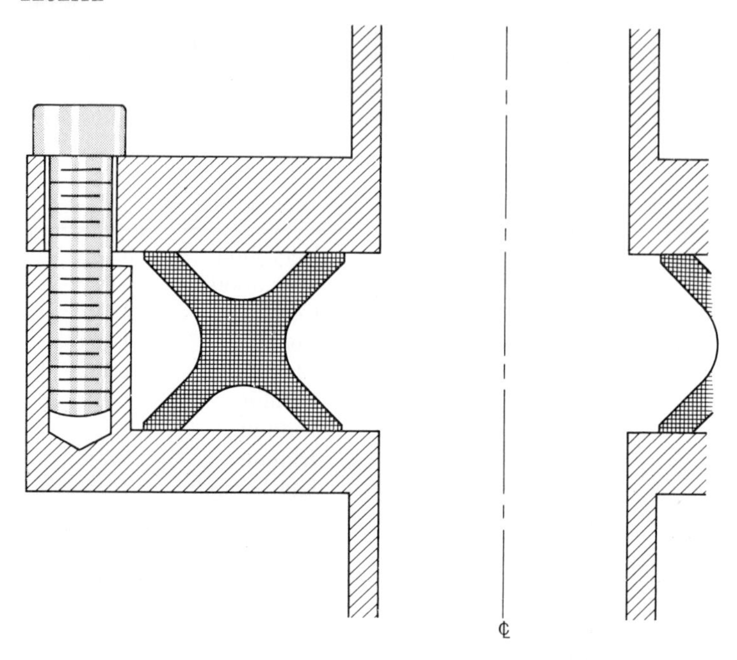

Fig. 154. Bakeable vacuum coupling employing X-ring.

housing. X-rings are manufactured by the E. B. Wiggins Oil Tool Company, Inc., Los Angeles 23, California (Bar-X Seals) and are available in a variety of sizes, in several kinds of stainless steel, and in Inconel X[1] (heat-treatable alloy) which will withstand repeated cycling up to 650°C. The contacting surfaces of these rings are fine-ground and can be obtained silver-plated to provide a cushion seat.

Although these rings are more expensive than the more common Neoprene, Viton, or Teflon O-rings, they have the very valuable advantage of bakeability.

A typical all-metal vacuum coupling employing one of these X-rings is illustrated in Fig. 154. Other types of seals for demountable systems will suggest themselves.

Zeolite. Natural zeolites, originally used as water softeners, are mainly sodium and aluminum hydrous silicates. The synthetic (or artificial) zeolites[2] differ only in that the grain sizes and porosity are greater.

The use of artificial zeolite and/or activated alumina for use in trapping oil vapors (minimizing of backstreaming) etc., has been described by Biondi[3] and Harris.[4] Such traps are placed between the diffusion pump and the vessel being evacuated, and contain built-in electric heaters for reactivating the vapor-absorbent material.

Zeolite can be reactivated by heating for 12 hours at 400°C.

---

[1] New designation is Inconel Alloy X-750.

[2] See Molecular sieves, p. 377. Molecular sieves are synthetic sodium and calcium aluminosilicates, dehydrated and formed into pellets of various more or less uniform sizes.

[3] M. A. Biondi, *Rev. Sci. Instr.*, **30**, 831, 1959.

[4] L. A. Harris, *ibid.*, **31**, 903, 1960.

Zinc. A bluish-white metal, one of the important constituents of brass and some bronzes (with copper). It has the following properties:

Atomic weight	65.38
Atomic number	30
Melting point (°C)	419.5
Boiling point (°C)	907
Specific gravity (gm/cc) at 20°C	7.14

Commercial zinc, containing about 0.1% lead, has the following properties:

Density (lb/in^3)	0.255
Specific gravity (gm/cc)	7.15
Melting point (°C)	419
Specific heat (gm-cal/gm/°C)	0.094
Thermal conductivity (cgs)	0.265
Coefficient of linear thermal expansion	
per °F, in/in	$13\text{–}18 \times 10^{-6}$
per °C, in/in	$23\text{–}32 \times 10^{-6}$
Electrical resistivity (ohms/mil/ft) at 68°F	36.6
(microhm-cm) at 20°C	6.1

Zinc is nonmagnetic, its susceptibility being -0.157×10^{-6} cgs units.

The vapor pressure of zinc is fairly high, as would be deduced from its relatively low boiling point (see the table on p. 148). Pressures of about 10^{-3} torr at 290°C and above 0.1 torr at the melting point (419°C) are found. This limits its usefulness as a constitutent of structural materials in vacuum equipment to temperatures not much above 120°C.

Galvanized steel is steel which has been coated with zinc by dipping in the molten metal, or by electroplating. Zinc is a common major constituent of die castings as well as of brasses and some bronzes, and also of German silver.

Zinc is widely used for making the negative (outer casing) electrode of semidry batteries such as flashlight and dry cells. It is a constituent of a number of hard (silver) solders, and these should be used with caution in the fabrication of vacuum devices.

Zinc oxychloride cement.[1] (Dental cement.) This is prepared by heating zinc oxide to a yellow color (calcining) to free it of carbonates. When cool, it is mixed with a 60% zinc chloride solution to the consistency of a thick paste. Setting takes place in a few minutes and results in a hard, adhesive, and water-resistant cement. (Prepared zinc oxychloride and variations of it can be obtained from dental supply houses.) This material may be used as a basing cement for tubes.

Zircon. A natural semiprecious stone having the composition $ZrSiO_4$ (zirconium orthosilicate). Small amounts of impurities produce colors ranging from pale yellow through gray, yellowish-green, brown, reddish-brown, to red. Its melting point is approximately 2500°–2550°C, with a safe temperature for continuous use of 1455°C. Zircon is very resistant to acids, including aqua regia and alkalies. Its density varies from 1.92 to 2.02 gm/cc.

---

[1] *Handbook of Chemistry and Physics,* forty-first edition, Chemical Rubber Publishing Co., Cleveland, Ohio, 1960.

Zircon porcelain (sometimes called **Zircon ceramic**). The addition of the semiprecious stone zircon to talc and clay ceramic bodies[1] increases their heat conductivity, decreases their thermal expansion and, therefore, improves their heat-shock resistance. At low frequencies zircon porcelains have a somewhat higher dielectric constant and a greater power factor than some other dielectric materials. At higher frequencies, however, the dielectric constant decreases slightly and the power factor decreases rapidly with an increase in frequency, so that the resulting loss factor at high frequencies is extremely low. Zircon porcelains are more expensive to produce than some of the other dielectric materials because of greater die wear caused by the abrasive zircon raw material.

A typical zircon porcelain, M81A,[1] has the following properties:

Specific gravity (gm/cc)	3.1
Density (lb/in^3)	0.112
Water absorption (%)	0–0.5
Modulus of rupture (psi)	26,500
Impact resistance, Charpy (ft-lb)	1.20
Compressive strength (psi)	70,000
Hardness, Mohs' scale	7
Safe temperature limit (°C)	1196
Linear coefficient of thermal expansion (in/°C)	
20°–100°C	2.95×10^{-6}
20°–400°C	5.15×10^{-6}
Dielectric strength (volts/mil)	250
Dielectric constant at 1 Mc	7.10
Power factor at 1 Mc (%)	0.008
Loss factor at 1 Mc (%)	0.0057
Volume resistivity at (ohm-cm) 20°C	10^{14}
200°C	5.6×10^{14}
300°C	1×10^{13}
500°C	1.2×10^{9}
Temperature at which 1 cm^3 has a resistance of 1 megohm (10^6 ohms) (Te value) °C	> 700

A vitrified zircon porcelain manufactured by the American Lava Corporation, Chattanooga 5, Tennessee (Alsimag 475, L-4A) has the following properties:[2]

Water absorption	0–0.02 (impervious)
Specific gravity (gm/cc)	3.7
Density (lb/in^3)	0.134
Color	white
Softening temperature (°C)	1440
Safe temperature for continuous use (°C)	1100
Hardness, Mohs' scale	8

[1] Indiana General Corporation, Electronics Division, Keasbey, New Jersey (formerly General Ceramics Corp.).
[2] Table courtesy of the American Lava Company.

Thermal expansion coefficient (in/°C)	
25°–300°C	4.4×10^{-6}
25°–700°C	4.1×10^{-6}
Tensile strength (psi)	12,000
Compressive strength (psi)	100,000
Flexural strength (psi)	22,000
Impact resistance, Charpy, ½-inch rod (in-lb)	5.5
Thermal conductivity (cgs) approximate	0.012
Dielectric strength, step 60 cycle, ¼-inch thick discs (volts/mil)	250
Volume resistivity ($ohm\text{-}cm^3$) 25°C	$> 10^{14}$
100	2×10^{13}
300	5.5×10^{11}
500	5.5×10^{8}
700	1.4×10^{7}
900	8.2×10^{5}
Temperature at which 1 cm^3 has a resistivity of 10^6 ohms (Te value)	870°C
Dielectric constant at 60 cycles	9.1
1 Mc	8.8
100 Mc	8.6
10,000 Mc	8.4
Power factor, wet, (%) at 60 cycles	0.0360
1 Mc	0.0010
100 Mc	0.0012
10,000 Mc	0.0027
Loss factor, wet, (%) at 60 cycles	0.327
1 Mc	0.009
100 Mc	0.010
10,000 Mc	0.023

Zirconia. One of the oxides of zirconium, ZrO_2. This is a white-to-salmon pink refractory ceramic material having a density of 5.6 to 5.74 gm/cc and a melting point of 2680°–2715°C, with a safe operating temperature for continuous use of 2316°C.

Stabilized zirconia can be applied to metals and other surfaces by a flame-spraying technique.[1, 2]

Fused zirconia[3] is a very good electrical insulator at low temperatures but becomes a conductor when heated to 1300°C, which makes it of possible usefulness as a high-temperature heating element.

---

[1] J. L. Bliton and H. L. Rechter, "Physical Properties of Ceramic Coatings," Armour Research Foundation of Illinois Institute of Technology, Phase Report, Project No. ARF 6921–4; also same authors, "Determination of Physical Properties of Flame-Sprayed Ceramic Coatings," *Amer. Ceram. Soc. Bull.*, **40**, 683–688, November 15, 1961.

[2] The Flame-Ceramic equipment is produced and marketed by Continental Coatings Corporation, 17706 Miles Avenue, Cleveland 28, Ohio.

[3] The Norton Company, Worcester 6, Massachusetts.

Chattanooga 5, Tennessee (Alsimag 508), has the following properties:
A zirconia ceramic body, manufactured by the American Lava Company,

Water absorption	12–16 (porous)
Specific gravity (gm/cc)	2.9
Density (lb/in³)	0.106
Color	orange
Softening temperature (°C)	2400
Safe temperature for continuous use (°C)	1600
Thermal expansion (in/°C) 25°–300°C	9.6×10^{-6}
25°–700°C	9.9×10^{-6}
Compressive strength (psi)	10,000
Flexural strength (psi)	4,000
Impact resistance, Charpy, ½-inch rod, in-lb	4.0
Thermal conductivity (cgs) approximate, at 1760°C	0.004
Volume resistivity (ohm-cm³) at 25°C	$>10^{14}$
100°C	$>10^{14}$
300°C	4.5×10^{9}
500°C	8.2×10^{6}
700°C	2.5×10^{5}
900°C	4.0×10^{4}
Temperature at which 1 cm³ has a resistance of 1 megohm/°C (Te value)	610

Zirconium. A refractory metal similar in appearance to stainless steel. It has a melting point higher than that of platinum and can be used as a flux[1] in spot-welding other refractory metals (see pp. 87, 253, 495). It has excellent corrosion resistance and a low neutron cross section (neutrons pass easily through it with low absorption).

Two grades of zirconium exist—commercial and reactor—as well as a number of alloys (Zr-Hf, Zr-Ti, Zr-Al, Zr-Ta, Zr-Cb, Zr-W, Zr-Cu, Zr-Mo, Zr-Ni, Zr-Cr, and others).[2]

Commercial-grade zirconium always contains some hafnium, which has similar properties resulting in separation difficulties.

The properties of zirconium are given below:[3]

Atomic weight (pure Zr)	91.22
Density (commercial Zr), hot-rolled (gm/cc)	6.586
(lb/in³)	0.2374
cold-rolled (gm/cc)	6.505
(lb/in³)	0.2345

[1] G. A. Espersen, "Zirconium for Electron Tubes," Philips Laboratories, Inc., Irvington, New York, circa 1945. See also G. A. Espersen, "Fine Wires in the Tube Industry," *Proc. I.R.E.*, **34,** 116W, 1946.

[2] F. B. Litton, "Ten Zirconium Alloys Evaluated," *Iron Age,* April 5, 1951.

[3] "Properties of Zirconium Metal," Zirconium Metals Corp. of America, subsidiary of National Lead Company, 1955; "Zirconium Data File," Carborundum Metals Company, Akron, New York, 1961.

Melting point (°C)	1830 ±40
Boiling point (°C)	3577
Specific heat (at room temperature)	0.067 ±0.001
Linear coefficient of thermal expansion (in/°C):	
20–200°C	5.4×10^{-6}
20–400°C	6.9×10^{-6}
20–700°C	8.9×10^{-6}
Thermal conductivity (cgs) at 125°C	0.035 ±5%
Electrical resistivity, wire, at 20°C (microhm/cm)	40
Electrical resistivity, wire, at 20°C (ohms/mil/ft)	320–360
Electrical conductivity, wire, at 20°C (%) IACS	2.7
Temperature coefficient of resistivity per °C wire, 0–100°C	0.0044
Thermionic work function (ev)	4.1
Paramagnetic susceptibility (cgs) room temperature	1.3×10^{-6}
Modulus of elasticity, annealed (psi)	$11\text{–}14.8 \times 10^{6}$
Ultimate tensile strength (psi)	21,750–36,000
Shear modulus (psi)	4.76×10^{6}
Yield strength, 0.2% (psi)	16,000
Elongation in 1 inch (%)	16.2–43.1
Hardness, Rockwell	A 21–30
Atomic number	40
Transformation temperature (°C)	863
Vapor pressure (torr) at 2000°C	0.01

Zirconium, like aluminum, chrominum, and other metals, forms a thin protective oxide film in air at room temperature. The rate of oxidation increases with temperature, especially above 538°C (1000°F), which is the practical limit for atmospheric use. The metal should not be exposed to sulfur dioxide, carbon dioxide, carbon monoxide, or hydrogen atmospheres. Hydrogen, in particular, is absorbed by and reacts with zirconium at elevated temperatures to form zirconium hydride, and this results in severe embrittlement.

Zirconium is useful as a getter in electron tubes because of its affinity for large quantities of gases,[1] especially hydrogen, nitrogen, and oxygen. The metal absorbs these gases in the temperature range 300°–1600°C. Oxygen and nitrogen are not released even when the temperature is raised to 1650°C. Zirconium wire used for gettering purposes is overwound on or twisted with tungsten or molybdenum wires, since the zirconium by itself is weak in tension and would not be self-supporting at the high temperatures. Because of zirconium's ability to absorb and hold gases at high temperatures, one method of gettering, due to Espersen,[1] is that in which a strip or cylinder of zirconium foil is attached to the filament leads or wrapped around the cathode sleeve at some point.

Zirconium has a low secondary emission (pp. 239, 475) and can be applied to the tungsten or molybdenum grids of electron tubes[1] either as a spray of zirconium metal powder or zirconium hydride, suspended in an aqueous or nitrocellulose lacquer. Subsequent heating in vacuum to 1650°C sinters the zirconium to the base metal.

[1] Espersen, *op cit.*

Working zirconium: The metal forms similarly to titanium. Cold bends of a radius of 5 times the thickness can be done with hand or power tools. Smaller radii can be attained by applying some heat (not over 538°C) to the work and the tools.

Zirconium can be welded with inert gas or vacuum-arc or beam techniques, and vacuum-brazing can be done with silver, copper, gold, and other filler alloys.

Machining can be carried out without difficulty using slow speeds, heavy feeds, and flooding with coolant. Fine chips should be avoided because of the pyrophoric (fire-hazard) nature of zirconium.

Zirconium can be etched in a solution containing 2 cc hydrofluoric acid, 3 cc nitric acid, and 95 cc water.[1] Electrolytic polishing can be done in a solution of 1 part hydrochloric acid (concentrated) and 3 parts ethyl alcohol. The parts are first cleaned with 2/0 emery paper and then immersed in the bath with a current density of 1 amp/ft^2. They must be removed from the bath while the current is on, and washed immediately with plain alcohol. Operation of the bath is done with the work as the anode and a piece of stainless steel sheet as the cathode. Use a glass or rubber-lined tank.

Zirconium hydride (ZrH_2) (*cf.* pp. 67 *et seq.*). This is one of the materials used in the "active metal" process of making metal-to-ceramic seals. It operates by reducing the oxides of other less active metals in vacuum at elevated temperatures. One gm of ZrH_2 contains 240 cc of hydrogen at STP. Atomic hydrogen is liberated as the temperature rises, reaching a high value at about 940°C. Heating to higher temperatures ultimately results in complete dissociation to zirconium metal (melting point 1875°C) and hydrogen.

A 99% pure ZrH_2 product in 325-mesh size (powder), designated MHI Zirconium Hydride, is available from Metal Hydrides, Inc., Beverly, Massachusetts. In the technique of making metal-to-ceramic, metal-to-quartz, metal-to-diamond, or metal-to-other nonmetal seals, the powder is suspended in a vehicle such as nitrocellulose lacquer, ethyl or amyl acetate, acetone, alcohol, or sometimes water. This is applied at the site of the seal by brushing and is allowed to dry thoroughly before firing.

Zirconium hydride is also used as a getter (*cf.* p. 107). In this application it has the advantage over zirconium metal, for which it is substituted, in that it does not oxidize during seal-in or exhaust operations. As the film of zirconium hydride is heated *in vacuo,* the hydrogen is liberated, ultimately leaving a deposit of clean, highly reactive zirconium metal for the adsorption of oxygen, nitrogen, hydrogen, carbon dioxide, and other gases (except the inert gases).

Z-nickel and **Z-nickel type B.** (see p. 395).

Zone melting, zone refining.[2,3,4] This is, in effect, a refinement of the classical technique of purification by fractional crystallization, in which separation is effected by the difference in solubility of a solute in the solid and liquid phases of a substance.

---

[1] A. H. Robertson, "Metallography of Zirconium and Zirconium Alloys," Metal Progress, **56,** 667, 1949.

[2] W. G. Pfann, *Trans. A.I.M.E.*, 194, 1952.

[3] W. G. Pfann, *Zone Melting,* John Wiley & Sons, Inc., New York, New York, 1958.

[4] J. K. Kennedy, Paper #6, Symposium: "Classical Purification Techniques, Electronics Research Directorate, Air Force, Cambridge Research Laboratories, February, 1961.

In zone refining, only a small part of the "solvent" is melted at any one time, and this allows a very close control of the degree of fractional crystallization.

In practice, particularly with reference to reactive metals such as tungsten, molybdenum, titanium, zirconium, etc., the charge can conveniently be in the form of a long rod or cylinder suspended in a vacuum and heated by induction with a concentrator (see pp. 221, 222, 231) which heats only a short "zone" and does not significantly heat the vacuum vessel (see below). Either the charge or the concentrator coil is moved axially with respect to the other at a slow, constant rate. This technique obviously requires the charge rod to be of reasonably uniform cross section.

For many substances, the impurities in the charge will become concentrated in the liquid and will travel with the molten zone. The degree of purification will, to some extent, be determined by the rate of travel and also the number of passes (in the same direction).

Induction heating has the advantage of producing a degree of turbulence or stirring in the molten zone due to the eddy currents, and this helps to speed up the process which, nevertheless, is quite slow.

No container in contact with the charge need be used. This has two advantages: contamination from the substance of the container is eliminated, and danger of rupture due to nonuniform expansion and contraction is minimized. In such a procedure,[1] called the "floating-zone" method, the rod or ingot is suspended vertically in the center of a nonconducting vacuum vessel (glass, quartz, etc.), and the concentrator coil is passed up or down along it, producing the molten zone. Surface tension keeps the rod from breaking off and dropping.

Many metals and semiconductors can be purified by zone-refining techniques.[2]

ZONE MELTING, ZONE REFINING—BIBLIOGRAPHY

See also: W. G. Pfann, *Rev. Sci. Instr.*, **29**, 904, 1958; L. Spailter and J. R. Riley, *ibid.*, **30**, 139, 1959; F. J. Baum, *ibid.*, **30**, 1064, 1959; L. R. Johnson and W. Zimmerman, III, *ibid.*, **31**, 203, 1960; L. R. Weisberg and F. S. Rosi, *ibid.*, **31**, 206, 1960; P. H. Brace, A. W. Cochardt, and G. Comentez, *ibid.*, **26**, 303, 1955; and E. Buehler, *ibid.*, **28**, 453, 1957.

Zytel. Trade name for a group of Nylon (polyamide) resins manufactured by DuPont. Zytel 101 has good bearing properties and a high melting point, and is easily machined. Zytel 31 is an electrical-grade Nylon with very low moisture absorption and good dimensional stability. It is somewhat less rigid than other Nylons. (*Cf.* NYLON, p. 399.)

[1] P. H. Keck and M. J. E. Golay, *Phys. Rev.*, 89, 1953.
[2] Kennedy, *op. cit.*

Indexes

Author Index

*Subject Index**

* The letters n and t after page numbers indicate that the matter referred to is in a footnote (n) or in a table (t).

ABCDE698765